N. C. EDSALL
1972

THE HOSPITALS
1800-1948

The LETTER to recommend IN and OUT-PATIENTS.

GENTLEMEN,

I recommend the bearer *Mary White* *residing at*
2 Queen St_____ for an
Out Patient if the Board shall consider h__ a proper object of the Charity.

day of *27th* *184*6

Your humble Servant,

To the GOVERNORS of St. GEORGE'S }
HOSPITAL, *near Hyde Park Corner.* }

Mary

CONTRIBUTORS are desired to observe the following ARTICLES: *viz.*

I.   RECOMMENDATIONS are to be delivered every *Wednesday* morning by half-past Eleven of the clock, and *none* will be received *after* that time.

II. When there is not room in the House for all the Patients recommended at one time to be received, *those* only are admitted, who, the Board is of opinion, will most effectually answer the ends of the Charity; and the rest, if proper objects, are admitted Out-Patients till there is a vacancy in the House.

III. No person labouring under any infectious distemper, deemed incurable, or whose case is consumptive or asthmatic, or having old ulcerated legs, more proper for a workhouse is to be received into the House.

IV. On account of the number of Contributors each Governor can have but *one* In-patient at a time, Subscribers of *three* guineas are allowed to recommend *three* In-patients every year; and no Governor can have more than *two* Out-patients on the books at one time.

V.   Each Patient, if able, to bring two shirts or shifts, but Patients are not required to find themselves with *Provisions of any kind* during their stay in the Hospital.

VI. If any Nurse or Servant receive any money, treat, present, or gratuity, either from a Patient, or any relation or friend of such Patient, or from any other person, in respect for the services of such Nurse or Servant in the Hospital, such Nurse or Servant shall be dismissed.

*The Contributors are requested to send their money to this Hospital upon
any* Wednesday, *from Ten till Three.*

*** The large number of surgery Patients requiring a great
quantity of Lint and Cloth for rollers, &c. if Ladies please to send
in some old linen, it will be a valuable present to the Charity.

Wellcome Historical Medical Library

ST GEORGE'S HOSPITAL
Letter of recommendation signed by Princess Mary
of Cambridge, Princess of Teck, 1846

BRIAN ABEL-SMITH

with the assistance of Robert Pinker

THE HOSPITALS

1800-1948

A Study in Social Administration
in England and Wales

HARVARD UNIVERSITY PRESS

Cambridge, Massachusetts

1964

© Brian Abel-Smith 1964
First published 1964

Printed in Great Britain

Contents

CONTENTS

List of Illustrations

Thanks are due to the following for permission to reproduce photographs:
The Central Middlesex Hospital, The Mansell Collection, The Passfield
Trustees, The Radio Times Hulton Picture Library, St Thomas' Hospital,
The Wellcome Historical Medical Library. The source of each photograph
is given on the page where it is reproduced.

Abbreviations

BHA	British Hospitals Association
BMA	British Medical Association
BMJ	British Medical Journal
BPP	British Parliamentary Papers
BRCS	British Red Cross Society
COS	Charity Organization Society
EMS	Emergency Medical Service
GCO	General Council Order
HofC	House of Commons
HofL	House of Lords
HSA	Hospital Saving Association
HSF	Hospital Saturday Fund
KEHF	King Edward's Hospital Fund for London
LGB	Local Government Board
MAB	Metropolitan Asylums' Board
MOH	Ministry of Health
PEP	Political and Economic Planning
PLB	Poor Law Board
PLOJ	Poor Law Officers' Journal
RCP	Royal College of Physicians
SSHS	Soldiers and Sailors Help Society
VADs	Voluntary Aid Detachments
WHO	World Health Organization
WINA	Workhouse Infirmary Nursing Association

Preface

RESIDENTIAL institutions for the use of the sick have been
known for hundreds of years. They have evolved in many
different societies to serve different purposes – to maintain the
suffering poor, to advance medical knowledge, to train apprentices, to save doctors' time, to test whether patients were
malingering, to promote much higher standards of medical care,
to undertake specialized treatments and operations, to protect
society and to serve as doctors' workshops. Many hospitals have
served several of these purposes at one time or have gradually
changed their role from one to another because of changing
demands of patients, doctors, hospital managements and society
in general.

This study attempts to analyse the changing role of the
hospitals for physical disease in England and Wales between
1800 and 1948 in relation to the needs and objectives of the
medical profession. Hospitals in Scotland have developed on
different lines in many respects. No reference is made to them in
this study. Except where otherwise stated, all the statistics refer
solely to England and Wales.

Most studies of individual hospitals have been concerned to
describe the character and achievements of the doctors who
staffed them and have emphasized the impact of changing
medical techniques and medical knowledge. Little is said here,
however, about methods of treatment. This is not to imply that
they are not important to understanding the work and organization of hospitals. The omission is partly due to my lack of
qualification to write about such matters. But more important
is the lack of systematic information. Little is known about what
hospitals actually did for particular patients and diseases, about
the cost of implementing new developments in medicine, the
number of staff required to operate them or the amount of floor
space allocated to different purposes. Detailed case studies of

individual hospitals are needed before any generalization can be attempted.

Hardly anything is said about the effects which developments in hospital services have had on mortality inside and outside the hospital. Once again, facts are far too few. It is generally agreed that hospitals could have had little effect on levels of mortality in the nineteenth century, except by isolating and eventually helping to eradicate the more virulent infectious diseases. The effect of hospitals on mortality levels in the twentieth century is much harder to assess. How great has been the contribution of hospital care to the increasing expectation of life at different ages? Detailed analysis of the case records of individual hospitals, allied to other systematic studies, would be needed before any conclusions could be reached about mortality or morbidity.

The study originated in 1956 when, with the help of King Edward's Hospital Fund for London, I started to explore the literature on the history of health services. It soon became clear that a history of hospitals should follow and not precede a history of nursing. Thus this study is in a sense a companion volume to my *History of the Nursing Profession* (1960). In part, it grew out of discussions with Dr Odin W. Anderson of the Health Information Foundation of New York (now at the University of Chicago), who was searching for answers to a number of critical questions. Why had Britain and not the United States nationalized its hospitals? Why were most general practitioners in Britain separated from hospital work? Why was there such a wide measure of clinical freedom for consultants and specialists? What were the underlying forces which had created the National Health Service? Why had it taken its present form? How far had differing political philosophies led to different systems of financing medical care in the two countries?

With the assistance of a grant from the Health Information Foundation, this book has been written in part to explain differences in the organization and administration of hospitals in Britain and the United States. I had the opportunity to make a first-hand study of medical care organization in the United States while I was attached to the Yale Law School, New Haven, for three months at the beginning of 1962.

I approached this research with the conviction that it was only possible to understand developments in hospitals against a fairly wide social and economic background. Thus I have attempted to outline the history of hospitals in the context of changes in the medical profession, in philosophies governing the administration of the Poor Law and in the whole system of medical care organization. The history of many other aspects of our health services has still to be written. Some of these studies are, however, fortunately already under way. It has been particularly valuable to discuss some of these issues with Mr Frank Honigsbaum, who is studying the development of general practitioner services, Mr Norman Holly, who has been working on the development of pharmaceutical services, Mrs Rosemary Stevens, who is studying the role and function of the specialist, and Miss Gwen Ayers, who has generously allowed me access to an early draft of her forthcoming study of the Metropolitan Asylums' Board.

This is a study of hospitals and doctors. Its focus may have tended to give excessive weight to economic and professional conflicts and too little to the leadership of great individuals – Florence Nightingale, John Simon, Henry Burdett, Beatrice and Sidney Webb, Lloyd George, Aneurin Bevan – to mention a few at random. There is no doubt that high ideals and noble philosophies have played their part in influencing the actions of both medical and lay experts – and even of politicians. The influence of pressure groups has also been important and these are stressed here because earlier studies have paid too little attention to them. But the more one draws attention to the forces which led to a particular course of action, the more one may give the impression that history was in some sense inevitable or predetermined. This I certainly do not believe. But when we know what did eventually occur, it is hard to identify all the alternatives which were available at particular turning points in history.

Although I am solely responsible for the facts and opinions presented in this book, many of the ideas and much of the material have been contributed by others. In particular, I have relied upon the careful and extensive researches undertaken by Mr Robert Pinker, who has acted as research assistant through-out the whole study. By assembling and comparing all available sources, he has been able to piece together a series of statistics showing the number of hospitals, the number of available beds, occupied beds, and patients treated in institutions for the physically sick for selected years between 1861 and 1938. Originally it was intended that these statistics, which are quoted throughout the text, would be included as an appendix. His work has, however, grown large enough to justify a book on its own – the second volume of this study.

Though we had two years to collect the material for this book, it was not possible to explore every possible source. There comes a time when one must make the ruthless if arbitrary decision to search no more. Inevitably we will be shown by later writers to have been wrong on a number of points. It will be clear from the footnotes that our reading of the *British Medical Journal* has been thorough from 1880 onwards, of *The Hospital* from its foundation in 1886 until it ceased publication in 1921, and of the *Hospital Gazette* from its foundation in 1904 to 1948 (this journal changed its title to *The Hospital* in 1930). We have been able to give *The Lancet* much less exhaustive treatment – dipping into it where we wanted a further view on certain developments or when other sources led us to look up a particular leader, article or correspondence.

We have made use of many libraries in the course of our work. We wish to acknowledge in particular the substantial help which we have received from the British Library of Social Science, the libraries of General Register Office, the Ministry of Health, the Royal College of Physicians and the Wellcome Foundation. We have also been given access by the Institute of Hospital Administrators to their sets of *The Hospital* and of *Burdett's Hospitals and Charities*. Mr F. A. Lyon kindly lent us his set of the *Hospital Gazette* and Mr A. R. J. Wise kindly lent us *The Poor Law Officers' Journal*.

In collecting the material we have made extensive use of modern aids to bibliographical research. Most of the quotations were recorded on tape and typed back with phenomenal speed and accuracy by Miss Sheila Benson, who has also filed the material and typed most of the drafts. The marshalling of the footnotes and the standardization of the typography have also been her responsibilities. The later drafts have been typed and corrected by Miss Kathleen Ewart. Nearly all the quotations have been checked back to their original sources by Mr Hugh Small and Mrs Carmen Hill. No author could ask for more painstaking assistants.

I have discussed many questions with those who played

important parts in shaping events – particularly Lord Beveridge, Sir John Charles, Dr James Mackintosh and Sir Wilson Jameson. And the following have been kind enough to read and comment on the book in whole or part: Miss Gwen Ayers, Sir Zachary Cope, Sir Guy Dain, Dr Somerville Hastings, Mr A. G. D. Ives, Dr John Lee, Professor Donald MacRae, Mr J. F. Milne, Dr Charles Newman, Dr Alexander Robertson, Mr Walter Stern, Captain J. E. Stone, Lord Taylor of Harlow, Professor R. M. Titmuss and Professor Peter Townsend. They have corrected many errors, inconsistencies and stylistic weaknesses and drawn my attention to many sources which I had overlooked. After all their valuable advice, the faults that remain are due to my own obstinacy or carelessness.

December 1963   *Brian Abel-Smith*

CHAPTER I

The Sick and Lame Poor

ONLY in the last hundred years have hospitals come to play an important role in the treatment of the sick. Though many hospitals were founded in the eighteenth century, there were only about 3,000 patients in hospitals in 1800.[1] Even in 1851, when the importance of hospitals was first recognized by a special category in the census of population, only 7,619 hospital patients were enumerated.[2]

At the beginning of the nineteenth century, medical knowledge consisted of 'nurses' gossip, and sick men's fancies, and the crude compilations of a blundering empiricism'.[3] Little effective medical care could be obtained by either rich or poor and it was better to receive what there was at home. In hospitals cross-infection was a constant menace. Some of those who did not have fatal diseases when they entered hospital acquired them after admission. 'The very first requirement in a hospital,' wrote Miss Nightingale, '[is] that it should do the sick no harm.'[4] The early hospitals failed to meet this requirement.[5] Not until the

[1] A list of hospitals is given in J. Howard, *An Account of the Principal Lazarettos in Europe*, London, 1789. To this list we have made additions for hospitals omitted and hospitals founded between 1789 and 1800 with the assistance of the librarian of the Royal College of Physicians, whose help is gratefully acknowledged. Complete information is not available but we estimate that there were about 4,000 beds and an average of 3,000 patients in 1800.

[2] This figure is an underestimate as many small institutions were excluded.

[3] J. Simon, *On the Aims and Philosophic Method of Pathological Research*, p. 21, London, 1848, Quoted in R. Lambert, *Sir John Simon (1816–1904), and English Social Administration*, p. 42, London, 1963.

[4] Florence Nightingale, *Notes on Hospitals* (3rd ed.), p. iii, London, 1863

[5] T. McKeown and R. G. Brown, 'Medical Evidence Related to English Population Changes in the Eighteenth Century', p. 125, *Population Studies*, Vol. IX, November 1955

late nineteenth century were hospitals of positive benefit to a substantial number of patients.

Thus illness of any kind was normally endured at home: patients who thought it efficacious purchased such medical advice and treatment as they could afford. There was a fairly clear class hierarchy of medical advisers as there was of patients. For the rich there were the fellows and licentiates of the Royal College of Physicians. The College had been established in 1518 but as late as 1800 it had only 47 fellows, 115 licentiates and 26 extra-licentiates.[1] They were the *élite* of medical practitioners, drawn exclusively from graduates of Oxford and Cambridge, which secured that they were all members of the Church of England. As late as 1834, membership of the College could be obtained for a down payment of fifty guineas after three examinations lasting some twenty minutes each.[2] A man could pass the examination 'who is a good classical scholar but knows nothing of chemistry, nothing of medical jurisprudence, nothing of surgery, little or nothing of anatomy, nothing of the diseases of women in childbed, and nothing of the manner of delivering them'.[3]

There were also the licentiates of the College of Surgeons, founded in 1800 and controlled by a restrictionist clique.[4] The Council and Court of Examiners did not insist on high professional standards and treated the licentiates 'with insult and contempt'.[5] The social status of surgeons was lower than that of the physicians. They were allowed to operate and treat externally but not to give medicines internally. By 1854, there were approximately 200 fellows and 8,000 members of the College of Surgeons. Most of their operations were performed at the patients' homes.

For those not so well endowed with the world's riches and those who lived far from any physician or surgeon, there were apothecaries who were drawn from a lower social class and allowed to charge for their medicine but not for their advice.

[1] *Catalogues of the Fellows, Candidate Licentiates in Midwifery and extra-Licentiates of the Royal College of Physicians*, London, 1778–1847
[2] *Report of the Select Committee on Medical Education* (H of C, 601-2), Pt. I, para. 2566 (evidence of Sir David Barry), London, 1834
[3] ibid., para. 2573
[4] J. F. Clarke, *Autobiographical Recollections*, p. 7, London, 1874
[5] ibid. The licentiates were made to enter the College by a miserable back door from Portugal Street.

Until the early nineteenth century the apothecary was no more than a tradesman who learned his job during a five-year apprenticeship. Although there were some surgeon-apothecaries, most of this 'Order' were qualified only in medicine; they were drawn from the lower middle-class families of tradespeople, and yeomen farmers. And for all classes there was a generous supply of quacks – persons who had not been required to take any examination, however casual. They were well patronized. In Lincolnshire, in 1804, it was estimated that the quacks outnumbered the trained men by a ratio of nine to one.[1]

The problem of nursing was often solved in wealthy households by engaging more domestic help in the house, but there were also women who had specialized in caring for or 'watching' the sick. For confinements, specialized help was more often engaged than for ordinary illness. There were persons who made their living by midwifery or by laying out the dead as occasion demanded.

For those who could not afford any paid assistance, it was possible to obtain help from the Poor Law. Although not expressly authorized under the old Elizabethan statute, a haphazard system of medical relief had grown up in the seventeenth and eighteenth centuries. Some parish councils had entered into contracts with local doctors who undertook to provide bottles of medicine and other relief in kind to sick paupers referred to them. The usual arrangement was for the doctor to be paid a lump sum, out of which he met the cost of the medicaments.

The main care of the sick poor came inevitably from within the family circle. A folklore or quasi-medical knowledge was handed down from mother to daughter and no doubt the advice of neighbours, friends and priests was taken if not always used. The patient was made as comfortable as the love and care of the family could make him. Illness was not regarded as a circumstance which required much positive action. All that could be done was to ask God to remove the affliction in his own mysterious way.

Such was the position of those who had a home and circle of kin to lend support and succour. Those who did not have these assets needed institutions. There were others who were driven

1 C. Newman, *The Evolution of Medical Education in the Nineteenth Century*, p. 59, Oxford, 1957

to seek institutional care either because sickness had made them destitute or destitution had made them sick. Finally, there were those who hoped, after everything else had been tried, that they might find relief or cure away from home.

There were two types of institutions which had come to cater for the sick by the end of the eighteenth century – the voluntary hospitals and the workhouses. The latter were a more recent development. These residential institutions which accommodated the indigent and their families and tried to provide them with some form of work had been constructed in the attempt to limit the cost of assisting the poor in their own homes. Parishes had been authorized to construct them by an Act of 1722.[1] Inevitably their inmates had come to include the sick. In 1782[2] adjacent parishes were authorized to combine into 'unions' so that they could build workhouses for the exclusive use of children, the aged and the sick. These permissive Acts were not widely used as many parishes thought it more economical to look after the poor in their own homes. Nevertheless, there must have been a considerable number of sick persons accommodated in workhouses early in the nineteenth century. It is indeed likely that the sick in workhouses exceeded those in hospitals.

A few voluntary hospitals were venerable institutions. For example, St Bartholomew's had been founded in 1123 and St Thomas' in 1207, but they had not always catered exclusively for the sick. It was during the eighteenth century that the idea of founding charities for the care of the sick really took hold. For example, the Westminster Hospital was founded in 1719, Guy's in 1721,[3] St George's in 1733, the London Hospital in 1740 and the Middlesex Hospital in 1745. Thus by the 1780's, there were seven general hospitals in London providing a total of some 2,000 beds. They housed about 1,600 patients in 1789. At the same date, it was found that about thirty provincial towns had acquired hospitals in the preceding fifty years.[4] But there were as many beds in London as in the whole of the rest of

[1] 9 Geo. I. c.7
[2] 22 Geo. III. c.83
[3] Mr Thomas Guy decided to set up the hospital in 1721, but the first patients were not admitted until 1725.
[4] These figures were calculated from a list prepared with the assistance of the present Librarian of the Royal College of Physicians from two main sources: Howard, op. cit., and *The Medical Register for the Year 1783*.

England and Wales. In 1800 there was a total of about one bed to 5,000 persons, compared with about one bed to 175 persons in 1961.[1]

The initiative in founding the early hospitals came largely from laymen. The venerable 'hospices' owed their origin to royal or civic initiative and many governors were drawn from the social *élite*. Later hospitals were founded by persons of high standing in their local communities and governed by persons at the top or keen to approach the top of the social pyramid. The twenty original governors of the Middlesex Hospital were 'desired to wait on the nobility and others for their subscriptions'.[2] The money for the Sheffield General Infirmary was put up by leading families of the iron trade and by the local vicar.[3] The office of President in the large London hospitals was held by members of the Royal Family, dukes and marquesses. Many of the aristocracy were governors of more than one hospital. In 1798, Charles James Fox and William Wilberforce were both vice-presidents of a London hospital.[4] Early on it was a mark of social status to govern a voluntary hospital. And early on many members of the House of Lords were closely associated with the voluntary hospital movement.

While the endowed hospitals such as St Thomas' and St Bartholomew's could support themselves on the income of their endowments, the newer foundations depended largely on current subscriptions to finance their expenditure. The progress of the voluntary hospital movement depended on the willingness of the rich to help the poor, and the money was provided for religious and wider humanitarian reasons. And the scale on which this money was given to hospitals over a period of two centuries indicated a tremendous sense of social duty and responsibility. Gifts were not, however, always disinterested. In some hospitals it was laid down that when purchases were made for the hospital, preference should be given to tradesmen who were subscribers.[5] There were even governors who had a

---

[1] See Vol. 2 of this study.

[2] H. St George Saunders, *The Middlesex Hospital, 1745–1948*, p. 12, London, 1949

[3] J. D. Leader, *Sheffield Royal Infirmary, 1797–1897*, pp. 7–8, Sheffield, 1897

[4] *The Royal Kalendar or the Complete and Correct Annual Register for England for the Year 1798*, p. 304, London, 1799

[5] Howard, p. 133

financial interest in providing the hospital with supplies.[1]

In many hospitals regular subscribers were obtained by giving them the right to nominate a certain number of beneficiaries of the charity. They wrote letters of introduction for prospective patients and occupied a place on the board. There was no limit to the number of governors as there was no evident limit to the need for funds. Old governors recruited new governors from their friends and those who wished to be their friends. These 'open boards' grew larger and larger. Inevitably attendance was poor but there was always a danger that policy might alter according to which governors happened to appear at each meeting. The system worked, however, because of the large measure of authority which actually resided in the unpaid chairman, but it remained possible for governors to turn up in force and change the whole policy of the hospital.

The early foundations had for centuries employed both physicians and surgeons and remunerated them in cash and kind for the duties required of them. The governors of the newer foundations also drew their medical attendants from the class of practitioners whom they consulted themselves but these doctors were generally unpaid. And as time went on, the older foundations did not revise their salary rates to take account of increasing responsibilities or the current value of the services they were obtaining. Though modest payments continued to be made in some hospitals, the physicians and surgeons gradually acquired honorary status. Just as the governors provided lay supervision without payment, so the medical staffs were regarded as providing medical supervision without payment.

For generations the ancient hospitals of London had received the services of distinguished doctors. For example, Dr Mead, the physician of St Thomas' from 1703 to 1715, was among the most eminent of the period. It became the mark of the confidence of distinguished laymen to be asked to be a member of the honorary staff of a hospital. The doctors who accepted these appointments were making their own personal contribution to the relief of the poor. They were also retaining the good will of their patrons. In addition, there was a good chance of becoming medical adviser to the other lay members of the board.

The duties of the honorary medical staff were not arduous. At St Thomas' Hospital it was laid down in 1760 that the

---

[1] ibid., p. 138

physicians should meet in the doctors' room every Tuesday morning to see all patients able to attend. Then they would visit their respective wards.[1] The physicians and surgeons had also to go around the wards on Saturday mornings. The assistant physicians had to attend in the wards on Mondays, Wednesdays and Fridays: male outpatients were seen on Wednesdays and women and children on Fridays.[2] They had also to fill any gaps in the seniors' attendance.[3] In 1820, the physicians of St Bartholomew's Hospital had only to attend twice a week:

> Each went his complete rounds once a week only. On another day he saw a crowd of outpatients, new cases, which were admitted only on that occasion . . . and any old cases in emergency. In his absence, his patients, as well as those of his two brother officers, were nominally under the care of the very worthy and very little apothecary of the hospital. . . . The patients were really under the care of such of the physicians' pupils as considered themselves qualified.[4]

Apothecaries were also employed in some hospitals to do the junior medical work. In 1771, the resident apothecary at the Manchester Royal Infirmary 'took charge of the inmates in the absence of the honorary staff' and was 'answerable for the teaching and good conduct of the apprentices'.[5] John Howard reported instances 'in which *rest, regimen* and *cooling physic* has *saved* limbs which gentlemen of the faculty would have removed'. An operation could be prevented 'by the spirited exertions of the *good* old house apothecary'.

The paid staff of the hospital was small. Apart from the apothecary, the other three senior appointments were the steward, the hospitaller (minister or chaplain) and the matron. At Guy's Hospital in 1725, the first two of these were paid the same salary of £80 per annum, only £13 more than the butler. At St Thomas' Hospital it was the hospitaller's task in 1752 to 'frequently and carefully visit the Sick and Lame Poor in this

[1] F. G. Parsons, *The History of St Thomas' Hospital*, Vol. II, p. 217, in three volumes, London, 1932–6
[2] ibid.
[3] ibid.
[4] *The Life of Sir Robert Christison, Bart.* (edited by his sons), Vol. I, pp. 189–90, Edinburgh, 1885
[5] E. M. Brockbank, *The Foundation of Provincial Medical Education in England*, p. 57, Manchester, 1936

House for their Instruction and Consolation'.[1] At the Radcliffe
Infirmary, the chaplain was assisted by a deputy. It was this
last officer's task to censor all books presented to the hospital.[2]

The larger hospitals found it necessary to employ a senior
administrative officer. At the Middlesex, the post of 'clerk or
registrar' dated from 1748. He was paid ten guineas per annum
to 'collect the subscription money from the subscribers and pay
the same into the hands of the treasurer'.[3] By 1824, the post of
secretary offered £100 per annum plus residence. He had to
attend all committee meetings, write all the minutes and letters,
keep the accounts and inventories, and visit the wards daily.[4]
At St Thomas' Hospital, the steward could deputize for the
treasurer in granting leave to nurses, in granting permission
for dead bodies to be 'Opened, Dissected or Dismembered', or
in punishing patients who were absent from chapel. It was his
duty to give permission to the patients to stay out or sit up late
at night.[5]

The matron was a subordinate official. Her duties at St
Thomas' in 1752 were to 'take care that the Nurses do their Duty
diligently and that they lodge not out of the House'.[6] From 1755
she was paid £60 a year.[7] She was little more than a domestic
supervisor and housekeeper. She ordered the food and watched
over all the female staff.

Some of the early nurses apparently needed close supervision.
They were little more than domestic servants of a rather rough
and coarse type. Hospital work did not attract those with more
refined ways. Some nurses drank to excess and others were not of
high moral character. Their most common faults at Guy's
Hospital were to stay out without leave and take money from
patients and relatives.[8] But there were others who had learnt
their duties carefully from the doctors and had gained a fund of
knowledge and skill from their long experience working on the
same ward. In the early days the nurses did not always live and

[1] C. Graves, *The Story of St Thomas's*, *1106–1947*, p. 29, London, 1947
[2] A. G. Gibson, *The Radcliffe Infirmary*, p. 197, Oxford, 1926
[3] E. Wilson, *The History of the Middlesex Hospital*, p. 255, London, 1845
[4] ibid., pp. 263–4
[5] Graves, pp. 29–30
[6] ibid., p. 29
[7] Parsons, Vol. II, p. 213
[8] J. C. Steele, 'A Statistical Account of the Patients Treated in Guy's
Hospital during 1869', *Guy's Hospital Reports*, 3rd Series, Vol. XVI, p. 552

eat in the hospital. When accommodation was provided, it was often unattractive – in basements or attics as would have been thought appropriate for servants.

The patients were accommodated in lines of parallel beds on each side of the ward – an arrangement whose origin might be traced more to the customs of monasteries than to any early theories of ventilation. When John Howard visited all the hospitals in England and Wales in the late eighteenth century, he found that wards usually held between fifteen (St Bartholomew's) and thirty (Guy's) beds. The ceiling height varied enormously: at Leeds Infirmary the ceiling was fifteen feet eight inches high. The width of wards varied from seventeen feet (Western Hospital) to twenty-four feet (Royal Haslar, Portsmouth). Some of the beds were iron: they were painted green at Winchester County Hospital to contrast with the blue and white furniture. Other beds were wooden: those at Guy's were infested with bugs. The beds were covered with hair or straw mattresses and linen sheets. Above the beds at St Thomas' Hospital were 'semicircular irons for the curtains in winter'.[1] Under each bed at Guy's was a box which 'makes a seat when drawn out'.[2]

The rough wood floors were either washed or dry-rubbed with sand. At the Radcliffe Infirmary, this last practice was 'almost as bad as hiding the dirt with sand'.[3] Walls were whitewashed, though this had not been done for some years at the London and Middlesex Hospitals. Standards of hygiene varied widely. In many hospitals, Howard complained of closed windows and of 'offensiveness'. He reported that beds were not beaten and brushed regularly outside and expressed regret that bedding was not 'more frequently washed and aired'.[4] At Leeds Infirmary, however, there was great attention to cleanliness and there were 'no bugs in the beds'.[5] At Norfolk and Norwich Hospital, the preservation of the urine was 'a perquisite of the nurses'.[6] There were baths at many hospitals but the one at the London Hospital which was housed in a dirty cellar was never

[1] Howard, p. 134
[2] ibid., p. 135
[3] ibid., p. 171
[4] ibid., p. 136
[5] ibid., p. 192
[6] ibid., p. 154

used nor was the 'good cold bath' at the Westminster Hospital.[1]

Some hospitals, such as the Hereford County Infirmary and the Winchester County Asylums, had dining rooms adjoining the wards. In the big London hospitals the food provided consisted of a pint of water gruel or milk porridge for breakfast, eight ounces of meat or six ounces of cheese for dinner and broth for supper. There were no fresh vegetables. Each patient was allowed twelve to fourteen ounces of bread a day and two or three pints of beer. Vegetables and milk were frequently included in the diet of hospitals outside London.

In some hospitals the medical staff were given the right to admit accident cases, but the governors usually kept in their own hands the decisions about who should benefit from their charity by admission to the wards. Decisions were taken at a weekly meeting of the governors. Thus patients were admitted to St Thomas' on 'Ordinary Court Days'.[2] The duty of selecting patients for admission fell upon a group of governors known as the 'almoners'. At St Bartholomew's the almoners had for many years guarded their rights from any interference by the medical staff.[3] At Guy's, patients were admitted on 'Thursday in every week at eleven o'clock of the forenoon precisely'.[4] One effect of this system of admissions was to keep out many of the acutely sick.

There were some hospitals which tended to concentrate on 'curable' cases. This had been the practice at St Thomas' from the seventeenth century.[5] But cure had been slow. Thus at the end of 1644, St Bartholomew's Hospital had 249 occupied beds, having discharged 1,122 patients and buried 152 during the year. St Thomas' Hospital had 265 occupied beds at the end of 1644 and had discharged 1,063 patients and buried 248 during the year.[6] It was generally true for most hospitals in

[1] ibid., p. 136

[2] Graves, p. 28

[3] There were complaints at the hospital in 1664 that 'the apprentices to the three surgeons show pressing importunity and bould saucey carriage to the allmoners to enforce such persons to be admitted as they recommend for the remedy thereof'. E. Moberley Bell, *The Story of Hospital Almoners – The Birth of a Profession*, p. 18, London, 1961.

[4] H. C. Cameron, *Mr Guy's Hospital 1726-1948*, p. 59, London, 1954

[5] Parsons, Vol. II, p. 208

[6] *A True Report of the great Cofts and Charges of the foure Hospitals, in the City of London, in the maintenance of their great number of poore, this present year, 1644* (24th April, 1644)

1800 that patients were admitted for rest and tendance during
a period rather than as now for an operation or a definitive course
of medical treatment.[1]

There were many ambulant patients and they were required
to help with the work of the ward.[2] At St Thomas' in 1752,
patients were forbidden to stay out of the house after seven
o'clock in winter and eight o'clock in summer.[3] John Howard
reported in 1789 that at both St Thomas' and Guy's 'the patients
easily get out, there being no proper attention to the gates so
that the adjoining gin-shops often prevent the efficacy of
medicine and diet'.[4] It was even practicable for the governors
of St Thomas' Hospital to lay it down 'that the patients do
constantly attend the Worship of God in the Chapel on Sabbath
and other Days, on pain of forfeiting of one Day's Allowance for the first Offence, without reasonable excuse'.[5] Many
patients must have had more contact with the minister than
with the doctor.

The lives of the patients were subject to detailed rules and
regulations. These were read weekly in each ward in St Thomas'
Hospital. Men and women were rigidly separated. Little or no
attempt seems to have been made to provide entertainment other
than religious observances and the sick poor were specifically
forbidden to engage in most of their customary recreations. At
St Thomas', they were not allowed to curse or swear, or to 'revile
or miscall one another . . . nor abuse themselves by inordinate
Drinking, nor incontinent living'.[6] At the Radcliffe Infirmary,
patients were not allowed to play cards, dice, or any other game,
to smoke within doors, or 'behave themselves indecently'.[7]
This was the discipline imposed on patients only a few of whom
were acutely ill. The discipline was to remain long after the type
of patient admitted had changed.

The beneficiaries of the charities, though poor, were not

[1] Gibson, p. 195
[2] In the Radcliffe Infirmary Oxford, they carried coal to the wards,
worked in the laundry, and 'in 1784 the physicians and surgeons were
requested to notify the Secretary weekly those patients who might properly
be employed on the water engine'. Gibson, pp. 197–8
[3] Graves, p. 30
[4] Howard, p. 135
[5] Graves, p. 29
[6] Graves, p. 30
[7] Gibson, p. 195

wholly destitute. One reason for excluding the very poor was that the hospitals did not want to incur opprobrium by consigning their dead to pauper funerals nor were they prepared to incur the expense of funerals. Thus patients were often made to guarantee funeral expenses before admission.[1] Patients were not normally admitted to St Thomas' unless they had a certificate from a church warden or 'other substantial Person'[2] that they would be buried in the event of death without cost to the hospital. At St Bartholomew's the sum of 17s 6d had to be deposited or guaranteed for burial except by cases of sudden accident.[3] Neither the London Hospital nor the Westminster, however, required any surety for burial.[4]

At Guy's Hospital in 1788, patients were required to arrive

... with a change of Body-Linen, Stockings, Neckcloth, Stock, or Handkerchief, and to pay to the Sister Two Shillings and Nine-pence, for *two Towels, a Tin pot, a Knife, a Spoon, an Earthen Plate, and five Pairs of Sheets*, and if any part of the Number of Sheets is not expended during their Continuance, the Sister shall return Three-pence per Pair; and if any more is used they shall pay three-pence per Pair . . .[5]

John Howard reports of this hospital that he 'saw a woman bring her child and with tears in her eyes leave the fee of 2s 9d for the nurse and sixpence for the steward'.[6] It cost two shillings for an ordinary patient to be admitted at St Bartholomew's and 3s 6d at St Thomas', quite apart from the deposit for burial. 'Foul' and venereal patients had to pay more – seven shillings at St Bartholomew's and 10s 6d at St Thomas' plus fourpence a day for subsistence. There were no fees or charges at the London Hospital or the Westminster.[7]

By the eighteenth century, some hospitals were beginning to exclude certain conditions to protect the health or moral welfare of other patients. It was laid down at St Thomas' in 1752 that 'no Person be received who is visited or suspected to be visited

---

[1] J. Langdon-Davies, *Westminster Hospital – Two Centuries of Voluntary Service, 1719–1948*, p. 63, London, 1952
[2] Graves, p. 28
[3] Howard, p. 132
[4] ibid., pp. 131 and 136
[5] Cameron, p. 74
[6] Howard, p. 136
[7] ibid., pp. 131–6

with the Plague, Itch, Scald-Head, or other Infectious Diseases'.[1] In London, smallpox cases were admitted to a special hospital set up to treat such cases. The Newcastle Infirmary admitted fever and skin cases until 1774 when the governors decided to exclude them. In the Chester General Infirmary there were still two fever wards in 1789. John Howard found them 'not in the least offensive'.[2] There were, however, very strict rules.

> No fever patients, nor their nurses, are suffered to go into other parts of the house . . . nor any stranger, unless accompanied by the apothecary or his assistant. . . . The floors of the wards are to be washed very clean twice a week, and near the beds every day. . . . All the bedclothes . . . are to be marked FEVER WARD, and all the knives, forks, pots, cups and other utensils are to be of a peculiar colour. . . .[3]

A number of hospitals also started to exclude venereal disease in the eighteenth century. The Westminster Hospital took this decision in 1738 and the Manchester Royal Infirmary followed in 1753. In 1805, the Middlesex Hospital restricted the admission of venereal disease patients to the relatively wealthy by demanding a payment of two guineas per week.[4]

The main provision for venereal diseases in London was at the Lock Hospital with about sixty beds in 1789. It was the policy of this hospital never to re-admit a patient who had once been discharged. As John Howard commented, 'This charity gives encouragement to repentance . . . yet it destroys all incentive to presumption.'[5]

Very few children were admitted to the general hospitals. Thus, for example, the Radcliffe Infirmary in its rules of 1770 refused to admit them at all.[6] One reason for such a policy was that children were frequently subject to infection. There were, however, other reasons for relatively few child patients. Dr George Armstrong, who founded the first children's dispensary at Red Lion Square in 1769,[7] refused to support a proposal for

---

[1] Graves, p. 28
[2] Howard, p. 208
[3] ibid., p. 209
[4] Saunders, p. 21
[5] Howard, p. 138
[6] Gibson, p. 195
[7] G. F. Still, *The History of Paediatrics*, p. 418, London, 1931

a children's hospital on the grounds that 'it very seldom happens that a mother can conveniently go into an hospital to attend her sick infant'.[1] During the eighteenth century it appears to have been accepted that the mother should live in the hospital with her child – an idea only recently revived. 'If you take away a sick child from its parents or nurse you break its heart immediately. . . .'[2] Dr Armstrong thought that it would be impossible to run a hospital where 'the Mothers and Nurses [would] be perpetually at variance with one another . . . if there must be a nurse to each Child what kind of Hospital must there be to contain any number of them?'[3]

There had been times in the medieval history of St Thomas' Hospital when unmarried mothers had been admitted for confinement,[4] and the Middlesex Hospital was in its early days partly used for maternity cases.[5] With these exceptions, institutional provision for maternity cases developed apart from the general hospitals. Although the fashionable man-midwives of the eighteenth century were licentiates of the College of Physicians, the practice of obstetrics was virtually a separate profession entered by a separate apprenticeship. It was known, moreover, that women in childbirth could be a dangerous source of infection.

Thus general hospitals were beginning to exclude certain types of cases. It was generally believed that children should not be admitted to hospital at all, that the management of confinement was not a proper responsibility for the physicians and surgeons who staffed the hospitals, and some hospitals had recognized the dangers of admitting cases which were infectious or contagious. In addition, St Thomas' Hospital had begun to concentrate on 'curable' cases. With these exceptions, and the exclusion of the indigent, whose needs were possibly the greatest, hospitals tried to meet all types of medical and surgical needs among 'the sick and lame poor'. In the endowed hospitals, a patient with an influential patron stood more chance of being admitted than a patient who lacked all influence. In the other

[1] ibid., p. 420
[2] ibid.
[3] ibid.
[4] E. M. McInnes, *St Thomas' Hospital*, pp. 19 and 36, London, 1963
[5] H. R. Spencer, *The History of British Midwifery from 1650 to 1800*, pp. 179–81, London, 1927

hospitals, the recommendation of a subscriber was almost essential.

Patients included those who required some active treatment and those who only needed custodial care. After St Thomas' formally laid it down that incurable cases should be excluded, one of its governors (Mr Guy) founded, with money he had made in speculation, a sister hospital specifically for incurable and mental cases. But the early decision of the governors of St Thomas' Hospital to concentrate on curable cases proved to be an important precedent. It was not many years before Mr Guy's hospital began to exclude the type of patient it was founded to treat.

CHAPTER 2

Material for Teaching and Research

THE scientific awakening of the eighteenth century affected the theory and practice of medicine. The abstract ideas of physicians and surgeons were beginning to be challenged by empirical research. There was a new interest in anatomy. In Paris and in Edinburgh, medical research workers purchased corpses through the criminal underworld so that they could learn by careful dissection more about the workings of the human body. New fields of medicine were opened up – the study of the bones, the eyes and ears. New diagnostic aids were gradually developed, particularly the stethoscope, which was invented in 1819. The new empiricism came somewhat late to London.

In the first half of the nineteenth century, the average number of patients in hospitals in England and Wales increased from about 3,000 to nearly 8,000. Old hospitals were enlarged and new hospitals were founded both in London and in the provinces. The interest in hospitals which had been growing in the later years of the eighteenth century broadened and spread to wider social groups and to remote communities. As villages expanded into towns and towns into cities in the great drift to urban living generated by the developing industries, there were more and more places where it became practicable to attract the staff and patients for a hospital. The growth of the hospital 'movement' was made possible by the money given by the public; but the major impetus in channelling charitable bequests and donations in this direction came increasingly from doctors. They wanted hospitals for teaching and research.

Before the founding of the hospital medical schools, medical teaching had been conducted by a combination of theoretical instruction and somewhat casual apprenticeship. In 1800, teaching was primarily conducted by private profit-making schools: only three London hospitals had schools attached.[1]

[1] St Bartholomew's, the United Hospitals (St Thomas' and Guy's) and the London

The foundation of the College of Surgeons in that year led to a closer association between medical education and hospitals. At the start of the College, the examination for membership could be taken after one course in anatomy and one in surgery.[1] In 1813, the College added the further requirement of a year's attendance on the surgical practice in a hospital.[2] The Society of Apothecaries required for its examination, under the Apothecaries Act of 1815, not only theoretical studies and five years' apprenticeship but also six months' hospital or infirmary or dispensary practice.[3] Many apothecaries took the membership examination of the College of Surgeons as well, to enable them to be dually qualified.

For these reasons, there was a rush of students to the hospitals in the second decade of the nineteenth century. It is reported that, in the early 1820's, the theatre of St Thomas' Hospital 'was crowded in every part by upwards of four hundred students of the most respectable description; in fact, we never before witnessed so genteel a surgical class: the sight was most pleasing, for they all appeared gentlemen of cultivated manners and good education.'[4] All these students paid three guineas or more and the greater part of the money went into the pocket of the lecturer.

Gradually more and more hospitals acquired associated medical schools: more hospital surgeons took on teaching responsibilities and more hospitals were founded: the supply responded to the demand. While in the eighteenth century hospitals had been founded by laymen to meet the needs of the sick poor, in the first half of the nineteenth century many hospitals were founded to serve the needs of medical students and their teachers. Thus in 1828 University College opened first a dispensary and shortly afterwards an inpatient department to provide teaching material for its medical school. Some teaching hospitals owed their foundation partly or wholly to the initiative of doctors. This was the case with both St Mary's and Charing Cross.[5] By 1858, there were twelve London hospitals with medical

[1] Newman, p. 18
[2] ibid.
[3] ibid., p. 70
[4] S. Sprigge, *The Life and Times of Sir Thomas Wakley*, p. 77, London, 1899
[5] *H of L Select Committee on Metropolitan Hospitals 1890–3*, First Report (392), para. 2169, HMSO, 1890

schools;[1] 80 per cent of the general hospital beds in London were in teaching hospitals.[2]

The hospitals offered many advantages for medical education. As the importance of practical illustration became recognized, a storehouse of different types of cases made it possible to give varied demonstrations to large classes of students. While the paying patient had a legitimate right to object to being observed and prodded by a group of students, a person in receipt of charity was hardly in a position to complain about such invasions of his privacy. Moreover, the collection of a large number of cases in one building made possible the classification of different cases. While the apprentice could only learn about such cases as his master happened to be attending on any particular day, the hospital student could 'walk the wards'. In the early days, such walks were casual and irregular; it was not until much later they became planned in a systematic manner.

The practice of having a group of patients with similar diseases sorted into separate outpatient clinics or placed in adjacent beds had advantages for research as well as teaching. Experiments with different forms of treatment became easier. And if an experiment failed, at least there would not be repercussions on the doctors' private practices.

With the development of organized teaching, a hospital could get £500 from a student articled as hospital-apprentice.[3] A resident pupil paid 1,000 guineas and gained thereby the first but not exclusive claim to a surgical appointment at the hospital.[4] Even a surgical dressership cost 10 guineas or more.[5] The direct earnings from teaching could be large. For example, in 1816, Mr Brodie earned £1,530 from fees and lectures at St George's Hospital.[6] Teaching was also a profitable investment because pupils sent their own wealthy private patients in later years for remunerative consultations. It became known by private

[1] St Bartholomew's, Charing Cross, St George's, Guy's, King's College, the London, St Mary's, the Middlesex, the Royal Free, St Thomas', University College, the Westminster. Newman, p. 115

[2] Calculated from statistics given in *Sixth Report of the Medical Officer of the Privy Council 1863*, 8034, Appendix No. 15, Dr Bristowe and Mr Holmes, *The Hospitals of the United Kingdom*, HMSO, 1864

[3] Newman, p. 121

[4] ibid.

[5] ibid.

[6] G. T. Bettany, *Eminent Doctors*, Vol. I, p. 292, London, 1885

patients that the hospital staffs possessed the most advanced knowledge. Charitable work became the key to fame and fortune.

Just as the governors purchased or inherited their position of honour in the hospital, so the practice grew up of the honorary medical staffs handing on their posts to close relatives or selling the right to succession by charging exorbitant apprenticeship fees. In the 1820's, appointments to hospitals 'were obtainable only by family or money influence. . . . At Guy's and St Thomas' . . . the surgeons and assistant surgeons formed a snug family party.'[1] The duties of surgeon at a large teaching hospital were not very arduous. As late as 1848, when there were 397 beds for surgical patients at St Bartholomew's, only about 400 operations were performed in the year. Between 80 and 100 of these were amputations.[2]

In view of the glittering prizes received by the 'great men' – the leading physicians and surgeons – and the wide opportunities for intellectual and professional satisfaction, it is not surprising that there were attracted to work in the hospitals many more enterprising and ambitious young doctors than could be accommodated on the staffs. The student who wished to reach the top of his profession had to get on the staff of a London teaching hospital and gain a fellowship of one of the Royal Colleges. Only the wealthiest young men could reasonably expect to reach such heights.[3] The cost of election (without examination) to a fellowship of the College of Physicians was over £110 and the same distinction at the College of Surgeons cost £31 but did involve an examination.[4]

There was not much room at the top of the medical profession. Out of about 15,000 practitioners registered in 1860, fewer than 1,200 were working in 117 of the larger voluntary hospitals.

[1] Clarke, p. 4

[2] H. Graham, *Surgeons All*, p. 362, London, 1939

[3] 'Fees ranged in the London School between £71 8s 0d at the Westminster and £100 16s 0d at King's for all the classes and hospital practice required for a diploma; in the provinces, fees were less, £52 10s 0d for the same provision at Queen's College, Birmingham, for instance. These fees were still, compared with modern money values, high.' Newman, p. 122

[4] The total examination cost of becoming a licentiate of the Royal College of Physicians was £56 17s 0d. Election to a fellowship cost a further £55 15s 0d. Membership of the Royal College of Surgeons cost £21 and the admission of a member to fellowship cost another £10.

Of these, only 579 were classified as being 'physicians and surgeons who have charge of inpatients'.[1] The remainder were assistants and junior housemen.

Promotion to the ranks of honorary physicians and surgeons was very slow, especially in London. The posts had a high monopoly value and there was little incentive then as now for those enjoying the benefits of hospital appointments to recommend that new posts should be created. There was a natural reluctance to share the spoils. Abernethy, a 'great man' of English surgery between 1814 and 1827, was kept in the subordinate position of assistant surgeon for twenty-eight years, before being elected principal surgeon.[2] A number of London hospitals introduced new rules by which physicians and surgeons had to retire on reaching sixty-five years.[3]

It was fairly common for candidates for positions on the staff to canvass the whole body of governors. In the smaller hospitals, extra votes could be purchased: 'as the votes were recorded, the friends of the losing candidate would take money from their pockets to make "faggot" voters, and so the battle would be waged between the combatants until the capacity to pay more was exhausted.'[4] Howard considered it a 'scandalous abuse, by which the lives and health of the poor are in a manner put up to auction'.[5]

In time, the system of purchase by 'faggot votes' or by exorbitant apprenticeship fees fell into disuse and gradually special committees were set up to recommend new appointments consisting either of laymen and representatives of the honorary staff or solely of the latter. But whichever system was adopted, the good opinion of the existing staff was essential. And to gain this, candidates were prepared to be blatantly exploited.

During years of anxious waiting, juniors did the routine work of the hospital. They selected suitable cases for their seniors from the herd of outpatients. They gave day-to-day supervision to their seniors' patients in the wards while they were absent. Thus 'at the Westminster, Sir Anthony Carlisle, the senior

---

[1] F. Buckle, *Vital and Economical Statistics of the Hospitals for the Year 1863*, p. 79, London, 1865
[2] E. Mapother, *The Medical Profession*, p. 118, Dublin, 1868
[3] ibid.
[4] Clarke, p. 299
[5] Howard, p. 97

surgeon, had between thirty and forty beds in 1838, but frequently left his patients in the care of former housemen'.[1] Gradually the juniors took over the work which had previously been that of the apothecary. The title of apothecary for the resident medical officer was abolished in the London Hospital in 1854,[2] in St Thomas' Hospital in 1871,[3] and in the Middlesex Hospital in 1886.[4] There was now no role for a general practitioner in a large teaching hospital.

In most hospitals, the juniors did all this work without payment. But gradually small salaries were introduced for resident medical officers – between £50 and £100 per annum with full board. There were also in some hospitals very junior posts available for 'diligent students' for which payment was demanded.[5] In many provincial hospitals, even the most experienced 'registrars' were forbidden to engage in private practice lest they take business away from their seniors.

Thus there accumulated in each hospital a group of exploited and frustrated young doctors. The lack of promotion opportunities was not the only reason for discontent. As the frontiers of medicine advanced, the younger generation of doctors developed special interests in particular diseases and techniques. Separate outpatient clinics were developed for cases which they made their special field of study. For further progress special equipment and a group of beds set aside for the new speciality were required and this needed the consent and co-operation of the senior medical staff and the governors, which were not readily forthcoming. Unless a hospital was rapidly expanding, a new speciality could only be accommodated at the expense of an old one.

The old guard of 'great men' fought against the sectionalization of medicine. They clung on to their beds and refused to see limited resources diverted to new departments. The aspiring specialist found himself blocked and thwarted by the older generation of physicians and surgeons, who were general practitioners in their respective fields and controlled the general hospitals.

[1] Langdon-Davies, p. 169
[2] E. W. Morris, *A History of the London Hospital*, p. 159, London, 1926
[3] Parsons, Vol. III, p. 172
[4] *Hospital Gazette*, May 1913, p. 174
[5] W. Dale, *The State of the Medical Profession in Great Britain and Ireland*, p. 47, Dublin, 1875

One reason for specializing was the pursuit of knowledge. The young doctor with a meagre practice had little hope of demonstrating to the influential patient that his total skill was greater than that of his senior. It was, however, easier to cultivate a reputation for special skill in treating one particular condition. Specialization was a form of self-advertisement.

Thus the reaction of some of the dissatisfied and ambitious specialists to the frustration of the general hospitals was to go off and found a special hospital. There was a rapid growth of special hospitals throughout the nineteenth century both in London and in the provinces. In the case of London it was estimated later that four new special hospitals were founded in the eighteen-thirties, seven in the forties, and eight in the fifties. In the sixties no less than sixteen special hospitals were started.[1]

The first special hospitals had been started to make provision for patients who could not be safely accommodated in the general hospitals and for patients whom the Royal Colleges were not interested in treating. The practice of obstetrics had developed apart from the main stream of medicine. The President of the Royal College of Physicians in 1827 held that 'midwifery was an act foreign to the habits of a gentleman of enlarged academic education'.[2] Questions on the subject were conspicuous by their absence in the examinations for membership of the Royal College of Surgeons and for the licentiate of the Royal College of Physicians. The surgeons regarded the subject as the responsibility of the physicians, but in the licentiate paper of the Royal College of Physicians only two questions on the subject appeared between 1848 and 1858.[3] Not until the 1850's were lectures in midwifery given in all medical schools.

Lying-in hospitals had been founded in London in the eighteenth century. The initiative for founding these early maternity hospitals came largely from doctors who had specialized in obstetrics. In 1739, Sir Richard Manningham, the leading man-midwife of his day, had started lying-in wards in a

[1] *H of L Select Committee on Metropolitan Hospitals 1890-3*, Third Report (321), p. iv, HMSO, 1893

[2] Sir Arthur Newsholme, *International Studies on the Relation between the Private and Official Practice of Medicine*, Vol. III, *England and Wales, Scotland and Ireland*, p. 146, London, 1931

[3] J. M. M. Kerr *et al.* (eds.), *Historical Review of British Obstetrics and Gynaecology*, p. 298, Edinburgh & London, 1954

house adjoining his residence in Jermyn Street.[1] In 1752, these wards became the General Lying-in Hospital (now Queen Charlotte's).[2] This hospital was used for teaching, which became a very substantial source of income to the staff of the hospital.[3] In 1791, the hospital was stated to be for 'poor pregnant women, as well married as unmarried'.[4]

The General Lying-In was not, however, the first lying-in hospital. The British Lying-In Hospital was founded in 1749 (now the British Hospital for Mothers and Babies, Woolwich), and the City of London Lying-In in 1750: the latter was founded for married women only. When the New Westminster Lying-In (now the General Lying-In)was opened in 1767, it was stated to be for 'wives of poor men and particularly of soldiers and sailors'.[5] It also admitted unmarried mothers 'such as are deserted, and in deep distress, to save them from despair, and the lamentable crimes of suicide and child murder'.[6] Two years later it had to report that in a period of five-and-a-half months, 14 out of the 63 patients had died of puerperal fever.[7]

While the separate development of the practice of obstetrics was originally responsible for the separate development of maternity hospitals, the danger of infection kept them separate. It was continuously observed that puerperal women in lying-in hospitals were 'highly susceptible to the poison of contagious fevers' and 'sensitive of those conditions on which pyaemia and erysipelas depend'.[8] Many leaders of opinion (including Miss Nightingale) doubted whether maternity hospitals ought to exist at all. It was obviously undesirable to expose pregnant women to the infections of a general hospital or general hospital patients to the infections which were known to develop in maternity hospitals. Thus the separate provision of maternity hospitals had a similar rationale to the separate provision of hospitals for smallpox and infectious diseases. The only London

[1] G. C. Peachey, *Proceedings of the Roya Society of Medicine* (*Epidemic & State Medical Section*) Vol. XXVII, 1924, p. 72. Quoted in Spencer, p. 16
[2] Spencer, p. 16
[3] Kerr *et al.*, p. 294
[4] H. Graham, *Eternal Eve*, p. 310, London, 1950
[5] ibid.
[6] ibid.
[7] Spencer, p. 105
[8] Bristowe and Holmes, pp. 567–8

smallpox hospital was founded in 1746,[1] and in the same year
the Lock Hospital for venereal diseases was started.[2]

A third type of specialist hospital began to be founded early
in the nineteenth century for reasons similar to those which
had led to the separate foundation of maternity hospitals. The
treatment of eye diseases had been 'tacitly abandoned, even
by the hospital surgeons, and turned over to the oculists'.[3] There
had been eye dispensaries treating outpatients in the late
eighteenth century,[4] but not until the beginning of the
nineteenth century were the first eye hospitals opened. Partly
because of the heavy incidence of trachoma in soldiers returning
from the Napoleonic Wars, two special hospitals were founded
in the early years of the new century – one under royal patronage
and the other with the full backing of the medical staffs of Guy's
and St Thomas' Hospitals.[5] Between 1808 and 1832 at least
nineteen eye hospitals were founded in the provinces, of which
eleven were to survive.[6] In London, there were six eye hospitals
in 1866; by that time, however, there were seven ophthalmic
departments in the general hospitals.[7]

It was not until 1851 that the first children's hospital (Liverpool Children's Hospital) was opened in Britain. This was also
a field of work which had been neglected by the general hospitals.
For reasons given in Chapter 1 it had been believed that a
children's hospital would be both cruel and impracticable. It
was known, moreover, that children were particularly likely
to develop infectious diseases.[8] Extremely few children had been
admitted to the general hospitals. When children had to be
admitted, Miss Nightingale favoured the usual practice of

[1] A. Highmore, *The History, Design and Present State of the various Public
Charities In and Near London*, p. 275, London, 1814
[2] ibid., p. 142
[3] E. T. Collins, *The History and Traditions of the Moorfields Eye Hospital*, p. 8,
London, 1929
[4] A. Sorsby, 'Defunct London Eye Hospitals', *British Journal of Ophthalmology*, February 1936, pp. 77–8
[5] The Royal Infirmary for Diseases of the Eye in 1804, and Moorfields
in 1805. See Sorsby, p. 80.
[6] Sorsby, 'Nineteenth Century Provincial Eye Hospitals', *British Journal
of Ophthalmology*, September 1946, p. 504
[7] Sorsby, 'Defunct London Eye Hospitals', p. 77
[8] T. Higgins, *Great Ormond Street 1852–1952*, p. 8, London, 1952. See also
A. H. Coughtrey, 'Growth of Children's Dispensaries and Hospitals',
Hospital Gazette, November 1916, pp. 21–3.

putting the younger children in female adult wards and the older in the men's adult wards as in her view the patients 'often became the child's best protector and nurse'.[1]

In London, the first children's hospital was Great Ormond Street, which was opened in 1852 for children between the ages of two and twelve suffering from diseases

> ... peculiar to, or modified in some important respect by their early age. . . . Infants and children under two years of age are not generally eligible for admission as inpatients, it being undesirable on account of their tender age to separate them from their mothers. Such young children, however, are eligible as outpatients and, under special circumstances ... may be received into the hospital with or without their mother.[2]

'At first there were so few applicants ... that it seemed as if the hospital was not needed.'[3] Soon, however, the new idea caught on: moreover, more and more infants were admitted, 'to the great anxiety of the Board of Management'.[4] And after this shaky start, children's hospitals spread all over the country. In 1853, children's hospitals were started in Norwich and Manchester. In the 1860's, at least six new hospitals for children were started in London and six in the provinces.[5]

Thus many special hospitals were started because there were needs which were not being catered for by the general hospitals. Fever, maternity, eye and children's hospitals certainly fall into this category, at least in their early days. So also does the Royal Hospital for Incurables at Putney, founded in 1854 by public subscription. The latter was far from adequate to meet the needs of this type of patient. By 1890 it accommodated only 38 men and 180 women.[6] Apart from this and some other small excep-

[1] Higgins, p. 18
[2] ibid.
[3] ibid., p. 24
[4] ibid., p. 32
[5] A. H. Coughtrey, 'Founders of Hospitals', *Hospita Gazette*, January 1917, pp. 59–61
[6] *Select Committee on Metropolitan Hospitals 1890–3*, Third Report, p. lxii and Evidence, para. 25708. Sir Henry Burdett found his attempts to visit this hospital 'a most amusing experience because it is unique; and it is unique in the sense that even in Russia they gave me greater facilities for entering the hospitals than I could get out of the Royal Hospital for Incurables at Putney.'

tions the main provision made for the chronic sick was by the
Poor Law authorities.

Occasionally the founding of special hospitals for particular
types of case was due to the sympathy of a group of laymen for
persons suffering from that condition. Thus Miss Johanna
Chandler found that no general hospital would admit her grand-
mother who was suffering from paralysis: she devoted many
years of her life to looking after her. She determined to start a
hospital for such cases though she was neither well-connected
nor affluent. She began raising funds by making and selling
artificial flowers and trinkets. In time, her cause won the support
of the Lord Mayor, David Weir, and interested some wealthy
City gentlemen. As a result, in 1860, the National Hospital for
Nervous Diseases was opened in Queen Square. Miss Chandler
had envisaged a home for incurables. Probably owing to Weir's
insistence, the hospital only admitted 'persons whose cases do
not appear incurable'.[1]

It was, however, unusual for the initiative for founding a
special hospital to come from laymen. Most of them were
founded by doctors and their motives were inevitably mixed.
At one extreme was the desire of doctors to help the sick and,
in the process, to advance science. At the other extreme was
the desire of a doctor who was excluded from the existing
hospitals or was denied promotion to advance his own career
by self-advertisement. In many cases, both motives were at
work. Some of the hospitals for eye diseases and for children
were not wholly founded to benefit the poor. Thus John Cun-
ningham Saunders was a protégé of Astley Cooper at St Thomas'
Hospital who had little hope of a hospital appointment as he had
not been articled for six years at the Royal College of Surgeons.
He went off to Gravesend, 'anxious about his future prospects',
but was summoned back by Cooper in a letter ending, 'I shall
endeavour to make your situation comfortable in a pecuniary
point of view, but I had rather make that the subject of conversation when I see you.'[2] Saunders was made comfortable
from a pecuniary point of view by the foundation of Moorfields
Hospital.

It was not difficult to start a special hospital. A grateful patient
might be persuaded to put up the money for the purchase of the

[1] G. Holmes, *The National Hospital, Queen Square*, p. 9, London, 1954
[2] Collins, pp. 5–6

premises. But failing this, the money could be extracted from the public by skilful advertisement. The process was described some years later to a Select Committee of the House of Lords:

> Someone would be got, a young man who had not a great deal to do, who would work the thing . . . and he would issue a number of advertisements pointing out that such a hospital had long been wanted, and supplied a great void . . . an arrangement would be made by which the secretary would receive a certain proportion of the receipts, and he would get some friend to advance a little money, and they would take an old house, perhaps a tumble-down house which no one else would be got to rent . . . and he would fit up a few beds in it, and open an outpatient department and then the thing is done.[1]

In time the field covered by the special hospitals extended from those treating conditions not properly catered for by the general hospitals to those treating conditions which were being handled by the general hospitals. The new specialists began to compete both with the hospital practice and with the private practice of the surgeons and physicians. The monopoly power of the clique of doctors who controlled hospital appointments in the London general hospitals began to be undermined. Hospitals were started to treat conditions such as cancer, the stone and fistula: to treat particular parts of the body such as the skin, ears and rectum. There were even hospitals founded to provide specific forms of treatment such as hydrotherapy or to practice particular theories of medicine such as homoeopathy. There was, however, no great urge to make adequate hospital provision for the diseases which caused the heaviest death rate among the poor (fevers and tuberculosis). Nearly all the special hospitals met needs which were common among the rich as well as the poor. They were, moreover, needs which the patient could recognize for himself. A patient with pain in his eyes, ears, nose or throat would have little doubt which hospital was purporting to treat his ailment.

Thus the distinctive feature of specialist hospitals was the fact that most of them were founded and controlled by doctors. While the general hospitals had been mostly started by charitable laymen who had solicited aid from doctors, the specialist

[1] *Select Committee on Metropolitan Hospitals 1890-3*, First Report, Evidence, para. 1092 (Dr H. Hardy)

hospitals were mostly started by doctors who solicited aid from laymen. The new hospitals met the needs of their founders in a variety of different ways. They provided clinical material and resources for the development of skill unhampered by the obstruction and surveillance of the 'great men'. Secondly, they could be used to attract private patients. An advertisement extolling the work of a hospital was a legitimate means of raising money to help the sick poor, but it had the effect of enhancing the reputation of the doctor who ran it. Some of the specialists were indirect beneficiaries of the charities they created.

There undoubtedly were hospitals providing somewhat spurious treatments and hospitals which involved an unnecessary duplication of facilities. This became more evident when belatedly the general hospitals set up special departments in the fields whose neglect had contributed to the growth of special hospitals. But these factors do not wholly account for the indiscriminate condemnation of special hospitals by the leaders of opinion, both medical and lay. Many doctors were opposed to specialization as a matter of principle, others resented the loss of 'teaching material'[1] and private practice: both the lay governors and medical staffs of the general hospitals objected to the diversion of charitable funds elsewhere.

In 1853, the *British Medical Journal* made a bitter attack on special hospitals: 'Half the special hospitals [were] founded in the grossest self-seeking on the part of some individual. . . . An energetic surgeon makes up his mind to step to fame and fortune by means of bricks and mortar.'[2] The matter came to a head in 1860 when it was proposed to set up a Hospital for Stone and Diseases of the Urinary Organs – St Peter's Hospital. A protest movement was organized and gathered in it all the leading figures and representative bodies of medicine. A manifesto was prepared condemning 'the modern practice of opening small institutions, under the name of hospitals, for particular forms of disease, in the treatment of which no other management, appliance or attention is required than is already supplied in the existing general hospitals'.[3]

In the same year, *The Lancet* spoke of the special hospitals as a 'monstrous evil – an evil which springs from within the pro-

[1] See *BMJ*, 29 July 1860, p. 582.
[2] ibid., 16 June 1860, p. 458
[3] C. Morson, *St Peter's Hospital for Stone 1860–1960*, p. 5, London, 1960

fession'.[1] The question of special hospitals was debated at the Annual Meeting of the British Medical Association at Torquay. It was resolved that a committee should be set up to investigate the whole question of hospital management throughout the country.[2] One speaker, W. O. Markham, later to become editor of the *British Medical Journal*, said that 'the gentlemen engaged in those [special] hospitals got their names spread all over England, but in the meantime the profession was being ruined'.[3]

In 1863, *The Lancet* launched an attack on 'this rampant evil of over-weening specialism'.[4] Three doctors responsible for 'the slough of selfish specialism' were named – Mr Lobb of the Galvanic Hospital, Mr Westlake of the Dispensary for Ulcerated Legs and Dr Mackenzie of the Dispensary for Diseases of the Throat. 'Next may come a Quinine Hospital, an Hospital for Treatment by Cod Liver Oil, by the Hypophosphates, or by the Excrement of Boa-Constrictors.' Mr Lobb of the Galvanic Hospital wrote to defend himself:

> ... the London Galvanic Hospital was not established until after I had failed in my endeavour to become connected with my 'alma mater', St Bartholomew's. I offered to undertake the treatment with galvanism of a certain number of picked cases from the out-patients to be handed over to me by the assistant physicians. This offer was backed by the sanction and with the encouragement of the whole medical and surgical staff of the hospital with the exception of Mr Lawrence (whose antipathy to all change is so well known), and the apothecary with whose privileges it would in some way have interfered. ...
>
> I am prepared at any time to relinquish the London Galvanic Hospital upon being placed in an established London hospital, in an honourable and independent position, a ward being set aside for the treatment of suitable cases with the aid of galvanism ...[5]

In 1864, the foundation of St Peter's Hospital for the Care of Stone in the Bladder and Urinary Diseases was derided by the *British Medical Journal*: 'Cutting for stone and crushing stones are very limited occupations. ... The establishment of a small

[1] *Lancet*, Vol. II, 1860, p. 88
[2] *BMJ*, 11 August 1860, p. 628
[3] ibid.
[4] *Lancet*, Vol. I, 1863, p. 183
[5] ibid., p. 219

home under the very shadow of Middlesex Hospital, is it not, in a charitable sense, playing the farce of charity?[1] The hospital had on its staff a Mr Walter John Coulson who was also a surgeon at St Mary's Hospital. St Mary's told him either to leave the staff of the hospital or give up the special hospital. He decided to leave St Mary's.[2] Similarly, the Treasurer of St Thomas' Hospital laid it down that no member of the medical staff could work in a special hospital.[3] In 1864, on the other hand, Moorfields laid it down that no surgeon could hold an *ophthalmic* appointment in another hospital.[4]

The doctors who founded special hospitals used more forceful methods of raising money than the more conservative general hospitals. They were in a hurry and not prepared to wait for subscriptions to come in. They employed secretaries to go out and raise funds. In some hospitals he was the senior administrative officer and delegated his other duties to a steward. There were, however, some older establishments such as the Brompton Hospital for Diseases of the Chest which used the traditional method of selling life governorships with the right to give subscribers' tickets for sums of thirty guineas or less. But it is significant that in the smaller institutions such as St Mark's and the Skin Hospital at Blackfriars, the doctors appealed for subscriptions without offering any rights to subscribers in return for their money. The doctors kept in their own hands the right to select the patients who were to benefit from the charity.

There were some hospitals which were not prepared to have their activities limited by the funds which could be collected from donors. They developed the practice of extracting charges from outpatients when this was practicable. Those who could afford it paid 1s or 2s 6d for 'advice'. This service attracted some better-off patients who would not have attended at a general hospital. They could not afford the customary guinea for a private consultation with a physician or surgeon, but the charges made at the hospital were within their means and broadly in line with those made by general practitioners. Teachers, clerks, and tradesmen were attracted to the special hospitals to the

[1] *BMJ*, 19 November 1864, pp. 582–3
[2] *Select Committee on Metropolitan Hospitals 1890–3*, First Report, para. 19559
[3] *BMJ*, 14 September 1889, p. 620
[4] Sorsby, 'Defunct London Eye Hospitals', p. 97

detriment of their general practitioners. For this reason, general practitioners joined in the general outcry against special hospitals.

There was a strong element of true charity in the motives of medical men who accepted honorary posts in the early days of the voluntary hospitals. Later there came others who used hospitals for research and teaching, and found that their hospital appointments brought them tangible rewards in fees for teaching and in the enhancement of their professional reputations. Most of the special hospitals were started to initiate medical work in fields which had previously been neglected but there were some which were started for less creditable reasons. Those who attacked the special hospitals greatly exaggerated the number of undesirable establishments. Many important advances in medical knowledge and techniques were made in the special hospitals and incorporated later on in the teaching and practice of the general hospitals.

CHAPTER 3

The Administration of Voluntary Hospitals

D URING the first half of the nineteenth century teaching
played a larger role in hospitals, and more teaching hospitals
were founded both in London and the provinces. The number of
operations increased and so did the number of patients who
were admitted and discharged. As hospitals became more active,
the task of running them became more complex and the problem
of financing them more burdensome. And the actions taken by
the lay governors became matters which increasingly concerned
their honorary medical staff.

Gradually the governors of the larger hospitals appointed
small sub-committees to supervise day-to-day management.[1]
Many of these 'house committees' found it necessary to appoint a
senior administrative officer of higher standing than had previously been required. The secretary or house governor took
over many of the duties which had previously been undertaken
by the unpaid treasurers and governors, particularly that of
fund-raising. Sometimes the appointment of a secretary preceded
the establishment of a 'house committee' but the direction of
change remained the same.[2] The process took place later in the
provinces than in London as the provincial hospitals were slower
to reach the size and complexity requiring it.

The secretary tended to be drawn from the governors' own
social circle – though he was often one of the less well endowed
members. At the Westminster Hospital, the secretary was
expected to notify deaths, admit inpatients between house
committee meetings, undertake fund-raising, see that hospital

[1] Some 'house committees' were started in the eighteenth century.

[2] An example of the way in which this transition occurred is shown in the
history of the Westminster Hospital. In 1826, a medical committee was
appointed to advise the executive committee of 300 governors. When a new
secretary was appointed in 1832, the post was vested with real authority and
status for the first time. Three years later a house committee was established.
Langdon-Davies, pp. 142–3

rules were maintained, dismiss unruly patients, visit wards daily, prevent smoking, visit kitchens, keep an eye on all provisions, supervise repairs and 'attend to every department of the Hospital with vigilance, discretion and activity'.[1] In some of the largest hospitals, the secretary was aided by a steward who concerned himself with provisions. Secretaries were paid salaries ranging from £100 to £300 per annum and were often resident. Occasionally they worked on a commission basis and received a percentage of all funds received. This system lasted at the Royal Northern Hospital until 1894.[2]

Thus the governors strengthened and streamlined their administration by the introduction of house committees and senior lay administrators to meet the needs of the large and complex charities they were controlling. The governors had in theory complete authority over everything that happened in their hospitals. In practice, there were limits to the authority that they could exercise over the senior professional men who were giving their services to the hospital. They were careful not to question the clinical judgement or examine the quality of the work of any of the doctors in the hospital unless they were forced to do so.

Except where matters of finance were concerned, the doctors were left to run the medical side of the hospital. In teaching hospitals, the doctors selected their students, planned curricula and divided out the receipts from teaching. They also divided out the beds. Sometimes they were divided equally among honorary staff members; sometimes senior doctors were given more beds than staff appointed later. Each full staff member was responsible for the treatment of the patients in his beds. It was not the duty of the senior physician or the senior surgeon to exercise any supervision over the work of other full members of the staff.

Gradually the doctors formed themselves into medical committees to co-ordinate their activities, to prepare advice for the lay governors and to ensure that their collective interests were properly represented in the management of the hospital. Thus a medical committee was established at the Westminster Hospital in 1826 'to inspect charges for drugs and to regulate the medical

---

[1] ibid., p. 153
[2] E. C. O. Jewesbury, *The Royal Northern Hospital 1856–1956*, p. 73, London, 1956

affairs of the charity'.[1] In St Bartholomew's Hospital, the initiative for such a committee came from the Treasurer, in 1843. Its duties were to include 'all matters relating to the medical part of the establishment and to the school'.[2]

There was no one 'system' of hospital administration; each body of governors was a law unto itself. The officials appointed under such titles as clerk, secretary and steward[3] had a variety of different functions in different hospitals. At Guy's Hospital, the most highly paid officer was a doctor. The 'resident superintendent' was paid £400 per annum, plus free residence.[4] The Treasurer still paid the bills, placed the contracts and supervised every appointment in the hospital. By 1890 the superintendent was directly responsible to the Treasurer for

> . . . the entire supervision of the hospital, in all departments, medical, nursing and administrative, with all necessary powers of control, including the power of suspension from duty for misconduct. He has the control of the admission of inpatients but in practice this function is for the most part deputed to the house physicians and surgeons. He is not a member of the medical committee.[5]

In general, the doctors were kept off the house committees, where the recommendations of the medical committee were considered. However, at Charing Cross Hospital the doctors were represented at the weekly meeting of the board.[6] This question led to a dispute between the doctors and the governors at St Mary's Hospital, Paddington, in 1863. The doctors wanted direct representation on the 'weekly managing committee'. Instead they were given a committee of their own.[7]

[1] ibid., p. 148

[2] N. Moore, *The History of St Bartholomew's Hospital*, p. 388, London, 1918

[3] At St Thomas' Hospital it was the Steward who was responsible, in 1848, for 'the whole police and internal management' of the Hospital. He received £200 per annum plus two gratuities of £100 each, and an allowance of £92 including residence. In contrast, Matron received £130 per annum, plus an allowance, including residence, of £79. Parsons, p. 101

[4] When this post was first advertised it attracted ninety-seven applicants including five army officers. The successful candidate was a doctor – the superintendent of Glasgow Royal Infirmary. Cameron, p. 192

[5] *Select Committee on Metropolitan Hospitals 1890–3*, Third Report, p. xv

[6] ibid., p. xxii

[7] *Select Committee on Metropolitan Hospitals 1890–3*, Third Report, p. xxviii

By 1860 the general hospitals had developed a system of bipartite administration. Power was divided between a house committee and a medical committee. Each had authority for independent action within a limited sphere but if it came to a clash of interest the house committee was the body which had the last word. This administrative structure represented the uneasy alliance upon which the voluntary system was based: there were the governors who gave in cash and the doctors who gave in kind.

In the early days, when hospital work represented a small and not wholly essential part of a doctor's activities, the system worked well as the doctors had little special interest in the policy of the institution for which they were working. When the hospitals became important to the profession for teaching and research, there came disputes between the governors and the doctors. Indeed, the whole process of forming medical committees represented the growing interest of the doctors in the administration of the hospitals.

One obvious area in which differences arose between governors and doctors was that of finance. As more active treatment was practised in the wards and in the outpatient departments, the cost of running hospitals was increased. At the Middlesex Hospital in 1821 the committee were horrified at the expenditure on drugs.

> The surgeons had adopted the practice of ordering medicine for their patients and were also addicted to the use of 'new and expensive drugs', quite unsuitable for a 'charitable institution'. . . . The amount of wine consumed had more than doubled in five years though the number of patients had not. . . . The apothecary had been equally lavish and had issued leeches at the rate of a hundred a day. The Board ordered that in future after the leeches had been used they should be properly preserved for further application.[1]

On the other hand, the governors were also raising standards. At the Radcliffe Infirmary in 1822 an order was made 'that sheets should be changed in ordinary cases at least once a month'.[2]
Another conflict of interest between doctors and governors

1 Saunders, p. 22
2 Gibson, p. 235

was over the question of subscribers' letters. The governors
wanted to retain in their own hands the selection of inpatients.[1]
The right to issue letters was the traditional way of enticing
members of the public to subscribe. But one consequence of
increasing indefinitely the number of governors was to increase
the number of 'tickets'. The doctors were opposed to the whole
system of subscribers' letters. The demand for beds was very
great, and they wanted to admit a patient for a short stay if this
could prevent death or permanent disability and enable the
patient to return to a full and useful life. They did not welcome a
chronic or incurable case who would 'block the bed' for an indefinite period of time and perhaps never be able to return home.
Medical teachers also wished to demonstrate quick results rather
than the careful and skilled management of a long and lingering
illness. There was no guarantee that the persons whom subscribers thought worthy of their charity would turn out to be
valuable material for teaching and research.

The 'ticket system' was prevalent in most of the hospitals.
From an inquiry conducted in 1863, Bristowe and Holmes found
that 'at the great majority of London hospitals which depend
entirely on private bounty, it has been found necessary, in order
to conciliate the subscribers, to allow them a kind of right of
nominating the recipients of this charity'.[2] The role of country
hospitals was especially limited by the requirements of the 'letter'
system which bore even less relation to the most urgent medical
needs of the rural poor. 'The right of the subscriber to nominate
... is far more rigidly enforced [and] the proportion of accidents
and urgent cases admitted without such nomination is smaller ...
consequently these establishments are practically reduced to
the treatment of accidents and cases of chronic disease.'[3] Moreover, 'subscribers expect their nominees to be admitted for the
full term of a letter which is customarily given for a period of
six to eight weeks'.[4] The wards of many provincial hospitals

[1] The Royal Free Hospital was, however, founded in 1828 as a protest
against this system of governors' letters.

[2] Bristowe and Holmes, p. 465. This inquiry into the sanitary circumstances of hospitals was ordered by Sir John Simon who was then the Medical
Officer of the Privy Council.

[3] ibid., p. 466

[4] ibid.

were filled with ambulant and infirm cases to the exclusion of the acutely sick.[1]

Bristowe and Holmes summarized the role of country hospitals in 1863: '. . . the hospital is looked upon by the poor as a private charity, as far as disease is concerned and admission into it is sought through private channels, just as into an almshouse. . . .'[2] Employers subscribed to hospitals to gain the right to send any of their employees who were ill: 'these country hospitals have become, in great measure, sick clubs, in which the employer pays instead of the patient.'[3] Bristowe and Holmes concluded that the smaller voluntary hospitals were maintaining a misleadingly high reputation for salubrity only by neglecting their 'most important duty' to the 'poor who are in the most grievous danger'.

Despite the generalizations of Bristowe and Holmes there were some provincial hospitals which did not admit chronic cases. In 1859, the rules of Salop Infirmary were very strict about the type of case which was ineligible for admission:

> That no woman big with child, no child under seven years of age (except in extraordinary cases, such as fractures, stone, or where couching, trepanning or amputation is necessary), no persons disordered in their senses, suspected to have smallpox or other infectious distemper, having habitual ulcers, cancers not admitting to operation, epileptic or convulsive fits, consumptions, or dropsied in their last stage, in a dying condition, or judged incurable, be admitted as inpatients, or inadvertently admitted, be suffered to continue.[4]

Despite the ticket system the doctors were able to have a

[1] Dr Bristowe described the Essex and Colchester General Hospitals as 'the very type of a country hospital, the persons admitted are almost exclusively agricultural workers; all cases where there is a suspicion of contagiousness are carefully excluded and with the exception of a comparatively small number of accidents and other cases of emergency, both surgical and medical cases are of an unimportant and trivial or chronic nature.' Ibid., pp. 639–40. Mr Holmes remarked of the Royal Portsmouth, Portsea and Gosport Hospital that '. . . it is difficult to avoid a feeling of very great regret on seeing an institution . . . in a busy and crowded town like Portsmouth used mainly as a refuge for a few chronic invalids who have had the good luck to recommend themselves to some subscriber.' Ibid., p. 666

[2] Bristowe and Holmes, p. 466.

[3] ibid.

[4] quoted in *Hospital*, Vol. 31, April 1935, p. 99

considerable influence on the admission policy of the hospitals. Bristowe and Holmes noted that 'the beds are allotted to medicine and surgery in proportions quite different from those in which cases occur in actual practice'.[1] Two-thirds of all urban hospital inpatients were surgical cases, while in the normal run of general practice over two-thirds of the patients were medical cases. The doctors got their way by introducing a ban on particular types of patients and limiting the beds available for different types of case. Thus at the three endowed hospitals (St Bartholomew's, St Thomas' and Guy's), admissions were 'subject to the regulations as to number of beds, exclusion of smallpox, and proportion of medicine and surgery'.[2] The doctors had the right to admit acute cases under the heading of 'emergencies' – a right which was increasingly used.

It remained true in the first half of the nineteenth century as in the eighteenth century that very few children were admitted. An inquiry carried out all over England and Wales in January 1843 indicated that there were only twenty-six children under ten 'suffering from Diseases peculiar to their age'.[3] At this time, the London Hospital excluded all children under seven except those requiring 'amputation' or 'cutting for stone'.[4] In the early 1860's at least half the children who were in hospital were accommodated in the eight London and provincial children's hospitals. At Great Ormond Street, the largest of these institutions, children were sent home as soon as they showed symptoms of infectious disease.

By regulating the class of patients the hospital would accept and by the admission of emergencies, the honorary staffs of the London hospitals could secure that the occupants of hospital beds became short-stay cases. The policy could be carried furthest in endowed hospitals: in other hospitals there were obvious limits to the amount of restriction the doctors could impose on the rights of those who found the money. But regular subscriptions were not the only way of obtaining funds. Boards of Guardians were empowered, under the Poor Law Amendment Act of 1851, to subscribe to voluntary hospitals and to send them pauper patients. Few Boards of Guardians took advantage of

[1] Bristowe and Holmes, p. 464
[2] ibid., p. 465
[3] Higgins, p. 10
[4] Bristowe and Holmes, p. 717

these powers and even fewer voluntary hospitals were prepared to admit paupers. The voluntary hospitals also held bazaars and fêtes, charity balls and charity dinners, and collected a variety of donations and legacies from all classes of society. When appealing for funds it was an advantage to be treating acute rather than chronic cases. The more acute the cases admitted, the greater were the number of inpatients that could be treated in a given number of beds during the year. Such statistics were valuable for appeal purposes.

As hospitals came to admit more acute sick, the work of the outpatient department acquired a new importance both in selecting patients and in gaining funds. The doctors wanted acutely sick patients with interesting diseases for teaching purposes. It was easier to achieve this if a pool of prospective patients was created from which the selection could take place. This was one function of the outpatient department. The sick crowded into the entrance hall of the hospital and the junior medical staff handed on to their seniors those they would find of interest.

Just as the policy of admitting only acute cases could be used to the financial advantage of the hospital when appealing for funds, so could the horde of outpatients not deemed suitable for admission. Their number could be added to that of the inpatients to produce a large but misleading total of work done. It was all useful copy for appeal purposes.

The need to appeal for funds led to distortion in such statistics as were collected by the hospitals. For this reason among others there are no wholly reliable figures which can be quoted for the nineteenth or early twentieth centuries. There was an obvious incentive to inflate the number of beds in the hospital and any measure of the work done. Many rural hospitals would have been seriously overcrowded if all their beds had been occupied. Many of the wards were too small to accommodate the official complement of beds. Some beds were always left vacant for emergency and other special cases. In the smaller teaching hospitals, wards were kept 'more empty in vacation than during session in order to economize funds'.[1]

It was a 'far from uncommon practice' to give inpatients after their first six to eight weeks' stay a renewed ticket and count them from that time forward as a new admission. The result of

[1] Bristowe and Holmes, p. 465

this and other falsifications was that 'in annual summaries as much as a sixth or even a quarter of individuals are counted as two patients. . . . In one instance, out of 626 nominal patients, no less than 169 were duplicates. Including this latter number in the computation, the death rate was 4·7; excluding this number, it mounted to 6·5.'[1] The motive behind these practices was 'to parade on one hand the large number of patients treated and, on the other hand, the great amount of benefit bestowed on them'.

> . . . Thus, in one institution . . . we were assured that one of the surgeons had been known, in a case of operation about to end fatally, to take down the original ticket; and to supply the patient with a new one in order that the case may be counted as two, and second, a case of death from erysipelas . . .[2]

For similar reasons, a perspicacious treasurer showed a deficit 'for appeal purposes' year after year. This could be done by allotting large slices of revenue to capital account. The revenue account could then be left with a deficit of whatever size was thought appropriate. Also, it was possible to hold back receipts so that they could be entered into a later year of account. Both these methods were used to falsify hospital accounts.

For what it is worth, one authority estimated the total expenditure of 117 voluntary hospitals for the year 1863 at nearly £372,000, of which £144,000 was spent by the Metropolitan hospitals.[3] This estimate excluded many special hospitals. A more comprehensive analysis was made of the London hospitals' revenue in 1861.[4] It included all the fourteen general and sixty-six special hospitals with thirty-nine dispensaries. Their revenue comprised £210,384 from dividends, property or trade and £155,376 from voluntary contributions. It seems probable, therefore, that the total revenue of voluntary hospitals in England and Wales during 1863 was at least £500,000. The annual cost per bed in London teaching hospitals varied in 1868 from £77 at University College to £40 at the Westminster. There were even greater variations amongst the special hospitals where

[1] ibid., p. 527
[2] ibid., p. 466
[3] Buckle, op. cit., Summary Table, p. 58
[4] Calculated from S. Low, *The Charities of London in 1861*, p. vii, London, 1862

annual costs per bed ranged from £124 at the Cancer Hospital to £48 at the Royal London Ophthalmic. In the provinces costs varied from £30 at the Sheffield Infirmary to £58 at the Brighton and Sussex County.[1]

With this income of about £500,000 per year the hospitals were servicing about 11,000 occupied beds in 1861. The voluntary hospitals had expanded rapidly. As many as 85 per cent of all London general hospital beds were in teaching hospitals. The London and provincial teaching hospitals contained 36 per cent of all voluntary beds and had a higher proportion of occupied beds than any other group of voluntary institutions. Nearly 40 per cent of all voluntary hospital patients were being treated in teaching establishments. It was, however, largely poorer persons[2] who were admitted. Of the 10,414 inmates classified in the census of 1861, only 157 were grouped as 'professional people' and half of these were local government officers, teachers and clergymen. Only fourteen were 'persons of Rank or Property not returned under any office or occupation'. The rest were wage-earners employed in industry, domestic service or agriculture. As many as 1,630 inmates were classed as being engaged in 'Attendance (Domestic Servants etc.)'.[3]

The basic design of the ward changed little except that there was greater emphasis on ventilation. Although there was little specific knowledge about the causes of cross-infection, it was believed that air in generous quantities was prophylactic. Thus some wards were built in noble proportions with windows on both sides to facilitate cross-ventilation and patients were constantly exposed to continuing draughts of the chilly and dirty air of urban England. There was, however, a further reason for the large open wards of the period with the generous corridors between the rows of beds. More space had been created for the bedside teaching of medical students. Some teachers had as

[1] These estimates were taken by Sir Henry Burdett from a report on hospital expenditure prepared by J. S. Wilkinson, the secretary of St Mary's Hospital. Burdett used them as the only reliable data available for the period and emphasized that they contained 'figures, prepared upon an identical basis with great care and accuracy'. H. C. Burdett, *Hospitals and Asylums of the World*, Vol. III, p. 171, London, 1892

[2] At one provincial teaching hospital in 1864, a 'poor person' was defined as being any wage-earner who received less than 18s a week. Gibson, p. 196

[3] *Census of England & Wales for the Year 1861*, Population Tables, Vol. II (5597), Table XL, p. xcviii, London, 1863

many as a hundred students following them round the wards.[1]

As yet, however, there were very few hospitals built on the pavilion plan. It was to be found at St Bartholomew's and the London Fever Hospital. Some small hospitals, however, consisted of only one 'pavilion', such as the Charing Cross Hospital and the Ipswich Hospital. Hospitals with an 'H-shaped' interior corridor were numerous: they included the Middlesex, St George's, Reading and Leicester. The most common design of all was the corridor plan – with numerous wards leading off a central corridor. Such hospitals were to be found at Westminster, Bath, Hull, Manchester and many other places.[2]

Iron-framed beds were more common than they had been when Howard had made his tour some seventy years earlier. Mattresses were of chopped straw, flock or horsehair though a few rural hospitals used 'husks of oats' as bedding.[3] It was common for mattresses to be stripped and pulled at regular intervals. Beds were sometimes curtained for privacy and warmth and at the Radcliffe Infirmary there were bedside rugs and Windsor chairs.[4] There were lockers or boxes under or by the side of the beds for the storage of personal possessions. Patients were allowed to 'bring their own clothes into the wards where they have the right to keep them until they leave'.[5]

The diet of patients was much the same as it had been seventy years earlier except for the introduction of tea. Meat was more generously provided in London hospitals than elsewhere while patients in rural establishments were given milk – a rare provision in some urban hospitals. The daily diet for males in St Bartholomew's consisted of half a pound of meat, half a pound of potatoes, one ounce of butter, fourteen ounces of bread, two pints of tea and two pints of beer.[6] Bristowe and Holmes observed generally that 'the allowance of stimulants is becoming every year more liberal' and it was generally held that alcohol was of medicinal value.[7] The diet provided by the hospitals

[1] Bristowe and Holmes, p. 490

[2] ibid.

[3] ibid.

[4] F. Oppert, *Hospitals, Infirmaries and Dispensaries* (2nd Eng. edition), p. 50, London, 1883

[5] ibid.

[6] ibid., p. 112

[7] Bristowe and Holmes, p. 484. 'At the Royal Free Hospital the expenses in 1862 amongst 1,254 inpatients was £484 11s for wines and spirits.' Ibid., p. 597

was supplemented by the patients' own supplies which were brought on admission and augmented by gifts from relatives. Patients were generally expected to have their own personal supplies of tea, sugar and butter. Some had personal supplies of 'bacon, cheese, butter, bread, cakes, apples, slices of meat etc.'.[1]

Detailed rules and regulations were still being laid down by the governors to control the lives of the sick poor. At the Royal West Sussex Hospital, 'patients were forbidden to curse or swear, to gamble, drink spirituous liquors, or smoke or chew tobacco...'[2] At the Radcliffe Infirmary, ambulant patients were forbidden to leave the hospital without permission – in order to stop them returning drunk.[3] Refractory and 'disorderly' patients were punished by being discharged. Patients who persistently smoked in wards were dealt with in this way. Whether all these rules were rigidly enforced depended on the quality of the nursing staff who alone were always on the spot. Bristowe and Holmes found that in Newcastle Infirmary, 'the wards seem badly supervised ... and patients smoke and commit other irregularities in them'.[4]

The introduction of teaching to the majority of the general hospitals in London and to some in the provinces, together with the new interest in medical research, had led to improvements in the nursing staff. The doctors needed a reliable assistant who was constantly in the wards and who could be relied upon to distribute the medicines and apply the poultices exactly as directed. Some of this work fell upon junior medical staff and senior medical students but much was left to the sister in charge of the ward. Thus a higher class of person was employed to do this work. Sisters were people who had been 'head servants in gentlemen's families', 'widows in reduced circumstances' or 'persons who have lived in a respectable rank of life'.[5] They were paid £20 to £40 per year.

Thus the sisters began to be separately recruited from the nurses. And in the larger London teaching hospitals more trustworthy working women were employed as nurses. They were under the supervision of persons who insisted on higher standards

[1] Gibson, p. 207
[2] Royal West Sussex Archives, No. 7, for period 1827–1899
[3] Gibson, p. 198
[4] Bristowe and Holmes, p. 617
[5] B. Abel-Smith, *A History of the Nursing Profession*, pp. 7–8, London, 1960

of hygiene than had been common in the eighteenth century. Thus the wards were scrubbed weekly or twice weekly and when funds allowed the walls were washed and painted or white-washed every year. While nurses were paid 2s 6d per week in Oxford, they were paid two or three times that sum in London. They worked very long hours and there were no clearly separated off-duty periods.

The standards of hygiene in the small provincial hospitals and in the small special hospitals which had been set up in unconverted private houses were much lower. Bristowe and Holmes described one hospital very unfavourably. 'The beds are crowded together . . . the water closets are offensive and open immediately out of the wards so that in certain states of the wind the bad odour is plainly perceived in the wards.'[1] At this hospital there was always a shortage of water although the tanks were kept filled 'by the labour of prisoners on the treadmill in the adjoining jail'.[2]

It was not only the sisters and nurses who were becoming more trustworthy in the well-run teaching hospitals. A much better class of woman was being sought for the post of matron. Mrs Wardroper, the matron of St Thomas' Hospital, who ran Miss Nightingale's training school from 1860 onwards, had been appointed many years earlier. The picture of the typical pre-Nightingale nurse as drunk and depraved, which was drawn by the nursing reformers, does less than justice to many of the nursing staff working in the hospitals in the forties and fifties. Nursing had been steadily improving over the years preceding the Nightingale revolution.

In the light of history, it may be said that the most significant change which occurred in the voluntary hospitals in the first half of the nineteenth century was the growing emphasis on the acute sick. To a considerable extent, the trend marked the triumph of the views of the 'honorary doctors' over those of the charitable public. Many of the latter were content to have their money used to give relief and comfort to those in pain: help to a patient whose suffering was of long duration might even be preferred to constructive treatment for a patient whose stay was short. Pain was what mattered, not any 'economic' return for money spent. The doctors on the other hand and those lay

[1] Bristowe and Holmes, p. 630
[2] ibid.

governors who were influenced by them wanted to show results in terms of cure, and they were naturally reluctant to surround themselves with cases which showed the limitations of their professional skill. Doctors who taught particularly wanted to demonstrate successes.

Thus the hospitals came to have 'more grave cases'.[1] The trend which was starting in the provinces was well advanced in London. This 'economical' use of beds was made at the expense of those whose needs went unmet. After Guy's Hospital was appropriated for the acute sick, there was only one charity in the whole of London for chronic cases – the relatively small Hospital for Incurables at Putney.

Many general hospitals continued to admit cases of infectious disease in the first half of the nineteenth century and, in some instances, for many years later. This was the practice in the Westminster, St Bartholomew's, St Thomas' and the London Hospitals. In the provinces, cases of infectious disease were admitted to Nottingham General Hospital, Manchester Royal Infirmary, Sheffield General Infirmary and Newcastle Infirmary.[2] In some hospitals such cases were treated in separate wards; in others they were accommodated in the same wards with other patients. But by 1860, the wisdom of accommodating infectious cases in general hospitals was increasingly being questioned and some hospitals were abandoning the practice. Despite the mushroom growth of special hospitals for other purposes, and although infectious diseases were the great killers of the poor and the main menace for the rich, there was only one hospital for fever cases and one for smallpox cases in the whole of London.

The general hospitals became more careful about admitting cases of infectious disease at the same time and for the same reason that the value of isolating *all* infectious cases became appreciated. As more epidemics raged across Britain's large and growing cities, more and more hospitals were excluding the victims. Thus, both for cases of infectious disease and for cases of chronic illness, the voluntary hospitals offered grossly inadequate accommodation. What was left undone by charity had eventually to be undertaken by public authorities.

[1] ibid., p. 465
[2] The author wishes to acknowledge extensive help on this point from Mr J. F. Milne of the Institute of Hospital Administrators.

CHAPTER 4

Sick Paupers

BY 1861, there were some 11,000 patients in voluntary hospitals which were presided over by the leading citizens and leading doctors of the period. While most of the country hospitals were serving the needs of poor persons who could secure the favour of a subscriber's letter, in London the patients were beginning to be more carefully selected to meet the needs of teaching and research.

The patients in the voluntary hospitals were not, however, the only group of sick persons receiving institutional care. Without causing much public comment or official notice, there had accumulated in the workhouses by 1861 a total of some 50,000 sick persons[1] under the care of workhouse medical officers. Many 'patients' were of a type which the voluntary hospitals would not accept.

The workhouses had grown enormously in both size and number in the previous thirty years as a result of the report of the Poor Law Commissioners of 1832–4, and the subsequent Poor Law Amendment Act of 1834. Public policy had aimed to stamp out able-bodied pauperism by refusing applicants outdoor relief. Instead they were to enter the workhouse where their condition was to be rendered 'less eligible' than that of the poorest paid labourer outside. It was hoped that the offer of accommodation in the repressive workhouse would separate the work-shy from those with genuine needs. The aged and sick were not intended to be covered by this rule: outdoor relief was to continue to be available to them.[2] If, however, they could not manage at home, it was suggested that they might be accommodated in separate buildings away from the punitive

---

[1] See Vol. 2 of this study.

[2] The position was made clear in the *Outdoor Relief Regulation Order* (1852).

establishments for the able-bodied so that 'the old might enjoy their indulgences'.[1]

The new régime was to be implemented by an administrative structure which might have worked if all concerned had wished to practise the same principles. There was a central supervisory body of three commissioners, with Edwin Chadwick as secretary, which had very limited powers and was not represented in Parliament, while the unit of local administration was normally an elected Board of Guardians: it was this body which raised the money and actually operated the service.

Within a decade it became clear that the central body could exercise no real authority. In practice, each Board of Guardians operated on whatever principles it thought fit. Moreover, those Guardians who tried to operate the service as the commissioners intended found that the task of separating the needs of the impotent, which had to be met from the needs of the able-bodied, which had to be discouraged, was much easier to state than to administer. Poor Law medical officers had neither time, prestige nor diagnostic tools to make clear and acceptable distinctions between the healthy and the sick – if such distinctions can be made in any community, particularly one at a low level of living.

In the last quarter of 1839 an inquiry showed that out of 260,000 recipients of outdoor relief, 87,000 were classified as *partially* able to work.[2] It was decided by the lay commissioners that these should have been submitted to the workhouse test. It was important to 'prevent medical aid from generating or encouraging pauperism'.[3] To protect the less-eligibility principle it was essential to apply the workhouse test to any cases of doubt lest malingering should be encouraged.

However logical the principles of 1834 may have been in theory, they were unworkable in practice. A system which offered relief at home to the sick and punishment in an institution to the able-bodied was thought to encourage malingering. It certainly made the work of the medical officer impossible. The latter was paid a small sum, out of which he had himself to provide medicine, for attendance on all the sick poor in the district. It did not pay him to linger over diagnosis or provide a

---

[1] *Report from His Majesty's Commissioners for Inquiring into the Administration and Practical Operation of the Poor Laws*, p. 307, London (Fellowes), 1834

[2] *Sixth Annual Report PLB, 1839-40* (1836), pp. 17-18, HMSO, 1840

[3] ibid., Continuation Report, 1840, pp. 44-5

course of domiciliary treatment which extended over a long period. As Mr Farnall, an inspector of the Poor Law Board, remarked in 1866: 'His object, therefore, is either to make them well as soon as possible, and get them off his hands, or to send them into the workhouse.'[1] Admission to an institution was more convenient not only for the doctor but also for the relieving officer. A series of assessments and payments could be avoided by admission to the workhouse. 'It is quite competent for a medical officer and an outdoor relieving officer to act together, and recommend that the pauper should be taken into the work-house, in doing which they both get rid of the *onus* of looking after him.'[2]

For the principles of 1834 to be fully operated there needed to be not only conscientious doctors and relieving officers but really adequate outdoor medical relief. The Guardians were generally unwilling to grant this, partly because of the burden on the rates and partly because of the fear of encouraging malingerers. Whatever the intentions of the central authority, some Boards of Guardians refused outdoor relief to every appli-cant while others gave it in grossly inadequate amounts. Approxi-mately a third of all outdoor relief was given in kind: the normal scale of provision was rarely more than 1s or 2s with a loaf of bread weekly. The London Unions were particularly noted for their unwillingness to give outdoor relief. As Mr Farnall ex-plained: 'When Guardians begin to distribute $7\frac{3}{4}d$ a week to an old man or woman in lodgings, the poor creature cannot live upon it, and he or she comes into the workhouse, out of which, I need scarcely tell you, he or she never goes until the day of his or her death.'[3]

There were, in addition, wider reasons for the growth of the number of the sick in workhouses. There were large groups of wandering labourers and it was a period of rapid migration from country to towns[4] where conditions were far from healthy.

[1] H. B. Farnall, Statement made to the Society for the Improvement of the Infirmaries of London Workhouses (private meeting), 8 February 1866
[2] ibid.
[3] ibid.
[4] The percentage of the total population of England and Wales living in towns of 20,000 and over increased from 17% in 1801 to 35% in 1851. A. Weber, *The Growth of Cities in the Nineteenth Century: A Study in Statistics* (Columbia Univ. Studies in History, Economics and Public Law No. 29), p. 47, New York, 1899

Traditional systems of family care were disrupted. There were more isolated people, more widows, aged persons and separated or deserted wives. Finally there was the rapid growth of the total population. All these factors contributed to the increase in the number of the sick in institutions from roughly[1] 10,000 in receipt of medical care in 1843 to some 50,000 twenty years later.

The problem of the sick poor was at its worst in London, partly because of the stern policy of the Guardians and partly because the needs were greater. Scales of outdoor relief which might have been adequate in a rural area were inadequate in London where rents were rising, where all food and fuel had to be purchased and where successive epidemics brought their own special burden of pauperism. Moreover, it was in London that the voluntary hospitals were becoming more and more selective in the cases they would admit. It was the Poor Law service which accommodated the bulk of the sick children, the mental cases, the skin conditions, those with epilepsy, tuberculosis and venereal diseases and the unexplored mass of the chronic sick.

In 1834 the commissioners had assured the Cabinet that it was their intention to assign 'distinct, quiet and comfortable abodes for the impotent'. The central authority, however, had never had any effective power to force Guardians to do so.[2] All categories of pauper were accommodated in one institution. By this means, costs were kept to a minimum: the major work of running the institution, including not only the domestic work but also the nursing care of the impotent, was done by such able-bodied paupers as happened to be available. For a number of reasons, including economy, all paupers were cared for in institutions which had been designed for the operation of the principle of less-eligibility. It is, therefore, not surprising that these buildings were unsatisfactory for hospital purposes.

The failure of Guardians to provide classified institutions not only led to unsatisfactory treatment of the sick; it also had the curious consequence of keeping at home many patients who most needed to be admitted for the health of the whole population. Only two of the forty London Boards were consciously prepared,

[1] Before 1849, the Poor Law statistics were not obtained on a nationally uniform basis and are far from reliable.
[2] It could not compel local bodies to spend more than £50 per year or one-tenth of the rates on workhouse buildings. Nassau Senior, MSS, Diary No. 173, pp. 68–71, University of London Library

because of the dangers to staff and other 'inmates', to admit fever patients. Instead cases were referred to the one voluntary hospital set up for this purpose.[1]

In 1866 two separate inquiries were undertaken into the state of London's workhouses. The first one was by commissioners appointed by *The Lancet*;[2] the second was by special inspectors appointed by the Poor Law Board (Mr Farnall and Dr Smith). From these accounts, a fairly comprehensive picture can be gained of conditions in London workhouses. The official inquiry was later extended to provincial workhouses.[3] In general, it can be said that the provision for sick paupers was in sad contrast to that for the sick poor in the voluntary hospitals. Standards, however, varied enormously from one Union to another: much depended on the interest and wealth of each Board of Guardians, and on the quality of the officials whom they employed.

According to one of the official investigators (Mr Farnall) nothing could be done to make thirteen out of the forty Metropolitan workhouses fit for use as hospitals because

> . . . in each sick ward of the above workhouses there is a great deficiency of cubical space for each patient . . . most of these workhouses are badly constructed and are closely hemmed in on every side by other buildings; the trades carried on in some of them taint the atmosphere; the airing yards are, generally speaking, wholly insufficient; there is no facility for supervision or inspection in any other; there is no room to erect sufficient bathrooms and lavatories where required; it is not possible to build water closets outside the walls of the buildings, and so remove them from the close proximity to the sick wards; and there are no means of giving day rooms to the convalescent.[4]

[1] The London Fever Hospital, Islington

[2] On the whole the official inspectors were less critical of what they saw than the *Lancet* commissioners but the latter pointed out that many minor improvements were made as the result of the reports published in *The Lancet* (*Report of the Lancet Sanitary Commission for Investigating the State of the Infirmaries of Workhouses*, p. iii, London, 1866)

[3] *H of C Sessional Paper 4*, 1867–8, BPP, Vol. LX, 1867–8 (*Report of Dr Edward Smith, Medical Officer to the PLB, on the Sufficiency of the existing Arrangements for the Care and Treatment of the Sick Poor in Forty-eight Provincial Workhouses in England and Wales*), p. 3

[4] *H of C Sessional Paper 387*, 1866, BPP, Vol. LXI, 1866 (*Report of H. B. Farnall, Esquire, Poor Law Inspector, on the Infirmary Wards of the several Metropolitan Workhouses, and their existing Arrangements*), p. 7

He went on to suggest that if the number of sick beds were reduced by a half in all but one of the remaining twenty-seven London workhouses, they would then be fit for 'hospital purposes'. The *Lancet* investigators visited one London workhouse where paupers were found sleeping on the floor[1] and in another forty young girls were stated to be sharing thirteen beds.[2] Mr Farnall found only one of the London workhouses which was 'sufficient for the purpose to which it was dedicated'. He based this opinion on the assumption that each patient should be provided with 'not less than 1,000 cubic feet of air'. The official requirement of the Board at this time was 500 cubic feet per resident but even this low standard was not enforced in many sick wards.

The dangers and discomforts of some of the overcrowded sick wards were increased by inadequate ventilation.[3] At one workhouse the air vents admitted only 'volumes of sooty or smoky air'. Elsewhere the windows were so badly designed that 'when opened by day they poured large volumes of air upon the patients beneath . . . and must have often caused injury to health. . . .' In those workhouses where the windows had been set very high in the wall 'to prevent improper communication between the classes of inmates', bedfast patients were literally cut off from all views of the outside world.

There was an almost universal practice of 'mixing up sick wards in the body of the House'.[4] Even 'contagious fevers of the most dangerous kind' were found warded with other sick paupers.[5] Prevailing systems of classification ranged from the reasonably well ordered and separate buildings at St George's Union to the chaos of the Strand Workhouse, where it was found that 'there are a greater or less number of sick cases existing at various times in nearly all the other wards'.[6] Very few of the

---

[1] *Lancet Commission Report*, p. 16

[2] *H of C Sessional Paper 372*, 1866, BPP, Vol. LXI, 1866 (*Report of Dr Edward Smith, Poor Law Inspector & Medical Officer to the PLB, on the Metropolitan Workhouse Infirmaries and Sick Wards*), Appendix, p. 149

[3] 'The ventilation of the workhouses is almost everywhere defective from the absence of efficient means of ventilation and the almost universal habit of covering . . . ventilators. The first cause is almost, and the second quite universal.' *H of C 372*, 1866, p. 20

[4] *Lancet Commission Report*, p. 14

[5] *H of C 372*, 1866 (Appendix), p. 97 and *Lancet Commission Report*, p. xviii

[6] *H of C 372*, 1866 (Appendix), p. 102

sick in country workhouses were segregated, and at Hatfield conditions were so bad that the inspector decided: 'It is not worth the trouble to examine this workhouse as a place for the sick.'[1] When patients were classified the result was not always satisfactory. The *Lancet* commissioners reported that the female itch ward at Chelsea was 'the nastiest place altogether that our eyes have looked upon'.[2]

The investigators found in the majority of workhouses a superficial veneer of hygiene. For example, the *Lancet* commissioners noted 'a special air of *bescrubbedness*, rather a powerful odour of soap and water, about the wards of the workhouse infirmaries'.[3] 'Except the presence of bugs,' remarked Dr Smith in his report on St George-the-Martyr, 'the wards, linen, tables, dressers, crockery and all appurtenances are kept clean.'[4] The cleanliness was, however, only on the surface. There was a general deficiency of toilet facilities, and the *Lancet* doctors found only one London workhouse where there were sufficient baths attached to sick wards.[5] Many dangerously unhygienic practices were tolerated. At Kensington and Paddington some of the sick were 'found washing in their chamber pots'. The inspector was told by one medical officer that the patients preferred to wash in this way but he later established that they did this 'against their will and their former habits at home'.[6] Only a few Guardians provided lavatory paper on the grounds that 'a very large proportion of the poor'[7] were not in the habit of using it. There were, however, 'numberless instances' of closets being blocked with 'old towels, dusters and dishcloths' – and leaves of Holy Scripture.[8]

The provision of towels was most inadequate. At Paddington, there was one towel for every twenty-four to thirty-one inmates.[9] The *Lancet* Commission found a syphilitic women's ward where

[1] *H of C 4*, 1867–8 (Appendix), p. 92
[2] *Lancet Commission Report*, p. 22
[3] ibid., p. 21
[4] *H of C 372*, 1866 (Appendix), p. 86
[5] *Lancet Commission Report*, p. 22
[6] *H of C 372*, 1866, p. 16 and Appendix, p. 180
[7] ibid., p. 17
[8] 'One or more Bibles, and sometimes a Prayer Book, were found in each ward, but in a more or less imperfect and dilapidated state – a circumstance connected with the subject just discussed.' Ibid.
[9] Ibid., p. 15

the eight inmates had one round towel a week. 'Usually, however,' Dr Smith explained, 'the supply for an ordinary ward is two or three round ones and they are changed twice a week.' The combs provided by the Guardians were 'usually broken' and there were 'extremely few' hairbrushes. The supply of soap was limited as 'it might readily be wasted',[1] and at the Strand Workhouse the head nurse (Miss Beeton) told an investigating committee that she was 'always afraid of seeing vermin on the patients or their bedclothes'.[2]

Few aspects of workhouse life escaped the touch of 'less-eligibility'. Flock beds were generally provided but 'mattresses were of very rare occurrence'. In one workhouse, the beds were made wholly of wood and in five others the beds had 'broad and rigid bands of iron for the bottom'.[3] Feather beds were more often to be found in the country workhouses but 'the rugs varied very much, but generally they were of cotton, and, with the blankets, were often very old and thin'.[4] The *Lancet* doctors complained that in nearly half the infirmaries the mattresses were too short or not as long as the bedsteads.[5] The quality of sheets varied from the 'faded, worn or ragged'[6] articles at St James' to those of Marylebone where 'three sheets are appropriated to each bed and one is changed weekly'.[7] At Bethnal Green 'where the master has recently held office in the army the bedding was neatly folded up and placed at the head of the bedstead throughout the day'.[8]

Apart from five workhouses where ornaments and flowers were displayed, the environment of the sick people was stark

[1] *H of C 372*, 1866, pp. 15–16. In commenting on these deficiencies Dr Smith suggested that, 'The practical test of these questions is the cleanliness of the inmates and this doubtless far exceeded that of the same class at their own homes and was not less than that of the inmates of other public institutions.' Ibid., p. 6

[2] *H of C Sessional Paper 362*, 1866, BPP, Vol. LXI, 1866 (Report made by R. B. Cane, Esquire, Poor Law Inspector to the PLB . . . into certain Allegations made by Matilda Beeton, in reference to the Treatment of the Sick in the Strand Union Workhouse), p. 11

[3] *H of C 372*, 1866, p. 11

[4] *H of C 4*, 1867–8, p. 23

[5] Dr Smith refers to beds in adult wards being only 4 ft 8 in. long and others that were 2 ft 3 in. in width. *H of C 372*, 1866, p. 11

[6] *H of C 372*, 1866, p. 11

[7] ibid.

[8] ibid., p. 12

and drab. 'The practice of painting the walls half-way up with hideous drab and finishing them off with glaring whitewash is still, barbarous though it be, nearly universal.'[1] Dr Smith managed to find some wards in which 'short curtains were economically represented by whitened window panes' and a few other Houses where curtains and blinds were provided but there was a 'very general deficiency' of scriptural prints.[2] The walls of the newest workhouses were left rough and undrawn but in others whitewash was commonly used. Some Guardians allowed green, blue and pink washes and at Poplar it was learnt that 'the Master changes the tint every six months'.[3] Windsor chairs were 'universally found' and there were plenty of 'narrow benches without backs or cushions'. It is surprising to note, however, that woollen capes and slippers were generally provided 'for such as use the nightstool during the night'.

All the reports commented on the monotony of daily life in the infirmary wards of 1866. The sick paupers at St Mary Newington had the use of about 800 books but in most other Unions the library was 'very small and the books old and perhaps not interesting'. Periodicals and newspapers were very rarely provided and Dr Smith was disturbed by the shortage of Bibles and the absence of picture books for the illiterate. The imbeciles were treated with kindness and imagination in most workhouses. At Marylebone they were given pets and 'pretty pictures'.[4]

Card games were not allowed in any workhouse. Dr Smith was told that the aged and infirm did not care for 'games and similar amusements'. He found that they were, in practice, 'rarely supplied to the children or the aged' and regretted seeing 'so many hundreds of persons, with nothing to amuse them, who, from defective education, and long residence out of the world, had nothing to think about, and who sat or lay looking at bare walls, or their scarcely more animated fellow inmates'.[5] A still more depressing picture is drawn of Cardiff Workhouse, where 'they lead a life which would be like that of a vegetable were it not that they preserve the doubtful privilege of sensibility to pain and mental misery'.[6]

[1] *Lancet Commission Report*, p. 19
[2] *H of C 372*, 1866, pp. 17–18
[3] ibid., p. 10. See also *Lancet Commission Report*, p. 19, quoted above.
[4] *Lancet Commission Report*, p. 17
[5] *H of C 4*, 1867–8, p. 25
[6] *Lancet Commission Report*, p. vi

The diet of the sick paupers appears to have been reasonably adequate if unappetizing. The *Lancet* doctors thought that 'the infirm and chronic patients decidedly require a diet of their own'[1] and heard 'many bitter complaints of the pea soup as causing pain and spasm in the stomach. . . .' Much wastage of food occurred amongst the old and toothless residents and their diet was, for this reason, 'uniformly insufficient'.[2] The medical officer had the power to provide a better diet for indoor paupers by certifying them as sick. Thus it was found that 'the number of sick is increased by fully one-third in most workhouses, simply in order to obtain for the aged and infirm a better dietary'.[3] One medical officer prescribed 'sick diet' for all patients except the 'undeserving'.[4] Workhouse medical officers could also order 'extras' such as 'chops, fish and various delicacies' including alcohol. Roasted food was rarely allowed to inmates, without the express recommendation of the medical officer.

Every investigator at this period criticized the prevailing systems of cooking and conveying food to the sick wards. Kitchen apparatus was defective in many workhouses and very few Guardians employed skilled cooks. In both London and the provinces 'the conveying of the food is seldom effected with as much care to keep the food warm'.[5] This conveyance of food was necessary in London because there were 'no hospital kitchens in the detached infirmaries, nor . . . separate kitchens attached to the sick wards of all the workhouses; and invariably there are no day rooms'.[6]

By 1866 only six of the Metropolitan Unions had appointed enough paid nurses to satisfy the very moderate requirements of the Board. In the forty London workhouses there were 142 paid non-pauper nurses attending roughly 21,150 sick and infirm patients. Of this small number, 35 were employed in two workhouses, leaving 107 to care for nearly 18,000 patients in the other workhouses. And there were only three paid night nurses in the

[1] ibid., p. 28
[2] ibid.
[3] *H of C 372*, 1866, p. 62
[4] 'No case of serious illness comes within this definition of course. What I call the undeserving are *all ordinary* cases of gonorrhea and chancre.' A. Sheen, *The Workhouse and Its Medical Officer*, p. 10, Cardiff, 1875
[5] *H of C 372*, 1866, p. 33
[6] *H of C 4*, 1867-8, p. 25

whole of London.[1] There were similar deficiencies in the provinces. Rural Guardians were reluctant to appoint paid nurses because of the smallness of their institutions. At Chorlton, one of the best provincial workhouses, the nursing was under the supervision of two Protestant Sisters and in larger towns, such as Derby, paid nurses were occasionally employed. Some Unions employed married couples who undertook the nursing as a joint appointment,[2] but these arrangements were not approved of by Dr Smith who believed that men lacked the necessary patience and tidiness to be good nurses.

It was most unusual for a paid workhouse nurse to have received hospital training:[3] often a scrubber or laundress would be promoted to paid nursing duties.[4] Many of them were resident in the workhouses but their accommodation was rarely such as might attract 'trustworthy and efficient' persons.[5] In 1866 their salaries varied between £12 and £50 per annum and it was 'a matter of surprise' to Dr Smith that reputable nurses 'could be obtained at Marylebone Workhouse at £14 per year'.[6] In addition to their wages the paid nurses also received board and an allowance of beer or porter.

The paid nurses spent much of their time supervising the large number of unpaid paupers who provided the bulk of the Poor Law 'nursing' staff. The standards of these attendants varied greatly. At Islington they were found to be 'zealous and well-managed, conscious that they are thoroughly looked after, and anxious to deserve good opinion'.[7] In other workhouses the paupers had been compelled to nurse by day as well as by night and thus became fatigued and disgusted.[8] Frequent instances of pauper nurses stealing the food and stimulants of patients were

[1] *H of C 372*, 1866, pp. 6, 24
[2] *H of C 4*, 1866–7, p. 13
[3] See Vol. 2 of this study.
[4] S. Lane-Poole, 'Workhouse Infirmaries', *Macmillan's Magazine*, July 1881, p. 223
[5] *H of C 372*, 1866, p. 56. The Head Nurse at the Strand described her quarters thus: 'My room was on the same floor as the Men's Sick ward; only a small lobby parted us. In this lobby was a sink and a dusthole; there was also all the soiled linen from the Men's Sick ward. . . . I often got the smell so strong from the same in my room that I could scarcely bear to remain in it.' *H of C 362*, 1866, p. 14
[6] *H of C 372*, 1866, p. 56
[7] *Lancet Commission Report*, p. 67
[8] *H of C 372*, 1866, p. 25

cited by the *Lancet* commissioners and other critics. Dr Smith
conceded that 'in one or two cases such charges had been proven
against a nurse but claimed that such practices were not
frequent'.[1] Drunkenness was a common fault amongst workhouse
nurses: it was encouraged 'by the allowance of one pint, or a
pint and a half of strong porter daily . . . with one or two more
glasses of gin for night duty or disagreeable work'.[2]

Aged paupers were frequently employed in nursing as they
were more likely to remain in the workhouse for long periods.
Some of them were too feeble to lift patients and those at the
Strand 'wanted good Nursing and Nourishment themselves,
trembling and coughing all day long. . . .'[3] Very few of them
could read: the common medicines were known by their
appearance to both nurses and inmates and 'moreover, should
the nurses forget, there are always some inmates of the ward
who can read and . . . the pauper nurse was accustomed to seek
their aid'.[4] The *Lancet* commissioners found, however, that
medicine was 'given with shameful and, so to speak, systematic
irregularity' and sometimes the doctor's instructions were
ignored.

Where paid nurses were employed it was customary to place
one in seniority over the others. She was variously known as
'Superintendent Nurse', 'Head Nurse' or 'Upper Nurse', but her
status was lower than that of the workhouse matron. The latter
was frequently the wife of the master. The duties of the matron
involved the superintendence of 'the whole internal working
of the establishment, the cleaning, the linen, the food, the
cooking, the distribution of food, the stores, etc. . . .' and in many
workhouses she was expected to superintend the care of the sick.
Dr Smith was not satisfied with the way in which matrons discharged their duties and remarked that 'more activity and
attention to duty on the part of the matron would be to the
advantage of the inmates and guardians'. He found them to be
the least efficient members of the senior staffs in workhouses.[5]

The position of workhouse medical officer was normally
held by a part-time officer who had little or no security of tenure.

[1] ibid., p. 25
[2] ibid.
[3] *H of C 362*, 1866, p. 14
[4] *H of C 372*, 1866, p. 26
[5] ibid., p. 70

The appointment was made by each Board of Guardians on terms and conditions which it thought appropriate. In sixteen of the forty London Unions the duties of workhouse and district medical officer were combined into one office. There were only four full-time residential posts in the whole of London, three of which were combined appointments. In the provinces, resident medical officers were employed in only a few of the largest workhouses. Many Guardians were content to hire their doctors at the lowest possible price by advertising vacancies and inviting the local practitioners to undercut each other.[1] In some Unions the posts were subject to annual renewal which entailed a yearly round of canvassing by all the local doctors.[2] Older practitioners had to compete for these Poor Law appointments in order to keep potential competitors out of their districts. Young doctors sought these posts in order to supplement their incomes during the early days of private practice and to gain experience in the lucrative business of midwifery.[3]

In some Unions the medical officer was reasonably paid. At St Marylebone Workhouse he received £950 per annum. After paying a resident assistant, a non-resident dispenser and the cost of his drugs he was left with an annual income of about £450. He devoted six hours daily to workhouse duties and the remainder of his working day to private practice. He was responsible for about 460 sick and infirm patients and 88 imbeciles and epileptics 'not upon his books, some of whom are occasionally ill'. This medical officer believed that his terms of service were 'advantageous to the poor, the Guardians and himself'.[4] The full-time medical officer of Portsea Island Union received a salary of £315 and extra payments of about £40

---

[1] On 16 June 1856 the President of the Poor Law Board told the House that 'the salaries of M.O.'s were fixed by the Poor Law Guardians and he was sorry to say that, with respect to many of them, the salaries were extremely low and the Poor Law Board had great difficulty in inducing the Boards of Guardians to raise them'. *Hansard* (*H of C*), Vol. CXLII, 16 June 1856, col. 1494

[2] *Bradford Observer*, 6 February 1851

[3] They were often disappointed at the infrequency with which such work came their way. Supplementary fees were paid to doctors for midwifery but the lowest fee payable to medical officers was fixed at 10s. As midwives could be hired for 7s 6d the medical officer was rarely called for except in cases of danger. *GCO 1847* and *Poor Law Chronicle*, 7 October 1865, p. 65

[4] *H of C 372*, 1866, Appendix, pp. 95–6

per annum. His only expenses were £12–14 a year for dispensing.[1]

Other medical officers did not fare so well. The 'aged and infirm' doctor at a West London workhouse received a salary of £110 a year, plus another £12 for extra duties. He provided his own drugs at a cost of roughly £45 a year. As he employed a deputy at £105 yearly to do the work he suffered an annual loss of £28 on his office.[2] Presumably he regarded it as essential to keep rivals out of the job.

At Rotherhithe Union the duties of workhouse and district medical officer were combined. There were between 50 and 60 patients in this workhouse of whom about a third were 'diet' cases. The district area included a population of roughly 20,000. The medical officer received £35 for workhouse duties, and another £105–110 for his district work. Out of these sums he spent £12 yearly on drugs and employed an assistant to do the district work.[3]

The medical officer at Bath received £150 per annum and paid for his own assistant and nearly all drugs. In a number of rural areas the workhouse medical officer was paid as little as £50 yearly and still provided most of his drugs.[4] There were other Unions in both London and the provinces where medical officers were precluded from private practice.[5]

Just over half of all the Metropolitan officers did their own dispensing and provided their own drugs. Extra fees were paid in all but five workhouses for midwifery, lunacy certification, removal of paupers and vaccinations. The incomes from these extras were sometimes as low as £10 and never higher than £70 per annum, but the sums paid were not always related to the amount of additional work involved. At one workhouse where midwifery fees were not paid, there was an average of over 300 deliveries a year.

The duties of the workhouse medical officer entailed much

[1] *H of C 4*, 1867–8, Appendix, p. 129
[2] The reports of Dr Smith and Mr Farnall on this workhouse make an interesting contrast. They each made different estimates of the cost of drugs, the income from extras and the time spent in the workhouse daily by the medical officer. They agreed that he was holding his office at a pecuniary loss to himself.
[3] *H of C 372*, 1866, Appendix, pp. 77–8
[4] *H of C 4*, 1867–8, Appendix, pp. 26, 40, 66 and 92
[5] *Lancet Commission Report*, pp. 158–9, and *H of C 372*, 1866, p. 76

more than giving attendance upon the sick. He was required to examine all new admissions, to direct and make suggestions regarding the diet, classification and treatment of sick and insane paupers, 'to report in writing to the Guardians on defects in diet, drainage, ventilation, warmth and all other arrangements of the workhouse, or any excess in the number of any class of inmates' and to tell the Guardians of 'any defect which he may observe in the arrangements of the workhouse or in the performance of the nurses'.[1] In the larger workhouses it would have been impossible for any part-time officer to discharge these numerous duties efficiently.

The medical officer was junior in both rank and status to the master of the workhouse. The latter was regarded as the 'head of the executive within the workhouse'.[2] He was responsible to the Guardians for every aspect of workhouse administration including 'the training of inmates to be useful in the workhouse, in improving the state of the yards, and, in general, in devising plans whereby the whole establishment may be more and more efficiently conducted'.[3] In 1866 the master was rarely provided with office assistance and much of his time was taken up in routine clerical duties.[4] It was 'very rarely found that a master can originally have had suitable training'.[5] Many of them were retired army NCOs and one had formerly been employed as a cheap lodging-house keeper. It is not surprising, therefore, that Dr Smith conceded 'that whilst some are in a degree careless, others are overbearing'.[6]

Thus the medical officer was working under an official who was '(save in exceptional circumstances) socially below him'.[7] As a result, the *Lancet* commissioners found that 'an antagonism is set up and in many cases leads to the most vexatious and mischievous interference by the master with the purely medical order of the surgeon'.[8] And the duties of the two officers were such that there inevitably would be friction unless they could work harmoniously together. The medical officer was answerable

[1] *GCO 1847*
[2] *H of C 372*, 1866, p. 65
[3] ibid., p. 66
[4] ibid.
[5] ibid.
[6] ibid.
[7] *Lancet Commission Report*, p. 32
[8] ibid.

directly to his Guardians for 'any defect which he observed in the arrangements of both the Infirmary and the workhouse'. These 'arrangements' were the responsibility of the master to whom he was officially subordinate. When conflict arose, the medical officer could rarely hope for support from either the Guardians or the central authority.[1] The concept of medical relief constituted both a limit to the authority of the Guardians[2] and a contradiction to the principle of 'less-eligibility' upon which the whole Poor Law was based.

Dr Smith blamed the medical officers for not being openly critical of the deficiencies in the Poor Law services. In view of the insecurity of tenure of these officers it is, however, remarkable that they criticized at all. Some certainly did. Thus the medical officer of Cheltenham Workhouse reported to the Board on 'the disgraceful unfitness of the Cheltenham Workhouse in September 1866'. The Poor Law Board acknowledged his letter during October 1867 but had not taken any action in November 1868, by which time the condition of the House was one of 'entire unfitness, disorganization, tyranny and terrorism'. The medical officer then wrote a strong remonstrance to the press and was immediately forced to resign by the president of the Board.[3] There was some truth in the assertion of the *Lancet* commissioners that medical officers were 'having to fight the battle of the poor, with terrible earnestness against the prejudices and gross material interests of the working members of their Boards of Guardians'.[4]

There were numerous instances of masters quarrelling with medical officers. It was Miss Beeton's experience that 'All

[1] 'In disputes between Guardians and their medical officers referred to the Poor Law Board, the bias has been so clearly towards the Guardians that complaint is practically useless.' *Poor Law Chronicle*, 7 October 1868, p. 65. This journal was so critical of the central authority that the Board prohibited the supply of any public document or information to it.

[2] After 1840 the Guardians had been openly encouraged to limit the power of their medical officers – 'In the absence of any positive provisions, medical aid has, nevertheless, been supplied to the poor. The arrangements for the purpose have been almost infinitely various. . . . Almost all, however, had the same object – the absence of all effective control over the medical officer, as well as respects his due attendance on the sick, as with regard to the amount of his charges. . . .' Continuation Report 1840, pp. 44–5

[3] See *Daily Telegraph*, 14 November 1868, and *Poor Law Chronicle*, 21 November 1868, p. 91.

[4] *Lancet Commission Report*, p. 31

masters seem to want to reign supreme over them [the medical officers], not liking them to order what they do not see needful for the pauper.'[1] At an inquiry at Farnham the master admitted that he 'threatened to pull the doctor's nose if he called me a perjurer'.[2] The central authority seems to have treated these officials with exceptional leniency. On one occasion it sanctioned the reappointment of a master who had given false and slander-ous evidence before an official inquiry.[3] As Dr Smith explained, 'The master and matron and medical officer should have a deeper sense of their responsibility to the Poor Law Board, and of the former two, some have well earned and should now receive a superannuation allowance.'[4]

The responsibility for the conduct of the workhouses rested on the locally elected Guardians. In the urban areas they were mostly shopkeepers, tradesmen, or retired businessmen, and in the rural areas they were mostly small farmers though some were county magistrates holding *ex officio* appointments. In London, Mr Farnall found that 'gentlemen will not generally act on these Boards'.[5] Except for the few *ex officio* members, Guardians were elected annually by the ratepayers, though some London parishes derived their powers from local Acts and in these districts the Guardians were appointed by vestrymen. The *ex officio* Guardians rarely attended Board meetings and decision-taking was generally left to the annually elected members. As Dr Smith remarked, 'The short tenure of office and the frequently recurring periods of election keep the guardians in fear of the constituents; and when any unusual expenditure of money is needed, they have often to choose between deferring the question until after the next re-election or voting in a manner which may

[1] *H of C Sessional Paper 362*, 1866, BPP, Vol. LXI, 1866, p. 47

[2] This inquiry was instituted after an epileptic pauper had been drowned in a cesspool from which he had been ordered to ladle manure by the master. *H of C Sessional Paper 372*, 1866, BPP, Vol. LXI, 1866, p. 33

[3] *H of C Sessional Paper 249*, 1867-8, BPP, Vol. LX, 1867-8. (Letters addressed to the PLB by the Guardians of the Strand Union . . . relative to Mr George Catch.) The lengthy catalogue of Mr Catch's misdeeds is also recorded in J. Rogers, *Reminiscences of a Workhouse Medical Officer*, London, 1889. He was eventually dismissed after chasing a female pauper up a chimney and then attempting to smoke her out by lighting hydrochloric acid in the grate.

[4] *H of C 372*, 1866, p. 70

[5] Farnall's Statement

prevent their re-election.'[1] Their duty, as they saw it, was to save the rates rather than to meet need.

Often they knew very little about what really went on in the institutions they controlled. There was a system of visiting committees but these were found to be 'the most defective part of the present system'.[2] 'They usually visit too infrequently and in too great a hurry and are too much disinclined to recommend changes.' Visiting committees in voluntary hospitals were thought to be more efficient as 'they are often gentlemen connected with and who know the practice in other hospitals'.[3]

Above the Guardians was the Poor Law Board which had become largely ineffective. Although 1,000 orders and advisory circulars were sent out between 1847 and 1866, it was extremely hard for the Board to force Guardians to raise and spend more money than they wished. In practice the Board itself had ceased to exist. By 1866 its *ex officio* members had stopped meeting as a Board and decisions were left to the officials. During the tragic winter of 1868, when the London workhouses were overcrowded with destitute poor, the president of the Poor Law Board was on holiday in the South of France.[4] When documents required signature they were taken round to the houses of Ministers who, 'it was alleged, frequently signed without reading the contents'.[5] There were only thirteen Poor Law inspectors, one of whom was responsible for the whole of London.[6]

Power really resided with the Guardians if they had wanted or had been able to use it. They were not drawn from the social *élite* which ran the voluntary hospitals. Few of them had ever known the benefits of skilled nursing or even adequate medical care and it is therefore less surprising that they declined to make these available to sick paupers. They were often drawn from a social class which had but recently risen from that which the

[1] *H of C 372*, 1866, p. 65
[2] ibid.
[3] ibid.
[4] Rogers, p. 69
[5] Rogers, p. 80, and *Poor Law Chronicle*, 7 July 1868, pp. 1–2
[6] The Metropolitan Inspector was required to meet each of the forty Boards of Guardians 'at least once a year', to inspect each workhouse 'thoroughly' every six months, 'to conduct numerous official enquiries and to perform routine duties in connection with his office. . . .' *H of C 372*, 1866, p. 68

Poor Law was serving, and they no doubt attributed their rise to virtues which must be encouraged in the poor. Their status was not wholly secure and it was not unknown for a Guardian to end his days in the workhouse sick wards. These unqualified and uneducated men believed from their narrow experience that 'less-eligibility' meant saving on the rates: better nursing and medical services would be extravagant.

When judged in terms of the less-eligibility principle, despite all its deficiencies the Poor Law service was already extravagant. The workhouses were providing more medical services than the independent poor could be expected to buy for themselves. While 'admitting the existence of many defects', Dr Smith pointed out that 'no one can walk through these great institutions without appreciating the fact that the inmates are better fed, better clad, better housed and better cared for than they were before their admission, and better than the great mass of the working classes who earn their own living. . . .'[1]

The Guardians shared with the Poor Law Board the belief in the principle of 'less-eligibility', but this principle was in sharp contrast to the principles which were beginning to be practised by medical officers granting medical relief, and in even sharper contrast to the principles which were being practised by the voluntary hospitals of London for those who were 'acutely sick' and of value as teaching material. The Poor Law medical officers had been trained in such hospitals and their conflicts with the administrators were challenging the whole philosophy of the Poor Laws.

Thus by the middle 1860's there were two free hospital services. The larger sector was run under the shadow of 'less-eligibility' with money raised by compulsory levies. The smaller sector was run to meet the needs of selected patients at a higher standard with money raised by voluntary contributions. The public was 'lavishing princely munificence on the splendid institutions which ostensibly supply the national hospital requirements' but 'ignored the *real hospitals of the land*'.[2] The two systems had developed for a variety of reasons: to give charity to the sick poor, to provide doctors for prospective patients and to provide patients for prospective doctors, to prevent abuse of cash relief

[1] ibid., p. 71
[2] *Lancet Commission Report*, p. ix

and to assist in medical research. But from this muddle of conflicting motives an important precedent had been established. The poor had gained the right to institutional care when they were sick.

CHAPTER 5

Nursing and Workhouse Reform

IN the first half of the nineteenth century the voluntary hospitals had expanded and developed as they became increasingly used by doctors for teaching and research. In the second
half of the century, the influx of medical pioneers was followed
by an influx of nursing pioneers; and in time the new doctors and
the new nurses joined forces with lay philanthropists to demand
improvements in the care of the sick in workhouses.

The movement for nursing reform arose out of the recognition
of the importance of bedside care, which was the result of wider
medical knowledge and more intensive treatments. But it took
the form it did because nursing was able to provide an outlet for
the social conscience and frustrated energies of the Victorian
spinster. The doctor needed a skilled auxiliary who would handle,
supervise and treat each patient as he directed. The condition
of each patient had to be accurately observed and the relevant
details reported to the doctor. Training was introduced to
develop these skills and to implant the necessary medical
knowledge.

The school which Miss Nightingale started in 1860 at St
Thomas' Hospital was not the first in Britain, but its influence
was certainly the most pervasive and lasting.[1] The training was
free and the 'probationers' were provided with tea, sugar and
washing, a certain amount of outer clothing and a payment of
£10 for the one year's course. Admission was not confined to
girls from the higher social classes. Miss Nightingale thought
that daughters of small farmers and well-educated domestic
servants would make the best nurses. Nevertheless, some of the
daughters of the prosperous families of Britain were included
among the early recruits. The religious zeal of Kaiserswerth[2], the

[1] For a more detailed description of the origin and development of
nursing reform, see Abel-Smith, op. cit.
[2] At Kaiserswerth, a few miles from Düsseldorf, a Protestant Institute

military discipline of Scutari, and the cultural pattern of Miss Nightingale's prosperous Victorian home were all combined and imposed on the first recruits to the Nightingale school. The probationers were under continuous supervision during the ten hours of ward duty, were compelled to keep a diary, and were reported on weekly. Any lapse in sobriety or truthfulness meant dismissal. Supervision extended also to the periods when the probationers were off duty. Special accommodation was eventually provided in a nurses' home where the pupils could be supervised by the home sister. The single bedrooms and communal sitting-room, although by no means luxurious, were greatly superior to the standard of accommodation previously thought adequate for nursing staff. Living-in was made part of the training.

The foundation of the nurse-training school was an event which attracted widespread attention. Miss Nightingale had started her school in a large and venerable hospital which commanded no small respect in the hospital world. Apart from the cost of acquiring or adapting accommodation which would be thought suitable for the new class of nurse, there were no financial obstacles standing in the way of reform. Indeed, probationers could be paid less than the traditional nurses while providing a higher standard of service. It is not, therefore, surprising that the experiment was quickly copied. Miss Nightingale engineered many of her early pupils into positions as matrons at other hospitals and the new order spread by geometric progression as each trained nurse trained others.

A higher standard of hygiene and a new discipline were introduced into the hospital ward. Everything possible was scrubbed and cleaned and exposed to the cold fresh air; medicines and dressings were handled with military efficiency. The patients drawn from the working class were put in the charge of young ladies who did not hesitate to impose their own culture upon them. It is possible also that the example of the nurses communicated itself to the doctors and made them also more conscientious. The introduction of hygiene and efficiency made possible

---

of Deaconesses had been founded in 1833 by Pastor Theodore Fliedner as a home for discharged female convicts and had grown until it included a hospital, a lunatic asylum, an orphanage and two schools. Miss Nightingale spent three months there in 1851.

the development of hospitals which were of positive benefit to their patients.

The introduction of trained matrons and probationer nurses meant a major change in hospital administration. In many hospitals the matron had previously played a small role in the control of nursing affairs. Her major work had been that of a housekeeper, and in these matters she worked under the orders of the lay administration. It was she who engaged the nurses, though in some hospitals she did this in consultation with the medical staff responsible for each ward. The doctors gave them such training and knowledge as they possessed. It was not the matron's duty to tell the sisters what they ought to be doing for the doctors. Moreover, the nursing staff tended to remain continuously in the same ward.

When a hospital was run on these lines it was clear that the introduction of a matron and a training school would bring conflict. To put it baldly, if the matron was to undertake what she considered to be her duties, she had to carve out an empire of her own. She had to take over some of the responsibilities of the medical staff and some of the responsibilities of the lay administration. In addition she had to centralize the administration of nursing affairs, lowering thereby the prestige of her sisters.

Thus the new matrons came into conflict with the lay administrators and the doctors. While the resistance of the former could be overcome fairly easily if the governors supported the matron, it was more difficult for the unpaid doctors to be forced to accept the new régime without public protest. In part it was a battle of the sexes. The new ladies had to fight the male doctors, the male administrators and the male governors. They had to win a position of power for their sex in an institution which was exclusively controlled by men.

In a remarkably short time the matrons got their way and took over positions of undisputed authority between the medical staff and the lay administration. A system of tripartite administration replaced bipartite administration. By 1880 the change had occurred in most of the leading voluntary hospitals of London. It came so swiftly because the pressure for it came from the top of the social hierarchy: the ladies who sought power in the hospitals moved in the same social circle as the committees that ran them.

It was to prove much harder to reform the workhouses. Guardians were seldom drawn from the same social background as the governors of voluntary hospitals and they tended to see their duty as the protection of the ratepayer rather than the pauper. The doctors who worked in the Poor Law service were not persons of high standing in their local community. Great powers had been vested in the masters, many of whom had risen from humble origins. There was, moreover, the whole philosophy of the Poor Laws and this was the most serious obstacle to overcome.

Within four years of the foundation of her training school at St Thomas' Hospital, Miss Nightingale had extended her campaign to improve nursing from the voluntary hospitals to the workhouses. In response to an approach by William Rathbone, the wealthy Liverpool philanthropist, she sent Agnes Jones to become matron of Brownlow Hill Institution. She arrived with a staff of twelve trained nurses and within a month had sacked thirty-five of the old pauper nurses and quarrelled with both the master and the Guardians, but she did succeed in introducing drastic changes before she died of an infection caught at the Infirmary.

Meanwhile, Miss Nightingale had become active in the growing movement for workhouse reform. In 1853, Miss Louisa Twining had protested publicly about the state of the workhouses after she visited the Strand Workhouse. She had gone to call on a respectable old woman who had been compelled to enter it when 'strength and eyesight failed her'. The old lady had 'begged that her friend and visitor would not forget or forsake her when shut up from the outer world'.[1] After a number of visits, Miss Twining planned to bring other ladies 'for the purpose of reading to the inmates, and giving comfort and instruction'.[2] The Poor Law Board objected to her proposal, pointing out that it was 'contrary to the general practice to admit strangers into the workhouse for the purpose of aiding the paid and responsible officers in the performance of their duties'. It would be an 'embarrassing and inconvenient precedent'.[3]

A year later, after Miss Twining had made a personal visit to

[1] Louisa Twining, *Recollections of Workhouse Visiting and Management during Twenty-Five Years*, p. 6, London, 1880
[2] ibid., p. 7
[3] ibid., p. 8

the Board, this decision was reversed provided the plan was 'quietly carried on'.[1] The ladies visited quietly, but they also assembled information on the state of the workhouses which Miss Twining published. Her revelations led to a somewhat ineffective debate in the House of Lords in 1857 and the withdrawal of permission for ladies to visit the Strand Workhouse.[2] The ladies responded by forming, in 1858, the Workhouse Visiting Society and successfully infiltrating a number of other workhouses. By 1860, 140 members were visiting twelve Metropolitan workhouses, and local branches had been established in several parts of England.[3]

The opposition to workhouse visitors had a number of causes. First, there was the natural fear of the officials that the ladies would obtain information which would be to their discredit. Secondly, there was the religious issue; if there were to be Protestant lady visitors, how could Roman Catholic ladies be kept out of the workhouses? Thirdly, there was the widespread prejudice of male Guardians against the interfering woman. One of the visitors commented sarcastically on this attitude:

> We do give credit to many ridiculous stories and pity many imaginary grievances, and sometimes go to the length of bestowing unmerited tea or even indigestible lozenges and Puseyite tracts upon our protégés . . . but perhaps, if the gentlemen to whom the guardianship of the poor is exclusively entrusted *never* made blunders . . . the state of our workhouses would not be precisely what it is at this moment.[4]

During the late 1850's, a further organization was formed which concerned itself partly with the cause of workhouse reform – the National Association for the Promotion of Social Science. Its members were leading citizens, male and female, of the same social standing as the male governors of the voluntary hospitals and higher in status than the male Boards of Guardians. They were not reformers in any radical sense; they sought to improve the Poor Law, not to destroy it. These influential citizens were able to see that workhouse scandals were not hushed

[1] ibid., p. 11
[2] ibid., p. 21
[3] *Journal of the Workhouse Visiting Society*, May 1860, p. 197
[4] Frances Cobbe, 'The Sick Poor in Workhouses', *Journal of the Workhouse Visiting Society*, London, 1861, p. 487

up but received the widest possible publicity. The Association was in touch with the more enlightened and courageous of the Poor Law medical officers.

The training of the general practitioner was now carried on in the leading voluntary hospitals, and the militant workhouse doctors wanted to raise the standards of care of the workhouse sick to a level which was not so wildly out of line with that of the hospitals in which they had been trained. By the Registration Act of 1858 the doctors had enhanced their professional and social status. By the sixties there were some doctors who were no longer willing to tolerate exploitation by Boards of Guardians and domination by workhouse masters, or to acquiesce in the neglect of the sick poor. Some, like Dr Rogers, were able and willing to protest even though protest led to dismissal. In 1866 he formed a Metropolitan Poor Law Medical Officers' Association.[1] The inaugural meeting was attended by thirty out of the forty Metropolitan workhouse medical officers.

Thus the Poor Law reform movement consisted of a loose alliance of three divergent groups: there were the doctors who wanted greater professional independence to provide their patients with the care they needed; there were the nursing reformers, headed by the formidable Miss Nightingale; finally, there were the well-intentioned laymen who had made it their business to ascertain what life was really like in the workhouses. The forces ranged against them were the parsimonious representatives of the ratepayers, an apathetic and ill-informed Poor Law Board, and a Parliament which still insisted on regarding the whole Poor Law as a service providing for able-bodied workmen.

In 1864 a Select Committee reported on the question of medical relief. It had been appointed in 1861 as a result of widespread concern about the failure of the Poor Law to deal adequately with the distress of the winter of 1860. The inquiry was conducted by the Poor Law inspectors under the chairmanship of the Board's own president. This hardly independent

[1] The Association was formed after a meeting called by Dr Rogers to co-ordinate replies to a circular letter sent out by the PLB. Rogers believed that the Board's aim was to elicit so many contradictory answers that it would be justified in taking no action. The Association was formed so 'that we might be prepared to deal promptly with any similar departmental trickery'. Rogers, pp. 56–7

inquiry recommended some minor changes but found 'no grounds for interfering with the present system'.[1] Within a few months of this complacent report, a sick pauper died in Holborn Workhouse as a consequence of gross neglect. This was followed by another death in St Giles's Workhouse in similar circumstances. The charges of neglect on the part of pauper nurses and other lay staff were not adequately refuted.

In 1865, James Wakley, the new owner of *The Lancet*, prompted by a number of workhouse medical officers, commissioned three doctors to visit the workhouses. Two of them were on the staff of leading London teaching hospitals (the Westminster and St Mary's) and they judged the workhouses by the standards which had been set in their own hospitals. Some of the facts published in their 'soberly sensational'[2] reports were summarized in Chapter 4. They noted that 'the average mortality of the Metropolitan workhouses is very high' even when allowances were made for 'the number of feeble aged persons and hopelessly diseased who enter the houses and the number of sickly infants who are born in it'.[3] They said that the medical officers were 'habitually overworked', that their remuneration was 'in most cases insufficient',[4] and that it was quite wrong to require them to pay for their own dispensing and drugs. Their general conclusion was uncompromising:

> Patch up the present system as we may, it will still continue to be a scandal and a reproach. . . . The State hospitals are in the workhouse wards. They are closed against observation, they pay no heed to public opinion; they pay no toll to science. They are under the government of men profoundly ignorant of hospital rules. . . . To perpetuate 39 bad hospitals when half a dozen good will suffice would be an act of gross and dangerous misgovernment.[5]

The publication of the *Lancet* Commission's report led to the formation of yet another organization – the Association for

[1] *H of C Sessional Paper 349*, BPP, Vol. IX, 1864 (*Report from the Select Committee on Poor Relief*)
[2] Hardy Gathorne, President of the Poor Law Board, told the House of Commons that he would be 'the last person to complain of the mode and manner in which that inquiry was conducted . . .' *Hansard (H of C)*, Vol. CLXXXV, 8 February 1867, col. 153
[3] *Lancet Commission Report*, op. cit., p. 34
[4] ibid., p. 31
[5] ibid., p. iv

the Improvement of the London Workhouse Infirmaries. The secretary was Dr Hart,[1] one of the three *Lancet* commissioners. Members included Sir Thomas Watson, President of the Royal College of Physicians, Charles Dickens and John Stuart Mill. The Association's publications reinforced the agitation aroused in the press and in Parliament.

To the complaints of doctors and laymen were added the courageous protests of two nurses who had known the standards of the voluntary hospitals and would not tolerate the neglect of workhouse patients. Joan Bateman complained about the Paddington Workhouse[2] and Matilda Beeton reported on both the Strand and Rotherhithe Workhouses. She even went so far as to allege that the Guardians and their officials had deliberately deceived the central authority as to the quality of care being given in the sick wards.[3] It took two deputations from the Workhouse Infirmary Association to force the Board to conduct an inquiry, but Miss Beeton's story was eventually substantiated. Mr Farnall ended his report to the Board on a note of despair: 'As your Board has no power to compel the Board of Guardians to build a new and sufficient workhouse, the old Rotherhithe Workhouse, with all its defects, still exists.'[4]

Meanwhile Miss Nightingale had been busy behind the scenes. With her experiment at Liverpool successfully if not peacefully launched, she was well aware that it was one thing to prove the advantages of reform by local demonstration and quite another

[1] Ernest Hart later became editor of the *British Medical Journal*.
[2] *H of C Sessional Paper 517*, 1866, BPP, Vol. LXI, 1866 (Evidence taken in the Recent Poor Law Inquiry at Paddington and the Report of Mr Farnall thereupon)
[3] 'I well remember, sir, your visit to the Rotherhithe Infirmary, the Master accompanied you. I answered yes when I ought to have said no; this I did fearing the Master or Matron would hear me or you would tell them, and then I might be reported, and that is anything but pleasant, inasmuch as they are told they must mind how they leave their appointment, or the Poor Law Board will not sign another for them. This rod was shook over me, sir. . . . The fourth nurse was a confirmed drunkard, so much so, that I was in constant fear of her doing bodily harm to the sick patients. She would beat them till they were black with bruises, more especially those who were unable to help themselves and friendless. . . .' *H of C Sessional Paper 518*, 1866, BPP, Vol. LXI, 1866 (*Report of the Inquiry lately held by the Metropolitan Inspector into the Complaints of Miss Beeton against the Management of the Rotherhithe Workhouse Infirmary . . .*), pp. 21–2
[4] ibid., p. 7

to secure its adoption all over the country within any reasonable period of time. It takes more than clear empirical evidence to defeat vested interests, to overcome public prejudice and to drive to action a timid administration. All this she had learned during her attempts to reform the medical administration of the army and the sanitary policies of the British administration in India. Workhouse nursing would not be altered all over the country without far-reaching changes in the whole system and principles of workhouse administration.

When she heard of the death in negligent circumstances of a pauper called Timothy Daly she wrote to the President of the Poor Law Board (Mr Villiers) and summoned him to her sofa-side. She persuaded him to undertake an investigation into the treatment of the sick poor with a view to reforming the whole field of workhouse administration. Shortly afterwards she received Mr Farnall, the Poor Law inspector for the Metropolitan district, and with his help drew up a 'Form of Inquiry' to be circulated to every workhouse in London.

In the same year the Poor Law Board appointed its first medical officer to the post of inspector, Dr Edward Smith. He 'was not expected to advise in any general, or any initiative sense, but only to answer in particular cases on such particular points as might be referred to him'.[1] But he had arrived on the scene at a critical time, as it was he and Mr Farnall who were instructed to inquire into the existing arrangements for the care of the sick in all the Metropolitan workhouses and to suggest 'such alterations as might appear advisable in the present system'.

These inspectors made many suggestions for improvements in the workhouses. Dr Smith suggested a capitation system for paying workhouse doctors: '10s per adult based on the average number of inmates in the workhouse at one time', with two children under the age of sixteen counting as one adult.[2] He advised the appointment of another 130 paid nurses[3] in the Metropolis and concluded that 'Paupers should be employed only as servants and in subordinate capacities'.[4] Mr Farnall was convinced that 'pauper nursing should be wholly abolished' as

[1] Sir John Simon, *English Sanitary Institutions*, p. 552, London, 1890
[2] *H of C 372*, 1866, p. 62
[3] ibid., p. 56
[4] ibid., p. 70

he had found them to be mostly illiterate and 'feeble old women' and 'because their previous careers have, in many instances, been vicious; because their love of drink often drives them to beg, or buy, or rob the sick . . . and because their treatment of the poor is, generally speaking, not characterized either by judgment or by gentleness'.[1] Dr Smith saw no reason 'to doubt that many of the evils which now exist would, long ago, have been removed, and I cannot but think that the system of Inspection is at fault and should be reconstructed on the model of the Lunacy Commission'.[2] Dr Smith suggested that there should be separate wards for certain special categories of inmate – those with scarlet fever and smallpox, noisy and dangerous lunatics, and children.[3]

Mr Farnall's report was strongly influenced by the views of Miss Nightingale, for he was in frequent contact with her.[4] Indeed, the similarity of the style suggests that large sections of it were written by Miss Nightingale herself.[5]

> . . . mere suggestions to rebuild or remodel the infirmaries of the metropolitan workhouses, so as to give not less than 1,000 cubic feet of air to each patient, nor less than 80 superficial feet to each bed, to abolish pauper nursing, to establish a sufficient staff of trained paid nurses by day and by night in each of the workhouses, to give each of the medical officers a sufficient salary, to appoint resident medical officers wherever necessary, to pay for the drugs out of the rates, to strictly classify patients in separate wards, and to provide day-rooms for the chronically sick, the aged and infirm, and the convalescent, will not, as it seems to me, secure the satis-factory treatment of the sick poor in workhouses, for there is no legal power vested in your Board which enables you to compel Boards of Guardians to adopt these suggestions in their entirety.[6]

Mr Farnall suggested that the Poor Law Board should seek legal powers to require all these things to be done. Hospitals, he insisted, should be built, wholly apart from the Metropolitan workhouses and paid for by a common rating extended over the

[1] *H of C 387*, 1866, p. 6
[2] *H of C 372*, 1866, p. 68
[3] ibid., pp. 35–7
[4] Cecil Woodham-Smith, *Florence Nightingale*, p. 351, London, 1951
[5] I am indebted to Miss G. Ayers for this suggestion.
[6] *H of C 387*, 1866, p. 7

whole Metropolis. 'The rates being intolerably unequal, no ingenuity or contrivance could render the majority of the present sick wards in any way equal to the just requirements of sound medical science.'[1] The plan was very similar to Miss Nightingale's 'ABC of Workhouse Reform' which she sent to Mr Villiers in December 1865. But she wanted to go further and hand over the care of London's sick poor to one central management.[2]

By the spring of 1866, the Whig Government was tottering and Mr Villiers was afraid to introduce such a controversial measure. On 18 June 1866, the Government fell and, with it, Miss Nightingale's hopes of a Bill. Miss Nightingale, however, sent copies of her plan to Edwin Chadwick, and to John Stuart Mill who was sitting on a Select Committee on Local Government in the Metropolis.

Mr Villiers' successor at the Poor Law Board was Mr Hardy Gathorne. His first action was to send a series of suggestions and recommendations to the Metropolitan Guardians. He then sought advice from the President of the Royal College of Physicians (Sir Thomas Watson) who set up an expert committee to report on 'the requisite amount of space and other matters in relation to workhouses and workhouse infirmaries'. This committee decided that each sick inmate should have 850 cubic feet with six feet between bed heads, rather than the 1,000 cubic feet recommended by Dr Smith. Fever and smallpox cases should have 2,000 cubic feet and be 'removed to separate hospitals'.[3]

On this last recommendation all authorities were agreed – the Poor Law inspectors, the physicians' committee and Miss Nightingale. Something had to be done to create an adequate number of isolation hospitals. It was a matter which affected all sections of the population and was vital to the health of the whole nation: and the need was greatest in London. In the interests of the other residents, nearly all the Guardians had by this time refused to admit fever or smallpox cases to their workhouses[4] and more and more voluntary general hospitals were adopting

    [1] ibid., p. 8
    [2] Woodham-Smith, p. 351
    [3] *H of C Sessional Paper 185*, 1867, BPP, Vol. LX, 1867 (*Report of the Committee appointed to consider the cubic space of Metropolitan Workhouses*)
    [4] Only two Metropolitan workhouses 'willingly or usually retained cases of fever and smallpox'. *H of C 372*, 1866, p. 4

the same policy. Thus Guardians had to try and secure admission for this type of case at the London Fever Hospital and at the Smallpox Hospital. The former had only 182 beds and the latter only 100 beds, and these hospitals were increasingly becoming occupied by paying patients. There was a grave shortage of accommodation for the diseases which constituted the greatest danger to the health of the people of London.

On 8 February 1867, as yet another epidemic of scarlet fever spread across London, Mr Hardy Gathorne introduced his Metropolitan Poor Bill. The main emphasis of his proposals was on the creation of separate hospitals for fever and smallpox cases. There was no risk of abuse of such a service as 'smallpox and fever are things the relief of which cannot be traded in. Nobody will go into a smallpox or fever hospital who has not one of those diseases.'[1] He wanted greater powers. He explained that the Board had been reluctant to put into force the compulsory powers it already possessed as 'it would have been difficult if not impossible to have proceeded by *mandamus*, and in the case of medical officers, legal and technical questions and questions of contract would undoubtedly have been raised'.[2]

He then defined the new policy which was to be implemented and stated its underlying principle with considerable emphasis:

> There is one thing . . . which we must peremptorily insist on, namely, the treatment of the sick in workhouses being conducted on an entirely different system, because the evils complained of have mainly arisen from the workhouse management, which must, to a great degree, be of a deterrent character having been applied to the sick, *who are not* proper objects for such a system. That is one thing that I should insist on as an absolute condition. I propose therefore, that power shall be given to combine such districts as the Poor Law Board may think proper – whether parishes and parishes, Unions and Unions, or Unions and parishes – under a more complete system of inspection and control.[3]

The larger districts would be better able to build 'asylums' and

[1] *Hansard*, 8 February 1867, col. 171

[2] ibid., 21 February 1867, cols. 154–5. 'These local Acts have been among the greatest impediments with which the Poor Law Board have had to contend. The Board has constantly been liable to be tripped up in the Courts of Law for if a notice were sent to the directors it was held that it ought to have been sent to the vestries and vice-versa.'

[3] ibid., 8 February 1867, col. 163

attract suitable women for training as nurses.[1] In addition he wanted the asylums to be used to teach medical students, as 'the attendance of medical practitioners and their pupils would amount to an inspection of the most efficacious kind'.[2]

Control was to be exercised through appointed nominees on the local Boards, who would not exceed one-third of the number of appointed Guardians. Nominees would be chosen from citizens rated at not less than £100, so that he (Hardy Gathorne) would not be criticized 'for putting on to the Board persons of lower qualifications than those possessed by the elected Guardians.'[3] They would serve as responsible persons 'who could be removed if they did not discharge the duty they had undertaken'.[4] In addition, the Bill gave the Board powers to direct the appropriate authorities to buy or adapt a building to the satisfaction of the Board, and to direct that any workhouse should be used as an asylum for the common use of the district. In the case of outdoor relief, the Bill gave the Poor Law Board power to direct Guardians to provide dispensaries in which medical officers were to work. They were to be assisted by dispensers.

Mr Hardy Gathorne estimated that the extra cost on current account would be about £60,000 each year; this could be raised by a rate, for the whole Metropolis, of one penny in the pound. The initial capital cost he estimated at about £400,000; a quarter of this would be needed for two buildings for accommodating fever and smallpox cases and a similar sum for school buildings.[5] A rate of two-thirds of a penny in the pound would be required for the annual repayments.

After assuring the House that he had no wish to 'equalize the rates', Hardy Gathorne explained that he wanted to set up a common fund for London with an income collected from all the parishes and Unions according to their rateable value. In the case of lunatics and patients suffering from fever and smallpox in asylums set up under the new plan, the common fund was to pay all the costs of maintaining the patients. In the case of other approved asylums, the salaries of all officers were to be

[1] ibid., 21 February 1867, cols., 163-4
[2] ibid., 8 February 1867, col. 165
[3] ibid., 21 February 1867, col. 778
[4] ibid., col. 777
[5] ibid., 8 February 1867, col. 173

reimbursed by the fund. All medicines and medical and surgical appliances were to be paid for by the fund for any patients wherever treated. As the whole cost of running the asylums for lunatics and infectious cases was 'being placed upon the Common Fund, it will be necessary to have a Central Board'.[1]

The Bill was cunningly devised. It was a carefully balanced compromise between central direction and local autonomy with some measure of rate equalization built into it. It made it possible for larger units of administration to be created for the sick poor but it did not destroy the Guardians or remove any function from their control, provided they acted together. On the other hand, the Poor Law Board had extreme powers to direct and it could appoint its own representatives on all the relevant committees. The Radicals had their attention drawn to these extensive powers, though the President was careful not to tell the House exactly what size of district he intended to create and how much he intended to use his new authority. The Conservative element with their fears of bureaucratic centralization and ugly memories of the early days of Chadwickian despotism were told 'there was nothing in the Bill to abolish self-government – indeed under its provisions local government would have the fullest scope for its exertions'.[2] Hardy Gathorne did not draw attention to the fact that he could use his control over the Common Poor Fund as an additional weapon to induce Guardians to establish separate infirmaries for the sick and to create dispensaries.

The Radicals, particularly those who had received copies of Miss Nightingale's brief on the subject, said that the Bill did not go far enough. Her brother-in-law, Sir Harry Verney, wanted 'one Board for the uniform management of the sick poor of London'. The costs of training nurses should be included among the items to be paid for by the Common Fund.[3] John Stuart Mill also argued the case for one Board for London. Answering those who suggested that such a Board would be a step towards centralization, he said 'the denial of it would be a far greater step towards centralization. The powers which such a body is best qualified to exercise have become indispensable and if not assumed by a central board, they will therefore be necessarily

[1] ibid., 21 February 1867, col. 776
[2] ibid., col. 753
[3] ibid.

assumed by a purely government board, the Poor Law Board.'[1]

Hardy Gathorne replied that, 'If the Metropolis were made one district, a central board would be created. If that experiment were tried it would be seen whether the powers of the Board might, with benefit, be applied to other purposes', but he thought it wise to proceed 'by steps'.[2] He did not propose to go all the way and establish several 1,000-bed hospitals in various parts of London. First, these would involve great expense and render useless existing workhouses; secondly, 'whereas in our smaller establishments, notwithstanding all their defects, gangrene, erysipelas and puerperal fever do not intrude, in the large hospitals those diseases not only intrude, but are often permanently fixed there'.[3]

Despite extended debate, the Bill was eventually passed with some enthusiasm. A Tory Minister without a straight majority had steered through the House an important measure of reform. He had achieved this without splitting his party. He had shown enough of his hand to win the support of the Radicals, and not so much that he lost the support of his own right wing. He had found the right balance between central and local government and made it possible to create a public body which would build isolation hospitals in London. It was a brilliant piece of political manœuvring.

Only six weeks after his Bill received the Royal Assent, the Board produced an order[4] under the new Metropolitan Poor Act that all the Unions in the Metropolis were to be combined into one district for cases of fever, smallpox or insanity. There were to be sixty members on the board of management of whom three-quarters were to be elected Guardians and fifteen were to be appointed members. It was the birth of the Metropolitan Asylums' Board.

Soon afterwards, orders were issued for the formation of the new sick asylum districts. Between January and November 1868, seventeen Unions and parishes were reorganized into six sick asylum districts.[5] Seventeen other London Unions and

[1] ibid.
[2] ibid., 8 March 1867, cols. 1610–11
[3] ibid., 8 February 1867, col. 164
[4] Order of 15 May 1867
[5] *Twentieth Annual Report PLB 1867–8*, 4039, pp. 17–18, HMSO, 1868

parishes were also required to provide their own separate
infirmaries.[1]

In theory, the president of the Poor Law Board had extensive
powers to direct all these authorities. He could give specific
orders by which all of London's sick poor would be accommodated in separate buildings. And if any authority failed to
comply with his directions he could take over the job and do it
himself directly. But as Hardy Gathorne had told the House of
Commons, it was very difficult, if not impossible, to do this –
particularly as it would have involved a savage rate in some parts
of London. *Mandamus* was no more of a political possibility after
the Act than it had been before it. It was for this reason that he
had provided for a nucleus of appointed members. But the most
powerful weapon which Hardy Gathorne had forged was the
Common Fund, about which he had said very little in the debates
on the Bill.

Where expenditure was borne by the Fund, an important
degree of separation had been created between those who raised
the money and those who spent it. In the extreme case of the
Metropolitan Asylums' Board, the majority of costs were covered
by the Fund: and the Guardians on the Board had to pay somewhat less heed to the impact on local elections of the expenditure
they were authorizing. In the case of other asylums, officers'
salaries were reimbursed by the Common Fund. If Guardians
chose not to create a sick asylum to the satisfaction of the Poor
Law Board, they had themselves to meet the salaries of officers
ministering to the sick. If, on the other hand, they did what the
Board asked them to do, the Common Fund paid the salaries.
As long as the initial capital expenditure was not too heavy,
there was a financial incentive in London to create separate
infirmaries. As seen from any local viewpoint, the system was

---

[1] *Twentieth Annual Report PLB 1867–8*, p. 18. The difference between a
'separate infirmary' and a 'workhouse' was not officially clarified until
much later. In 1914, the LGB explained that 'In previous reports "separate
infirmary" has been used to denote a separate building or separate block of
the workhouse, whether separately administered or not. This definition has
now been abandoned and the term restricted to those cases where the
administration of the infirmary is governed by a set of regulations
distinct from those relating to the workhouse.' Only in London were the
separate infirmaries invariably under the control of medical superintendents. *Forty-Third Annual Report LGB 1913–14*, Cd 7444, p. ix, HMSO,
1914

equivalent to a high percentage grant on officers' salaries and all medicines.

The Act applied only to London. In the following year, the Poor Law Amendment Act[1] empowered provincial authorities to provide separate infirmaries, but there was no common fund to induce them to do so. And even in London it was not clear whether separate infirmaries would be created in every area. Much depended on how the Poor Law Board used the new authority that Parliament had granted it.

Nevertheless the Metropolitan Poor Act of 1867 was an important step in English social history. It was the first explicit acknowledgement that it was the duty of the state to provide hospitals for the poor. It therefore represented an important step towards the National Health Service Act which followed some eighty years later.

[1] 31 & 32 Vict. c. 122. S.8

CHAPTER 6

The Creation of Pauper Hospitals

FROM the legislation which followed the revelations of 1866, the Poor Law Board had gained new powers. It had also gained a clearer policy and a new sense of purpose which was gradually communicated in greater or lesser measure to the hundreds of public authorities housing the sick poor. One section of the 'impotent' (the sick) was to be given more comfortable and fitting abodes. Hospitals were to be provided.

The reorganization of the London Guardians into sick asylum districts did not last for long. In 1868, Hardy Gathorne was promoted to Home Secretary and his place was taken for a brief period by the Earl of Devon who in turn handed over to Goschen at the end of the same year. Under the latter's presidency, all but two of the newly formed districts were dismantled. The two which survived were the Poplar and Stepney district, which had already built an infirmary (now St Andrew's Hospital), and the central London district, which was instructed to carry on with the plans to build one.[1] Their existing arrangements had come in for special criticism in the recent inquiries.

The reason given for that sudden change of policy was the high cost of the first new building. Poplar and Stepney had spent £45,000 on its infirmary which contained 562 beds. Hardy Gathorne had estimated that only £120,000 would have to be spent all over London on the new sick asylums. The figure was now put at £600,000. For reasons of economy it was decided to create infirmaries by 'upgrading' one of the workhouses in each Union.[2] To ensure that each Union had enough buildings to introduce the necessary minimum of classification, the number of separate Metropolitan Unions was reduced from thirty-nine to thirty.

[1] *Twenty-First Annual Report PLB, 1868–9*, 23650, pp. 16–18, HMSO, 1869
[2] *Twenty-Second Annual Report PLB, 1869–70*, C 123, pp. xxxvi–xxxvii, HMSO, 1870

G

Though this change was a retreat from the more ambitious proposals for the accommodation of the sick poor which had been envisaged in 1867, Goschen genuinely intended to provide a proper medical service. He saw the value of early access to medical care. In his last annual report he went so far as to say that

> . . . the economical and social advantage of free medicine to the poorer classes generally as distinguished from actual paupers, and perfect accessibility to medical advice at all times under thorough organization, may be considered so important in themselves as to render it necessary to weigh with the greatest care all the reasons which may be adduced in their favour.[1]

Goschen defined the functions of the proposed new dispensaries and infirmaries in positive terms. The relation between the two services was intended to be based on the needs of the sick. Addressing Guardians who were hesitating about providing proper infirmaries, he told them it was wrong to imagine that

> . . . when the dispensaries are brought into full operation in the Metropolis, a fewer number of sick poor will be sent into workhouse hospitals than at the present time. Indeed, such a result has never been anticipated by us. . . . The sick poor are not sent into infirmaries on account of outdoor medical relief being inaccessible to them, but either on account of the character and condition of their homes, or on account of some special requirement of their disease, or on account of the patients having no one to nurse them at home.[2]

Goschen's interpretation of the proper role of the hospital would still be acceptable today.

Guardians did not hasten to develop dispensaries of their own accord and the Poor Law Board used its power over the Common Fund to force recalcitrant authorities to do what it wanted. In 1869 the Poor Law Board reported that the provision 'for withholding repayment from the Common Poor Fund of the salaries of medical officers and the cost of medicines in those cases where the Guardians neglect or refuse to establish a dispensary have had the anticipated effect of promoting to a considerable extent the adoption of the system'.[3] Six

[1] ibid., p. lii
[2] ibid., p. xlvii
[3] ibid., p. xliv

dispensaries had been opened. Each of them had 'the indispensable requisites of a waiting room for patients, a dispensary room, and what is most essential for the proper working of
the system, consulting rooms for the district medical officer'.[1]

The Board laid down two principles for planning dispensaries.
They were to be sited not more than a mile 'and in most cases
it should be much less, from the dwelling of any patient'.[2]
Secondly, there should be enough work to occupy a full-time
dispenser.[3] For the medical officer, the dispensary system represented an enormous improvement over the previous practice.
He was saved a number of home calls and he had neither to
pay for nor dispense the drugs. All he had to do was to 'visit at
specified hours, for an hour, say, in the morning'.[4]

In March 1871, Goschen was made First Lord of the Admiralty
and the brief period during which the Poor Law Board was
controlled by men of vision came to an end. The next president,
Stansfeld, knew nothing about the subject of poor relief and
'had no independent or original views of his own'.[5] He was
content to ratify the decisions of John Lambert,[6] who was
brought in as permanent secretary with the strong backing of
Gladstone, the Prime Minister. Lambert believed above all else
in the principles of 1834. He accepted that medical care had to
be given to the sick, but to prevent abuse of this right it should be
given only in institutions. The creation of a chain of infirmaries
would make it possible to abolish all outdoor relief. Secondly,
he saw real hospitals as the key to real workhouses: it would be
possible 'to restore due discipline among the able-bodied'.[7]
And it was believed that the stigma of a pauper institution which
had grown up when all institutions were harsh would survive
the creation of well-run infirmaries. The Fulham Guardians
found that 'where the worst form of pauperism exists, the
inhabitants prefer the filth and squalor of their own wretched

[1] ibid.
[2] ibid., p. xlvi
[3] ibid.
[4] H of L Select Committee on Metropolitan Hospitals 1890–3, Second Report
(457), p. 619, para. 23366, HMSO, 1891
[5] J. L. & Barbara Hammond, James Stansfeld – A Victorian Champion of
Sex Equality, p. 110, London, 1932
[6] Lambert had been an inspector from 1857, drafted the 1867 Act and
had served on the Adderley Commission. See R. Lambert, pp. 524–8.
[7] Thirteenth Annual Report LGB 1883–4, C 4166, p. xxxi, HMSO, 1884

abodes . . . it is almost impossible (unless by threatening to withdraw all relief) to get them to consent to enter the infirmary'.[1] It was argued from this and many other instances that the poor had an overriding preference for home care. Just as the offer of the primitive workhouse had deterred the able-bodied, so the offer of the therapeutic workhouse would prevent malingering.

Outdoor relief had been increasing throughout the sixties. It was estimated in 1869 that 'the proportion of acute cases is on the average nearly twice as great among the outdoor paupers and shows to how great an extent important disease is treated in the homes of the poorest classes'.[2] The drive to limit outdoor relief came not only from the bureaucracy of the Poor Law officials but from influence brought to bear by the powerful Charity Organization Society, which urged the Board to put into practice the current theories of the political economists.[3] In 1870 Professor Fawcett published his Cambridge Lectures on Pauperism in which he strenuously advocated the abolition of outdoor relief. John Lambert and his chief assistant, Inspector Henry Longley, were simply reflecting the fashionable dogmas of the day.

Thus the Poor Law Board attempted to apply the twin policies of creating infirmaries and eradicating outdoor relief. Though it had little power to enforce its wishes in London and virtually none in the provinces, it had considerable influence over officers and Guardians, which it exercised not only by orders and circulars but by the persuasion of its inspectors. There were, however, only two medical inspectors: the others had no formal qualifications for their jobs which they learnt by apprenticeship as junior assistants. Some of them were 'men of inferior ability, education and manner who were put in as a reward for political or other services'.[4] But there were some keen and able men who impressed upon the Guardians the new militancy of the Board they served.

[1] *Twenty-Second Annual Report PLB 1869–70*, C 123, p. 41, HMSO, 1870

[2] *H of C Sessional Paper 468*, 1870, BPP, Vol. LVIII, 1870 (Poor Law Board Return), p. xiv, HMSO, 1870

[3] C. Woodward, *The Rise of the Charity Organization Society*, Cambridge University Ph.D. thesis, 1961

[4] S. Gwynn and Gertrude Tuckwell, *The Life of Charles Dilke*, Vol. I, p. 504, London, 1917

The policy of eliminating outdoor medical relief by the offer of institutional care was likely to discourage early diagnosis and treatment and thus to conflict with the preventive principle which was gaining acceptance in the field of public health. Soon after Stansfeld was appointed to the Poor Law Board, the Commission which had been appointed to investigate the sanitary circumstances of England and Wales published its report.[1] Its principal recommendation was that the Poor Law Board, the Local Government Division of the Home Office and the Public Health Division of the Home Office should be brought together under one Minister. The Government implemented this recommendation. The medical officer at the Privy Council was John Simon,[2] one of the leading enthusiasts for preventive medicine. Thus John Simon was brought under Stansfeld, the first president of the Local Government Board, a Minister who remained blind to the potentialities of preventive medicine[3] and allowed Simon to exercise no influence over Poor Law policy. The latter's small department was gradually overwhelmed by the Poor Law bureaucracy and Simon himself resigned in 1876. The prevention of abuse was thought more important than the prevention of the spread of disease.

Thus the officials of the Poor Law Board emerged triumphant from the reorganization of 1871. Under a malleable president they had absorbed and silenced the Public Health Department. During the next ten years, under the presidencies of Stansfield and his successor, Sclater-Booth,[4] the inspectors made the Poor Law into a system of deterrence in which the new medical

[1] *H of C Sessional Paper 1*, 1871, BPP, Vol. XXXV, 1871 (*Second Report of the Sanitary Commissioners*)

[2] Sir John Simon gained national fame as first Medical Officer of the City of London (1845–55). In 1855 he became Medical Officer to the Board of Health and to the Government – again the first post of this kind. As Medical Officer to the Privy Council and Local Government Board (1858–76) he advanced sanitary law and opinion, made health administration scientific in outlook and method and extended the technique and range of social inquiry. See R. Lambert, *Sir John Simon (1816–1904)*.

[3] H. Preston-Thomas, *The Work and Play of a Government Inspector*, p. 50, London, 1909

[4] '. . . whose mental requirements were not of a high order but whose geniality and humour have given him a popularity in the House'. He was dominated by the intellectual superiority of Lambert 'and obediently spoke from his brief without venturing outside it'. He remained in office until 1880. Ibid., pp. 52, 56

institutions played a most vital role. They campaigned against outdoor relief at a time of heavy unemployment and acute agricultural depression. Wet summers and a cattle epidemic caused a fall in agricultural wages and a steady drift of unemployed rural labourers into the towns. The inspectors encouraged the urban Guardians to greet the influx of labourers with the 'workhouse test'. They were unable to find 'that the special conditions of locality, trade, season, weather or population interfere with its universal applicability'.[1]

The campaign against outdoor medical relief altered the role of the relieving officer in those Unions which adopted the new principles. In many areas it had become the practice for the relieving officer to visit an applicant for medical relief not only to see whether he really was a pauper but also to see whether the district medical officer was shifting cases to the institution to relieve himself of the trouble of looking after them. An inquiry had been conducted in 1867 by the central authority to find out the policies of the Guardians regarding the use of institutional services. The Lambeth Guardians reported that they expected their district medical officers 'to act honestly in recommending patients to the workhouse'.[2] At West Bromwich the Guardians felt that 'great care should be taken to prevent patients being sent into the workhouse infirmary for the purposes of lessening the work and responsibilities of the District Medical Officer'.[3] The Doncaster Board, amongst others, found it necessary to act on the relieving officers' advice in order 'to prevent abuse on the part of a medical officer in getting rid of a burdensome patient'.[2] In the Clifton Union, the Guardians did 'not as a rule feel themselves bound by the recommendations of the District Medical Officer'[4] as they believed this course might 'place an unfair burden on the workhouse medical officer'.[5] The district medical officers of Coventry were not allowed to 'dictate to any

[1] *Fourth Annual Report LGB 1874-5*, C 1328, Appendix 12: H. Longley, 'Report to the LGB on Poor Law Administration in the Metropolis', p. 47, HMSO, 1875

[2] *Twenty-Second Annual Report PLB 1869-70*, p. 46

[3] ibid., p. 72

[4] ibid. These Guardians believed that, 'The removal of the sick into the uncongenial influence of the workhouse cannot, in almost any point of view, compensate for the loss of cheering sympathy and kind attentions of relatives and friends at home.'

[5] ibid., p. 67

extent as to what sick should be removed to the workhouse'.[1]

In future it was to be the duty of the relieving officer to see the patient before the doctor so that he could force the patient into an institution as a condition of receiving medical relief. Only in very exceptional circumstances were there to be any breaches in this procedure. This doctrine was set out by Inspector Longley in 1873 in what Chief Inspector Davy called some thirty years later 'the most uncompromising defence of the workhouse system ever penned'.[2] The new rule was to apply to all but the 'exceptionally urgent and for the most part rare cases'. It was not the duty of the Poor Law 'to protect the community generally, and beyond these limits, against the scandal of death by starvation or to seek out recipients for relief'.[3]

All medical relief should be granted with intent to deter so that it might act as 'an incentive to provident habit'.[4] Longley was especially anxious to check the pauperizing influence of the grant of meat and stimulants as 'persons who would otherwise receive medical aid from public hospitals are unduly attracted to Poor Law medical relief, because the latter is, while the former is not, commonly accompanied by a grant of nourishment'.[5]

The most effective deterrent of all was to offer

> ... none but indoor relief to the patient, where it is possible to do so, as insisting that his family, except in special cases, and where opportunities of providing against sickness have been manifestly neglected, shall receive indoor relief also.[6]

It was equally important that

> ... the stamp of pauperism is plainly marked upon all relief given ... the words 'Dispensary' and 'Infirmary' should never be used in forms, advertisements and addresses without the prefix 'Pauper' or 'Poor Law' or 'Workhouse', which should indeed appear as far as possible in every document supplied by Guardians to those relieved by them.[7]

[1] ibid., p. 69
[2] *Royal Commission on the Poor Laws & Relief of Distress 1905–9*, Appendix Vol. I, Cd 4625, p. 181, para. 3297, HMSO, 1909
[3] Longley (*Fourth Annual Report LGB*), p. 24
[4] ibid.
[5] ibid., pp. 59–60
[6] ibid.
[7] ibid.

In this way, the founding of the Poor Law hospital service was attended by a second campaign, the aim of which was to ensure its maximum use by paupers. The inspectors saw the two policies as being complementary to one another.

The plans for the establishment of a chain of dispensaries were overtaken by the campaign against outdoor relief. The fewer the patients treated outside hospital, the fewer were the areas able to justify the appointment of a full-time dispenser. A few dispensaries were, however, established in the provinces[1] and by 1890 there were 44 dispensaries operating in London. In that year there were 53,272 home visits and 54,149 attendances at the dispensaries. There were 158 medical officers at work on an average salary of £115 per annum. In 1886, the cost of drugs and appliances was about £7,000. The cost per patient of this service was estimated to be 4s 3d.[2] It could, however, be shown that the number of attendances at dispensaries in the whole of London was about half the outpatient attendances recorded by the London Hospital alone.[3]

Where the dispensary system did not operate, however, the terms of service of district medical officers remained very unsatisfactory. As late as 1909 it was reported that in most Unions the district medical officers

> . . . still have to find their own drugs and medicines and any dressings or bandages that are required, and they are paid fixed stipends which vary; as little as £10–£15 a year up to as much as £300 or £400, a very usual figure being £100; together with additional fees for midwifery cases and operations.[4]

Furthermore:

> The doctor takes these positions in order to further his private practice and I am afraid the poor very often have to suffer for that reason; he takes it too cheap.[5]

In status the district medical officer was junior to the relieving officer.[6] The latter had the 'right, at his unaided discretion, to

[1] *Report of the Royal Commission on the Poor Laws & Relief of Distress 1905–9*, Cd 4499, p. 250, para. 60, HMSO, 1898
[2] *Select Committee on Metropolitan Hospitals 1890–3*, Third Report, op. cit., p. lxx, para. 404
[3] ibid., Second Report, p. 727, para. 25807
[4] *Report of Royal Commission on Poor Laws 1905–9*, Cd 4499, p. 848
[5] ibid., p. 851
[6] *Royal Commission on Poor Laws 1905–9*, Vol. I, Cd 4625, Q. 2898

refuse the sufferer' access to medical relief. He rarely exercised this right, even when supported by his Board, for fear that 'anything untoward' might happen to the patient. Whenever a relieving officer marked a medical order 'urgent' he could 'require the doctor himself immediately to visit the patient's residence'. A medical officer's definition of 'urgency' was not considered to be so authoritative. If a Poor Law doctor attended a case which he thought was urgent without first obtaining a relieving officer's order, 'he not infrequently finds himself refused, on some frivolous pretext or other, the midwifery fee or other emolument to which he would normally have been entitled'.[1] There were some relieving officers 'who would vex or harass the doctor in revenge for some former lack of compliance on his part with an unwarranted request'.[2]

The doctors could not risk a quarrel. As one of the Poor Law inspectors pointed out many years later, doctors had to accept and keep these jobs because 'some of their most valuable patients may be either members of the Board of Guardians or people who have . . . interests with the members of the Boards of Guardians'. The Poor Law appointments 'gave them a certain status'. When a medical officer depended partly on Guardians for his private income, he was unlikely to 'quarrel with his bread and butter' in the interests of reform.[3] Moreover, the medical officer had no financial incentive to look after more pauper patients in their own homes. 'It was a very natural tendency that a patient who needed an enormous amount of attention, and who also did not bring an increased income to the medical practitioner should be given an order for admission to the infirmary, which was a very simple way out of the difficulty.'[4]

The individual medical officer was powerless and had every incentive to comply with the wishes of the Board and the Guardians. A group of Poor Law medical officers did, however, send the Board a memorial of protest against its policy. They asked for higher salaries, to be given the status of established civil servants and to be allowed to give relief in the home without the intervention of the relieving officer.

[1] *Report of Royal Commission on Poor Laws 1905–9*, (Minority), p. 849
[2] ibid., pp. 852–3
[3] *Royal Commission on Poor Laws*, Vol. I, Cd 4625, Q.9320
[4] ibid., Vol. II, Cd 4684, Q.14912

Instead of the 'workhouse test' being applied to the sick poor, they should be treated at home or removed to a cottage hospital, or to an infirmary, as may be favourable to their rapid and complete cure, and early return to the position of breadwinners. Sickness, one of the most prolific and pitiable sources of pauperism, ought, we submit, to be placed upon a footing quite apart from that of ordinary causes of want and dependence on the rates. It is cheap and wise to cure the sick poor with the greatest promptitude.[1]

These arguments did not weigh with the Local Government Board. It reminded the doctors that the system of medical relief had been carefully considered by a parliamentary committee in 1866. There was nothing to suggest that 'a different conclusion would be arrived at if the matter were again brought under consideration of parliament'.[2] As regards the request to become established civil servants, it was pointed out that servants of the state were prohibited from engaging in private practice.[3] On the question of remuneration the Board stated that 'the facility with which, when the office of medical officer becomes vacant, competent medical men are found to fill the vacancy, affords a strong presumption that on the whole the remuneration is not deemed to be insufficient'.[4]

Thus the Board pursued its 'crusade' against outdoor relief. It was actively supported by the Charity Organization Society. The Unions which were controlled by members of the Society or influenced by it[5] hastened to implement the new principles and bestow upon them a flavour of their own. At Whitechapel, the plan to abolish outdoor relief was based on a 'perfect understanding' between the Guardians and the Charity Organization Society, and medical assistance 'was as far as possible made educational'. Every applicant was asked, 'supposing we tide you over your present difficulties, will you join a sick club so as in the case of future sickness you will not have to rely on the parish?' The 'dependants of the deserving sick received charity' and it was explained that 'although the

1 *Eighth Annual Report LGB, 1878-9*, C 2372, pp. 86-8, HMSO, 1879
2 ibid., p. xlv
3 ibid., p. 89
4 ibid., p. 90
5 Leading 'orthodox' Boards were in the Metropolitan Unions of St-George-in-the-East, Bethnal Green; Whitechapel; St George's, Hanover Square; Stepney; and Paddington. Their provincial counterparts were Brixworth, Bradfield, Birmingham, Reading, Wallingford and St Neot's.

infirmary is an institution almost equal to a general hospital, the very fact of its separating the man from his family is in itself a certain test'.[1]

In some of the strictest Unions 'deserving applicants' were still allowed outdoor medical relief. Membership of a provident dispensary or sick club was one mark of the 'deserving'.[2] A few Boards were even prepared to overlook one-half of the amount of a sickness benefit in assessing need – a practice which the central authority officially condemned in 1870.[3] Others granted all first orders 'on loan'. In some cases the relieving officer was allowed 'a commission of 20 per cent on what he can recover'.[4]

There was a marked diminution in the amount of outdoor medical relief granted between 1871 and 1900. The new Poor Law dispensaries were fully operative by 1873 but the number of dispensary orders granted fell steadily from 144,676 in that year to 102,470 in 1900.[5] During the same period the growth in the membership of sick clubs and provident dispensaries was immense. The Poor Law Board and the Guardians between them managed to direct the organization of general practice in Britain from the publicly owned dispensary or 'health centre', with its salaried dispenser to the club or 'panel' practice and the commercial pharmacy.

The switch from domiciliary care to institutional care which had been started soon after 1834 by the deliberate policy of restricting outdoor relief, and which had been assisted by

[1] *Report of the H of L Select Committee on Poor Relief 1888*, 492, paras. 4454 & 4450 (evidence of Mr Vallance), HMSO, 1888. By 1880 there were only 63 outdoor paupers in this Union and between 20 and 30 of these were receiving medical relief. The remainder were boarded-out children (para. 4620).

[2] ibid., para. 124. Sir Henry Owen, secretary of the LGB, was asked whether in many Unions the question as to an applicant's membership of a sick club was 'applied as a kind of test, whether it is indoor or outdoor relief that is to be given?' Sir Henry replied that, 'No doubt that is so and reasonably so.'

[3] Under the Act of 1894 it was left to the local Boards of Guardians to decide whether friendly societies were to be taken into consideration when granting relief. A further Act of 1904 enacted that Guardians were not to take into consideration weekly sums of 5s or less received from friendly societies. *Royal Commission on Poor Laws 1905–9*, Vol. I, Cd 4625, Qs. 1120 and 2037

[4] *Report of Royal Commission on Poor Laws 1905–9* (Minority), p. 853

[5] *Royal Commission on Poor Laws 1905–9*, Vol. II, Cd 4684, Q. 23233 (evidence of Dr Downes)

medical officers who took a narrow view of their responsibilities, gained momentum in certain areas with the almost total denial of such relief. This policy was sanctioned and supported by the central authority. It was hoped that the costs of the separate infirmaries could be paid for by savings on outdoor relief.

It was the 'orthodox' Unions who were most willing to build new infirmaries or adapt and extend old workhouses for the sick poor who were denied outdoor medical relief. By November 1873, nine separate infirmaries had been opened in London, but there remained six Unions without any special institutions for their sick.[1] Attempts to encourage the voluntary combination of Unions for building purposes were met 'in the majority of instances, by the keen opposition of Boards of Guardians'.[2]

By 1883, the central authority was able to announce that in the Metropolis all but three of the thirty Poor Law areas were provided with separate infirmaries as 'contemplated by the Metropolitan Poor Act of 1867'.[3] There were also encouraging reports from the provinces. The Birmingham Guardians opened a 'test' workhouse and began building a new infirmary for over 1,000 beds during 1887.[4] In Yorkshire, 'the new detention infirmaries at Selby and Great Ousebourne were completed . . . and the new block for the sick containing about 100 beds at Hull Workhouse was opened'. The Chesterfield Guardians were less co-operative and their inspector was reporting as late as 1902 that 'until the sick wards . . . are erected the Guardians cannot put into force the workhouse test'.[5] Little progress was made in the country districts and the few rural Boards who built new infirmaries found it almost impossible to recruit suitable nursing staff.

When the Local Government Board carried out a national census of sick paupers in 1896[6] it was revealed that 58,550 patients were being treated in 'separate infirmaries' and other 'wards for

[1] *Third Annual Report LGB, 1873–4*, C 1071, p. xxi, HMSO, 1874
[2] Longley (*Fourth Annual Report LGB*), p. 45
[3] *Twelfth Annual Report LGB, 1882–3*, C 3778, p. xxxii, HMSO, 1883
[4] Now one of the largest mental hospitals in the country
[5] *Thirty-First Annual Report LGB, 1901–2*, C 1231, p. 116, HMSO, 1902
[6] *H of C Sessional Paper 371, 1896*, BPP, Vol. LXXII, 1896, pp. 6–43. These returns were made during the summer (1 July 1896) and therefore understate the mean number of sick persons in Poor Law establishments. For further details on this and later censuses, see Vol. 2 of this study. The above figures are rounded to the nearest ten.

the sick'.[1] Of these patients 22,100 were in 'separate infirmaries', leaving 36,450 sick in the general mixed workhouses. The 27 London infirmaries alone were accommodating 11,050 patients, almost all of whom were classed as 'sick and bedridden'. The great majority of the 'aged and infirm' were not receiving the benefits of a classified institution.[2]

The creation of infirmaries which were physically separate from workhouses involved higher costs. Many of the tasks which had previously fallen to the lot of the able-bodied paupers had to an increasing extent to be performed by paid staff. The workhouse had been able to support itself at a low cost on pauper labour. Apart from the workhouse officers, a few porters and such paid nurses as were engaged, all the rest of the workers were unpaid paupers. They manned the kitchen, the laundry, the linen rooms; they made and repaired the clothes and did all the domestic chores. It was obviously less satisfactory to attempt to draft paupers to work in a separate institution. Moreover, separation involved duplication: instead of one kitchen there were two to be staffed. Inevitably workhouse masters were unwilling to release satisfactory workers for duties in another institution. It was often hard enough to find persons who had the health and competence to staff one institution. Thus, one consequence of the creation of a separate infirmary was a sharp increase in paid staff on the payroll of Boards of Guardians for routine duties.

There was a second reason for the increase in cost which followed the creation of separate infirmaries. The change represented a new attitude to the care of the sick in institutions. The Central Board made it clear that infirmaries should be supplied with 'all reasonable and proper appliances for the treatment of disease of every kind', and that everything should be provided which might 'tend to promote a cure or alleviate suffering'.[3] The fittings of the sick wards were to be such as were 'usually provided in the wards of general hospitals'.[4] No

[1] The term 'separate infirmary' was used for institutions ranging in size from a Birmingham infirmary with 1,300 beds to a building in Church Stretton containing 4 infirm patients.
[2] The London 'separate infirmaries' contained only 94 'aged and infirm' persons. There were over 6,000 sick paupers in the Metropolitan workhouse sick wards, the majority of whom were grouped as 'aged and infirm'.
[3] *Twentieth Annual Report PLB, 1867–8*, p. 28
[4] *Twenty-First Annual Report PLB, 1868–9*, pp. 44, 47

longer were the standards of care of the pauper patients to be judged by the standards enjoyed by the lowest paid labourer. Though it took time before the full consequences became apparent, the principle of need had triumphed over the principle of less-eligibility.

The change was marked by the development of a new administrative pattern. While previously the chief officer in a workhouse had been a lay official – the workhouse master – and while the chief administrator in the voluntary hospitals was generally a lay clerk or secretary, the leading official in the new infirmaries was a doctor – a whole-time medical superintendent. Although not every Board of Guardians adopted this pattern it became increasingly prevalent. By 1888, every London infirmary had its own superintendent who was aided by one full-time assistant medical officer. Many superintendents were former resident housemen from voluntary hospitals who had failed to establish themselves as consultants. By 1905, London Guardians were paying their superintendents between £350 and £500 a year[1] and granting them spacious accommodation, coal, gas and laundry.[2] There were additional fees for vaccinations and the certification of lunatics.[3]

Assistant medical officers in Poor Law infirmaries were mostly recruited from young practitioners who found the work a useful introduction to general practice. Junior medical assistants were paid £100 a year and the senior assistants started at an annual salary of £120. The maximum to which they could rise was only £160.[4] They had little incentive to remain with the Poor Law infirmaries and the majority resigned after two or three years service.[5] Some Guardians only appointed their assistant medical officers for a period of one year.[6] As the majority of

[1] *Royal Commission on Poor Laws 1905–9*, Vol. II, Cd 4684, p. 306, para. 14 (evidence of Mr Spurrell). The average salary in London was £422 a year.

[2] *Hospital*, Vol. LIII, 8 March 1913, p. 618. See also *Departmental Committee on the Nursing of the Sick Poor in Workhouses, 1902*, Pt. II, Minutes of Evidence, Cd 1367, p. 187, HMSO, 1902. Only 44 of the 692 Unions making returns in 1900 employed resident medical officers in their workhouses.

[3] *Royal Commission on Poor Laws 1905–9*, Vol. II, Cd 4684, Q. 23479

[4] ibid., p. 306, para. 14 (evidence of Mr Spurrell)

[5] ibid., Qs. 23442–4 (evidence of Mr Spurrell). The St Pancras Guardians engaged all their juniors on annual contracts 'so that we get a relay of young medical practitioners for the infirmary' (Q. 18734, evidence of Mr Millward).

[6] ibid., Q. 18734 (evidence of Mr Millward)

superintendents were appointed 'from outside' the Poor Law, there was a 'strong possibility' that senior assistants would never attain the highest rank.[1]

The creation of the infirmaries brought with it, as had the creation of teaching hospitals a generation earlier, the problem of frustrated juniors, but the change from lay to medical administration crystallized the new function of the infirmaries. Moreover, Guardians were faced with professional chief officers who could make demands for resources which it was hard for laymen to refuse. The concept of less-eligibility has been a concept which could as well be judged by the Guardians as by anyone else: they were obviously far less qualified to assess medical needs.

The standards which the new medical superintendents attempted to introduce in the infirmaries were strongly influenced by those of the voluntary hospitals where some of them had worked and all of them had been trained. And the major shortcoming which they identified in the Poor Law sector was in the quality and the quantity of nursing staff. It was, moreover, this aspect of the care of the pauper patients which had received special attention in the exposures of the sixties. To a considerable extent the whole movement for workhouse reform had been an integral part of the nursing reform movement.

Even if all the Guardians had been willing to engage an adequate staff of trained nurses at current rates of pay, this would not have solved the problem. The attempt to create workhouse infirmaries followed very soon after the nursing revolution had spread throughout the principal voluntary hospitals of London. The new criteria of what was required of a nurse and the number of nurses that were required had led to an acute shortage of nurses in the voluntary hospitals. Trained staff were not available to staff both the hospitals and the infirmaries, let alone the workhouses. Moreover, work in voluntary hospitals was for many reasons much more attractive to the trained nurse.

The reformers decided early on that the only really effective means for the Poor Law to obtain nurses was to train its own. This was how the voluntary hospitals got most of their nursing work done and the fact that probationer nurses were cheaper than trained nurses was an argument which was likely to appeal to the Poor Law authorities. But the key to the development of a training school lay in the construction of proper living

[1] ibid., Qs. 23441–2 (evidence of Mr Spurrell)

accommodation and the recruitment of a fully qualified matron and sisters.

Such a policy was easier to implement in the new infirmaries than in the workhouses. The system of lay administration in the latter was an obstacle to nursing reform. Workhouse masters were unwilling to delegate part of their authority to superintendent nurses and their wives had traditionally performed many of the functions which a matron performed in a voluntary hospital. Good trained nurses were not willing to work under an autocratic administrator of lower social class than themselves or to tolerate interference from his untrained wife. The creation of separate infirmaries under the control of medical superintendents removed a major obstacle to nursing reform. The doctors in charge had learnt to appreciate and respect the position of the matron in the voluntary hospitals.

Miss Nightingale herself created the nursing school of the first new London infirmary. She supplied the matron and nurses from St Thomas' Hospital for the infirmary at Highgate which opened in 1871. In 1873, the Central London Sick Asylum District was authorized 'to receive single women or widows between 25 and 35 years of age as probationers who were to remain as such for at least a year and were to be employed under the control of the medical officer and matron'.[1] Two years later, the central authority expressed the hope that the system of training and supplying nurses would extend to each of the new infirmaries being built in the Metropolis.[2] At the same time, some provincial Boards of Guardians began to employ more trained nurses.[3]

With the creation of separate infirmaries came the creation of nurse-training schools and the steady substitution of paid nurses for pauper nurses. In 1879, the Local Government Board went so far as to claim that 'in all the sick asylums and separate infirmaries' the system of employing pauper inmates as nurses 'had been entirely superseded' by the employment of paid nurses. This statement was untrue. There was one separate infirmary, containing 150 sick and infirm, where there were only

[1] Elizabeth M. Ross, 'Women and Poor Law Administration 1857-1910' (M.A. thesis, unpublished), Chapter VIII, p. 19
[2] The Chorlton Union were employing 23 paid nurses in 1869. *Twenty-Second Annual Report PLB, 1869-70*, p. lxiii
[3] ibid., p. 19

two paid nurses, both of whom were untrained. The matron was responsible for both the infirmary and the workhouse which contained another 400 inmates. 'Pauper women of more or less bad character' were doing most of the nursing, and there was 'no paid supervision at night'.[1] There were said to be many similar establishments, both in London and the provinces.[2]

Only by the narrowest definition of 'nursing' could it be said that paupers were not doing such work. 'Almost all provincial infirmaries', wrote a contributor to a contemporary monthly magazine, 'are nursed by paupers under the control – or not under the control – of one paid nurse, who is herself under the authority of the ignorant matron of the workhouse.' There was an infirmary in London where the matron stated that she did 'not expect nurses to do the nursing themselves, but only to superintend the paupers'.

The Local Government Board was being diligently watched and prodded on to greater efforts not only by Miss Nightingale but also by Miss Twining and her lady visitors. In 1879, the ladies formed the Association for Promoting Trained Nursing in Workhouse Infirmaries at a meeting held 'at the house of Constance, Marchioness of Lothian', and by 1885 the Association was paying for the training of nurses, and was itself employing in the workhouses 53 nurses with one year's training. By 1898 it had trained and secured appointments for over 800 nurses.

In some of the infirmaries the working conditions for nurses were far from attractive. Thus at the Central London Sick Asylum, the seventeen day- and seven night-nurses were responsible for 264 beds. 'Most of the nine head nurses were hospital trained' but the rest were former ward maids. Matron 'did not pretend to interfere with the nursing at all'. Although the nurses' working day began at 7 a.m. and ended at 8 p.m., it was claimed that they 'had more recreation than the other officers'. Their medical officer claimed that the conditions of service in the Poor Law were so bad that it was 'impossible, within the present structure, even to raise the nursing staff to the efficiency it ought to arrive at'.

The recruitment of suitable nurses was the main problem of

[1] Paper read to WINA, 25 July 1879, p. 4
[2] *Select Committee on Metropolitan Hospitals 1890–3*, Third Report, paras. 24419–79

the infirmaries. There was no difficulty in erecting buildings once the money had been voted and there were many doctors willing to take salaried posts at fairly modest salaries, but nurses could not be obtained until training facilities were extended. From the start, the infirmaries were faced with the essential problem of nursing recruitment. The infirmary which needed nurses most imposed such strenuous duties on the nurses it had that the vacant posts were unattractive to prospective applicants.

Although this problem remained, the Local Government Board had in many areas of the country succeeded in its aim of creating hospitals. One motive for this policy had been economy and in this respect it was temporarily successful. Between 1872 and 1882 the cost of in-maintenance increased from £1·5 million to £1·8 million, but the cost of out-relief fell from £3·6 million to £2·6 million.[1] A second motive had been the desire to restrict the use of the Poor Law to those who desperately needed it. Its failure in this respect is discussed in Chapter 13. A third motive had been the desire to abolish outdoor relief. Though the savage policies of some Guardians undoubtedly stimulated the growth of private insurance to cover doctors' fees, some of the provision of outdoor relief was shifted from the Poor Law to the voluntary hospitals.

[1] *Twelfth Annual Report LGB, 1882–3*, p. xiv

CHAPTER 7

Hospitals and General Practitioners

ALONGSIDE the voluntary hospitals supported by voluntary contributions, there had come to be public hospitals – the separate infirmaries for the pauper sick which were supported by local taxation. At the same time, a crusade against outdoor relief was being waged. But this crusade did not put an end to the provision of free care for the sick poor resident in their own homes. Many of those who were denied outdoor relief were treated in the outpatient departments of the voluntary hospitals. And in time these departments became as heavily criticized by general practitioners as the system of outdoor relief was criticized by the Local Government Board. The Charity Organization Society criticized both systems of free medical care – outdoor relief and outpatient departments.

By 1860, there had been major changes in the standing of those who purveyed medical advice and administered medical treatment. The dually-trained apothecaries were beginning to challenge the privileges and compete with the practices of the fellows of the Royal Colleges. The hierarchy of the old orders of medicine was becoming less distinct and the new general practitioners were firmly established as the doctors of the growing middle class. While there were great improvements in the College of Surgeons, the College of Physicians did not put its house in order despite the challenge of the apothecaries. Nepotism and snobbery rather than empirical tests remained largely the means by which this College recruited its Fellows.

Although the number of doctors in England and Wales was not increasing as fast as the population,[1] the practice of medicine was highly competitive. Some doctors went not only into the provinces but also into the rural areas. General practitioners

---

[1] The census figures show that there was one doctor to about 1,400 persons in 1861; to about 1,550 persons in 1871; to about 1,700 persons in 1881; and to about 1,500 persons in 1891.

who were already in an area accepted appointments under the Poor Law on the best terms that could be secured, and scrutinized the activities of voluntary hospitals to see whether patients who could pay were being treated free. There were also constant demarcation disputes between general practitioners and consultants. These were the main points of controversy which filled the leaders and correspondence columns of the medical press during the second half of the nineteenth century and they reacted upon the hospitals in many subtle ways.

By 1861, there were about 11,000 occupied hospital beds in England and Wales for a population of about 20 million: hospitals had been started in most of the principal towns. In general, they were 'closed list' hospitals. Just as the Royal Colleges dominated medical appointments in the London general hospitals so a limited group of doctors in each local town controlled the local hospital. The status which had always gone with a hospital appointment in London went with a hospital appointment in the provinces.

From the late 1850's, the hospital movement spread into the rural areas. Small 'cottage hospitals' were built. One of the first, if not the first, was opened at the initiative of Mr Albert Napper, FRCS, at Cranleigh, Surrey, in 1859.[1] By 1865 there were eighteen cottage hospitals: by 1880 the number had increased to 180.[2] In some cases, cottage hospitals were started by a legacy or donation from a philanthropist, in other cases the money was raised from a number of local subscribers. At Weston-super-Mare, on the other hand, a hospital was started by the working classes with subscriptions of 1d per week.[3] There was usually a small committee of management in which the local parson played a leading part. The medical staffing of a cottage hospital was organized differently from that of a general or special hospital,

> ... though as a matter of necessity one medical man must be the surgeon or medical intendant in ordinary to the establishment, yet that every medical man in the neighbourhood is entitled to send his patients to it, supposing them to be suitable cases; that in case of an operation being required he is to have the option of performing

[1] H. J. MacCurrich, *Treatment of the Sick Poor of this Country*, p. 15, London, 1929
[2] H. C. Burdett, *Cottage Hospitals, General, Fever, and Convalescent*, p. 17, London, 1896
[3] E. J. Waring, *Cottage Hospitals*, p. 20, London, 1867

it; and should any fee be forthcoming, for such operation, as from the Union, he is entitled to it.[1]

In general, cottage hospitals were open to all the local general practitioners.

Right from the start the hospital at Cranleigh took payments from the patients varying from 3*s* to 10*s* 6*d*. About a quarter of the cost of the hospital was raised in this way. Often the subscriber who issued the letter of introduction paid the difference between the patient's payment and the total cost. The benefits of the system were not enjoyed exclusively by those of limited means. As one early writer pointed out, 'The lessons he [the surgeon] learns day by day in these hospitals are, in time of need, of value in the ancestral hall.'[2]

Thus the new generation of general practitioners who had been taught in hospitals began to acquire hospitals of their own in the rural areas. This raised the local doctor's professional status and, it was claimed, 'enabled him to treat, under the most favourable circumstances, serious surgical cases, which before its institution, had to be transferred to the nearest county hospital'.[3] Far away from the towns where the 'old orders' controlled hospital beds, the rural patient was able to enjoy a continuous relationship with one doctor and had the 'privilege of being able to pay something, however small, according to his means, for the treatment he receives'.[4]

The system of asking the patient to pay what he could afford had been practised by the endowed London hospitals in the sixteenth century.[5] The practice had, however, been tacitly abandoned. Nearly all the general hospitals provided free care:[6] the only exceptions were a few provincial hospitals which levied modest charges. Charging was more common in the special hospitals and they had attracted a somewhat higher class of patient than the voluntary general and teaching hospitals.

The use of such hospitals as there were had not been confined to the indigent class in the eighteenth century. This is shown by

[1] ibid., p. 15
[2] ibid., pp. 17–18
[3] Burdett, *Cottage Hospitals*, p. 7
[4] ibid., p. 5
[5] McInnes, p. 33
[6] Apart from the requirement that new patients should provide their own butter, tea and sugar. See Jewesbury, p. 35.

the fact that the hospitals were able to ask and receive deposits from patients on their admission. There had been no criticism of the system. When the role of the hospitals had become larger and when there had arisen a class of doctor who won a precarious living from the modest payments of skilled workers and the lower middle class, these doctors launched a campaign for a more stringent definition of the class of person who was to be granted medical charity.

At the Fifth Annual Meeting of the British Medical Association in 1836, concern had been expressed at 'the vast amount of gratuitous medical assistance'[1] which was being given and being expected of the profession. In 1853, the *British Medical Journal* rampaged against 'the abuse of Hospitals and Dispensaries – a monster evil of the Day'.

The campaign was principally directed against the outpatient department which 'diminishes the earnings of the Physicians, surgeons and general practitioners practising within the sphere of operations of a hospital. . . . Gentlemen's servants, clerks and well-to-do tradespeople with their wives and children absolutely encumber the waiting-rooms of the London hospitals.' In country districts 'yeomen' were going to the nearest county hospital and depriving local doctors of their fees. 'We would commence by driving forth, with indignation, from the waiting-rooms, the over-paid and pampered menials of the pseudo-charitable societies.'[2] Month after month the journal continued its tirade.[3]

It was not just the fact that the total earnings of the medical profession were diminished by misdirected charity that angered the general practitioners. The articles also implied that consultants and specialists were using their positions in the hospitals to steal patients from general practitioners. 'Our leading men,' wrote the *British Medical Journal* in October 1853, 'who have risen over the breakers and billows of fortune's sea . . . should hesitate before dispensing indiscriminate gratuitous medical advice. . . . We know of cases in which such persons have been given their fee of £20 or £30 for the attendance of the very surgeon under whose care they had meanly placed themselves

[1] quoted by Edward Crossman in *BMJ*, 14 July 1883, p. 64

[2] *BMJ*, 28 January 1853, p. 76

[3] ibid., 11 March 1853, p. 201; 15 April 1853, p. 315; and 20 May 1853, p. 429

to obtain gratuitous medical advice.'[1] In the same year, a Medical Ethical Committee was set up which took steps 'to prepare a draft code of the ethical laws'.[2]

It is not possible to judge whether, by the 1850's, the hospitals were attracting a higher proportion of patients who could have made some payment or whether the average patient could have paid more. There had been large changes both in the social structure of Britain and in the hospitals. Out of the industrial revolution there had emerged a small class of clerical workers and a larger class of skilled workers. There were more people in the middle ranks of society than there had been a hundred years earlier and these were the customers of the new general practitioners. The hospitals had also improved greatly and though the population feared admission to hospital, it was becoming known that they were the centres of medical knowledge. On the other hand, it is very unlikely that subscribers to hospitals in 1800 would have denied a letter of recommendation to a patient on the grounds that he or she was able to make *some* payment for medical care. The endowed hospitals had served 'the sick and lame poor' without defining very closely the meaning of the word 'poor'. The 'subscription hospitals' had admitted those whom subscribers wanted to help without any close examination of their means. While it is clear that no one in affluent circumstances would have wanted a place in the rough hospitals of the day, the use of voluntary hospitals had not been confined to indigent patients.

Whether there was more 'abuse' of charity in the second half of the nineteenth century than in earlier times will never be known. It was clear, however, that 'abuse' of hospitals could have been restricted by demanding payments from patients who could pay. The introduction of payments in the cottage hospitals which were controlled by general practitioners was welcomed by the medical profession. In January 1866 the *British Medical Journal*, in a general discussion of the dangers to both patients and the profession of gratuitous medical services, had feared that 'village hospitals will become extensions of the evil system'.[3] These fears did not materialize. Two months later it welcomed the fact that Dr Spencer Williams who was responsible for a new

[1] ibid., 28 October 1853, pp. 939–40
[2] ibid., 11 November 1853, p. 998
[3] ibid., 20 January 1866, p. 76

cottage hospital near Tamworth held the view that 'when people are in receipt of good wages the hospital should not be on a purely charitable basis . . . the medical men should receive an adequate remuneration for their services'.[1]

The attitude of the profession to payments in general and special hospitals which the general practitioners did not control was very different. If a patient could purchase a specialist opinion for only 1s or 2s 6d why should he go and pay the same price for a non-specialist opinion from his general practitioner? The system amounted to undercutting. So while payments were encouraged in cottage hospitals controlled by general practitioners, similar payments were regarded as a menace in hospitals controlled by specialists. Patients who lived near such hospitals were to be strictly divided into those who were expected to pay the customary fee and those who could pay nothing.

The general practitioners were joined in their campaign against outpatient abuse by the Charity Organization Society. An 'influential committee' on outpatient administration was set up in 1870 with two sub-committees to investigate general hospitals and special hospitals respectively. It was estimated that a quarter of outpatients at general hospitals had a 'probable income' of over £1 10s a week. It was held that such people 'should, as a rule, and especially when unmarried, be expected to belong to a sick club or provident dispensary'.[2] The subject was discussed at the 1870 annual representative meeting of the British Medical Association. *The Lancet*, on the other hand, thought that abuse of outpatients' departments was impossible as 'conditions in them were so appalling'.[3]

A doctor wrote in the *Quarterly Review* for 1874 that, 'From five per cent at some of the general dispensaries to fifty per cent at some of the special hospitals, belong to a class to which the medical profession have not covenanted to give their gratuitous services.' Much was made of extreme cases – 'the wife of a gentleman possessing an income of £800 a year', 'the daughter of the musical instrument maker who has two establishments and employs many hands'. It was alleged that Messrs Truman, Hanbury and Company made a large subscription to the London Hospital to get free care for their employees. There was

[1] ibid., 10 March 1866, p. 260
[2] ibid., 30 December 1876, pp. 870–1
[3] quoted in E. Moberley Bell, pp. 19–20

the story of the Scotsman who, when complimented on his subscription of £10 to the local hospital, replied: 'When I came here the firm paid £300 a year for the doctor. I get them to subscribe £10 a year and now we do without a doctor.'[1]

One solution to the 'abuse' of outpatient departments lay in the development of provident dispensaries. This was one of the schemes advocated by the Charity Organization Society. It argued that a high proportion of the working class could afford to pay for its own doctoring 'if that payment could be made in the form of a small weekly payment during times of health as well as of illness, while they would generally be unable, especially when ill, to meet the lump sum for doctors' bills'.[2] Dispensaries or hospitals run on these lines were developed in many provincial towns such as Brighton, Coventry, and Northampton but the system made little impact on Central London. If the 'great men' accepted small sums for their opinions they would be undercutting the local practitioners. The London physicians and surgeons could 'never consent to allow this system to be tried at the hospitals to which they are attached'.[3]

Although the system of provident dispensaries was used to limit the abuse of outpatient departments in some provincial towns, it had some advantages as the doctor working in a dispensary did not have to dispense his own medicines. The system was not, however, popular with the British Medical Association as it led to what the profession regarded as abuses of its own. 'Those people,' wrote the *British Medical Journal*, 'who can best afford to pay their medical attendant liberally are usually the first to avail themselves of the means of defrauding the medical profession by obtaining their treatment at a nominal sum.'[4] Unless there were strict wage limits, the dispensary system interfered with the system of discriminatory charges practised by the profession. Moreover, some dispensaries were governed by committees of working men which 'it is not a pleasant matter for an educated gentleman to serve under'.[5]

In 1873–4 a number of doctors formed an association called

[1] *BMJ*, 30 December 1876, p. 870
[2] quoted in H. C. Burdett, *Pay Hospitals and Paying Wards throughout the World*, p. 14, London, 1879
[3] ibid., p. 20
[4] *BMJ*, 27 March 1875, p. 416
[5] ibid., 10 April 1875, p. 484

the Hospital Outpatient Reform Association. Circulars were sent to all the principal hospitals of London asking them not as a rule to issue medicines and to appoint a special officer to see that 'the place was not abused by persons coming who were able to pay'. 'We could not get anything done,' complained a member of the Association; 'in the most cases our circular was simply acknowledged and nothing was done by any hospital, as far as I know.'[1]

At the beginning of 1875, the *British Medical Journal* published a memorial on outpatient abuse and in the next year the BMA set up a Hospital Outpatients' Reform Committee which reported that 'the outpatient relief at hospitals was unsatisfactory and justly complained of by the profession'.[2] There was, however, little the British Medical Association could do about it. Giving his report at the BMA Conference at Cambridge in 1880, Mr Timothy Holmes said that

> he had addressed himself to the hospital authorities until he was sick of them, and they of him. . . . The fact was that the public have been pressing all these years to come to the outpatients department; and the hospitals have pressed their claims for support, not upon the quality of their treatment, but upon the fact of the numbers who have flocked to the outpatient department.[3]

Some London hospitals had, however, taken some not very resolute action. At St George's Hospital, where Mr Holmes was a surgeon, inquiries began to be made from 1872 into the means of outpatients and doubtful cases were referred to the Charity Organization Society. The London Hospital started the same practice a year later – yet in this case the inquiries were made by the honorary medical staff.[4] But the medical staff of the hospitals had little interest in keeping out patients who could pay – particularly if they were 'interesting cases'. Though such patients may have been business lost to local general practitioners, they certainly could not have paid the sums which the fellows of the Royal Colleges would have asked for a private consultation. When the Charity Organization Society inquired into abuse at

[1] *Select Committee on Metropolitan Hospitals*, First Report, 1890–3, para. 1219
[2] *BMJ*, 21 August 1880, p. 300
[3] ibid., p. 301
[4] *BMJ*, 23 October 1875, p. 529

the Westminster Hospital and the Royal Free, surgeons complained that they were losing many of their most interesting
patients.[1] 'The outpatients' departments were essential for
teaching purposes.'[2]

In the late 1870's, the general practitioners widened the
target of their attack. They expanded their criticisms of free
treatment given by consultants and specialists and their juniors
in outpatient departments to allegations of unethical behaviour
by consultants in their own private practices. They accused them
of accepting small fees[3] and giving bad service for them.[4] Even
some of the very great did 'not ask more than a guinea or two for a
visit or two guineas per consultation'.[5] There were consultants
who held on to a patient referred to them without any communication with the general practitioner.[6] As a result general
practitioners became reluctant ever to refer patients to consultants lest they would never get them back.[7] Some consultants
let their visits run on and took alternate fees with the general
practitioner.[8]

One consultant wrote to defend himself in the following
terms:

… Though my position in the profession is very good, yet circumstances have prevented my getting a footing in the good graces of

[1] Moberley Bell, pp. 22–3
[2] *BMJ*, 6 July 1889, p. 48
[3] ibid., 29 December 1877, p. 941
[4] ibid., 19 January 1878, p. 111
[5] ibid., p. 112
[6] ibid., 4 May 1878, p. 666. 'A gentleman who has been attended by me
for some time and who has a cancer of the rectum went without my knowledge
to consult the celebrated physician, at the same time telling him that he was
under my care, and that I had informed him he had a tumour of a serious
nature in the rectum. The physician prescribed a simple mixture of Salts,
etc., without making any rectal examination (although my patient was
passing blood per rectum etc.) and did not in any way communicate with me,
so that I really only found out by accident on my next visit. Again, a lady that
I had attended for years and who is still under my care, went at the solicitation
of her friend to consult an eminent oculist for an infection for which I was
then treating her. This gentleman, although my patient told him that she
was under my care, did not communicate with me, but simply wrote a
prescription for a different tonic from what she was then taking, and I only
heard of it by my patient handing me the prescription.' (Letter from 'MB
LOND. and FRCS')
[7] ibid.
[8] ibid., 9 February 1878, p. 197

the upper classes, and I have few patients indeed of social rank equal to my own. The names in my case book are those of farmers, tradesmen, artists, literary hacks, the inferior clergy, clerks, publicans, artisans, and even domestic servants. . . . it is evident that there is not enough strict old-fashioned consulting practice to feed one-twentieth of that formidable list which I have just received from the Royal College in Pall Mall. Moreover, the efforts of the Charity Organization Society to purge the outpatient department of hospitals augment considerably our clientele. . . . But I cannot conceal from myself that we are diminishing the aggregate income derived by the profession from the public, nor can I see how that result can be avoided.[1]

In the last sentence the author had expressed the heart of the matter. There was not enough consulting practice to go round. While the term 'consultant' ought to mean 'a medical man who sees patients only in consultation with an ordinary medical attendant', in fact this type of consultant hardly existed. The *British Medical Journal* produced a working definition of a consultant:

> . . . a gentleman, no doubt as a rule of superior culture and knowledge of his profession, who sees patients at his own house at stated hours, who is quite willing to visit them at home if requested to do so; it being understood that he confines his practice to medicine or surgery, as the case may be; and that the rate of his remuneration is higher than that usually accorded to the practitioner. He is, in fact, a practitioner (though exclusively medical, surgical or obstetrical) among the rich, or among those who are willing to pay a guinea or more for each consultation or visit. As, in point-of-fact, the ordinary general practitioner so-called finds the bulk of his work in medicine and obstetrics, the difference between him and the consultant really resolves itself into a difference of fees. We are not objecting to this. The difference of remuneration generally corresponds with a superior value of the opinion of the consultant.[2]

The real difficulties came when patients did not confine themselves to one class of practitioner and when the patient was referred from a general practitioner to a consultant. There was always the danger of a consultant stealing a patient from a general practitioner. He might take no steps to find out whether

[1] ibid., 2 March 1878, p. 321
[2] ibid., 9 February 1878, p. 197

the patient already had another doctor. Alternatively he might take a patient who had been referred to him into his own higher class of general practice.

Hybrid relationships breed mongrel results. Between the patient who calls and who frankly adopts the 'consultant' as his sole personal adviser for the occasion; the patient who calls for his 'medical man'; the patient who calls with a letter from his 'medical man'; the patient who calls at the request of his 'medical man', or with his consent, and with the expectation of the latter to see his patient at once again with a letter expressing the consultant's opinion; and the patient who, being dissatisfied with the results of his former personal attendant . . . desires to change his adviser and take 'higher advice' – there are many shades of difference; and in the course of an active morning's work, the consultants are sometimes apt to disregard the finer nuances. . . . By treating a patient who calls alone and without a letter from his doctor as his own, the consultant is probably for the moment more likely to consult his own pecuniary interests; and although very few London hospital physicians or surgeons are not willing to place conformity to its established professional customs above pecuniary considerations, still the unconscious bias of other palpable considerations is evidently to obliterate the faintly seen lines of a course which, by stripping the case of all superficial details, became more distinct. . . .[1]

According to the *British Medical Journal*, in February 1878, 'There must always be men who are partly consultants and partly practitioners; and we venture to think that it is well both for the profession and the public that it should be so.'[2] Three months later the *British Medical Journal* retreated from this position:

Whether it might be feasible, or whether, if feasible, it might be desirable, to establish a class of 'pure consultants' in the medical profession, is a question which is, we think, ripe for discussion. Such men would, on application to their Colleges, receive recognition as 'consulting physicians' or 'consulting surgeons', as Barristers of more than ten years' standing in recognized positions may, upon application . . . be called 'within the Bar' or 'taking silk' as it is called. They can then only 'lead'. They have precedence in seniority, they receive higher fees, but they must always have

[1] ibid., 4 May 1878, p. 647
[2] ibid., 9 February 1878, p. 197

associated with them in every case a junior. The opinion of a consultant of this recognized position would be dignified and well marked. . . . Their incomes would not be less; their lives would be longer; their work would be of the highest and most noble kind; and their field of action would be defined in a most satisfactory sense.[1]

The legal analogy was constantly quoted by the profession and received increasing support. One writer carried the analogy further:

> . . . there should be two grades of consultant, corresponding to the outer barrister and the Queen's Counsel; and as the outer barrister must sit without for a certain number of years before he is called within the bar as Queen's Counsel, so the junior consultant should be required to practise for a given time before he is called to the position of select consultant. The practice of the former would be in consultation with the general practitioner, but the select consultants would be precluded from practising except in those difficult cases in which a third opinion is required; and as the junior consultant would only be brought into contact with the patient through the general practitioner, so the select consultant should only be allowed to practise with a junior.[2]

Three consequences were recognized to follow from this reasoning. First, the consultant should be a specialist rather than a consultant.

> . . . the very *raison d'être* of the consultant would be that he had devoted special attention to one particular subject. No general practitioner . . . can in the present day keep pace with the advance in every branch of practice, and it would be to obtain the opinion of a specialist that, in the majority of instances, a consultation would be desired.[3]

Secondly, that consultants should raise the general level of their fees. And thirdly, 'to enable consultants to live during the earlier years of their career, gratuitous hospital service must cease, the

[1] ibid., 4 May 1878, pp. 647–8
[2] 'An Address on the Maintenance of the Honour and Respectability of the Medical Profession', Edward Crossman, MRCS, LRCP, LSA. *BMJ*, 14 July 1883, p. 63
[3] ibid., p. 64

medical officers, like all other officers, must be paid for their services'. The writer pointed out that the Medical Act Amendments Bill before Parliament

> paves the way for the establishment of professional grades by providing first, a class of general practitioners, licentiates of the Medical Council in medicine, surgery and midwifery, and then recognizes a distinction between the qualifying titles and higher titles, and requiring them to be separately registered.[1]

This far-sighted address did not put an end to the correspondence. Complaints continued to pour in from general practitioners that consultants were stealing their patients.[2] As the *British Medical Journal* remarked,

> ... more especially in London, the general practitioner is apt to find the proximity of his more favoured colleague whom he has called in to give his opinion, result in injury to his dignity and curtailment of his income. ...

> ... it would be very difficult to find a consultant in London who understood it to bear any such meaning, or who would refuse to see, or even visit, when patients requested.[3]

The journal's conclusion went much further than its article of two years earlier.

> The need has arisen for a class of men who will practise as consultants in the strictest acceptance of the term, who will see patients only by the intermediary of their ordinary medical attendant, and who, consequently, could never be the cause of the latter losing his patient. The evil has assumed enormous proportions since the habit of demanding further advice has become universal on the part of patients to whom money is no particular object and the irritation and disappointment of the unfortunate practitioner who sees himself ousted leads to disagreeable scenes and undignified struggles, which, in the interests of all ranks of the profession, it is desirable should cease, and give place to genial relations, more in harmony with the dignity and honour of their calling.

[1] ibid., 65
[2] ibid., Vol. I, 1884, pp. 744, 838, 881, 926, 1184
[3] 'The Duties of Consultants', *BMJ*, 29 May 1886, p. 1030

The wholesome change will not be brought about by any fresh rules and regulations on the part of the governing bodies, all that can be expected by these means has long since been attained, and it is only by the strict enforcement of the laws of etiquette, and prompt complaint when they are infringed, that the general practitioner can hope to secure his rights and privileges.[1]

The letters received in the next fortnight became so bitter that the *British Medical Journal*

. . . declined to publish correspondence between individual practitioners and consultants in which questions of this kind have been somewhat acrimoniously discussed . . . the communications which we have received sufficiently indicate that there exists a feeling of grievance in this, which is rightly or wrongly pretty generally felt, and the cause lies deeply.[2]

In June 1886, a circular letter was issued in London and the suburbs and reproduced in the *British Medical Journal*. It announced the formation of a new Association of General Practitioners, with the aim of forcing consultants to confine themselves to consulting practice. After repeating the analogy with the legal profession, the letter expressed the view that

. . . the consultant should be applied to for advice by the practitioner and not by the patient; that the advice should be given for the instruction of the practitioner in the management of the case, and not for the instruction of the patient, who, having no technical knowledge, can profit little by it.

Since the practice of medicine has been more scientific and more specialized it follows that the practitioner is required, in the interests of his patient, to seek the advice of a consultant more frequently than it was considered necessary in the past and 'a need has arisen for a class of men who will practise as consultants in the strictest sense of the term'.[3]

The members of the Association were prepared to have 'nothing whatever to do' with 'so-called consultants who practised as general practitioners. . . . It will not seek to

[1] ibid.
[2] ibid., 12 June 1886, p. 1114
[3] ibid., p. 1124

Wellcome Historical Medical Library

IE 'DREADNOUGHT' BATTLESHIP, used to accommodate smallpox patients, 1871

REFUGE FOR THE DESTITUTE – FEMALE WORKHOUSE WARD, 1873

Mansell Collection

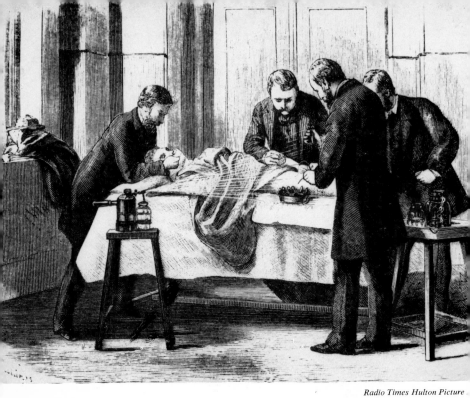

Radio Times Hulton Picture

ANTISEPTIC SURGERY WITH A CARBOLIC SPRAY, first introduced in 1865

HORSE AMBULANCE CARRIAGE IN 1886, showing end of movable stretcher

Radio Times Hulton Picture

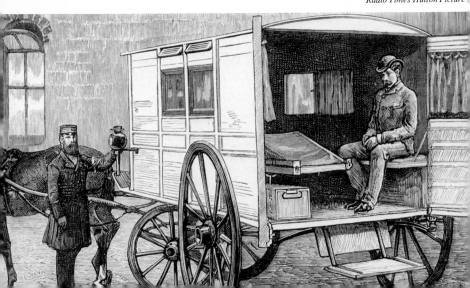

discredit them, nor will its members refuse to meet them when required to do so; but it will exert all its individual and collective influence in favour of those who act as consultants as the term is understood by this Association.'[1] Consultants were to be kept out of general practice by a system of boycott.

The foundation of the Association prompted many letters of support in the *British Medical Journal*. One writer went so far as to suggest that, 'The Association might keep a list of the black sheep for the private use of members, on the principles adopted by the Society for the Protection of Trade.' The writer suggested that the Association should not be confined to the London area. It was the country consultants

> . . . who work more evil than their brethren in London. In the great majority of instances the country consultant is the general practitioner who owes his position to the fact of his holding an appointment in connection with a country hospital. . . . When we find these men charging for bottles of medicine, attending low midwifery and taking clubs at the lowest possible scale, I think it is time for the profession to cry out. . . .[2]

A very frank letter came from Dr Robert Rentoul, one of the most militant defenders of the general practitioner:

> The whole struggle between the general practitioner and consultant is one of bread. Specialists, like other folk, must make their bread and butter or else 'go out'. In order to be fairly success-ful in their efforts, they must, like other men, be fairly dishonest. If he be called in by friends to consult with the usual medical adviser, he must necessarily try to find out what points of difference exist between the friends and their medical man. Then if he is a fairly dishonest man and wishes to be a successful consultant, he will strongly back up the relatives.[3]

By the end of 1886, there were 228 members of the Association of General Practitioners. It was announced that

> The Association has been formed in no spirit of hostility towards any corporate body, or to any existing organization in the pro-fession; but self-help lies at the base of independence, freedom and

[1] ibid.
[2] ibid., 19 June 1886, p. 1196
[3] ibid., 10 July 1886, p. 89

just principles, and it is only by the combination that GPs can relieve themselves of having their most momentous interests dealt with by small or irresponsible councils, self-elected or elected by small constituencies of which the general practitioners, who form the immense majority of the profession, and who are its backbone, have no share.[1]

Whatever was said, the Association was an organized attack upon the Royal Colleges.

This bitter dispute between general practitioners and consultants is vital to the study of the history of hospitals as it indicates the antagonism between the two groups of doctors – those who in the larger towns held hospital appointments and those who did not. It shows also the gradual emergence of the concept of referral as the essence of the relationship which many desired to create. This is not the place to discuss whether or not this restrictive practice was in the public interest. What is relevant to this present study is that once referral became accepted as the relationship which ought to exist between the private practitioner and the private consultant, it was not many years before it was held that a similar relationship should exist between the general practitioner and the outpatient department of the hospital.

At the end of the 1880's, attention was again concentrated on the 'abuse' of outpatient departments. Letters became more and more shrill. A correspondent who signed himself 'Victim' suggested that, if there were to be a fund for bankrupt hospitals, then there ought also to be a fund for bankrupt practitioners.[2] Another called for action from the British Medical Association. 'There is no other body to which we can look for aid. It is no use going to the Royal Colleges: they never did anything for us, and never will.'[3] A third complained that, 'The cant about teaching is intolerable. On any lecture morning what is the proportion of patients "carefully examined" to those sent away with a bottle?'[4] A fourth said that, 'The so-called provident dispensaries and the sham sixpenny dispensaries have already eaten up the heart of the profession . . . and are fast converting the profession of medicine into a bad form of retail trade.'[5] The editor of the

[1] ibid., 11 and 18 December 1886, p. 1190
[2] ibid., 30 June 1888, p. 1420
[3] ibid., 3 August 1889, p. 286
[4] ibid., p. 287
[5] ibid., 19 October 1889, p. 901

journal intervened in this year to ask that 'the tone in which the debate is carried on should be one of moderation and mutual respect. Hard words will rather alienate than persuade those from whom our correspondents so stoutly differ.'[1]

The battle against abuse was mainly conducted against the London hospitals, though the problem was to be found to a lesser extent in the provinces. In one provincial hospital, the medical staff of the hospital met local general practitioners and a joint committee was set up. It was decided that the circumstances of every patient were to be inquired into, and 'their claim for gratuitous treatment determined upon a proper wage scale. A detailed "means test" was developed.'[2] Similar action was taken in one London hospital.[3] Correspondents called for a similar wage limit strictly enforced in all London hospitals.[4] The Charity Organization Society offered to act as a 'clearing house' for London charities, but *The Hospital* invited subscribers to tell the Charity Organization Society secretary 'to mind his own business'. It did not want brought into the hospitals 'the frigid influence of the Arctic organization of Buckingham-street'.[5]

By 1890 many of the London hospitals had taken steps to check the number of outpatients. From 1876, inquiries were made of outpatients at King's College by an official who had previously been employed by the Charity Organization Society: cases of abuse were found to be 'extremely rare'.[6] At St Bartholomew's, from 1883, an 'educated man' was appointed at a salary of £150 per year[7] 'to take down names and addresses and to ask certain questions of the applicants as they came in; then, if he saw occasion, reference was made to the Charity Organization Society'.[8] At the London Hospital a similar system was introduced for cases with governors' letters but not for casualties.[9] The man employed on this work was not 'anything special, not a soldier or a policeman, but a man picked out by the house

[1] ibid., 27 July 1889, p. 202
[2] Jewesbury, p. 57
[3] ibid.
[4] For example, see *BMJ*, 3 August 1889, p. 223.
[5] *Hospital*, Vol. IX, 3 January 1891, p. 214
[6] *Select Committee on Metropolitan Hospitals*, Second Report, 1890–3, p. 457
[7] ibid., Q. 10385
[8] ibid., Third Report, op. cit., p. xli
[9] ibid.

governor'.[1] At St George's, inquiries were made but by the ordinary staff of the hospital.[2] Guy's Hospital took payment from patients and also limited the numbers of outpatients as well.[3] The number of new outpatients seen was limited at St Thomas', the Westminster and the Royal Free Hospitals though there were exceptions in cases of emergency.[4] No steps were taken at the Charing Cross Hospital,[5] or the West London.[6]

The voluntary hospitals were under attack not only for undercutting general practitioners by dispensing too many free consultations but even for dispensing poor medical care. But there was a limit to what they were prepared to do about it. The hordes of outpatients were good for appeal purposes and were wanted by the medical staff both for teaching and for the selection of interesting inpatients. Part of their problem could have been solved by extending the system of charges, but this would have raised an even greater howl of protest from local doctors. Above all else, the general practitioners wanted the hospitals they did not control to be free. This had its long-term importance for the development of medical care in Britain.

[1] ibid., First Report, Q. 1771
[2] ibid., Third Report, p. xlii
[3] ibid., p. xlii
[4] ibid.
[5] ibid.
[6] ibid., Second Report, Q. 20531

CHAPTER 8

The Transition from Pauper Hospitals
to Public Hospitals

ENCOURAGED by the Act of 1867, the reduced number of
London Guardians had constructed or adapted infirmaries
for the exclusive use of the destitute sick. There had been a
similar development in the provinces, but progress had been
slower partly because classification was much more expensive to
introduce in sparsely populated areas and partly because there
was no common Poor Law fund. The 'crusade' against outdoor
relief had ensured that the new infirmaries were fully used.

Under the Act, the responsibility of providing London with
hospitals for indigent fever and smallpox cases had been given
to a separate body, the Metropolitan Asylums' Board,[1] on which
the Poor Law Board had its own nominees. The cost of this
service[2] fell upon the Common Poor Fund. This class of illness
had been given special treatment for three reasons. First, the
voluntary hospital movement had failed to make more than
token provision for it: the most urgent medical requirements of
the people of London had attracted the attention of few donors
and few doctors. Secondly, the need for effective segregation
made it essential that there should be separate and special
hospitals. Thirdly, the growing knowledge of the process of
infection made it urgent to give protection to all classes of
society as well as to care for individual patients.

The new Board set about its task with zeal and determination.
The members appointed by the Poor Law Board and by the
London Guardians were of a somewhat higher social class than

[1] For the material on the Metropolitan Asylums' Board which is included
in this chapter, the author wishes to acknowledge substantial help from
Miss Gwen Ayers who has generously given access to the draft of her forthcoming study of the work of the Board.
[2] excluding the cost of maintenance

the general run of Guardians. They included among their number five doctors, of whom one was a fellow of the College of Surgeons and another a fellow of the College of Physicians. One of the doctors (Dr William Brewer) was elected chairman and he held the post for the first fourteen years of the Board's existence.

Within a few months, the Board had purchased three sites for hospitals at Hampstead, Homerton and Stockwell. Construction was, however, delayed while the Local Government Board made dilatory and ill-informed criticisms of the plans. And Sir Rowland Hill,[1] a prominent resident of Hampstead, was given time to create further delay by protesting against the use of land adjoining his property for the accommodation of infectious paupers. At the end of 1869, while these questions were under consideration, an epidemic of relapsing fever broke out in London. The Poor Law Board hastily sanctioned the erection of a ninety-bedded temporary hospital on the Hampstead site. It was constructed, equipped and staffed within a month. Work also went ahead on permanent structures on the other two sites and these hospitals were opened early in 1871.

By this time a smallpox epidemic was raging across London. The Board's total accommodation of 1,200 beds was inadequate to meet the need. An old workhouse was appropriated from the reluctant Guardians of Islington and handed over to the Board. The hospital ship *Dreadnought*, which was anchored at Greenwich, was borrowed from the Admiralty and used for convalescent patients. By putting up extra beds and erecting tents borrowed from the War Office, the Board achieved a total of 2,000 beds at the peak of the epidemic. But in 1871, 7,912 people died from smallpox in London out of a population of about three-and-a-quarter million.

The Board acquired further sites at Fulham and Deptford and, after prolonged delay caused by the Local Government Board, two further hospitals were built with a total of nearly 800 beds. These were opened in 1877, during the next smallpox epidemic. Meanwhile, the influential Hampstead residents led by Sir Rowland Hill had lodged a more formal protest against the use of property in their neighbourhood for infectious and smallpox cases. A select committee was appointed which defended the actions of the Metropolitan Asylums' Board but the Hampstead ratepayers were not satisfied: they took legal

[1] a former Postmaster-General and pioneer of the penny post

proceedings to recover damages for the 'nuisance' caused by the Hampstead hospital. The jury decided that the hospital was a nuisance and an injunction was issued that it should be closed.[1] And this decision was upheld on appeal in 1881 while a third epidemic swept across London. With all its hospitals about to be closed if residents of less prosperous areas followed Hampstead's example, the Board had to improvise accommodation by erecting huts and tents in Kent and borrowing old wooden battleships from the Admiralty.

Criticisms of the Board's hospitals spread to Fulham and a detailed study was ordered by the Local Government Board. The inspector reported that the number of houses invaded by smallpox in an area within a mile radius of the hospital was four times greater than in districts further out. The hospital at Fulham was closed and in 1881 a Royal Commission was appointed. Though the mode of conveying infection was not established, the Commission recommended that cases of small-pox should in future be treated in isolated positions on the banks of the Thames and in floating hospitals and that extra accommodation should be built for fever cases in the country.[2]

The Metropolitan Asylums' Board implemented these recommendations. For fever cases a new hospital was built at Winchmore Hill. For smallpox cases, the borrowed battleships were purchased from the Admiralty and an aged cross-channel steamer was also bought and adapted for hospital use. These arrangements were completed in time to handle the last major outbreak of smallpox (1884–5) without any difficulties.

The Board was driven to extraordinary lengths to fulfil its functions but its achievements were real. All advances were made despite constant interference from the central authority, not only in broad matters of policy but also in matters of administrative detail. Right from the start the central department expressed firm views about the way in which the hospitals were to be run. There was to be no deviation from the administrative structure which it had laid down for Poor Law

[1] The Hampstead case was eventually settled out of court in 1883. The sum of £9,000 was paid over as damages and Sir Rowland Hill's house and land in Hampstead were purchased by the Board for £13,000 – the site of what is now the Hampstead General Hospital.

[2] *Report of the Royal Commission on Smallpox and Fever Hospitals, 1882*, C 3314, pp. 56–7, HMSO, 1882

infirmaries. Thus at the beginning of 1871, regulations were sent out which specified that the medical superintendent was 'to govern and control all the officers, servants and other persons employed in the asylum'. The members of the Asylums' Board chose instead to govern their hospitals on a system adapted from that of the voluntary hospitals before nursing reform. They gave their medical superintendents responsibility for medical matters and their stewards responsibility for non-medical matters – including the discipline of all but the medical staff. The matron was little more than a housekeeper, working for two masters, the steward and the medical superintendent. She was in charge of the female domestic staff and responsible for the conduct of the nursing staff while off duty. Nurses while on duty were responsible to the medical superintendent. Co-ordination was effected by the management committee which met weekly at the hospital.

The Metropolitan Asylums' Board wrote and asked the Local Government Board to approve these arrangements and quoted the experience of voluntary hospitals:

> The Board believed that in all large London hospitals the duties of the medical men are strictly confined to those of a medical character and they are sure that such an arrangement is a wise one; . . . in some other institutions where a contrary plan has been tried, it is well-known that the Medical Superintendent has become for all practical purposes a medical steward, leaving the treatment of the patients to the Assistant Medical Officer.

Eventually a compromise was reached in the ambiguous formula that the medical superintendent was to assume over-all responsibility, though authority was to be divided between the medical superintendent and the steward.[1]

The asylums were provided under the Poor Laws, which required that they should only be used by paupers. It was the duty of the ordinary local authorities, the vestries and district boards of works, to make provision for patients who could afford to pay. They failed to do so. Thus, during the smallpox epidemic of 1871–2, the hospitals of the Metropolitan Asylums' Board, 'although provided at the cost of the poor rate, were resorted to extensively by persons not of the pauper class'.[2] Over a third of

[1] letter to the MAB of 18 February 1875
[2] *Sixth Annual Report LGB, 1876–7*, C 1865, p. xxxi, HMSO, 1877

the patients had not been paupers at the time of their admission.[1] Many had been admitted without relieving officers' orders and some had even paid for their care. When the 1871 population census was taken, it was found that 82 per cent of the patients in Hampstead Hospital were in gainful employment – the majority as skilled artisans.[2] During the epidemic of 1876–7 the social background of the patients was similar. An inquiry conducted on the night of 15 February 1877, in all the hospitals of the Metropolitan Asylums' Board, revealed that only 10 per cent of the patients admitted to having ever had poor relief before.[3]

This development was not provided for in the legislation and conflicted with the whole philosophy of the Poor Laws. The Metropolitan Asylums' Board was, however, prepared to accept the situation and even decided to refer to the inhabitants of its hospitals as 'patients' rather than 'paupers'. The central authority, however, had laid it down in the regulations that all inmates should be admitted on a relieving officer's order; it also maintained that 'the term "pauper" was the correct one and there is not sufficient reason for substituting "patient" '.[4] It held, despite the facts, that the admission of non-pauper patients was 'altogether exceptional'.[5] Thus for the next twelve years the Local Government Board referred to 'paupers' and the Metropolitan Asylums' Board referred to 'patients'. The latter also continued to admit patients without a relieving officer's order. The Local Government Board eventually agreed to allow this, but only when refusal to admit would have dangerous results. The Board was given statutory authority to recover costs in these 'exceptional circumstances'.[6] This was a large loophole as the danger of refusing admission to any case of smallpox could hardly be questioned.

The responsibility of providing accommodation for paying patients rested with the local sanitary authorities under the 1866 Sanitary Act. The Act was, however, permissive and not

[1] *Metropolitan Fever and Smallpox Hospitals: Returns of the Number of Cases Received up to 24th June 1872*, 424, BPP, Vol. XLIX, 1872
[2] See Gwen Ayers' forthcoming study.
[3] ibid.
[4] ibid. Letter of LGB of 22 December 1874
[5] *Sixth Annual Report LGB 1876–7*, p. xxxiii
[6] *Divided Parishes and Poor Law Amendment Act 1876*, 39 & 40 Vict., C 61, Section 42

mandatory. The power for these authorities to provide hospitals was repeated and widened by the Public Health Act of 1875 so that general hospitals could be provided. This power was, however, very seldom used,[1] and it certainly did not lead to the construction of hospitals in London for paying patients with infectious diseases. In 1877, the Local Government Board had to remind the vestries and district boards of works in the metropolis that it was their responsibility to provide hospitals for non-pauper patients.[2] But the replies still showed that 'with exceptions, the authorities had not provided and were not likely to provide'[3] such hospitals.

The Metropolitan Asylums' Board decided to undertake its own inquiries. It ascertained that five of the thirty vestries and district boards had made some attempt to use their powers; seven said they had not; six advocated the creation of a central board to provide hospitals for infectious diseases and the remainder assumed, erroneously, that it was the duty of the Asylums' Board to make provision for all cases.[4] The Asylums' Board recommended, therefore, that it should take over the functions of the sanitary authorities and provide for the needs of all cases, non-paupers as well as paupers.[5]

The Local Government Board did not accept this recommendation. Instead it secured the passage of an Act in 1879[6] which empowered but did not compel metropolitan local authorities to contract with the Metropolitan Asylums' Board for hospital facilities for non-pauper patients with infectious diseases. The Act did not alter the fact that admission to a Metropolitan Asylums' Board hospital still deprived patients of their right to vote. Moreover it made the problem of meeting the needs of those who were neither destitute nor able to pay the full cost of a hospital stay extremely complex.[7] No authorities made use of the Act and the system of irregular admission to the Board's hospitals continued as before in the epidemic of 1880.

[1] Thirty years later, it was found that only two sanitary authorities in the whole of England and Wales had taken advantage of the Act and opened their own *general* hospitals.
[2] *Sixth Annual Report LGB 1876–7*, p. xxxiii
[3] ibid.
[4] See Gwen Ayers' forthcoming study.
[5] Resolution of 22 February 1877
[6] *Poor Law Act 1879*, 42 & 43 Vict., C 54
[7] See Gwen Ayers' forthcoming study.

Once again the vast majority of patients had never before received poor relief.[1]

The Royal Commission of 1881 expressed strong views on the question of the admission of non-pauper patients and un-compromisingly recommended the preventive principle. It held

> ... emphatically and *in limine* that such a question is not to be treated as one of parochial relief, with primary reference to the case of the indigent sick ... but as one of public safety with primary reference to the general prevention and extirpation of epidemic infectious disease, subject to the obligation of doing all that humanity demands for the benefit of individual sufferers.[2]

The Commission concluded that the interests of public health and the concept of 'less-eligibility' were not compatible. It therefore advised that all existing infectious hospitals should be 'entirely disconnected from the administration of the Poor Law, and treated as part of the sanitary arrangements of the metropolis'.[3] The Commissioners were not sure whether it was wise to claim payment from cases in the ordinary wards even if the patient could afford to pay without difficulty. The Commissioners were prepared to contemplate not only state hospitals but free hospitals.

The government was not prepared to go as far as the Commissioners had proposed. The Metropolitan Asylums' Board was kept under Poor Law control: but under an Act of 1883,[4] patients admitted to its hospitals were no longer denied the vote except in parish elections. This last disqualification was removed in 1885.[5] The Board had at last got its way: its patients were no longer paupers. But apart from the exceptional circumstances which it interpreted so leniently, the Board could still only admit non-pauper patients from sanitary authorities which had made contracts with it. Despite several offers, the Board could not persuade any sanitary authority to enter into a contract. Such a contract would have meant that the authority itself would have had to meet the cost if any patient failed to pay, while under the

[1] ibid.
[2] *Report on Smallpox & Fever Hospitals 1882*, p. vii
[3] ibid., p. xxxi
[4] *Diseases Prevention (London) Act, 1883*, 46 & 47 Vict., C 35
[5] *Diseases Prevention (Metropolis) Act, 1885*, Section 7

customary but irregular procedure of admission to an Asylum, the cost fell on the Common Poor Fund. Eventually in 1889 after further prevarication from the Local Government Board, the Asylums' Board was empowered to admit persons who were not paupers and thus became the hospital authority for all cases of infectious disease in London.

In the same year the hospitals were entitled to admit medical students[1] and thus fill an important gap in medical education which the selective policies of teaching hospitals had created. It was now possible to prevent the 'ignorance of infectious diseases which hitherto has prevailed among young practitioners'.[2] No attempt was made to correct the ignorance of chronic diseases, which were on the increase for similar reasons.

Two years later a further important step was taken. Under the Public Health (London) Act of 1891[3] magistrates were given power to direct the detention in hospitals of persons suffering from infectious diseases, in cases where they appeared to have no proper place to go outside the hospital. The same Act removed the power of the Poor Law authorities in London to charge patients with infectious diseases. Every citizen of London had become entitled to free treatment from the Metropolitan Asylums' Board. If free and universal medical services are socialistic, one principle of socialism had been established before the founding of any socialist political party in Britain.

The term 'infectious disease' was gradually widened. Originally the Board was only authorized to admit cases of scarlet fever, enteric fever, typhus and smallpox. This range was greatly extended:[4] as more diseases became excluded by the voluntary hospitals, the free public medical services widened in

1 *Poor Law Act, 1889*, 52 & 53 Vict., C 56
2 *Select Committee on Metropolitan Hospitals 1890–3*, Third Report, op. cit., para. 413
3 54 & 55 Vict., C 76
4 Diphtheria patients were admitted in 1888, certain classes of children afflicted with ophthalmia and ringworm in 1897, and destitute measles and whooping-cough cases in 1910. During the following year non-pauper measles and whooping-cough patients were also admitted. The Board was empowered to admit all sick, debilitated or convalescent children sent by the Guardians (*Forty-First Annual Report LGB 1911–12*, Pt. I, Cd 6327, pp. lx–lxi, HMSO, 1912). A clause was inserted in the National Insurance Bill during 1911 which authorized the Board to receive tuberculosis patients. The clause also provided that, for this purpose, the Board should not be deemed a Poor Law authority. Ibid., p. 59

scope.[1] Thus the Metropolitan Asylums' Board developed into one of the largest and most effective hospital systems in the world. It did so while operating nominally as a branch of the Poor Law. By 1907, its annual expenses amounted to nearly a million pounds but the Local Government Board was already excluding these sums from the annually computed cost of pauperism.[2] This was a significant technicality.

In the provinces, the main provision for infectious diseases was made by the sanitary authorities. By 1891, about 400 of the 1,600 sanitary authorities had provided some form of hospital. The standard of these services varied from 'the model hospital at Walker-on-Tyne [to] . . . a wooden shed with its space for 40 beds forming a portion of the hospital provision at Preston'.[3] After the Infectious Diseases Notification Act in 1889, there was a large increase in provincial hospitals. By 1893 there were reported to be 'excellent isolation hospitals' at Bournemouth, Portsmouth, Poole, Weymouth, Winchester, Fareham, Calne, Havant, Catherington and other places. But many important centres were 'without any accommodation whatever for infectious diseases, and the omission of the sanitary authorities to avail themselves of the powers with which they are invested entails a most serious responsibility upon themselves, and constitutes a danger to the public health'.[3] The failings were greatest in the rural areas. In 1893, provincial county councils but not county boroughs were empowered to provide hospitals for infectious disease.[4]

By 1911, there were about 32,000 beds available for infectious diseases. The size and quality of these institutions varied from the splendid fever hospital for nearly a thousand patients at Liver-

[1] 'From 1840, when it suddenly doubled its mortality in England and Wales, until 1880, scarlet fever was the chief cause of death among infectious maladies and accounted for from 4 % to 6 % of all deaths. . . . By 1900, first measles and then diphtheria had surpassed it. These infectious diseases also outstripped smallpox.' W. H. Bradley, 'Notifiable Infectious Diseases: A Reassessment', *Royal Society of Health Journal*, Vol. 79, No. 4, July-August 1959, p. 4

[2] *Report of the Royal Commission on the Poor Laws and Relief of Distress 1905–9*, Cd 4499, p. 877 (Minority), HMSO, 1909

[3] *BMJ*, 28 January 1893, p. 185

[4] *Twenty-Second Annual Report LGB 1892–3*, op. cit., pp. 83–4

[5] *Isolation Hospitals Act 1893*, 56 & 57 Vict., C 68; also *Twenty-Third Annual Report LGB 1893–4*, C 7500, p. xxv, HMSO, 1894

pool to the twenty-two beds placed in 'an old warehouse on the river bank'.[1] There were, however, large areas of the country which still made do with 'the cottage or shed with two or three beds set aside for the occasional smallpox patient'.[2] As these 'hospitals' stood empty for months at a time they were frequently found to be unfit for use when needed. There was also the difficulty of obtaining trained nurses at short notice. This exigency was not always planned for, with the result that a patient could be left to the caretaker's attention![3] At least one local authority (Tunbridge Wells) was sued by a neglected patient for its 'scandalous arrangements'.[4] As *The Hospital* explained in 1907, 'there is at present a lamentable lack of uniformity in the public health powers and duties of the various sanitary authorities'.[5]

The sanitary authorities had powers to charge for their hospitals. In the great majority of instances, however, charges were not enforced as 'it was desired to get these hospitals generally used'.[6] The authorities who made charges usually adjusted them either to the means of the patient or to the rateable value of his home; in both cases they allowed free treatment for the poor.[7] The means test for this purpose was on a personal basis: relations were not chargeable – even a parent for a child. Patients, however, who arrived in these hospitals via the Poor Law authority could find themselves still disqualified for the franchise and both they and their relations had to pay.[8] Some authorities, such as Brighton, Eastbourne and Shrewsbury, levied very high charges. In the latter case, the charges were so

[1] By 1913 there were 755 fever hospitals with 31,149 beds and 363 smallpox hospitals with 7,972 beds in England and Wales. These totals include the hospitals of the MAB. Port sanitary authorities also maintained 30 isolation hospitals for 420 patients. LGB, *Return as to Hospital Accommodation in England and Wales*, p. 4, HMSO, 1915. Roughly a third of these beds were in London. By 1911, there were 6,528 fever beds and 2,040 smallpox beds in the hospitals of the MAB. In addition, there were 1,650 beds in the two MAB hospitals for sick and convalescent children. *MAB Annual Report for the Year 1911*, pp. xxv–xxvi, London, 1912

[2] *Report of Royal Commission on Poor Laws 1905–9*, p. 876 (Minority)

[3] *Hospital*, Vol. XLI, 13 October 1906, p. 21

[4] ibid., 10 November 1906, p. 83

[5] ibid., Vol. XLII, 27 July 1907, p. 451

[6] *Report of Royal Commission on Poor Laws 1905–9*, p. 941 (Minority)

[7] ibid.

[8] ibid., p. 943

prohibitive that the hospitals remained practically empty.[1]

Practices over charges for isolation hospitals varied widely and were thick with anomalies. Nevertheless, there had developed in many parts of the country a chain of free hospitals available for the use of the whole public without loss of the rights of citizenship. And while the critics of the voluntary hospitals could complain and did complain about abuse, such a term could have little meaning for isolation hospitals. An important precedent had been established for the whole future of Britain's public services. A personal service had developed which was available without charge. It was not long before the precedent was extended.

The first step in this direction was the extension of the right to vote in parliamentary elections to all persons receiving medical relief. While the right to vote had been confined to a small moneyed minority, the denial of it to sick paupers had little real significance: few of them would have ever been able to exercise it. After the Third Reform Act of 1884, the issue became one of real substance. Moreover, it was extremely difficult to see how the exclusion of paupers could ever have been accurately administered. As the next election approached, the matter was raised in the House, first in the case of Ireland and then in the case of Britain. The Government decided at the eleventh hour to give sick paupers the vote and introduced a Bill to achieve this. Those members of the House who wanted to keep disfranchisement argued that the Government was acting for reasons of expediency – to win pauper votes. But the Bill won the support of a majority of members. There were some who supported disfranchisement because of the anomalies created by allowing the vote only to patients with infectious diseases. Others, such as Sclater-Booth, pointed out that disfranchisement was unfair to the rural poor who had no access to voluntary hospitals.[2] Finally there were some who believed as a matter of principle that sickness should no longer be regarded as a justification for disfranchisement. In addition, there was reason to doubt whether disfranchisement could in fact be operated impartially now that the vote had been extended. One Member[3], who regarded disfranchisement as 'political economy run mad', said that the

---

[1] ibid., p. 942
[2] *Hansard*, H of C, Vol. CCXLIX, 16 July 1885, col. 1006
[3] Mr Collings

doctor and relieving officer in a parish in Somerset were members
of the Conservative Party and that they were deliberately dis-
criminating against Liberal voters. 'Unless a large number of
voters who had received medical relief were placed on the list
before the General Election, the Franchise Bill might as well not
have been passed at all.'[1]

Thus, in 1885 the sick pauper won the vote.[2] And this was
applied to sick paupers in workhouse institutions where the law
was interpreted locally to have this meaning.[3] In such cases, the
term 'medical relief' was interpreted to include 'food, lodging,
nursing and all other concomitants of treatment of the sick on a
scale equal in many respects to the best equipped general
hospitals in the country'.[4] One cause for the reluctance of people
to make use of Poor Law infirmaries had been removed. But
there remained the stigma of any institution run by the
Guardians and fear of hospitals of all kinds. But though this fear
remained, experience in the voluntary hospitals had taught a
section of the working class that admission to a hospital could be
beneficial. In some areas, however, there were no voluntary
hospitals: the infirmary offered the only institutional care for the
sick. Moreover, there were cases which the voluntary hospitals
would admit only for a limited period or not admit at all. The
more selective the voluntary hospitals became, the more the
deserving poor were denied an alternative to the Poor Law
service, if they could not be looked after at home.

Policy had been based on the assumption that the stigma of the
Poor Laws and the reluctance of the poor to leave their homes
would prevent any 'abuse' of the new infirmaries. It was believed
that these attitudes would survive when the infirmaries became
general hospitals. But just as the asylums became used by persons
not of the pauper class, so the infirmaries began to attract non-
pauper patients. A distinction grew up in the minds of the local
population between the infirmary and the workhouse.

A Select Committee of the House of Lords was told in 1888
that 'in consequence of the excellence of the treatment in these
infirmaries and their separation from the workhouses, the poor are

[1] *Hansard*, H of C, Vol. CCXLIX, 16 July 1885, col. 978
[2] *Medical Relief Disqualification Removal Act 1885*, 48 & 49 Vict., C 46, S 2
[3] Interpretation of the law varied in different areas. *Report of Royal
Commission on Poor Laws 1905-9*, p. 1021 (Minority)
[4] ibid., p. 231 (Majority)

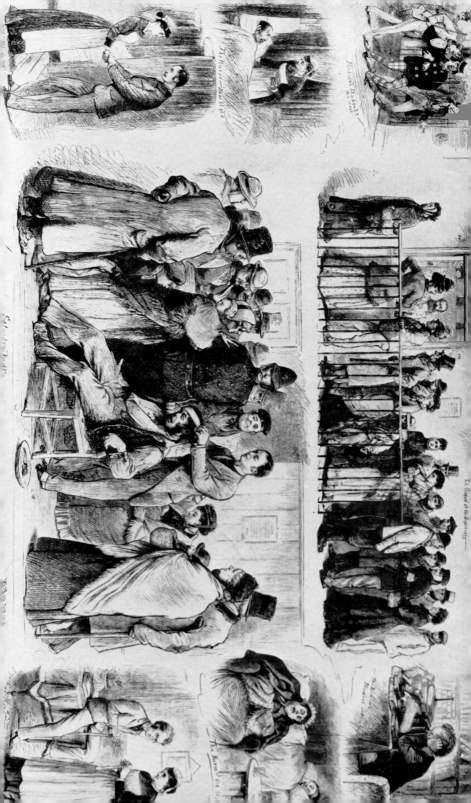

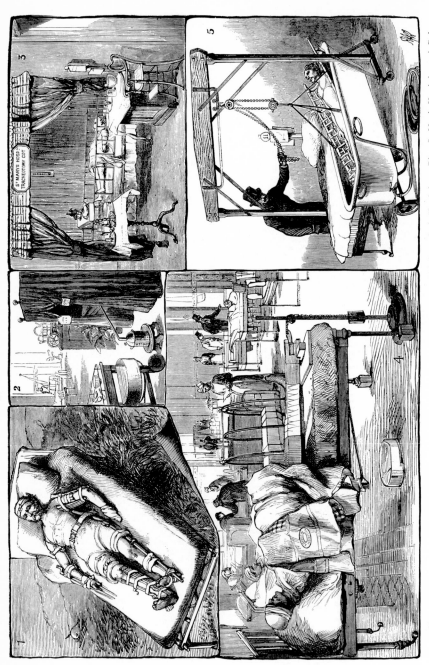

1. Extempore Dressing on the Battlefield.—2. Ward Tent and Apparatus for Steaming Throat and Bronchial Cases, Guy's Hospital.—3. Ditto, St. Mary's Hospital.—4. A Bad Accident Case: London Hospital.—5. Bath Lift: Middlesex Hospital.

so ready to resort to them that there is a tendency to regard them as a kind of "state hospital", entrance into which does not imply that the patient is a pauper'.[1] Arthur Pell, MP, a governor of Guy's Hospital, and a Guardian for forty-six years, said that he considered 'the infirmary of St-George's-in-the-East to be as perfect in its way as any hospital in London'.[2] Faced with this problem, some Guardians, with the full support of the Local Government Board, tried to accentuate the association with the Poor Law as far as possible. The Birmingham Guardians 'determined to make all persons who come to their infirmary pass through the gate that leads to the workhouse ground, so that they may not draw a distinction between the workhouse and the infirmary'.[3]

The evident quality of the new infirmaries was beginning to break down the stigma of the Poor Law. To stop the 'abuse' of outdoor medical relief, the attempt had been made to provide relief only in the institution: now institutional care was itself becoming 'abused'. And there was little the Guardians could do about it. They could, however, do their best to see that all patients paid who could afford to do so. Even this was not easy. One Guardian explained that when the attempt was made to extract a contribution from a patient with a broken arm before treatment, 'the man might use some very coarse expression to us and walk out of the room. He goes straight to the London Hospital, where he gets treated for nothing.'[4]

As the standard of the infirmaries improved, more patients 'not of the pauper class' made use of them. And presidents of the Poor Law Board issued circulars aimed not only at improving the standard of medical care in the infirmaries, but also the standards of amenity. Authority was given for the supply of such articles as books, toys, tobacco, snuff, dry tea, milk and sugar.[5] In 1893, all Guardians and their women's visiting committees were given the right to inspect workhouses at any time without notice.[6] Charitable ladies were allowed to come and entertain the sick and aged. At Bethnal Green they visited the workhouse

[1] *Report of H of L Select Committee on Poor Relief 1888*, (239), p. viii, HMSO, 1888
[2] ibid., para. 1457
[3] ibid., p. vii
[4] ibid., para. 1460
[5] General Orders of 1891, 1892 and 1894
[6] General Order 1893

K

to sing and play 'the violin and guitar every Friday afternoon'.[1] Such good intentions were not always welcomed. The infirmary committee at Lambeth had to discourage some Baptist ladies on the grounds that 'the doctor did not wish for any increase in the services nor did the patients . . . some of whom were very ill, some dying'. They 'did not want so much singing and talking'.[2] The able-bodied paupers were offered more serious forms of entertainment.[3]

A completely new situation was developing. The creation of public hospitals had proved such a success that they were used not only by paupers who had been refused outdoor relief but by persons above the pauper class. Following the precedent of the Metropolitan Asylums' Board in creating hospitals for patients of all classes, the whole character of the Poor Law infirmaries was beginning to change. This development was in complete contrast to the whole philosophy upon which the Poor Laws were based.

---

[1] *Royal Commission on the Poor Laws and Relief of Distress 1905-9*, App. Vol. II, Cd 4684, Q. 24147, HMSO, 1909

[2] *PLOJ*, 7 January 1901, p. 474

[3] The Whitechapel Guardians employed 'mental instructors' to read to their able-bodied paupers between the hours of 6.30 and 8.00 every day. Topics were chosen from 'paragraphs and reports touching labour, emigration, providence, temperance and kindred subjects'. These classes operated 'as a salutary restraint upon conversation and conduct'. *Select Committee on Poor Relief 1888*, para. 4506

CHAPTER 9

Paying Patients

I N the panic of the smallpox epidemics, skilled artisans and even professional people had entered the new public hospitals. The Metropolitan Asylums' Board had catered for patients far above the pauper class. And in the seventies and eighties patients above the pauper class were admitted to the Poor Law infirmaries. There were complaints that the voluntary hospitals were being similarly 'abused'.

Nursing reform had led to improvements in the comfort and probably in the curative potentialities of a stay in a voluntary hospital: there were higher standards of hygiene, and care was more intensive. Physically the patients were better looked after: they, like the probationer nurses who tended them, were under constant or nearly constant observation. Hospital care had become advantageous for a wider social group.

Throughout the sixties and seventies, the patients of the voluntary hospitals remained, with few exceptions, working-class. The wealthy showed no inclination to enter any sort of institution when they were ill. There were, however, some institutions which catered for the convalescent. Though never formalized, this had been the role of the fashionable spas of the eighteenth century and the faith in water cures had gradually extended to seaside resorts. Thus the Southport Convalescent Hospital and Sea-Bathing Infirmary had been founded in 1806 and the Convalescent Institution for Women and Children at New Brighton in 1847.[1] And in 1877, Messrs Cook & Sons, 'the well-known Tourists' Agents, decided to open a convalescent hotel for invalids at Luxor, Thebes, Upper Egypt'.[2] But apart from the convalescent stage, the wealthy suffered their sicknesses at home and took advantage of nursing reform by hiring nurses who were, or whom they thought to be, trained. If they needed a

[1] See *Burdett's Hospitals and Charities, 1889*, London, 1889.
[2] *BMJ*, 3 November 1877, p. 655

London consultant, they would pay large sums to have him come and visit them in remote parts of the country or would move house to London, where he could attend them regularly.

The not-so-wealthy, on the other hand, who had no homes in London and wanted the services of the great London 'names', would come and take lodgings in the area where the physicians and surgeons had their consulting-rooms. This enabled them to visit the great men or to be visited by them as often as they chose. Thus in 1865 Sir Henry Thompson, Bart., who earned £6,648 plus other large fees for visits abroad 'was in the habit of having breakfast at 8 a.m. and commencing his private operations which were performed in the "lodging houses" . . . near his residence at 8.45 or 9 a.m. The rest of the morning was spent in seeing his private patients at Wimpole Street.'[1] These lodging houses appear to have made no special arrangements for the accommodation of the sick.

If the difficulties could be overcome, the voluntary hospitals had an incentive to make provision for patients who could pay. They were finding it difficult to raise the money to run their hospitals at the new standards which were being introduced. Inpatients were costing much more to maintain. Although the first impact of nursing reform was not costly, as a probationer was paid less than the untrained nurse whom she replaced, it was not long before the cost of the nursing care given to each patient rose sharply. Not only did the new matrons demand and get a higher ratio of staff to patients, but they also required a much higher standard of accommodation to house the probationers and 'lady pupils' whom they were recruiting. And more nursing staff led in turn to more domestic staff to look after them.

Some hospitals managed to make a modest income out of the nurses they were training or had trained. The girls who had joined the hospital to nurse the poor were sent out to nurse the rich for fees which greatly exceeded the nurse's salary. This enterprise proved to be quite profitable for some of the hospitals that undertook it. Nurses were asked to help the hospital 'with both hands'.

Hospitals continued to raise money by the traditional means. Subscribers were canvassed and every type of appeal was used.

[1] Z. Cope, *The Versatile Victorian, Being the Life of Sir Henry Thompson, Bt., 1820–1904,* p. 47, London, 1951

But still the hospitals had not enough money from the well-to-do to meet all the commitments which they wished to undertake. They had now added to their senior officers powerful lady matrons who were constantly asking for more money to employ more staff. In the 1870's, two national organizations were set up to raise money for the hospitals – the Hospital Sunday Fund and the Hospital Saturday Fund.

The Sunday Fund was an organization to raise money through the Churches. For many years special collections had been organized to help the local hospitals.[1] In 1873, a central organization was created to stimulate the raising of money and rationalize its distribution. In its first year it collected £27,000; by 1889 the annual sum collected had increased to £41,700.[2] The money was distributed by the Council of the Fund according to the 'needs and merits' of each institution.[3] The Fund was often criticized for the way in which it interpreted this criterion but the money made a useful addition to the money raised by the hospitals themselves.

The Saturday Fund was a workman's fund. From the 1850's there had been organized workmen's collections to support local hospitals. The largest schemes were those supporting the Glasgow and North Stafford infirmaries.[4] The Saturday Fund was an organization controlled by working men elected from the workshops. The main aim of the Fund was 'to collect small weekly subscriptions from the classes who cannot give considerable sums at one time'.[5] In 1874, £258 was raised in street collections and £5,000 in workshops. In 1890 the respective sums were £5,096 and £15,237. The money was distributed according to the work, economy and efficiency of the different institutions. 'There were seven or eight actual working men on the executive committee. . . . The committee work is done in the evenings to enable the working men to attend.'[6]

The Saturday Fund, as distinct from the Sunday Fund, took subscribers' letters in return for the grants it made, sometimes

[1] See, for example, F. H. Jacob, *A History of the General Hospital near Nottingham*, p. 311, Bristol and London, 1951.
[2] *Select Committee on Metropolitan Hospitals 1890–3*, Third Report, op. cit., p. xcvii
[3] ibid.
[4] *Hospital*, Vol. LIII, 28 December 1912, p. 343
[5] *Select Committee on Metropolitan Hospitals 1890–3*, Third Report, p. xcvii
[6] ibid.

on the same scale as letters allocated to ordinary subscribers and
sometimes on a special scale. The letters were distributed through
the collectors in the workshops. By 1890 the managers of the
Fund were seeking also to become governors of the hospitals
to which the Fund subscribed. Henry Burdett[1] thought it quite
wrong for them 'to purchase privileges and governorships at
medical institutions, as they do not represent in any real sense
the contributors of the funds so collected for the hospitals'.[2]

When the Saturday Fund devised a penny-a-week fund, the
British Medical Journal regarded it as a dangerous precedent.
The Fund 'will be essentially provident and will establish a
moral if not a legal claim'[3] to treatment. Medical men 'may
hereafter find themselves suffering some material loss from the
gathering of the working classes generally into the outpatients'
departments of hospitals which are already sufficiently resorted
to by persons having no apparent claim to charitable relief'.[4]
The working men were already claiming a right to treatment in
return for their modest contributions. *The Hospital* pointed out
that they had no rights at all but only privileges.

> The question is – will the working men because they subscribe,
> say, one pound of every £100 to the cost of hospital maintenance,
> run the risk of losing the other £99 by claiming rights which have no
> existence, instead of taking gracefully the privileges and advantages
> which the voluntary supporters of hospitals have hitherto so
> generously conferred on them? . . . If they behave like unthinking
> and irresponsible children, they must not be surprised if they find
> the timid birds of voluntary charity flying away beyond the reach
> of their foolish clamour.[5]

Despite the Sunday Fund, the Saturday Fund, the special
appeals, subscriptions, legacies, donations and endowments,
the voluntary hospitals were still short of money. They wanted

[1] Henry Burdett was born in 1847, the son of a parson. He had wanted to
become trained as a doctor but this was not possible for financial reasons.
After a job in a bank in Birmingham, he became secretary of the Queen's
Hospital, Birmingham, and later resigned to take up a post in the share and
loan department of the Stock Exchange. In London he joined the committee
of the Seamen's Hospital, where he was elected vice-president. The publications he started included the *Nursing Mirror*, *The Hospital* and *Burdett's
Hospital Annual*.

[2] *Burdett's Annual, 1890*, p. xxxv
[3] *BMJ*, 26 May 1889, p. 1187
[4] ibid.
[5] *Hospital*, Vol. XXVII, 18 January 1890, p. 240

to expand their activities and it was partly for this reason that the possibility of asking for payment from some of the inpatients was seriously considered by the voluntary hospitals. But this development did not come solely from the desire to raise money; it arose also out of a gradual recognition that there was a class above 'the poor' who needed hospital care. Indeed, the whole subject of pay beds first arose out of public discussion of the need to provide hospitals specifically for those who could afford to make some payment.

In 1842, through the initiative of Dr Southwood Smith, a pay hospital was opened in London 'for the nursing and medical and surgical care of persons belonging to the middle classes'.[1] The president of the association was Prince Albert, who thought that the project was 'calculated to work much good'.[2] There were eight single-bedded rooms which by the third year were kept constantly occupied. Patients were required to pay up to two guineas per week. When the three-year lease of the original premises expired, the project was discontinued. One reason for the demise of the first pay hospital in Britain was the fact that the project had been launched with inadequate capital.[3]

By the 1870's pay hospitals were to be found in many other countries: for example, in France, Switzerland, Spain, Germany, Austria, Norway, Sweden, Italy, the United States and Canada.[4] Such hospitals were not to be found in Britain. Many reasons can be suggested for the late development of British pay hospitals. The general hospital had developed in Britain largely out of the endeavours of charitable laymen and they were thought of solely as facilities for the poor. Moreover, it was believed that the receipt of payments from patients would have harmed appeals for funds. And if payments had been received from patients it would have raised the awkward question of whether the payments should be received wholly by the lay governors or should be divided with the honorary medical staff. The British system of the 'orders' of medicine and of the 'closed list' hospitals created difficult problems concerning the professional relationship between general practitioners and the physicians and

[1] H. C. Burdett, *Pay Hospitals and Paying Wards throughout the World*, pp. 94–5
[2] ibid., p. 95
[3] ibid., p. 99
[4] ibid., pp. 37–84

surgeons. A German hospital which was controlled by a doctor could discriminate between different classes of hospital patient just as a doctor could discriminate between different classes of patient outside hospital. Such a system was not acceptable in British hospitals controlled by laymen and staffed by honorary physicians and surgeons.

Where hospitals were controlled by general practitioners, payments from patients were accepted. Thus the system of patients' payments grew up with the cottage hospitals. When a general practitioner arranged for his own patient to be admitted to such a hospital it was clear that he was not depriving other local practitioners of their livelihood. If, however, the large general hospitals had accepted paying patients, it would have been said that the hospitals were taking money which would have been received by the general practitioners if the patient had stayed at home.

There were, however, some special hospitals in Britain which took payments from patients. The practice was to be found largely in children's hospitals and women's hospitals.[1] Thus the women's hospital in Soho Square took sums varying from half-a-guinea per week to three guineas per week. After 1877 a uniform charge of two guineas was introduced.[2] There were also pay beds at the London Fever Hospital.[3] The paying system was, moreover, used extensively in Dublin.[4]

A scheme for a pay hospital for general cases had been suggested by *The Lancet* in 1875,[5] but the suggestion did not attract much attention. Not until it received the forceful backing of Henry Burdett did the idea get off the ground. In April 1877, he wrote a letter to *The Standard*. Burdett 'advocated the formation of an association for the purpose of founding a hospital replete with every possible comfort and provision for the privacy and proper treatment of well-to-do patients to which admission should be by payment alone'.[6] The *British Medical Journal* gave the scheme qualified approval. 'There is much to be said in favour of this project from every point of view; but, on the other

[1] *BMJ*, 10 July 1875, p. 48
[2] Burdett, *Pay Hospitals*, p. 87
[3] ibid., p. 89
[4] ibid., pp. 88–9
[5] *Lancet*, 6, 13 and 20 March 1875
[6] *Hospital*, Vol. XXXII, 23 August 1902, p. 255

hand, to be properly carried out, it requires to be organized on a basis which places it above suspicion.'[1]

The Lancet also saw the need to provide better care for patients who could pay. 'It is no reproach to private nursing to say that it is necessarily inferior to the best hospital nursing.'[2] It thought that a separate hospital for the purpose would be 'an immense boon'.[3] But it also suggested that part of the necessary accommodation might be provided by existing London hospitals by adapting a ward for the purpose. It found, however, that,

> on the part of many there would be a natural objection to entering a general hospital. . . . Hospitals supported by charity are afraid that they will not be able to show a deficit, or to appeal *ad miseri-cordiam*, if they introduce the system of paying patients.[4]

The Lancet made it clear that it was not advocating

> . . . any plan which shall deprive the general practitioner of his hardly earned fees, or increase the unpaid labour of the hospital physician and surgeon. Were such the effect of the scheme we should be amongst the first to protest against it. But there is no reason why this should be the result. In the case of existing hospitals some difficulty might be raised as to the introduction of medical men not on the staff of the hospital. . . . But in a separate institution, or a distinct division of the general hospital, there would be no reason why the patient's own doctor should not attend the patient, and the resident medical officer be responsible for carrying out his instructions. Where the patient elected to be under the ordinary hospital staff, the fees might go into a common fund, and this would remove any jealousy between members of the staff. In fact, nothing could be easier than to arrange a system which would meet with the concurrence of general and consulting practitioners.[5]

A week later the *British Medical Journal* came out strongly against pay wards attached to general hospitals. 'It will be necessary to erect special hospitals for this purpose, if the wants of the public and the profession are to be adequately met.'[6]

---

[1] *BMJ*, 21 April 1877, p. 491
[2] *Lancet*, 28 April 1877, p. 614
[3] ibid.
[4] ibid.
[5] ibid.
[6] *BMJ*, 5 May 1877, p. 557

The professional difficulties involved in pay beds in the voluntary hospitals were

> ... numerous and insurmountable; for which of the great hospitals would allow a general practitioner, for instance, or any member of the profession, to attend a patient in its wards because such patients were able to remunerate him for such attendance? And if the treatment of paying patients is to be confined to the members of the hospital staff, the opposition of the majority of the profession would necessarily be excited.[1]

In addition, 'the well-to-do patients would decline to submit to treatment in any institution partaking of the nature of a charity whether they were asked to pay or not'.[2]

Though the *British Medical Journal* poured scorn on the proposals of *The Lancet*, it gave its support to Burdett's scheme for a separate 'Home Hospital'. In less than a fortnight, 'on May 14th, 1877, a deputation of public, city and medical men waited on the Lord Mayor and presented a memorial on the subject.'[3] The scheme had the support of leading members of the medical staff of all the Metropolitan hospitals; the presidents of the Royal College of Physicians, the Royal College of Surgeons and the General Medical Council; and a battery of bishops, judges and barristers.[4]

Two months later, in July 1877, the president of the Metropolitan Counties branch of the British Medical Association devoted his presidential address to the subject. A Home Hospital was needed for

> ... individuals who are in a social position which renders them ineligible as hospital patients and, at the same time, for want of relatives and friends leaves them in a painfully isolated position, frequently to contend with painful illness with such imperfect attendance as may be obtained in an ordinary London lodging. It is by no means desirable to remove a sick person from his home surroundings, where there are relatives and friends to attend to the wants of the invalid, unless under exceptional circumstances. The class to whom such accommodation would be useful is those who

[1] ibid.
[2] ibid.
[3] *Hospital*, Vol. XXXII, 23 August 1902, p. 255
[4] ibid.

are comparatively friendless and alone, such as clerks and young
men living in town away from their relations, governesses and
others. . . . Patients of the class of which we are speaking . . . would
require a greater amount of privacy, with separate rooms, or, at all
events, wards containing only two or three beds in each.[1]

In August of the same year, Burdett addressed the Public
Medical Section of the British Medical Association at Manchester
in similar vein. It was not 'proposed to take people away from
their comfortable homes to a hospital because they are ill'.[2]
The Home Hospital was intended 'for the benefit of a large class
of the community who have no homes, or whose homes are ill-
adapted for the successful treatment of serious illness'.[3] It would
be 'an inestimable boon' for the 'lodger class' – 'governesses and
young men – clerks, students and such like . . . left to the tender
mercies of their landlady . . . to the above may be added clergymen, lawyers, officers in the army, navy and civil services, men
who are engaged in private and public offices, persons of education with limited means.'[4]

In addition to all these categories of person named by Burdett,
The Lancet thought a Home Hospital would be useful for those

> . . . who, residing in the country and abroad, are compelled to seek
> advice, and perhaps to undergo operations in London. They can,
> it is true, get lodgings and nursing, but the former are, in our
> opinion, as a rule far less suitable for their purpose and far more
> cheerless than the majority of ordinary hospital wards, the attend-
> ance is insufficient and the prices are exorbitant.[5]

The Lancet's only fear of the project was that there were to be
no medical men on the committee of management. 'When the
medical element is wanting to guide and correct, the most
astonishing blunders are committed.'[6]
The medical profession was not, however, unanimous in its
support for the Home Hospital project. A Dr Boyd Mushet gave

[1] *BMJ*, 25 August 1877, pp. 243–5
[2] ibid.
[3] ibid.
[4] ibid.
[5] *Lancet*, 23 June 1877, p. 914
[6] ibid.

notice of a motion for the annual meeting of the British Medical
Association to be held in Bath in 1878. He held the view that

> ... the institution of home hospitals for the well-to-do classes [was]
> calculated to impair the already far from universal recognition of
> payment for medical and surgical services; would tend to degrade
> the recipients of the benefits of the proposed homes, by extending
> charity to persons who, it is conceded, are able to pay; would
> aggravate the existing flagrant abuses of the hospital system, and
> be fraught with injustice to the profession, at present burdened by
> the exaction of its unpaid and gratuitous services.[1]

Despite Dr Mushet's opposition, the project went through.
A sum of over £20,000 was raised. The first Home Hospital was
opened on 27 June 1880 in Fitzroy Square. By 1902, 5,376
patients had been treated by a total of 1,476 doctors.[2] In 875
cases, the patient was accompanied by a friend during the stay
in hospital.[3] The hospital always showed a slight margin of
profit. Within a few months of opening, one significant change
in the arrangements was reported. The four-bedded ward which
had been opened up was abandoned. 'When a visitor comes to a
patient in a ward with more than one bed, those who have no
friends quietly overhear all the visitor has to say.'[4] When patients
were first given the choice, they insisted on privacy.

The Home Hospital was not, however, first in the field with
a pay hospital. In 1879, Mr Barr of Northampton persuaded
the Northampton Nursing Institution which supplied domiciliary
nurses from a central nurses' home, to rent two adjacent houses
and furnish one of them as a small pay hospital. Patients paid
one guinea for a back room and two guineas for a front room
and chose their own doctor. The first patients included 'clergymen, farmers, and tradesmen, their wives and families, governesses and tutors, schoolmasters and ladies in reduced circumstances'.[5] And in the same year the Hospital for Women,
Soho Square, provided a wing for 'a superior grade of sufferers
who are able to pay for their own support'.[6]

[1] *BMJ*, 21 July 1878, pp. 113–14
[2] *Hospital*, Vol. XXXII, 23 August 1902, p. 255
[3] ibid.
[4] *BMJ*, 8 January 1881, p. 61
[5] ibid., 22 March 1879, p. 437
[6] ibid., 17 May 1879, p. 791

Meanwhile, one of the great hospitals of London, St Thomas', had decided to admit paying patients. It had been financially embarrassed as the result of what Burdett called 'the folly of overbuilding'.[1] The construction of the new buildings opposite the Houses of Parliament had proved to be very expensive. At one time only thirteen of the twenty-one wards were in use.

The initiative in proposing to use one of the empty blocks for paying patients came from the Home Hospital Association which communicated with the hospital in April 1878.[2] After examination of all the relevant figures, the Association decided that the project would be too costly. However, the Treasurer of the hospital, Alderman Stone, produced a plan of his own. He calculated that it was possible to earn £7,400 from an expenditure of £4,300 and thus increase the revenue of the hospital by about £3,000 a year. To have raised this sum, however, the pay beds would have needed to be fully occupied.[3] Moreover, it was assumed that the medical staff would provide free services to the paying patients.[4]

The plan was adopted by the governors in November 1878. The British Medical Association thought the matter sufficiently important to make an immediate comment:

> It does not appear that Mr Stone has yet consulted the medical staff; perhaps it would have been better if he had done so before committing the Governors to a definite resolution at a public meeting ... it will be interesting to see what allowance is made here for payment of medical services. It will, of course, not be expected that the medical staff attached to the charity shall earn £3,000 a year for the hospital by unpaid services.[5]

The question was pursued in a long letter in the *British Medical Journal*. The letter started by taking it for granted that the medical staff would be paid for their services. This would bring them into competition with general practitioners. At present hospital cases were selected so that they were 'of the same class as in the daily practice of the staff would be the subject of a consultation if the

---

[1] H. C. Burdett, *Hospitals and the State*, p. 11, London, 1881
[2] Burdett, *Pay Hospitals*, p. 133
[3] ibid., p. 134
[4] ibid., p. 136
[5] *BMJ*, 23 November 1878, pp. 774–5

patients were of a less indigent character'.[1] As anyone who could pay 6s a day could be admitted to the proposed pay wards,

> ... the attendants of these wards would be *pro tanto* reduced to the functions of general practitioners and come into competition with them ... under the conditions of artificial preference, furnished by the original outlay of charitable funds; for if 6s a day were to furnish board, lodging, nursing appliances, medicines, dressings and the medical attendance by hospital consultants of high reputation, it is obvious that such a competition would leave the general practitioner nowhere, and put the St Thomas' staff in a position of outbidding the world for cheap doctoring to well-to-do people.[2]

The reaction of the general practitioner might be to

> ... avoid all consultations with St Thomas' men if he bore in his mind the anticipation that the result of bringing the two into contact might end at some future time in the transfer of his patient to a ward where a few shillings a day would pay for keep, while the doctoring by the same consultant would be thrown in for nothing by the lay governors as an unconsidered trifle.[3]

It was argued, therefore, that the consequences might be 'of very seriously disagreeable character to the staff, and likely to compromise most seriously their popularity, repute, and even their position in the profession as consultants'.[4]

The same issue carried a vehement letter of protest from a Dr Farquharson:

> ... Forty beds constantly filled with wealthy patients naturally implies a large annual deficit in the returns of their usual medical attendants; and I for one most emphatically protest. ... Some scale of payment for the medical staff may be conceded, but this I venture to think involves a still more objectionable principle. It is not for one moment to be supposed that these fees ... will in any degree approach the usual tariff for consultations or operations outside. ... Allowing, as I gladly do, the eminence of St Thomas' Hospital staff, it seeems to me that they would occupy a most

[1] ibid., 30 November 1878, p. 807
[2] ibid.
[3] ibid.
[4] ibid.

invidious position were they to accept such inferior payment as might be given them, and thus practically under-sell their professional brethren elsewhere.

> ... Are we members of the general profession outside to certify their fitness (also gratuitously), or are we eventually to see an out-patient department for the well-to-do from which the selection is to be made? ... the system of gratuitous medical relief by medical men, already far over-strained, and only too disastrous to the social well-being of our profession, will thus receive a wide extension, if the staff be not paid; that the principle of 'taking silk' by our leaders, and charging increased fees for the privilege of a fashionable opinion, will be imperilled if the St Thomas' Hospital staff be insufficiently paid; that the practitioners of London will be defrauded if this large cottage hospital be made a closed borough, and they be not permitted to follow up and treat their own cases, that the principle of well-to-do hospitals in London will receive a fatal blow if this most effective reversal of all their well-considered economic laws be permitted quietly to become *un fait accompli*. ...[1]

The medical staff of the hospital had been warned: a week later they expressed their views in a long letter to the *British Medical Journal*. Dr Bristow, the chairman of the medical committee, started by complaining about the *fait accompli* arrived at 'without any previous conference with us. ... It would, on principle, be unreasonable to require the staff that was elected for quite other purposes to give their gratuitous services to me.'[2] If the proposed charge was intended to include remuneration for medical and surgical attendance, it was

> ... altogether inadequate. ... If we consented to receive a salary, or a payment at so much a head, or chose to ask a half-a-crown or 5*s* per visit to each patient, we should be first laying ourselves open to the charge of competing unfairly with the general practitioners; if we were allowed to claim consulting fees, I need scarcely say that it would appear, and with good reason, that the department was established for our especial benefit.[3]

The only possibilities were for the patient to pay his own medical attendant privately or for a salaried resident medical

[1] ibid., pp. 817–18
[2] ibid., 7 December 1878, pp. 853–4
[3] ibid.

officer to be employed, 'with no other source of professional income'.[1]

Dr Bristow went on to suggest that the governors' proposals would impose 'heavy, unscientific, doubtless unremunerative, extra labour'.[2] The patients would be 'probably particularly uninteresting' and 'unduly exacting of time and attention'.[3] If they were drawn 'from the lower middle class' and

> . . . admitted by Governors' letters, they will necessarily be un-selected, and in large proportion, unsuitable for hospital treatment. If they be received on the recommendation of private practitioners, they will certainly comprise an excessive number of old cases of dyspepsia, and other chronic and incurable cases; if the physicians and surgeons have much to do with their selection, there is some reason to fear that sooner or later the department will be worked more or less in connection with their private practice . . . they should not be treated by a staff who carry an exterior practice as well, and who are likely, therefore, to make these institutions subservient to their private practice.[4]

Paying patients, the medical staff thought, should be looked after in separate institutions, either by their own doctors or by a whole-time salaried medical officer, but as a temporary measure Dr Bristow said he would do all that he reasonably could to help the governors. If paying patients had to be in the hospital, then they should be under the sole charge of separate whole-time salaried medical staff.

In a leader in the issue in which this letter appeared, the *British Medical Journal* emphasized points it had already made but did not support the proposal for a full-time medical officer. Well-to-do patients had to choose their own medical attendants. Medical men were being called upon 'to annihilate the existing distinction between general and consulting practitioners'.[5] The governors of St Thomas' Hospital were seeking to obtain success 'by degrading their consultants and putting their hands into the pockets of general practitioners'.[6] In the same week the London

[1] ibid.
[2] ibid.
[3] ibid.
[4] ibid.
[5] ibid., p. 843
[6] ibid.

branch of the British Medical Association met and resolved 'that it would not become the staff of St Thomas' Hospital to hold any official relations to the patients admitted to that hospital by payment'.[1]

A meeting was held between representatives of the governors and the medical staff at which the views of the doctors were repeated. The governors asked whether 'there might be less objection to the admission under their care of a more necessitous class of patient, who might, however, still be able to afford to pay the hospital their cost of maintenance'.[2] 'The new proposition,' commented the *British Medical Journal*, 'has its own perils.'[3] It involved 'the probabilities of unlimited abuse, unless hedged round by safeguards of an expensive and rigidly organized character'.[4]

At this stage a new and clearer formulation for a proposal to admit well-to-do patients was considered by the governors of the Hospital. It was to admit patients for charges of a minimum of two guineas, allowing them to choose and pay privately their own doctor. No patient was, however, 'to be entitled to introduce into the ward any medical practitioner not on the staff of the hospital, except by the written order of the Treasurer and House Committee, or in cases of emergency of the Treasurer alone'.[5] In a memorandum dated 18 January 1879, the medical staff had told the governors that while the admission of outside doctors did not infringe their position, they 'could not be blind to the many dangers which might be incurred to the reputation of the Hospital'.[6] It appears to have been for this reason that this safeguard was introduced. It was not acceptable to the *British Medical Journal*. 'So serious an infringement of the independence of the relations of patient and practitioner would, under any circumstances, be open to much objection.'[7]

Ultimately, with the approval of the Charity Commissioners, the governors of the hospital introduced two schemes. Under the first, patients were admitted to a separate part of the hospital and paid the hospital above cost for the services it provided,

[1] ibid.
[2] ibid., 14 December 1878, p. 884
[3] ibid.
[4] ibid., 21 December 1878, p. 928
[5] ibid., 14 March 1879, p. 404
[6] St Thomas' Hospital Archives
[7] *BMJ*, 22 March 1879, p. 432

which included a salaried medical officer. Patients were allowed to bring into consultation *any medical man* they chose without any restrictions. The second scheme contemplated admission of patients to the ordinary wards at a guinea a week, calculated only to pay the cost of maintenance. This second scheme was introduced despite the firm opposition of the majority of the medical staff. On 7 July 1879, the Grand Committee of the hospital was told that 'the physicians and surgeons objected strongly to be called upon to treat poor paying patients admitted into the general wards'.[1] The *British Medical Journal* did not like the scheme either as it involved 'the attendance of the honorary members of the staff without remuneration for their services'.[2]

The governors were not unanimous in wanting even the first scheme introduced. There is a memorandum in the archives of the hospital signed by Mr (later Sir) John Simon on 11 June 1879, suggesting that the whole project was too risky. There might be found very few persons who were prepared to pay the sums involved. Nevertheless, on 1 March 1881, St Thomas' Home for Paying Patients opened its doors. There were two single rooms at 12*s* a day. The large wards were 'divided up into compartments by means of curtains made of thick striped linen. Each compartment is furnished as a bedroom and containing every needful requirement: each has a separate window.'[3] Accommodation in a cubicle cost 8*s* per day. 'It is at present doubtful,' wrote the *British Medical Journal*, 'if the curtained compartments of the large wards will ever be popular as it is evident that there can be little real privacy under such an arrangement.'[4]

The Home did, however, attract patients. In 1889, there were forty-two beds and each patient paid the hospital a minimum of three guineas. The total received in this year was £5,600 representing a net profit of £500 to £600.[5] The pay beds in the general wards were little used. In 1889, only £120 was received from this source.[6]

1 St Thomas' Hospital Archives
2 *BMJ*, 12 June 1880, p. 895
3 ibid., 5 March 1881, p. 348
4 ibid.
5 *Select Committee on Metropolitan Hospitals, 1890–3*, Third Report, p. cxv
6 ibid.

In 1884, Guy's Hospital followed St Thomas' lead and decided to take charges from ward patients who could pay. Its finances had been 'seriously crippled by the continued agricultural depression'.[1] Most of the paying patients were referred by local medical practitioners. 'Times have changed,' wrote the *British Medical Journal*. 'The lowest strata of society,' it continued with some exaggeration, 'have now their palatial workhouse infirmaries, and a Poor Law system of medical relief which was never so systematic is at their door, and there is no small ground for the contention that the hospital now administers for the wants, and legitimately so, of those not absolutely paupers.'[2] There were, however, 'great, and we believe valid, objections to any such plan as a home set apart from the rest of the hospital' for 'those not absolutely paupers'.[3] The governors of Guy's were well advised in not adopting this scheme. Admission to the general ward was far preferable 'but we have heard that it has already been tried at St Thomas' and not been found very successful'.[4] Eventually, Guy's decided to admit patients in the common wards at one guinea a week and patients in cubicles at three guineas per week.[5] If a patient in a three-guinea bed was too poor to pay a first-class surgeon, the operation was performed free by the senior surgeon of the week.[6]

The system of patients' payments for care in hospital spread to other hospitals during the 1880's. In 1878, while cottage hospitals received about 12 per cent of their income from paying patients, only one or two other hospitals raised as much as 1 per cent of their total income in this way. By 1890, patients' payments amounted to 5 per cent of the income of the London hospitals (including those run by the Metropolitan Asylums' Board). In the provinces, patients' payments raised 15 per cent of hospital income. Five out of eleven London teaching hospitals, twenty-nine out of fifty-two special hospitals and thirty-seven out of eighty general hospitals admitted paying patients.[7]

[1] *BMJ*, 26 January 1884, p. 184
[2] ibid., 9 February 1884, p. 276
[3] ibid.
[4] ibid.
[5] *Select Committee on Metropolitan Hospitals, 1890–3*, Second Report, para. 9929.
[6] ibid.
[7] The statistics were collected by Burdett. See *The Hospital*, Vol. XXVIII, 26 April 1890, p. 47.

Separate nursing homes and pay hospitals also developed rapidly in the 1880's. In 1880, a pay hospital was opened at Bolingbroke House, Wandsworth Common. There was a resident medical officer and payments ranged from 'IOs to £3 a week according to the social position of the applicant and the accommodation required'.[1] In 1881, the provident dispensary at Hampstead decided to open a general provident Home Hospital.[2] In 1887 a Miss Pollock, a sister from Guy's, opened a nursing home in Weymouth Street.[3]

A private nursing home was opened with 120 beds at Bourne-mouth called the 'Mont Tore Establishment'. The Mont Tore treatment was said to be efficacious for 'the rheumatic, gouty, scrofulous, tuberculous and many other states, asthma, con-sumption, bronchitis, emphasima etc.'[4] General practitioners started advertising in the *British Medical Journal* for institutions which would take 'a weak-minded epileptic child', 'a paralysed old lady', 'an inebriate', 'a hysterical lady whose friends will gladly pay for her maintenance'. By 1890 there were 'many houses where nursing is carried to great perfection and many in the neighbourhoods where the doctors most congregate, such as Harley Street, and officered by former sisters of hospitals and other ladies'.[5]

Thus in a decade a number of different hospital facilities had been developed for selected groups of middle-class patients. Home Hospitals took the place of general lodging-houses for patients without the means or the relatives to be properly looked after in their homes. The movement to find accommodation for paying patients had arisen largely out of the nursing reform movement: it became more advantageous to provide institu-tional care for those of modest income who could not be con-veniently nursed at home. This led to the creation of separate nursing homes and Home Hospitals. Some of the voluntary hospitals took the opportunity to try and ease their financial difficulties by opening separate wings for paying patients on a profit-making basis. Under pressure from general practitioners, whose views were forcefully expressed in the *British Medical*

[1] *BMJ*, 4 March 1882, p. 312
[2] ibid., 23 July 1881, p. 140
[3] ibid., 4 June 1887, p. 1253
[4] ibid., 7 November 1885, p. 885
[5] *Select Committee on Metropolitan Hospitals*, First Report, 1890–3, para. 3785

Journal, these wings were open to all doctors. Thus the voluntary hospitals found themselves running an 'open list' hospital for private patients within a 'closed list' hospital for charity patients.

In addition, some of the voluntary hospitals forced on their reluctant medical staff a system of part payment in the general wards. This was similar to the system operated by rural general practitioners in their own cottage hospitals. It was only introduced in urban areas in the teeth of opposition from practitioners who were not on the staff of the hospitals. To maintain the size of their practices and the level of their fees, urban general practitioners wanted hospital patients to be rigidly divided into those who paid the full cost of their treatment and those who were treated free. Such a system was to be formally introduced for the whole population some sixty years later.

CHAPTER 10

The Demand for Hospital Planning
in London

BETWEEN 1861 and 1891 there was a rapid expansion in
hospital facilities. The number of both hospitals and beds
provided by charitable foundations more than doubled during
this period and the accommodation for the sick provided by
public authorities increased by over 50 per cent. The population
was also increasing rapidly but accommodation in hospitals
more than kept pace with the growth in the population.[1] It was
in London that provision was most generous and it was here that
the need for hospital planning was first recognized.

More hospital accommodation was needed because improvements in both medicine and nursing were making it more
advantageous for the sick to be admitted. Anaesthetics had been
introduced from the late 1840's, thus extending the type of
surgery which could be attempted. The development of antiseptic and aseptic techniques in the seventies and eighties had
begun to increase the safety of surgery.[2] The trained nurses who
were now to be found in virtually all hospitals did much to
increase the quality of bedside care and the comfort of patients.
Hospitals were still regarded with dread by the vast majority
of the population but many more poor persons were prepared to
accept admission.

The increased use of hospitals was also encouraged by the
campaign against outdoor relief. By 1890 there were only about
100,000 cases of outdoor medical relief each year in the whole of

[1] The number of beds per thousand of the population increased from 3·2
in 1861 to 3.9 in 1891. See Vol. 2 of this study.
[2] A surgeon at University College Hospital wrote a review of the success
of surgery in 1874. He pointed out that mortality from all forms of amputation
was between 35 % and 50 % and following certain forms as high as 90 %.
See McKeown and Brown, p. 120.

London. Many skilled workers were by this time protecting themselves against medical indigency by joining a friendly society or provident club. In addition, there were about 125,000 consultations in provident dispensaries in London though these tended to be on the outskirts of the city.[1] But the unskilled worker and his family, and perhaps also the families of skilled workers who were not covered by any provident system, looked increasingly towards charitable bodies to provide them with general practitioner services. In London, in the late 1880's, there were over 150,000 consultations at free charitable dispensaries and about 100,000 consultations in part-pay dispensaries.[2] But the largest system of free care was that provided by the hospitals, which in 1887 counted more than a million-and-a-half outpatient attendances.[3] In this last year the population of London was just over four million.

While patients could receive free medical advice if they were prepared to wait long enough at one of the voluntary hospitals, only in exceptional circumstances could they gain the means to support themselves and their families while they were too ill to work. Admission to a hospital did at least mean that they (but not their families) were fed and cared for. Thus the campaign against outdoor relief increased the demand for inpatient care. Moreover, the concentration of patients at the outpatients' departments gave the doctors a wide choice of cases from which they could choose those whom they regarded as of value for teaching and research – even though some of them could have been looked after at home if all the necessary services had been available.

A further reason for the growth of hospital facilities was the desire to isolate cases of infectious disease for the protection of the public at large. While there were virtually no public hospitals for infectious diseases in 1861, by 1891 there were over 350.[4] They varied from the large hospitals run by the Metropolitan Asylums' Board to the large number of small institutions operated by the sanitary authorities outside London.

In the voluntary sector, the largest increase had been in general hospitals. There were 130 in 1861, and 385 in 1891. Only

[1] *Hansard* (H of L), Vol. CCCXXXVIII, 29 July 1889, cols. 1553–5
[2] ibid.
[3] ibid.
[4] See Vol. 2 of this study.

one new teaching hospital was started during this period: the
Royal Free. After the registration of doctors in 1858, there was
hardly any increase in the number of hospitals which offered
medical training. Parallel to the development of voluntary
general hospitals was that of workhouse infirmaries. By 1891
there were eighteen infirmaries with nursing schools.[1]

While before 1861 there had been a great variety of different
architectural designs, in the seventies and eighties the vast
majority of new hospitals and rebuilt hospitals conformed to
one basic plan – a series of separate pavilions placed parallel
to one another. This uniformity was due to the general acceptance of the miasmic theory of disease and the logical application
of it to the problem of hospital construction. This was yet another
field in which Miss Nightingale had a decisive influence. The
pavilion plan for hospitals had been worked out by an expert
committee set up in France in 1787 to consider the advisability
of rebuilding the Hôtel-Dieu after it had been partly destroyed
in the great Paris fire of 1772. Not until 1854 was a hospital built
according to the committee's recommendations – the Lari-
boisière. This was the model to which Miss Nightingale constantly referred in her Notes on Hospitals, published in 1859.[2]
She argued that the essentials for the 'health of hospitals' were
fresh air, light, ample space and subdivision into separate
buildings.[3] The latter was needed to stop dirty air from going
from one ward to another. Lavatories should be placed at the
end of the ward so that they would be ventilated from three sides.
The most desirable air was that which was 'vitalized by sun-
shine': night air was not highly recommended. Patients had
to be kept in large open wards for better ventilation and so that
the head nurse could overlook the whole ward.[4]

These new spacious hospitals[5] were expensive to build and
expensive to run. They were administered in much the same
way as the hospitals of fifty years earlier, except that matrons
had risen in status and become solely responsible to the governors
for their departments. At the three endowed hospitals (St

[1] See Vol. 2 of this study.
[2] Nightingale, Notes on Hospitals, p. 100
[3] ibid., p. 12
[4] ibid., p. 17
[5] Miss Nightingale recommended 1,500 cubic feet per patient and 100
square feet per bed.

Bartholomew's, Guy's and St Thomas') the position of 'Treasurer' was still one of great authority. Elsewhere extensive powers were exercised by sub-committees of the governors. There were two main sub-committees – a committee or group of lay governors which met weekly or monthly, called the House Committee, and a committee of the medical staff. The medical staff were seldom directly represented on the Board.[1] In the special hospitals, on the other hand, the medical staff played a very active part on the governing body. Usually the House Committee at a general hospital reported to the full body of governors every quarter. At the London Hospital where the subscription system had been developed very fully there were four thousand governors entitled to attend.[2]

The chief executive officers of the general hospitals were laymen, except at Guy's where the position was occupied by a doctor. They controlled the lay staff in most hospitals but exercised no power over nursing staff. Even in hospitals where they had the power to do so it was 'a well understood arrangement' that they never interfered in that department.[3] 'It seems everywhere to be fully admitted that practically the matron is supreme in her own department, subject only to her responsibility to the managing body. . . .'[4] Each of the leading London hospitals had a chaplain. He often performed 'services lying outside his strict duty by interesting himself in the circumstances of patients, communicating with their friends, and particularly in recommending grants out of the Samaritan Fund'.[5] Chaplains were paid between £100 and £300 a year and given a residence.

The system of admission by governor's letter was much less rigid than it had been thirty years earlier.

The usual practice at the general hospitals appears to be to give very slight preference to applicants bringing letters over those (and they are the vast majority) who come without them. An outpatient letter will sometimes open the way direct to the outpatient department when a person not so provided must first pass through the

[2] St Mary's and the Great Northern did, however, have doctors on their Boards. *Select Committee on Metropolitan Hospitals 1890–3*, First Report, Qs. 2138–9

[1] ibid., Third Report, para. 49
[2] ibid., para. 462
[3] ibid.
[4] ibid., para. 297

casualty room and take his chance of being passed on or treated summarily there. But any person whose illness is sufficiently serious appears to be considered equally in either case a proper subject for treatment. So, in regard to admission to the wards, the only privilege attaching to a letter seems to be that, where two cases are of equal gravity, the preference will be given to the recommended case; but disease, it is said, and not the recommendation of a subscriber, is the real passport of admission; and the selection of the applicants to be taken in rests practically with the officer whose duty it is to admit to the hospital (usually the house physician or surgeon).[1]

The hospitals did not admit hopeless cases (unless the symptoms were very urgent) nor any chronic cases.[2] Some hospitals had a book in which the names of patients who had been in the hospital for over two months were recorded. Infectious cases were excluded but cases of measles, typhoid, and in some hospitals cases of diphtheria, were admitted. With regard to lock cases, though the practice varied, there was 'a prevalent tendency at the general hospitals'[3] to reject them. The main provision for lock cases was at the Lock Hospital which accommodated over a hundred cases but was often very short of funds. Patients were 'in the habit of quitting the hospital in a diseased state on such occasions as the Derby week fairs, etc., for the purpose of pursuing their avocation'.[4]

The general hospitals were being even more selective about the cases they would admit than thirty years earlier. There was greater emphasis on acute sickness. Medical needs as understood by the medical staff had in practice triumphed over the recommendations of lay governors. Owing to the pressure on the hospitals and the grave shortage of convalescent homes, patients were discharged even though not thoroughly cured. Some of these patients found their way to the Poor Law infirmaries.[5]

While the major growth in the thirty years up to 1891 had been in general hospitals, there was also an increase in the number of special hospitals. In this period the number of such hospitals in England and Wales increased by about 70 to make a

[1] ibid., First Report, para. 9709
[2] ibid., Third Report, p. xcix
[3] ibid., para. 188
[4] ibid., pp. ci–cii
[5] ibid., p. xcix

total of 160 in 1891.[1] In London the rate of growth of special hospitals was slowing down. Compared to the sixties, when sixteen new special hospitals were established, seven new ones were started in the seventies and only six more in the eighties.[2] Some of the special hospitals which had been founded earlier had become accepted by leading members of the medical profession. Thus, Mr Jonathan Hutchinson, FRCS, stated in 1881 that, while he had been opposed to the foundation of a hospital for the treatment of stones and diseases of the bladder some twenty-five years earlier, he no longer held this view.[3]

In 1889, the *British Medical Journal*, which had tended to be critical of all special hospitals, stated in a leader the reason why many of them had been set up:

> ... How many men are there waiting outside the hospitals, doing dreary drudgery at the dispensaries; or, who, having at length been received within the coveted circle, are exhausting their best efforts in the outpatients' department, waiting anxiously for promotion and relief from the thraldom of seniors! What these men, and many more who are not aspirants to the general hospitals, want is opportunity for independent work. And they want it while they are young, with energies unimpaired, still burning with the fresh spirit of original research.
>
> Those who by good fortune or merit – the two qualifications are not always united – have achieved hospital rank are apt to lament the multiplication of special hospitals. To some extent they themselves are responsible for this evil – if evil it be. Enjoying what approaches to a monopoly they should not be surprised if young men seek independent outlay.[4]

Some of the special hospitals had been founded owing to lack of prospects for younger men in general hospitals and because of the unwillingness of the general hospitals to make room for the development of new specialities. Some arose out of quarrels between doctors. In some cases new special hospitals were founded by doctors from existing ones. Two such hospitals were founded in 1887. A former member of the staff of St John's Hospital, Leicester Square, founded the British Hospital for Diseases of the Skin. The other new special hospital was founded

---

[1] See Vol. 2 of this study.
[2] *Select Committee on Metropolitan Hospitals 1890–3*, Third Report, p. lv
[3] *BMJ*, 13 August 1881, p. 309
[4] ibid., 22 June 1889, pp. 141–2

by doctors who had left the Throat Hospital in Golden Square.[1]

This last hospital had been very much in the public eye ten years earlier. Dr Morell Mackenzie combined the roles of founder, principal physician and medical superintendent, and was described by the *British Medical Journal* as 'a semi-autocrat in all medical and lay management'.[2] An inquiry into the management of the hospital conducted by the Duke of Grafton led HRH The Prince of Wales to withdraw his patronage. The dispute concerned the role played by Dr Mackenzie's clinical assistant, Mr Prosser James, who wrote an arrogant and un-repentant letter defending himself to the *British Medical Journal* from his address in Park Lane. 'If laymen presume to pronounce it [his clinic] faulty I can afford to smile at their opinion, which is about as valuable as that of the noblemen and gentlemen who, from their innate knowledge of therapeutics, are able to testify to the wondrous virtues of quack medicines.'[3]

The Throat Hospital was particularly unpopular with general practitioners because it had instituted an extensive system of part payment. There was a graduated system according to the occupation of the patient: 'a man who is a bricklayer, perhaps, would be charged 6*d* a week, and a stonemason would be charged 1*s* or 1*s* 6*d* a week, according to the earnings of the trade.'[4] Three-quarters of the patients made some payment and they were of a higher class than the patients of the general hospitals.[5] Inpatients paid a minimum of 7*s* per week.[6]

General practitioners had their own reasons for attacking special hospitals – in particular those which took payments from patients. The hospitals under attack were those which competed most obviously with the work of general physicians, surgeons and practitioners. 'It is, we believe,' wrote the *British Medical Journal* in 1888, 'the general opinion of the profession that, if half the throat, skin, ear and rectum hospitals and dispensaries in the kingdom were to be closed tomorrow, the public would not be the losers.'[7]

[1] ibid., 12 March 1887, p. 580
[2] ibid., 27 October 1877, pp. 596–7
[3] ibid., p. 686
[4] *Select Committee on Metropolitan Hospitals 1890–3*, First Report, para. 2124
[5] ibid., para. 2118
[6] ibid., para. 2340
[7] *BMJ*, 3 November 1888, p. 1001

Specialization was growing within the medical profession and many general hospitals had opened special departments which performed similar functions to the special hospitals. For example, Guy's Hospital had developed a full department (with both inpatient and outpatient facilities) for ophthalmology by 1831, and for obstetrics and gynaecology by 1842. A clinic for skin diseases was started in 1851, and for aural diseases in 1862.[1] St Bartholomew's Hospital had a full department for ophthalmology by 1869 and by 1880 had special clinics for diseases of the throat and skin, and for orthopaedics, obstetrics and gynaecology.[2] At St Thomas' the ophthalmic ward was opened in 1851,[3] and at the London Hospital departments were opened for obstetrics in 1853, for ear, nose and throat in 1866, and for orthopaedic cases in 1875.[4]

Physicians and surgeons were more cautious about what they had to say about special hospitals by the end of the 1880's. In 1889 only 31 out of the estimated 195 medical staff in London general hospitals did not hold some office in a special hospital as well. 'With scarce an exception every special hospital in London has attached a Fellow of the College of Physicians or a Fellow of the College of Surgeons who holds office in a general hospital.'[5] A number of them did not mention in the *Medical Directory* their connection with a special hospital.[6]

This did not mean that all special hospitals were reputable establishments. There undoubtedly were some special hospitals which were founded by doctors solely as a means of promoting their own practices. And there were doctors who made use of their hospital connections to promote their private practice. In 1892, the husband of a prospective patient received the following letter written on the writing paper of a special hospital in Sheffield from a Dr Hardwicke who claimed to cure cancer:

I have just received your letter and hasten to reply at once from here in order to save a post. I do think cancer curable, having proved it so. I shall be glad to see your wife next Sunday morning,

[1] Cameron, *Mr Guy's Hospital*, p. 357
[2] Sir D'Arcy Power & H. J. Waring, *A Short History of St Bartholomew's Hospital 1123–1923*, pp. 99–113, London, 1923
[3] Parsons, Vol. III, p. 124
[4] *Hospital Gazette*, Vol. 10, p. 208
[5] ibid., 14 September 1889, p. 620
[6] *Select Committee on Metropolitan Hospitals 1890–3*, First Report, para. 3804

or the Sunday morning following if convenient to you. The fee will be 20 guineas (twenty-one pounds) and will include the supply of remedies for one month, after which all the necessary remedies will be supplied at the rate of one guinea per month. I presume you desire me to see the case alone, and undertake the treatment, which in a case like your wife's, can be easily carried out by post, provided that I see and carefully examine the case once to start with. I enclose some printed slips done by our committee for the use of patients afflicted with cancer, etc.[1]

A hospital appointment undoubtedly promoted the private practice of the doctor concerned. The reasons for taking such an appointment were, however, inevitably mixed – a desire to help the poor, a desire for opportunities to gain experience and experiment with varied treatments, quite apart from a desire for self-advertisement. It could, however, be argued that an appointment at a special hospital provided peculiar opportunities for the acquisition of skill and it was this skill which led to the popularity of the doctor rather than the fact that he held a hospital appointment. Nevertheless, as *The Hospital* remarked in 1890, the law did allow 'the unrestrained licence which permits any adventurer, who is so minded, to start a hospital for his own whim or profit'.[2]

There was, moreover, no control over the use which was made of money contributed by the public. It was suggested that in the case of a hospital for skin diseases, the secretary had worked the system for his own benefit. He got 15 per cent of all receipts. Within a few years he was receiving £450 a year as his share of patients' payments and contributions of the charitable, to whom it was represented that 'the hospital was doing a most important work, and had to be supported'.[3]

Although there were some special hospitals whose administration could be justly criticized and a number of doctors working in them whose behaviour was less than ethical, other special hospitals had established for themselves a reputation which could not be seriously questioned. The major problem which they did present was one of unplanned and haphazard growth. Nor was this confined to special hospitals alone. The whole

[1] *BMJ*, 9 April 1892, p. 795
[2] *Hospital*, Vol. VII, 8 March 1890, p. 366
[3] *Select Committee on Metropolitan Hospitals 1890–3*, First Report, para. 1094 (evidence of Mr A. N. Hardy)

development of hospitals had been unco-ordinated and the over-all development did not follow the medical needs of the population. This problem became manifest first in London as it had attracted the largest number of beds. While the built-up area had expanded rapidly in every direction, nearly all the hospitals remained 'within an area of about two square miles'.[1] On the south side of the river, St Thomas' and Guy's were the only general hospitals. There was a great shortage of accommodation to the east of London Hospital in Whitechapel Road. 'A very large district in north-west London [was] served practically by a single hospital, St Mary's.'[2] An accident case might at the maximum need to be taken six miles to reach a hospital.[3]

It was hard to see how this problem could be solved. A hospital in an outlying district would have found it difficult to get 'the amount of attendance from distinguished doctors which the chief London hospitals now enjoy'.[4] It would also have found it difficult to obtain a good committee of management as many of the most useful members of such committees had businesses of their own and 'could not conveniently attend at a great distance'.[5] Nor would it have been found easy to obtain public contributions for a remote hospital.

A voluntary hospital, it was thought, had to be within easy coaching distance from the centres of private consulting practice. Thus, where there were fewest poor was the greatest provision for them. Within a radius of a mile from the Middlesex Hospital there were eight general and twenty-six special hospitals.

The siting of new voluntary hospitals was not only completely unplanned: it was also unco-ordinated with the development of the Poor Law infirmaries. While the construction of infirmaries depended on the availability of cheap sites and on the policy, wealth and energy of the thirty Boards of Guardians, the construction of voluntary hospitals was at the mercy of factors even less relevant to the needs of each area.

Demands for an inquiry into the problems of hospital development came from a number of different quarters. In 1882, the Metropolitan Counties branch of the British Medical Association

[1] ibid., Third Report, p. xlv
[2] ibid.
[3] ibid.
[4] ibid., p. xlvi
[5] ibid.

had resolved to ask the Home Secretary to appoint a Royal Commission to inquire into the working of hospitals. The demand followed from resolutions passed earlier in the year 'that the medical staff should be adequately represented on the governing body of the hospital; and that the necessary arrangements regarding treatment should be under the control of the medical staff'.[1] No action followed. At the annual general meeting of the British Medical Association in 1888, a paper on 'The Breakdown of the Hospital System' was read by a Dr J. Francis Sutherland. He advocated parliamentary grants to the voluntary hospitals and the abolition of subscribers' letters: disease should be 'the sole passport for admission'.[2] A committee should be set up in each town to limit the growth of small hospitals and determine the number of beds needed. People with grave diseases should not have to become paupers to enter a hospital. He called for a Royal Commission.[3]

A year later the British Medical Journal received a letter from the militant Dr Rentoul saying that 110 doctors had signed resolutions condemning the abuse of outpatient departments, deploring the fact that local practitioners were kept off the staff of their local hospitals and maintaining that pay beds and pay hospitals had taken patients 'out of our hands without any necessity'. If a Commission were appointed general practitioners should be represented on it by general practitioners.[4] The latter were particularly concerned about hospital developments in London because the provision both of inpatient and outpatient facilities was more generous in the Metropolis and because the hospitals were almost wholly staffed by doctors of a higher 'order' than themselves. While under the Poor Law the district medical officer wanted the right to provide free medical care to the indigent without interference from the lay relieving officer, many of the London general practitioners wanted a lay officer to be introduced into the voluntary hospitals to prevent physicians and surgeons from dispensing free medicine to anyone who could afford to pay. The attacks on the voluntary hospitals by the rising numbers of general practitioners were in reality all part of the major war being waged against their senior colleagues.

[1] *BMJ*, 8 July 1882, p. 48
[2] ibid., 25 August 1888, p. 416
[3] ibid.
[4] ibid., 10 August 1889, p. 342

Meanwhile, some members of the Royal Colleges and some governors of old-established hospitals, prodded to action by the Charity Organization Society, had also asked for an inquiry. On 29 July 1889, a petition was presented to the House of Lords 'signed by various members of the medical profession and by others also on behalf of various medical charitable institutions, in regard to the financial and general management and the common organization of medical institutions, endowed and voluntary, and in regard to the administration of Poor Law institutions for the aid of the sick in the Metropolis'.[1]

The case for an inquiry was presented by Lord Sandhurst. He started his speech by maintaining that 2,000 beds in London were closed through lack of funds. In 1887 the total deficit of the teaching hospitals had exceeded £32,000: it was now about £100,000. The special hospitals on the other hand had a surplus of £90,000. Sir Andrew Clark, President of the Royal College of Physicians, had condemned those 'improper hospitals, which divert funds in a direction in which they ought not to be employed, and rob the great hospitals of the support which they ought to receive'.[2]

He went on to quote a recent address given by Michelli who had referred to 'the excessive costs of special hospitals. . . . The maintenance of a bed in the small hospital is often 50 to 75 per cent greater than in a large one.'[3] He also condemned 'the excessive amount spent by hospitals in advertising and collecting, printing stationery and postage, and the small net percentage of profit that goes to hospitals out of the receipts from bazaars, fancy fairs'.[4]

Lord Sandhurst also attacked the 'improper hospitals' on more general grounds:

> The origin and management of some of the special hospitals have been such as to cause suspicion, where suspicion exists, as to the conduct of hospitals as a whole. They are not unfrequently started for private advantage by those who wish to make themselves consulting physicians or surgeons to them, some are started for speculative purposes and in neither case is the public welfare or the advantages of science considered. . . . There are no schools; there is

[1] *Hansard* (H of L), Vol. CCCXXXVIII, 29 July 1889, col. 1548
[2] ibid., col. 1551
[3] ibid., col. 1552
[4] ibid.

M

no advance of science, and the management leaves much to be
desired. . . . They are sometimes found in insanitary premises, and
are built without regard to existing local needs or perhaps in
proximity to hospitals; the advice is not of first-rate description,
and it is not infrequently the case that there are more beds provided
in the general hospital hard by for the treatment of such special
cases than in the special hospital itself. By the names they assume
they deprive the larger hospitals of cases which in the latter would
be better attended and from which instruction would be gained.[1]

As a result of the sporadic growth of special hospitals and the
unco-ordinated development of the Poor Law, medical facilities
were very badly distributed.

I will just take a case which shows the system. In Marylebone alone,
with a population of 155,000, there were in 1885 – one Poor Law
Infirmary with 700 beds, one general hospital, ten special hospitals,
four free dispensaries, one provident dispensary, two Poor Law
dispensaries, and one or two charities for gentlewomen. I should
think it very likely that a great number of patients came from
adjoining parishes, while the people in Marylebone went to St
George's and other adjoining parishes. There is no system at present
by which we can deal with that. Then again, take Fulham, which is
a long way from the centre of the Metropolis. With a population in
1885 of 152,600 there were one general hospital, two sick clubs,
one Poor Law infirmary, and one Poor Law dispensary.[2]

Lord Sandhurst also referred briefly to the abuse of outpatient
facilities:

Now my Lords, I come to another subject on which there is considerable diversity of opinion among those best qualified to judge,
and that is the outdoor departments of the hospitals of which the
dispensaries are really an extension and development. In 1887, the
outdoor patients were more than one million and a half, and the
number keeps on increasing. These patients often have an almost
interminable time to wait, and I have no doubt that many of them
are able to pay for attendance and medicine. This is very hard on
the small local practitioners who work hard for small fees, and it
tends, I fear, to the pauperization of a very large number of the
community. Therefore, my Lords, I should like to put it to the
House whether there is not here a legitimate cause for inquiry, and

[1] ibid., col. 1550
[2] ibid., cols. 1554-5

whether something might not be done to check this pauperizing system of outdoor relief, so that those in absolute want would be left to the resources of the larger institutions.[1]

He concluded his speech with the following words:

> I have no wish to bring forward any Motion which would have the ultimate result of placing these hospitals on the rates, though I have no doubt I shall be told that is the tendency of my Motion by those who do not take the trouble to read my remarks.
> I have framed this Motion with reference only to the hospitals of the Metropolis, although in Provincial towns there is a very general opinion in favour of a similar inquiry with respect to their hospitals. I may also say that we have with us nearly the whole of the rising medical profession.[2]

In his reply on behalf of the Government, Viscount Cranbrook was cautious and evasive. He feared

> . . . lest, if we were to impose an inquiry, the flow of means to the institutions might not be in some cases checked. Hospitals generally possess a fixed income from endowments, and there are a great number of them, I have no doubt, offer a proper subject of inquiry, but it is a very different thing when we come to deal with charities which are receiving aid by subscriptions from day to day. There has been, no doubt, an unnecessary multiplication of special hospitals. But they have been set up and are conducted by those who are breaking no law and infringing no rule of society, and who themselves find the means by which they are carried on. That seems to me to be the great difficulty in interfering with them. With regard to the Motion, I can say, on the part of the Cabinet, that the case for the inquiry will be considered.[3]

Nine months later when Lord Sandhurst raised the subject again, Viscount Cranbrook said that the proposal to set up a Committee would have the hearty support of the Government.[4]

Soon after it had been announced that a committee was to be appointed, a new association of general practitioners was formed to give evidence to it – the General Practitioners' Union. The

[1] ibid., cols. 1553–4
[2] ibid., cols. 1555–6
[3] ibid., cols. 1556–7
[4] ibid., Vol. CCCXLII, 20 March 1890, col. 1235

chairman was a general practitioner called George Brown who had been appointed to a Committee set up by the British Medical Association to consider the question of hospital abuse which, however, had never met. He claimed that 'the Association has met with a very great deal of support from the profession, especially in London'.[1] The proposals of the Association were drastic. The hospitals were to be put under a central board with statutory powers.[2] No case was to go to an outpatient department without a certificate from a medical man outside or a clergyman or some organization such as the Charity Organization Society.[3] If a patient who could pay got into a hospital despite this protective network, the central board should be empowered to recover the expenses and fees as if the patient had been treated privately.[4] The Union objected to the paying system in outpatient departments *in toto*: 'we think that it is subversive of all medical charity, and that it is demoralizing.'[5]

The establishment of the committee was welcomed in an outspoken leader in *The Hospital*:

> The whole country is a rickyard of hospitals; and incendiaries in the shape of dissatisfied general practitioners are carrying blazing torches in all directions . . . [the] weak place is the outpatients' department . . . The number of cases that a 'physician' – save the mark! – will see, examine and treat in an hour is incredible, and absolutely destructive of professional honesty. The plain truth is that some outpatient physicians do not care one straw for their outpatient work except in so far as it is a stepping stone to a permanent hospital appointment.[6]

Its welcome was not, however, unqualified: '. . . nothing will so infallibly ensure its [the committee's] failure as its appearance on the public stage in the capacity of a performing bear led by so sinister a master as the Charity Organization Society.'[7]

The Lords Committee accumulated two large volumes of evidence in 1890 and 1891 and finally produced a report in

---

[1] *Select Committee on Metropolitan Hospitals 1890-3*, Second Report, para. 25517

[2] ibid., para. 25615

[3] ibid., para. 25529

[4] ibid., para. 25589

[5] ibid., para. 25590

[6] *Hospital*, Vol. XXVIII, 26 April 1890, p. 43

[7] ibid., p. 44

1892. A petition from a group of doctors to get the terms of reference widened to include provincial hospitals met with no success.[1] Thus the report was confined to London.

Much of the evidence presented to the committee came from general practitioners. They complained about the 'abuse' of outpatient departments, the system of pay beds and the 'monopoly' of hospital appointments held by the Royal Colleges. On the first question they gave many isolated examples of the type of patients whom they had heard had gone to outpatient departments: a man who had paid £1,600 for his house,[2] a man with a pony carriage,[3] a footman who had the gout,[4] a gentleman with an MA.[5] The result was that 'in the area bounded by Oxford Circus to Holborn to Cheapside to the Thames to Whitehall and back to Oxford Street, there were only about forty to forty-five general practitioners' when the area should 'be able to keep two hundred medical men hard at work'.[6] Within the previous twenty years seventeen general practitioners had been starved out within ten minutes' walk of the London Hospital.[7] A general practitioner with a middle-class practice in St John's Wood alleged that the growth of free relief had lowered medical fees over the previous ten or fifteen years.[8]

In answer to these criticisms the hospitals with medical schools said that the outpatient departments were of the utmost importance for the sake of the training afforded to students. It was suggested that the experience gained in the outpatient department was the most valuable part of a student's training.[9] The medical staffs did not want to receive only cases which were referred to them as they found that 'the cases which would be the most useful for teaching purposes would not reach them, or would reach them in insufficient number'.[10]

Charles Loch of the Charity Organization Society said that every hospital ought to limit the number of outpatients it would

[1] *BMJ*, 3 May 1890, p. 1035
[2] *Select Committee on Metropolitan Hospitals 1890–3*, First Report, para. 4475
[3] ibid.
[4] ibid., Second Report, para. 25635
[5] ibid., Second Report, para. 16642
[6] ibid., para. 25579
[7] ibid., First Report, para. 4478
[8] ibid., para. 3609
[9] ibid., Third Report, p. xl
[10] ibid.

take and each case ought to be investigated 'by an almoner who should be an officer of experience in charitable work'.[1] He was prepared to allow the 'abuse' of the charity where it was necessary for medical education but the almoner system would make it possible to refer to the Poor Law cases requiring food. 'The almoner, being a trained man (or woman), would ask a few questions to the point and then possibly it might be a case for immediate reference to the relieving officer.'[2] This was social work.

The Committee came down in favour of keeping the out-patient departments much as they were. It decided that 'the charities were not abused to any serious or appreciable extent',[3] nor was it 'proved that patients were carelessly treated'.[4] There were many patients who could not afford a doctor and medical treatment. Each hospital should, however, limit the number of its outpatients and 'wherever experienced officials think there is a cause for suspicion',[5] inquiries should be made. The Committee did 'not attach too much importance to the statements as to the reduction of fees of practitioners among the poor by the free work of the hospitals' though it was 'obvious that the existence of the charities must tend to reduce them'.[6]

On the second main issue which was worrying general practitioners – the question of pay beds – the Lords Committee took evidence but made no pronouncement. Some witnesses argued that any system of part payment was wrong in principle. It was a 'malversation of funds' left 'for purely charitable purposes' to enable people 'for half or a quarter of the necessary payment outside to be attended by equal skill and equal nursing'.[7] It was said that even patients who paid the full cost were taking up 'the room that ought to be given to the poor'.[8] 'If it became a habit for a rich man to go to the hospitals they would oust the poor from them, just as the boys at Eton, Harrow and Winchester have ousted the poor for whom these schools were intended.'[9]

[1] ibid., p. xliii
[2] ibid., Second Report, Q. 26119
[3] ibid., Third Report, p. c.
[4] ibid.
[5] ibid.
[6] ibid.
[7] ibid., First Report, para. 4261
[8] ibid., para. 3739
[9] ibid., para. 4576

The general practitioners objected to part-pay beds because it led to patients going into hospital who could stay at home and pay their doctor. 'Many patients have been taken out of our hands without any necessity, and without any corresponding advantage accruing to the patients themselves.'[1] Provident hospitals in particular were 'spoken of very bitterly by practitioners in the neighbourhood'.[2] It was alleged that even pay wards which were in principle open to any doctor in the neighbourhood had brought 'a monopoly of practice to the doctors connected with the hospitals'.[3] 'It would be exceedingly difficult for a surgeon to get the same access to, and the same treatment of, a patient in the paying part of St Thomas' if he was not connected with the non-paying part of the building.'[4]

General practitioners wanted not only the right to admit their patients to pay beds in voluntary hospitals: they also wanted the chance to join the medical staff. They objected to the 'monopolies' of the Royal Colleges and particularly criticized the way by which the Royal College of Physicians selected its fellows. The defence of the system given by its president (Sir Andrew Clark) was that the physician had first and foremost to be a teacher.

> We hold that there are not only intellectual qualifications necessary but we hold that there are practical qualifications necessary and moral qualifications necessary: and so we give them an examination of a different kind, and we submit them to the ordeal of a double ballot before they are admitted. . . . Were it not so, my experience in London would lead me to believe that the last cancer-curer from America would be made physician to a London hospital.[5]

Despite Sir Andrew's valiant defence of the system of 'examination' employed by the Royal College of Physicians, the Committee were not convinced.

> The Committee suggest that the fact of not holding the diplomas of the Royal College of Physicians and Royal College of Surgeons

[1] ibid., para. 1680. See also para. 4561
[2] ibid., para. 1554
[3] ibid., para. 3787
[4] ibid., para. 3784
[5] ibid., para. 9709

of London should not exclude practitioners who have graduated elsewhere from becoming members of the staffs of the general hospitals in London.[1]

On the question of special hospitals, the Committee found a wide divergence of view among the medical staffs of general hospitals about the role which they should play. It was agreed that there needed to be special hospitals for lying-in cases and cases of venereal or infectious diseases. Beyond this there were some who held in principle that the separate development of specialities was undesirable. The words of Professor Virchow were quoted:

> ... no speciality can flourish which separates itself entirely from the common source of science; that no speciality can develop fruitfully and beneficially if it does ... not take the other specialities into account, and if all the specialities do not mutually assist one another.[2]

This led to the view that the task of the special hospitals should be undertaken by special departments of the general hospitals. 'The progress of discovery might be retarded, but it would not be less sure; and, at all events, its results, when gathered, would be fully utilized.'[3]

On the other hand, it was argued that the governing body of general hospitals did not take the same interest in special departments and were not so liberal in adopting improvements. It was this that created the special hospitals. It was only after a special hospital had been set up and had advanced the practical treatment of disease that the general hospitals started special departments. Moreover, the existing general hospitals had not the space to accommodate all the necessary specialities.

Their lordships did not pronounce on this question but contented themselves by lashing out at the less reputable establishments 'instituted by medical men for the purposes of their own advancement'.[4]

> Such a course of action leads to the establishment of hospitals where they are not wanted, to waste of money incident to the

[1] ibid., Third Report, p. xcix
[2] ibid., p. lvii
[3] ibid., p. lviii
[4] ibid., p. cii

creation of badly managed and small institutions, and to the deception of the public by inducing them to subscribe to undertakings alleged to be of public benefit, but which are in reality mere schemes for private emolument, and also are useless for teaching purposes.[1]

There were small hospitals which were not 'of any real benefit either to the sick or to science'.[2]

The existence of this undesirable fringe of special hospitals led a number of witnesses to advocate a central board, either to license or register hospitals or to express dissent about the establishment of undesirable new ones. The Charity Organization Society, in particular, suggested that a supervising body should be set up to report publicly upon every new proposal for a hospital. If that were not effective, there ought to be a system of licensing. The wider need for co-ordination and planned development was mentioned by several witnesses who supported some sort of central board, quite apart from the obvious requirement of the introduction of a standard system of hospital accounts. It was also suggested that some sort of bed bureau might be started.

The Committee recommended that a central board should be set up. Such a board should, however, have no connection with Government. And 'as there is no government grant, the interference of a government officer for inspection would be unwise. . . . Such interference would tend to check the flow of voluntary contributions, and to some extent interfere with the responsibilities of the unpaid Boards of Managers.'[3] Such a board should have 'no statutory powers as regards the formal licensing of any hospital built, or about to be built'.[4] It should, however, be granted a charter to enable it to receive monies for distribution to medical charities.

The board which the Committee tentatively suggested was to consist of forty-nine members, twenty of whom were to represent the general hospitals, and twenty the special hospitals and dispensaries. There were to be five representatives of the profession – one each from the General Medical Council, Royal

[1] ibid.
[2] ibid.
[3] ibid., p. cv
[4] ibid.

College of Physicians, Royal College of Surgeons, Society of Apothecaries and general practitioners. The other four bodies to be represented were the University of London, the London County Council, the Sunday Fund and the Saturday Fund.

The board was to receive audited copies of accounts and statistics from all hospitals. It was to visit all medical charities and report on proposals for new hospitals. It was to publish in its annual report all the statistics it had collected, and also proposals for the establishment of new hospitals and for the removal of hospitals and dispensaries to places where further hospital and dispensary accommodation was required. The board's task was to get medical charities to co-operate with one another. It was hoped that 'the fear of adverse comment in the reports of the board . . . would have a powerful influence in preventing the building of useless hospitals and in securing proper administration in existing institutions'.[1]

The Committee ended on a sombre note:

> It should always be borne in mind that the establishment of Poor Law infirmaries, and rate-supported asylums, under the Metropolitan Poor Law Act 1867, has in great measure altered the relations between the poor and the hospitals, and everything associated with medical charity; and the Committee cannot shut their eyes to the possibility that if some such organization as they have recommended is not adopted, a time may come when it will be necessary for hospitals to have recourse either to Government aid or municipal subvention.[2]

The Lords Committee had seen the writing on the wall.

[1] ibid., p. cvii
[2] ibid.

CHAPTER II

Royal Intervention in London

THE report of the Lords Committee led to no immediate action. It was one thing to show that some central board was needed but quite another to get one set up, in view of the rivalry and jealousy of the different hospital authorities. Nor was it clear that the constitution proposed for the board would have been acceptable to the medical profession. The *British Medical Journal* hastened to point out that 'the scheme appears to propose a degree of representation of the medical profession which would be clearly deficient'.[1]

The views of the Committee concerning the running of out-patient departments had not supported those of the militants of the profession and the Charity Organization Society. The Committee had seen a need for numbers to be limited and some investigation undertaken into the circumstances of patients, but it had not recommended the system of referral – the use of the hospitals solely for consultation purposes. Nevertheless, the *British Medical Journal* noted in July 1892 that 'the practice of using these departments [outpatient] for consultation purposes appears to be on the increase. . . . The general practitioners, if they wish it, can, it is clear, use the hospital very much more than they now do for consultation purposes, and keep their cases in their own hands.'[2]

At the annual general meeting of the British Medical Association in 1892, the medical charities committee produced a report defining a wage limit for free care for use in the London area. A majority of three on the committee suggested a figure of forty-five shillings per week. Dr Rentoul, the fourth member, suggested fifteen shillings for single applicants and twenty shillings for married applicants. If the figure of forty-five shillings were adopted, he suggested that '65 per cent of the population

[1] *BMJ*, 9 July 1892, p. 89
[2] ibid.

of the East End would be eligible for free treatment. . . . They had free education and now the British Medical Association was asked to recommend the principle of free medicine.'[1] Despite Dr Rentoul's opposition, the figure of forty-five shillings was adopted. A year later it was reported to the next annual general meeting that seven or eight institutions had agreed to accept the recommendations of the Committee.

Although the Lords Committee had not specifically endorsed his ideas, Mr Loch went ahead with his proposals to establish almoners in the hospitals and he now produced a more coherent account of the role they were intended to play. Essentially he argued for better co-ordination of existing services. 'To be effectual . . . medical charity must act in alliance with general charity.'[2] A free dispensary for drugs could not benefit destitute persons if they lacked the necessary food. The 'gadding about to hospitals and dispensaries' had to be checked. 'If we cared enough about outpatients as individuals, we would combine for their better all-round treatment.'[3] He thought that the doctors should first select their outpatients and then, if these patients needed other charitable help, the 'almoners' should attend to it. Those who could afford a provident club or dispensary should be referred to one.

> Some might be told they should go to a general practitioner. . . . Those who were destitute might be referred to the relieving officer of their district. . . . The provident dispensaries would be promoted and kept in touch with the hospitals, and while medical interests had a first consideration, something would be done to utilize both general charity and the poor law.

What was needed was 'a trained experienced person . . . a man or woman of some insight, prompt decision and firmness'.[4]

In 1895 an almoner was appointed at the Royal Free Hospital whose salary was paid by the Charity Organization Society.[5] Strictly speaking, this was not a new departure, as there had been officers carrying out similar duties in earlier years and they had

[1] ibid., 5 August 1893, p. 327
[2] C. S. Loch, 'The Confusion in Medical Charities', p. 304, *Nineteenth Century*, August 1892
[3] ibid.
[4] ibid.
[5] E. Moberley Bell, op. cit., p. 25

included educated persons who had worked with the Charity Organization Society. The original features of this appointment were the title and the fact that the post was occupied by an exceptional woman – Mary Stewart. By 1903 seven London hospitals were employing 'almoners'.[1] The Charity Organization Society continued to pay their salaries in the initial stages. From 1911 almoners were required to hold the certificate in sociology from the London School of Economics and to do practical work with the Charity Organization Society.[2]

An example of the work of an almoner in 1907 is given in *The Hospital*. At the Royal Free Hospital outpatients were sent from the dispensary to the almoner's office where they were interrogated by Miss Brummell, the outpatient lady almoner. 'This interrogation is searching and definite – He is asked, if an adult, whether he is married, whether employed, and if so, what his earnings are.'[3] If a patient was found to be in a position to afford private treatment he was not permitted to attend again. The inpatient lady almoner, Miss Lacy, made it a rule 'to ensure that each patient is able to pay something towards the cost of any apparatus provided for him'.[4]

Such practices inevitably brought the hospitals into conflict with the Saturday Fund, whose members held that their regular payments had given them the right to be admitted to hospitals without inquiries into their means. Three patients complained at St George's Hospital in 1903. The hospital decided that in future patients should only be referred to the almoner by the clerk to the hospital board.[5] There were similar complaints at Swansea, where a meeting of hospital governors was attended by a solid body of workmen 'who declared that they would not allow any investigations to take place into their circumstances'.[6] They believed that their payments entitled them to free treatment. A working-men's committee at Belfast also objected because of their payment of a penny a week. They refused to be 'interrogated'.[7]

By these means the voluntary hospitals kept in check the use of

[1] ibid., p. 46
[2] ibid., p. 91
[3] *Hospital*, Vol. XLII, 6 July 1907, p. 435
[4] ibid.
[5] Moberley Bell, pp. 43–4
[6] *BMJ Supplement*, 3 August 1907, p. 106
[7] ibid.

their outpatient departments, but progress was not fast enough to satisfy the medical profession. In 1894 thirty letters on out-patient abuse were printed in the *British Medical Journal* in a period of six months. A number of correspondents suggested that the number of outpatients should be reduced not by almoners but by the patients' general practitioners. With the exception of accidents and emergencies, only referred patients should be seen.[1] It was argued that there were patients who could afford to pay a general practitioner but were quite unable to pay for a specialist – particularly if it meant travelling to London and taking lodgings to be able to attend regularly at a private con-sulting-room.[2] Such patients should be referred to outpatient departments. If almoners sent such patients to dispensaries, they would be deprived of skilled advice, and specialists of high standing would not seek hospital appointments. It was not the general practitioner who had cause for complaint in such cases but the specialist who had to see these cases without payment. 'To pay the staff according to their earnings would be a new and possibly doubtful departure from the traditions of hospital practice.'[3] Another correspondent wrote to say that the real trouble was that the lay boards did not want to limit abuse. The doctors could not resign in protest as 'their places would be filled at once by men only too glad to have these lucrative appoint-ments'.[4]

Interest was revived in the question of abuse, and the repeated suggestion that outpatient departments should be confined to referred cases occurred at the same time as a renewed and acrimonious dispute broke out about the correct role of con-sultants. According to one doctor there was a fierce struggle for existence, not only among the humble ranks of the general practitioners but even among the lofty circles of the 'consultants'. The results were the prevalence of underselling, and the growing reluctance of general practitioners to 'send cases to London . . . knowing often they shall see the faces of their patients no more'.[5] One correspondent to the *British Medical Journal* wrote to deplore 'the undignified competition among the lower classes of the

[1] For example, *BMJ*, 14 April 1894, p. 840
[2] ibid., 20 January 1894, p. 158
[3] ibid., 17 March 1894, p. 605
[4] ibid., 21 August 1897, p. 498
[5] ibid., 5 May 1894, p. 977

profession'. The sixpenny dispensary was the answer to the 'free charity' of the casualty department where the leaders of the profession offered 'in the market place their own gratuitous services to the multitude in the public shrines of philanthropy'.[1] Another correspondent said that 'the time has come for some stand to be made against the house-to-house visitations of so-called consultants in the absence of the usual medical attendant.'[2] The Lancashire and Cheshire branch of the Incorporated Medical Practitioners' Association found it necessary to resolve 'that it is undesirable for those holding honorary hospital appointments to see patients for a fee at such charitable institutions, and unprofessional to transfer "hospital patients" to their own private practice'.[3]

The *British Medical Journal* tried once again to define the proper role of consultants. 'We are disposed to think that "consultants", surgical or medical, should not attend patients alone in their homes, and that patients should not be encouraged to call so continuously upon a consultant as to make the calls an "attendance".'[4] His fee on each occasion should be not less than one guinea and it should usually be paid at the time.[5]

One FRCP complained that some practitioners had decided to have no consultations at all. 'Let them agree with each other to call in, and to send patients to, those physicians only who refrain from acting as general practitioners by taking sole charge of the patient at their own homes.'[6] The *British Medical Journal* urged all local branches of the British Medical Association to form their own ethical committees 'to promote fair and honourable practice, to exercise judicious supervision of matters touching medical interests, and to prevent abuse of the profession'.[7]

The official view of the British Medical Association was in line with the suggestions of the Lords Committee. Thus it welcomed the decision of the Charity Organization Society and also of the Sunday Fund to encourage the appointment of special officers in outpatient departments to deal with the problem of abuse.[8] The

[1] ibid., 23 April 1893, p. 929
[2] ibid., 13 October 1892, p. 873
[3] ibid., 31 October 1896, p. 1350
[4] ibid., 13 January 1894, p. 93
[5] ibid., 27 January 1894, p. 210
[6] ibid., 26 May 1894, p. 1158
[7] ibid., 11 January 1896, p. 98
[8] ibid., 6 November 1897, p. 1351

Association drafted a poster saying that patients would be required to give information as to their means and circumstances, and tried to induce hospitals to display it in their outpatient departments.[1] By 1900 nearly every hospital in the country had been sent such notices. Among the provincial hospitals, thirty-seven agreed to display the poster, twenty refused and eleven 'declined altogether to take the matter into consideration'.[2]

In 1897 a new and separate organization was formed to agitate about the problem of hospital abuse – the Hospital Reform Association. The solution it favoured was referral. Patients with notes from medical men were to have a prior claim to treatment. In the general hospitals, patients coming from outside districts were to be requested to bring notes from medical men before being treated. In the special hospitals, payments from patients should cease and eligibility for free treatment should largely depend on the recommendation of private practitioners.[3] Such a system operated in a small hospital in Eastbourne.[4]

Two separate policies were therefore being advocated at the end of the century – restriction by a test of means and restriction by referral. There was, however, a third solution which had no support from the medical profession. In an article headed 'Hospital Abuse and Its Cure', *The Hospital* advocated patients' payments. 'We fail utterly to see why the [special departments of the great hospitals] should be conducted on an entirely free principle.'[5] A system under which patients paid was 'a more wholesome and better system of relief'.[6] The *British Medical Journal*, however, condemned the one-shilling charges for outpatients levied at the Queen's Hospital, Birmingham, and at Guy's, for undercutting the general practitioner. Those hospitals were spreading 'the sweating system further in the community'.[7] And when the Westminster Hospital decided to introduce a charge of threepence for drugs and dressings, general practitioners in the area were most indignant. The executive committee of the Westminster division of the BMA resolved 'that

1 ibid., 16 July 1898, pp. 175–6
2 ibid., 13 July 1901, p. 113
3 ibid., 26 February 1898, p. 589
4 ibid., 4 October 1902, p. 1051
5 *Hospital*, Vol. XXIX, 17 November 1900, p. 124
6 ibid.
7 *BMJ*, 15 April 1893, p. 809

such payment by patients is inadvisable, and further that in the interests of hospitals and their work it is advisable, as suggested by the Council of the BMA, that local medical practitioners should nominate representatives for election to the Board of Management'.[1]

Meanwhile the BMA had decided to try and promote its views on the conduct of voluntary hospitals by sponsoring a conference: it was dissatisfied with the progress made by writing letters. In March 1905, the Hospitals Committee of the BMA organized a United Hospitals Conference which was attended by representatives of many hospitals both from London and the provinces. It was agreed to set up a joint committee of the BMA and hospital managements to draft a set of principles of hospital management which were to be circulated to hospitals and considered at a second conference.[2]

At this second conference held in 1906 and attended by delegates from 150 hospitals, Dr Frank Pope, the chairman of the Hospitals Committee, made a frank statement of the Association's views:

> The unchecked distribution of free medical relief has a twofold effect on the general practitioner . . . it actually took away his patient . . . and it created in the mind of the public an idea that medical advice was not a thing to be paid for . . . or to be paid for in such small sums as indicated its comparative worthlessness. . . . Subscribers' letters were, from the point of view of the BMA, pernicious. They gave the applicant a sense of being treated as of right and not of favour, and made it difficult for the medical staff to give the more deserving a preference over the less. . . . [They] were given as rewards for Church attendance and membership of trade unions and shop associations, and when a body of working men received, in return for a subscription, a certain and stipulated number of subscribers' letters, no more and no less for each guinea given, it was impossible to argue – or at any rate to convince them – that they had not a right to exact in return so much attendance . . . the free gift of the doctors' time was passed over as of no importance. . . .[3]

The Conference agreed the following principles. Only patients who were unable to pay for adequate treatment were to

[1] *BMJ*, 24 July 1909, p. 238
[2] *BMJ*, 15 December 1906, p. 1731
[3] *Hospital*, Vol. XLI, 15 December 1906, pp. 198–9

be admitted to hospitals. Medical charities were to employ an almoner or other agent to investigate the circumstances of applicants. The production of subscribers' letters was to cease to be compulsory and wherever possible the system was to be abolished. All patients were to see a doctor at their first visit: serious cases were not to be denied treatment, but trivial cases were to be referred elsewhere. It was laid down that the function of outpatient departments was to be primarily consultative. Notices were to be displayed advising applicants of the existence of provident dispensaries in the neighbourhood.[1]

The *British Medical Journal* expressed qualified satisfaction with the results of the conference. Hospital managers had been found to be genuinely more willing to put their house in order than many people thought. It continued:

> . . . it is clear that the forces of reaction and inertia render it necessary for the BMA to press on with more speed than the Conference seems at present inclined to display, and it may be necessary for the Divisions to take action at an early date to press reforms on hospitals in their area if they are not administered satisfactorily.[2]

The question of hospital abuse continued to be actively discussed in the *British Medical Journal*: there were twelve letters on the subject in the first six months of 1907. In 1908 another hospital conference was held. It was decided that unsuitable cases applying to hospitals should be referred to local general practitioners, approved provident dispensaries or the Poor Law officer. It was agreed that 'the appointment of trained almoners constitutes one of the best methods for checking the misuse of hospitals', and that 'some definite steps should be taken to ascertain the ability or contrary of each patient at a cottage hospital to pay for his maintenance'.[3] 'A motion to the effect that the general body of the profession in a locality should have the right to nominate representatives for election to the Board of Management of a local hospital was rejected by a considerable majority.'[4] The *British Medical Journal* regretted this as it thought that 'representation of the outside medical profession was

1 *BMJ Supplement*, 15 December 1906, pp. 322–6
2 *BMJ*, 15 December 1906, p. 1731
3 *BMJ Supplement*, 20 June 1908, p. 432
4 *BMJ*, 11 April 1908, p. 163

necessary as an additional safeguard against abuse, not at present generally enforced'.[1]

At the 1909 annual representative meeting two further resolutions were passed which aimed at restricting the activities of voluntary hospitals. The first was that 'no fresh public medical institutions shall be opened without previous consultation with the local medical profession'.[2] The second resolution was 'that a medical certificate of suitability for hospital treatment be required as a condition of hospital treatment except in the case of casualties'.[3] Thus after twelve years, the policy which had been advocated by a group of extremists who had formed themselves into the Hospital Reform Association was adopted as official BMA policy.

The militant attitude of some sections of the profession is shown in a letter published in the *British Medical Journal* from the secretary of the Liverpool and Birkenhead combined divisions of the Association:

> The greatest problem before the profession today is the problem of hospital abuse and the tyranny of lay committees and the subordination of the medical staffs, and that while the lay committees are getting greater and greater control they are actually ceasing largely to be the actual people who subscribe the money that supports the hospital ... now there is a decided tendency to make actual contracts with public and private bodies to do work at a price.... It should be driven home to medical men that they will be held responsible for improper acts of the lay committees of the hospitals to which they are attached. Such pronouncements would enormously strengthen the hands of the staffs of hospitals.[4]

By 1909 the Association subscribed to every possible means of preventing the growth and restricting the activities of outpatient departments. And it used every means within its power to thrust its views on hospital managements. But this was only one of many matters which had been considered by the Lords Committee. The principal recommendations had concerned the question of planning. The Committee had suggested that a voluntary board should be set up to try and create some order in the jungle of

[1] ibid.
[2] *BMJ Supplement*, 31 July 1909, p. 146
[3] ibid., p. 144
[4] ibid., 8 May 1909, p. 238

voluntary bodies. The board was to have no statutory powers. As
it was to be composed primarily of hospital representatives, it was
unlikely to act very vigorously against any individual hospital.
Given money, it might achieve results by the power of the purse
but there were already two entrenched funds collecting money
on behalf of all the hospitals.

However unlikely such a project might have appeared at the
time, only four-and-a-half years after the publication of the report a body came into existence which performed with only
minor amendment the functions of the recommended committee.
It was *The Prince of Wales's Hospital Fund for London to Commemorate
the Sixtieth Year of the Queen's Reign* – later, *The King Edward's
Hospital Fund for London*. What was impossible by any other means
was achieved through the almost mystical influence of the
monarchy. Royalty could gain instantly the respect of hospital
authorities which neither the Church (Hospital Sunday Fund)
nor the consumer (Hospital Saturday Fund) could ever command. It could also raise money at a pace and on a scale which
no hospital authority could ignore. The personal intervention of
a King helped to postpone the day when the voluntary hospitals
were controlled by his Ministers.

Prince Edward had long interested himself in hospital affairs.
The project for the fund grew out of discussions of a centenary
dinner for Guy's Hospital which was being planned with the help
of Henry Burdett. When there were difficulties, Alfred Fripp, a
young surgeon at Guy's who had treated successfully one of the
young princes, appealed directly to the Prince of Wales. Thus
both Fripp and Burdett went to Marlborough House and the
latter eventually had full opportunity to lay his ideas before the
Prince. As a result of the talks, the idea of setting up a Diamond
Jubilee fund emerged.[1]

The Prince invited to a meeting held at Marlborough House
on 21 January 1897 a group of people who, he hoped, would help
him with his project. They included 'leaders in religion, medicine,
surgery, commerce, administration and industry, some of them
his close personal friends'.[2] They agreed unanimously to set up a
fund and consented to act as the first General Committee. Two
weeks later the Fund was in existence. As distinct from the

[1] F. D. Long, *King Edward's Hospital Fund for London: The Story of its
Foundations and Achievements 1897–1942*, p. 2, London, 1942
[2] ibid., p. 3

Saturday Fund and Sunday Fund it was intended right at the start that the capital raised would be invested: only income on the investments would be distributed.

It was hoped that the money would be raised from 'persons who have not hitherto acquired the habit of giving regularly to these institutions'.[1] The first quarter of a million pounds was raised in eleven months, a further £139,000 in the next three years, and in 1902 with the help of a special Coronation appeal £434,000 was collected. At this time the total income of London hospitals reporting to Burdett's Annual was about £1·7 million per year. While the Fund received many small sums, the bulk of the money came from large subscriptions. Burdett had reason to complain that 'the great majority of Londoners who may be generally denominated as prosperous citizens have so far failed to accept the privilege of personal service through this Fund'.[2]

The accumulation of capital and the total scale of the operations were not the only novel features of the Fund. Such money as was distributed was not handed out according to any simple arithmetical formula. Visits were made to each hospital so that the needs and capabilities of each management could be assessed on the spot. The Fund laid great stress on efficiency and tried to encourage permanent improvements rather than pay off debts. One essential preliminary was to set up a standard form of hospital accounts. By withholding grants from hospitals which refused to present their accounts in the standard form, the Fund introduced uniform accounts into most of the hospitals of London.

The first major task it set itself was to 'open closed beds in the larger hospitals'.[3] In the first four years 433 beds were opened.[4] Next the Fund turned to the more difficult task of securing the amalgamation of small hospitals by persuasion backed up with the promise of substantial grants. By these means the National and Royal Orthopaedic Hospitals were amalgamated in 1903, and three years later the City Orthopaedic Hospital was brought into the same fold. The five ear, nose and throat hospitals proved less tractable. A sum of £1,000 was set aside for a combined hospital in 1906 and doubled the next year. By 1911

[1] ibid., p. 5
[2] *Hospital*, Vol. XLI, 22 December 1906, p. 203
[3] *KEHF, First Annual Report, 1897*, p. 8
[4] Long, p. 25

£20,000 was set aside for this purpose. Not until 1914 did any of the fish reach for the bait and then only two hospitals were amalgamated.

The Fund could do little to correct the maldistribution of existing hospital buildings. Extra money was, however, given to the King's College Hospital and the Belgrave Hospital to help them move south of the river. And it did its best to stop further unplanned growth. New hospitals and hospitals contemplating major reconstruction were asked 'before taking definite action to submit their proposals to the Fund'.[1]

Little could be done to correct the concentration of hospitals within two miles of Oxford Circus. In 1906 the Treasurer of St George's Hospital wanted to remove the hospital from Hyde Park Corner to a site further out but he could not gain the support of the governors, who, according to Burdett, included 'a number of worthy men [who] have grown old with the institution'.[2] He reported that the King's Fund and other funds were fully aware of what was needed and 'until that course is followed money will no doubt be withheld from the institution'.[3] Despite this threat, St George's Hospital stayed where it was. As Burdett had said three years earlier, the King's Fund was performing all the functions of the Lords Committee central board 'except the enforced removal of hospitals to new sites'.[4]

Many of the grants given by the Fund had conditions attached to them. Some hospitals were given grants on condition that they remedied overcrowding. The establishment for Gentlewomen, Harley Street, got £75 'on the understanding that a properly constituted committee is elected forthwith'.[5] The Grosvenor Hospital was given a grant but attention was called to the high cost per inpatient per week.[6] More discreetly, the North Eastern Hospital for Children was given £250 'in anticipation of improvements being made in the direction indicated by the Visitors'.[7] The Queen's Jubilee Hospital was given no grant as 'this institution does not appear to be a hospital in any true sense of the word, and its buildings are quite unsuitable for hospital

1 *KEHF: Sixth Annual Report, 1902*, p. 7
2 *Hospital*, Vol. XL, 7 July 1906, p. 241
3 ibid.
4 *Burdett's Hospitals and Charities 1903*, p. 59, London, 1903
5 *KEHF: Second Annual Report, 1898*, p. 9
6 ibid.
7 ibid.

purposes'.[1] The Middlesex Hospital was told that the hours its nurses worked were too long.[2] Even the august St Thomas' had to take with its grant of £1,800 the criticism that 'an inquiry is needed to prevent abuse by outpatients'.[3] The Fund also exerted its influence on general matters of management. In 1900 hospitals were told of the objections, hygienic and general, against making inpatients supply their own tea, sugar, butter, personal linen, washing, etc. The Fund requested that 'the articles in question in future be provided by the hospitals'.[4]

The board which the Lords Committee had recommended was intended to be representative of the hospitals. And in the original letter of appeal which the Prince signed on 3 February 1897, it was envisaged that 'representatives chosen by the hospitals' might help with the distribution of the money. In practice, however, King Edward retained the power of appointment to the committees in his own hands. The Fund was never in any sense democratic. The aura of royalty, the high social standing of the members of the council and the high calibre of the Fund's visitors probably gave it greater power. But despite this advantage and the fact that within ten years it was channelling about a tenth of the income of the hospitals of London, the Fund was unable to make much progress in rationalizing the hospital structure. It could help to prevent the situation from getting worse but it could do little to alter the haphazard system which was then in being. It could help to break down the isolation of hospital managements but it could do little to create co-ordinated action. Finally, it could do nothing to plan a rational division of responsibilities between the voluntary hospitals and the public infirmaries.

The voluntary hospitals became continuously more selective in the patients they would treat. The provision made for patients with tuberculosis and venereal diseases remained grossly inadequate. Thus, the public sector was left to cater for the patients which the voluntary hospitals did not want or wanted only for the 'acute' phase of their illness. And as the availability of voluntary beds varied widely from one area to another, the function left for the public authorities varied correspondingly.

[1] KEHF: Third Annual Report, 1899, p. 9
[2] KEHF: Fourth Annual Report, 1900, p. 9
[3] KEHF: Third Annual Report, p. 9
[4] KEHF: Fourth Annual Report, p. 7

Where there was a generous supply of voluntary hospital beds, the public authorities were left only with the long-stay cases: where there was a shortage of voluntary hospital beds, the public authorities had also to provide acute hospitals. The arrangements made by different public authorities are described in Chapter 13.

CHAPTER 12

Pay Beds or Nursing Homes?

THE Lords Committee had taken evidence but had come to no decision on the controversial question of pay beds. Throughout the nineties, general practitioners continued to oppose pay beds in the voluntary hospitals. They wanted patients to be divided into two distinct categories – those who paid the full cost of hospital care, including the remuneration of the doctor, and those who paid nothing. When the patient could not afford the whole cost he should be induced to make a 'gift in the nature of a thank-offering in return for the charity freely accorded him'.[1]

Nonetheless there was a modest increase in the number of pay beds. In 1894, the Great Northern Central Hospital, on the instigation of Burdett, introduced pay wards 'for the reception of patients a little above the poorest class'.[2] The medical staff agreed to give such patients free services, provided no patient was admitted without 'the consent, in writing, of his or her own medical attendant'.[3] This action led to a protest in which 201 medical practitioners in North London took part.[4] A delegation was received by the hospital committee which demanded 'the immediate withdrawal of the whole scheme of Pay Wards in the Hospital'.[5] They said that the medical staff were

> giving their professional work for the enrichment of a lay corpora-
> tion and inflicting a proportionate pecuniary injury upon the
> Medical Practitioners in the neighbourhood. . . . The insertion of
> advertisements in the newspapers about the pay wards was doing

[1] *Select Committee on Metropolitan Hospitals 1890–3*, Third Report, para. 230
[2] *BMJ*, 3 November 1894, p. 1006
[3] ibid., 24 November 1894, p. 1201
[4] ibid.
[5] Jewesbury, *The Royal Northern Hospital*, p. 67

great harm to the medical practitioners of the neighbourhood. . . .
Every pay bed was a bed taken from the poor.'[1]

Dr Hugh Woods, a member of the Medical Charities Committee of the British Medical Association, wrote to say that he was 'pleased to hear on all sides firm resolves to abstain from calling into consultation any member of the staff who gives his services gratuitously in "these pay wards" '.[2] He would do all in his power 'to check subscriptions to the Great Northern Hospital as long as these "pay wards" continue'.[3] The pay wards did, however, continue. In 1900 the maximum charge was two guineas per week.[4]

By the turn of the century, more of the middle classes were seeking care away from home when they were ill. The discussion about pay beds in the middle seventies had been conducted in terms of meeting the needs of certain groups of middle-class persons from out of London, of persons in lodgings and of persons without families. Such people needed hospitals because they could not receive proper nursing care in their own homes. Everyone agreed that no one with a good home, ample domestic staff and a substantial income would ever need to leave it when they were ill.

The important changes in the practice of surgery which had occurred in the last twenty-five years of the century (asepsis and the use of anaesthetics) made possible operations which would never have been attempted earlier. As a result, the equipment and maintenance of an operating theatre had become much more complex than it had ever been before. If a room in a private house was used for the purpose, very careful preparation was now required. A book published in 1904 explains the procedure:

> To prepare a room for an operation, carpets, curtains and all hangings must be removed. The ledges over doors and windows must be cleansed and freed from the dirt which is apt to rest on them. Ceilings must be rubbed with a brush covered with a damp cloth and floors scrubbed until they are clean and sodden. . . .[5]

[1] ibid.
[2] *BMJ*, 24 November 1894, p. 1201
[3] ibid.
[4] *Hospital*, Vol. XXVIII, 30 June 1900, p. 229
[5] J. Aikman, *Surgical Operations in Private Practice*, pp. 171–2, London, 1904

It is not surprising that many families wanted to avoid this sort of upheaval. Moreover, it is unlikely that the standard of cleanliness actually obtained was comparable with that of a specially-designed theatre. An article in the *British Medical Journal* in 1903 emphasized this point: 'In these days of elaborate asepsis it must be recognized that almost no ordinary dwelling-house can provide the environment that is considered necessary for the achievement of the best surgical results.'[1] The author noted 'a growing disinclination on the part of surgeons to operate in private houses'.[2] The trend was not confined to surgery. Physicians were also beginning to believe that hospitals provided better supervision of a patient and prevented the spread of disease to relatives and friends. 'Medical homes are almost as necessary as surgical homes.'[3] There was 'an increasing desire on the part of physicians to have certain forms of disease removed from the influence of home surroundings'.[4]

Though a number of hospitals had provided pay beds, the majority had not. There were some hospital managements which wanted as a matter of principle to confine their work to the poor. There were others who feared the opposition from their medical staff and from local general practitioners. According to Burdett, most hospitals were not enthusiastic for financial reasons. They believed that 'the presence of pay-patients in their hospitals would prejudice fund-raising activities'.[5] For all these reasons, by far the majority of beds for paying patients were in separate hospitals or nursing homes. In 1891 there were about 9,500 beds in England and Wales in nursing homes and convalescent homes; by 1911 this number had increased to 13,000.[6] In 1900, there were at least fifty nursing homes in London.[7] 'Nursing homes are plentiful,' wrote a correspondent in the *British Medical Journal* in 1903, 'in which non-infectious ailments, whether medical or surgical, may be treated.'[8]

Many of them were started by ladies with or without a nursing qualification. According to one proprietor, it was essential to

[1] *BMJ*, 12 January 1903, p. 147
[2] ibid., p. 148
[3] ibid.
[4] ibid.
[5] *Hospital*, Vol. XXXI, 22 March 1902, p. 426
[6] See Vol. 2 of this study.
[7] *Hospital*, Vol. XXIX, 3 November 1900, p. 89
[8] *BMJ*, 17 January 1903, p. 147

obtain assurances of good cases from local doctors before starting.[1] Sometimes one surgeon would 'dominate one of these houses by filling most of the beds.... The surgeon who dominates the management by making habitual use of the home . . . may thus gain to himself the advantage of proprietorship without incurring any financial or personal liability.'[2] In other cases, surgeons or physicians set up their own homes. There was, therefore, 'a certain temptation to a man who has such an establishment to do his best to find patients for it'.[3] The *British Medical Journal* thought in 1905 'that it is on the whole better that neither physicians nor surgeons should be pecuniarily interested in running such homes'.[4]

While some of the nursing homes were 'admirably conducted and in every respect satisfactorily equipped',[5] there were others which left much to be desired. In some of them no trained nurses were employed, the food was meagre and badly cooked and the accommodation inconvenient, noisy and dirty. From 1900 onwards, complaints from patients and others were printed in the *British Medical Journal* and *The Hospital* about the low standard of care received in some homes where exorbitant charges were demanded.[6]

Homes for the chronic sick were the worst. An extreme case was reported in *Truth* in 1902. Thirteen patients, most of them senile, were accommodated in a little two-roomed house.

> Beds seem only to have been made at intervals of several days; bed linen, however foul its condition, to have been changed only at intervals of several weeks.... Cruelty of a very real and active kind appears to have been practised, presumably in the way of punishment, upon these feeble and half-witted creatures, while some of them were tied down in bed in a manner which would not be permitted in either workhouse or asylum.[7]

The Hospital pointed out that there was a 'not inconsiderable class of friendless people who, being in receipt of small pensions, or having invested in small annuities drift into "homes" of

[1] *Hospital*, Vol. XXXV (Nursing Section), 5 December 1903, p. 129
[2] ibid., Vol. XL, 23 June 1906, p. 206
[3] *BMJ*, 7 October 1905, p. 909
[4] ibid.
[5] ibid., 17 January 1903, p. 147
[6] See, for example, *BMJ*, 15 December 1900, p. 1749.
[7] quoted in *Hospital*, Vol. XXXII, 7 June 1902, p. 173

various degrees and when once there find themselves unable to get away without the assistance of outside friends whom they do not possess'.[1]

A private sanatorium for cases of consumption and cancer was operated by a Mr J. H. D. Jenkinson who was a chemist and druggist but had no medical diploma. He had previously been a manufacturer of poultry, pigeon and dog medicines. The residents of the home paid only ten shillings per week. The *British Medical Journal* estimated that the food alone should have cost eight shillings a week. The proprietor contented himself with giving patients a 'high class tonic' and sent for the doctor only when the patients were dying.[2]

The institutions which were set up as 'nursing homes' included a number which offered unusual forms of treatment. There were 'homes for rest cures, and for the fresh air cure, and for cure by vegetarian diet'.[3] Nearly all these establishments were for women. For men there were 'massage homes'. A nurse who applied for a job in one of these was asked if she had treated patients who were not really ill and to send a photograph by return of post. She was told that 'assistants here made a great deal by gratuities'.[4] Another nurse who accepted a post by correspondence arrived to find a lot of healthy men wandering around in dressing-gowns – 'one of whom took the head of the table at dinner so attired, having been "at the office" all day'.[5] There was no lock on the nurse's bedroom door.

All these abuses led to the demand for the licensing and inspection of private hospitals and nursing homes. Much was made of the contrast between the whole system of medical care available to the rich, and the service available to the poor. In an article entitled 'The Advantages of Poverty', *The Hospital* drove the point home. By going to the hospital, the poor man could get the best consultants' opinions. 'He either waits his turn, or, if endowed with tact and a little current coin, may secure the porter's favour and early admission to the consulting-room.'[6] The rich man would be treated first by his general

[1] ibid.
[2] *BMJ*, 16 January 1909, p. 173
[3] *Hospital*, Vol. XXXVI (Nursing Section), 24 September 1904, p. 43
[4] *BMJ*, 24 November 1894, pp. 199–200
[5] *Hospital*, Vol. LIII, 19 October 1912, p. 81
[6] ibid., Vol. XXXIII, 28 March 1903, p. 438

practitioner and only if this failed referred to a consultant whom he might or might not see the same day. If surgery was necessary he again got the inferior care.

> Any arrangements that can possibly be made in a private house are at the best merely makeshift, while it is doubtful, with the exception named [the Home Hospital], if there is a single nursing home in existence in which conditions are not passed which, in a hospital, surgeons would absolutely condemn. The rich man with all his wealth does not, and practically cannot, obtain the scientific advantage which the poor man can and does obtain for nothing.[1]

The campaign for the control of nursing homes had the full support of – if it was not actually conducted by – the leaders of the nursing profession. The representatives of the trained nurses had their own reasons for wanting public control of nursing homes. They wanted not only to protect the public from neglect but also to protect trained nurses from the competition of untrained nurses. Thus when a committee was set up in 1904 to consider the registration of nurses they pressed for action. In 1905 this committee recommended not only the compulsory registration but also the inspection of nursing homes.

The proposal had the hearty and continuous support of *The Hospital*. 'In the event of even the mildest measure for the regulation of nursing homes becoming law, 90 per cent of these establishments would be compelled to close their doors.'[2] There followed a somewhat garish account of the treatment which might be given to the supporters of voluntary hospitals if they went into a nursing home. They might occupy a room which had not been properly cleaned after a septic case had just been discharged.

> The details resulting from the operation . . . [might be] set aside in some secret receptacle until late at night, when, servants and nurses being safe in bed, the proprietors can steal downstairs and empty the contents on to the kitchen fire, where all the meals for the household are to be cooked on the morrow. . . . Had these helpless victims been destitute, their cause had long since been pleaded effectually.[3]

[1] ibid.
[2] ibid., Vol. XLIII, 16 November 1907, p. 192
[3] ibid.

The root of the claim for legislation lies then in the defenceless condition of the persons who use nursing homes.[1]

Thus not long after an extensive network of separate 'hospitals' had been developed for paying patients, the demand arose for public inspection and control to protect defenceless patients. There was no similar demand to protect poor patients from abuses in the voluntary hospitals. Although they were not profit-making and although well-run hospitals had committees who carried out regular visits, some scandals did come to light. In 1892, the insanitary condition of St Bartholomew's had been condemned by the Lords Committee. Reflecting contemporary ideas about the spread of infection, the Committee had stressed the importance of inspecting hospital drains:

> Notwithstanding the universal recognition of the importance of maintaining a thoroughly efficient system of drainage, and notwithstanding the experience which some hospitals have had of sore-throat and other serious diseases pointing to insanitary conditions, the practice of making periodical examinations of the drains ... does not appear to have been generally adopted.[2]

In 1894 the local medical officer of health had had his attention drawn to the Chelsea Hospital for Women by cases of scarlet fever breaking out among the nurses. He attributed this to the fact that the drains were leaking and that sewer air escaped into various parts of the hospital. The medical staff had continued to practise operations involving great danger in spite of numerous deaths from septicaemia.[3] In 1905 it was found that 'the arrangements for cadavers in the dead houses in connection with certain medical schools in London reveal that abuses have crept in and are allowed to continue, which are opposed to public decency and attended by dangers to the living'.[4] There was a large provincial hospital where the dead patient was stored in a screened-off corner of the casualty department.[5]

This was to be by no means the last exposure of the unsatisfactory state of a voluntary hospital. In 1913 charges were

[1] ibid., 7 December 1907, p. 275
[2] Select Committee on Metropolitan Hospitals 1890–3, Third Report, para. 290
[3] BMJ, 11 August 1894, p. 321
[4] Hospital, Vol. XXXVIII, 26 August 1905, p. 381
[5] ibid.

proved against a hospital at York, ranging from the inadequacy of the nursing staff to the misconduct of a sister and negligence in reporting deaths: one live person had actually been taken to the mortuary in error.[1] The existence of a committee had not prevented these faults. The chairman of the House Committee was 'an esteemed divine who is 85 years of age, and has been completely deaf for very many years. . . . The control has been practically in the hands of one of the honorary staff and a former Matron who is married to one of the staff.'[2]

In general, however, scandals in voluntary hospitals were on a smaller scale than scandals in nursing homes. Many of the latter were not only unsatisfactory but expensive. Their charges varied from four guineas a week to twenty guineas a week, though for the latter price it was often possible to get a room with a private bathroom, and accommodation for a friend or relative.[3] The Home Hospital remained among the cheapest of the nursing homes. It was rebuilt in 1902 with thirty beds at a cost of £10,000,[4] and raised its charge from three to four guineas a week: no patients were received for less than this sum.

Thus hospitals were fairly rigidly divided into full cost hospitals and free hospitals: to this rule there were few exceptions. There was a great need for hospital beds costing a guinea or two per week, but Burdett argued on the basis of his experience with the Home Hospital that it was not possible to provide a properly staffed and equipped nursing home for less than about four guineas per week. There were three possible ways of getting around the difficulty quite apart from the use of subsidies from public funds.

One possibility was price discrimination. Drawing upon continental experience, Burdett had long advocated payment according to means. In 1900 he suggested that there might be four grades of patients with the Poor Law authorities paying for the lowest grade.[5] He recognized that the doctors would need to be paid for their services.

[1] ibid., Vol. LV, 1 November 1913, p. 119
[2] ibid., p. 105
[3] ibid., Vol. XXXIX, 17 March 1906, pp. 399-400
[4] £2,000 of this sum was subscribed. Attempts to raise the remaining £8,000 failed and so the sum had to be gradually repaid by means of a sinking fund (*Hospital*, Vol. XXXVI, 14 May 1904, p. 125).
[5] *Hospital*, Vol. XXIX, 10 November 1900, p. 107

In 1906 a scheme was under discussion which would provide a surgical home in London for eighty to a hundred patients. There were to be three classes of patients – those who were admitted free, those who paid three guineas which was to cover all expenses of treatment, and those who were to pay more than the cost. The first two classes were to be given free medical attention from a permanent medical staff and the third group was to choose its own doctor and pay him separately. The *British Medical Journal* did not favour the scheme. It argued that it was not fair to try to cover the losses on poorer patients by increased charges on the richer patients. Moreover, 'it would . . . be superfluous and disadvantageous . . . to limit the power of choosing their own medical attendants to those who pay the highest rate'.[1] The scheme was never implemented.

A second possibility was to bring the actual cost of a place in a nursing home within the pockets of a wider segment of the population by some system of insurance. This alternative was also suggested by Burdett in 1900: 'a great insurance company should offer a policy for treatment in a pay ward.'[2] By 1906 Burdett was to be found saying that 'actuaries had been working at a suggested scheme for years and now saw their way to providing the proposed policy giving patients the necessary hospital treatment and some weeks at the seaside for the period of convalescence for an annual premium of little more than the ordinary accident policy'.[3] Later in the same year, the president of the Royal College of Physicians advocated the construction of 'big provident hospitals'.[4] No action was taken.

The third possibility was a large-scale development of pay beds in conjunction with the existing voluntary hospitals. By the sharing of overheads and some direct or indirect subsidy from the parent hospital, the price of a bed could be reduced. Burdett also proposed this in 1906.[5] The suggestion was no more popular with the medical profession than it had been in earlier years. The *British Medical Journal* hastened to the attack:

Consultants may find it convenient to have a certain number of beds at their disposal to which they can admit patients who . . .

[1] *BMJ*, 14 July 1906, p. 104
[2] *Hospital*, Vol. XXIX, 10 November 1900, p. 107
[3] ibid., Vol. XXXIX, 31 March 1906, pp. 445–7
[4] *BMJ*, 15 December 1906, p. 1732
[5] *Hospital*, Vol. XXXIX, 17 March 1906, pp. 399–400

they know to be able to pay operation fees, but to place their service at the disposal of all-comers is quite a different matter. If there be any solution of the question at all, it undoubtedly lies not in multiplying the number of pay wards attached to ordinary hospitals . . . but in the establishment of a sufficient number of conveniently placed public nursing homes. Even these, too, would fail to be successful unless it were open to every registered medical man to treat in them his own patients if they so desired, and unless safeguards were established against reduction of the ordinary charges for attendance and operation on the inmates except on due cause shown to the approval of a managing committee.[1]

The *British Medical Journal* was just begging the question, as Burdett wrote to point out. Nursing homes could not be run at a low enough price. Such a system must 'entail a large expenditure of capital and must indefinitely multiply the cost of maintenance, because each home would require separate management. . . . I am afraid, therefore, that if we are to wait till such a system of nursing homes is forthcoming, hospital abuse must continue to increase.'[2]

In so far as the British Medical Association was prepared to face up to the issue, it favoured some modest price discrimination in separate nursing homes. It was, however, prepared to endorse pay beds attached to voluntary hospitals under certain conditions. This was the policy adopted at the hospital conference it arranged in 1906. The conference resolved that pay beds were not incompatible with the voluntary system 'provided that they are open to every member of the medical profession who shall be paid any fees to be arranged between him and his patient'.[3] In the case of cottage hospitals, however, it was resolved that all patients who could contribute should do so. A certificate signed by a medical practitioner within the area was to be a sufficient recommendation for admission.[4]

On the question of nursing homes, the conference resolved that 'it is desirable that self-supporting public nursing homes should be established for patients who, being ineligible for the voluntary hospitals, are yet unable to pay the customary professional fees as well as the charges usually made in private

[1] *BMJ*, 31 March 1906, pp. 760–1
[2] ibid., 7 April 1906, p. 830
[3] *BMJ Supplement*, 15 December 1906, p. 327
[4] ibid., p. 323

nursing homes'.[1] Such homes were to be managed by committees on which the medical profession was adequately represented. Patients were to have free choice of doctor and were only to be admitted if they had a certificate saying they were 'suitable' from their own doctors. 'Some assistance should be available to patients unable to pay the entire cost but such subsidization should be subject to the approval of a committee.'[2]

After the conference, the BMA proceeded to define more closely the principles which had been agreed. Definitions were produced of the terms 'hospital' and 'cottage hospital'. Further principles were laid down. At the annual meeting in 1907 it was resolved that 'compulsory payment by patients to hospitals other than cottage hospitals should cease'.[3] This resolution was particularly relevant to the Liverpool and Manchester areas where the local divisions were busy protesting to the local hospitals.[4]

The BMA watched to see that the principles it had laid down were observed. In 1909, Hampstead Hospital decided to open a private wing and would not allow general practitioners free access to it. With the support of the central council of the BMA, the local division published a warning notice that no doctor should apply for an appointment without consulting the division or the medical secretary.[5] At the annual representative meeting later in the year, the council was instructed to secure the observance of the warning notice which had been issued and to take all steps 'to redress the injustice which has been occasioned, as its long continued existence is conducive to the disintegration of the Association'.[6]

Nothing came of the BMA's proposal for large private nursing homes with a few beds for patients who would pay less than the full cost. It was stated in 1908 that the subject was not 'ripe for general action'. However two substantial nursing homes were opened just before the First World War – one in London, and the other in Birmingham.

In 1911 a company was formed to build a nursing home in Vincent Square, London. It was to be run 'on strictly business

[1] ibid.
[2] ibid.
[3] *BMJ Supplement*, 3 August 1907, p. 105
[4] *BMJ*, 24 June 1907, p. 1564
[5] *BMJ Supplement*, 31 July 1909, p. 147
[6] ibid., 30 October 1909, p. 288

lines' with free choice of doctor, and medical bills were to be paid separately. The minimum charge for maintenance was to be three guineas a week. The home was described as being built to meet the needs of 'the poorer middle classes',[1] and was to be carefully designed 'for the patient's comfort as regards quiet and open space'.[2] Two years later the Empire Hospital for Paying Patients opened its doors.[3]

The nursing home at Birmingham was owned and run by doctors. There was a medical committee but every member of it had to be a stockholder. Patients could only be admitted to the hospital through a member of the medical staff. The general practitioner had free access to the patient and was, where practicable, invited to assist in the treatment. This was particularly the case 'with regard to the administration of anaesthetics and assistance at operations'.[4] All the doctors on the staff were on the staff of one of the Birmingham hospitals.

Most of the patients paid an inclusive fee varying from five guineas per week to ten guineas per week which covered both maintenance and professional attendance. There were also some private patients who paid their doctors separately. The hospital had sixty small private wards and four large wards with accommodation for six patients in each. There were two operating theatres, a small dispensary, a pathological laboratory and X-ray rooms.[5]

Despite further complaints about the failings of many nursing homes, the Government took no action to introduce registration and inspection. In 1912 an Association was formed for the protection and registration of nursing homes. Its objective was to ensure that the Matron and nurses had certificates from a recognized training school.[6] At the end of 1913, the London County Council decided to try and introduce a bill to gain powers to regulate maternity hospitals in its area and 'nursing homes and other establishments (not being public hospitals), where massage, manicure or curative treatment by light, electricity, baths or similar means is carried on'.[7] The parliamentary

[1] *BMJ*, 4 November 1911, p. 1221
[2] ibid., 23 December 1911, p. 1676
[3] *Hospital*, Vol. LV, 20 December 1913, p. 304
[4] *BMJ*, 21 February 1920, p. 264
[5] ibid.
[6] *Hospital*, Vol. LII, 14 September 1912, p. 615
[7] ibid., Vol. LV, 1 November 1913, p. 103

committee of the Council stated that one object was 'to prevent immorality'.[1]

By 1914 virtually all nursing homes were run on business principles. While there were beds where the patient had to pay substantially more than the cost, there were extremely few pay beds in Britain outside the cottage hospitals where patients paid less than the cost. There was nothing to stop almoners extracting substantial donations from inpatients in voluntary hospitals but such patients were in theory treated in exactly the same way as other patients.

In separate nursing homes, the profession was prepared to tolerate some subsidization of poorer patients but it was held to be 'unfair' for richer patients in nursing homes to pay extra to help poorer patients, though such discrimination was common in the fees levied by doctors on their patients. Moreover, if a nursing home was run on this principle, it was unlikely that richer patients would knowingly choose a home which charged more than cost in preference to a home which took no poor patients.

Burdett was among the few persons connected with British hospitals who advocated payments according to what the market would bear. This had been the original intention of the Home Hospital and of the Central Northern Hospital – two projects with which he was closely connected. He pointed out in books and articles that systems of varying charges were common in the United States, Germany and many other countries. The development of medical care in these countries had, however, been very different. In Britain, all hospitals except the small cottage hospitals were 'closed list' hospitals. General practitioners feared a loss of income if patients were allowed to pay hospitals what they could afford.

[1] ibid., 20 December 1913, p. 303

CHAPTER 13

The Acute Sick and the Chronic Sick

IT was not only the middle classes who were increasing their demands for medical care away from their homes. Between 1891 and 1911, the total number of beds for the sick in hospitals, infirmaries and workhouse institutions increased from about 113,000 to about 197,000.[1] This expansion was much more rapid than that of the population of England and Wales. The number of beds per thousand of the population increased from 3·9 to 5·5 in only twenty years.

The voluntary hospitals were providing a total of about 43,000 beds by 1911 – 14,000 more than in 1891. Though there were about forty more tuberculosis hospitals and thirty-five more chronic hospitals in 1911 than in 1891, the greatest expansion was in general hospitals. The number of these hospitals increased from 385 to 530 during this period. The public sector increased its provisions for the sick faster than the voluntary hospitals. It provided about 83,000 beds in 1891 and about 154,000 beds in 1911. The number of separate infirmaries with nursing schools increased from eighteen to seventy-five. The proportion of all beds for the sick in voluntary general and teaching hospitals and in these separate infirmaries increased from 31 per cent to 36 per cent, and the proportion of all beds which were in public hospitals for infectious diseases increased from 9 per cent to 16 per cent. Though the proportion of all beds in mixed Poor Law institutions fell from 54 per cent to 41 per cent the number of such beds changed little. There were 61,000 of these beds in 1891 and 80,000 in 1911. The new separate infirmaries represented additional accommodation rather than replacement of accommodation in mixed institutions.

The rapid expansion of separate Poor Law infirmaries was not only due to the need to meet urgent demands. The demands

[1] For the sources of the figures in the first two paragraphs of this chapter, see Vol. 2 of this study.

themselves were generated to a considerable extent by improvements in the quality of care provided in the infirmaries. Boards of Guardians were expressing new attitudes to the care of the sick. This was partly due to changes in the methods by which they were appointed. In 1894, the Local Government Act[1] swept away the old financial qualifications and abolished *ex officio* Guardians. It also made it possible for more women to join the boards: married women were no longer barred from service. The number of female Guardians increased from 193 in 1893 to 883 in 1894[2] and over 1,200 in 1909.[3] They generally came from a higher social class than their male colleagues: Guardians were also encouraged to appoint visiting committees consisting of women. These changes were later described by Davy, the Chief Inspector of the Local Government Board, as 'the inrushing tide of Political Democracy' which 'opened wide the way to a demagogic dispensation of relief'.[4]

Some of the Guardians who were elected differed from the Local Government Board in the way in which they interpreted their duties. For example, the Camberwell Guardians adopted the attitude of some of those who used the infirmaries. They refused to regard infirmary care as poor relief and refused to preach thrift to 'people who have not got anything to be thrifty on'.[5] They favoured the nationalization of all medical institutions and the provision of free treatment in them. National taxation was to be brought in to finance the system. The election of socialists to the Poplar Board of Guardians in 1894 caused much anxiety to the central authority. In response to complaints from some local ratepayers, Chief Inspector Davy was eventually sent down to conduct a special inquiry in 1905. In his report he had much to say about the Guardians' extravagances and bad management. Beatrice Webb also considered that the Poplar Guardians' administration was 'utterly reckless'.[6]

After the abolition of *ex officio* Guardians, the influence of the

[1] 56 & 57 Vict., C. 73

[2] Elizabeth M. Ross, *Women and Poor Law Administration 1857–1910*, pp. 217–18, London M.A. thesis, 1956. The first women Guardians were elected at Kensington in 1875.

[3] M. Bruce, *The Coming of the Welfare State*, p. 109, London, 1961

[4] *Twenty-Fourth Annual Report LGB 1894–5*, C 7867, pp. 14–15, HMSO, 1895

[5] *Royal Commission on Poor Laws 1905–9*, Vol. II, Cd 4684, Q. 16386

[6] Sidney & Beatrice Webb, *Our Partnership*, p. 337, London, 1948

Charity Organization Society diminished. It was, however, still to be found at St George's-in-the-East Parish, where a Guardian believed that 'sympathy is outside the educating system for the Poor Law to adopt'.[1] The Chairman of this Board thought that his Guardians should be given police protection at their meetings 'at any rate, during the winter'.[2] Stepney Board of Guardians – considered to be one of the strictest in England – quarrelled with the Charity Organization Society because 'they were too severe in time of war'.[3]

As infirmaries were improved, more and more non-paupers were admitted to them. Year after year, the inspectors complained about 'the annually increasing number in the infirmary [who] are recruited from a class far removed from destitution'.[4]

> The dress and the general appearance in many instances of the relatives and friends of the patients met with in the wards on visiting day suggest the inference that not a few among the latter are recruited from a class far removed from destitution, a status which was understood to be the condition entitling to relief from the rates in this or any other form when separate Poor Law infirmaries were first established.[5]

And though the authorities were meant to be charging those who could pay, very little money was collected.[6]

The sick of all classes had every incentive to use the best infirmaries. The majority of the Royal Commission on the Poor Laws of 1909 classed their wards, with some exaggeration, as 'quite equal to those of a first class general hospital'.[7] During 1906 'about 3,000 operations, some of them of a most serious and important character' were performed in the London infirmaries. Camberwell Infirmary was 'quite up to the standard of a

---

[1] *Royal Commission on Poor Laws 1905–9*, Vol. I, Qs. 5362–4. There was deadlock between the Guardians who wanted a cheap infirmary and the LGB who refused to sanction their plans.

[2] ibid., Q. 24

[3] ibid., Vol. II, Cd 4684, Qs 21602–3, HMSO, 1909. During the Boer War the Society refused help to soldiers' wives, if it could trace any record of relief having been given to the family.

[4] *Twenty-Eighth Annual Report LGB 1898–9*, C 9444, p. lvi, HMSO, 1899

[5] ibid., p. 86

[6] *Report of Royal Commission on Poor Laws 1905–9*, Cd 4499 (Majority), p. 273

[7] ibid., p. 347

first class general hospital'.[1] During October 1907 nearly all its 819 beds were occupied and there were approximately 500 patients whose condition was that of ordinary 'hospital' cases.[2] Accident cases were frequently taken in. About 500 operations were performed annually and the building was equipped with 'all the most modern appliances used in medical treatment – X-rays, Finsen lights, electric baths, etc.'[3]

The medical staff consisted of a superintendent and five assistants. The nursing staff was composed of a matron, fifteen 'head sisters', two night superintendents and forty-three staff nurses with three years' training. There were also two male nurses and fifty-five probationers.[4] Reports were made daily on all acute patients. There were some infectious cases in the children's wards and 'boy patients' under five years of age and 'girl patients' aged under eight were not allowed visitors. All patients slept in beds 'of the best quality' and the walls of their wards were 'painted or varnished on the plaster'.[5]

There were also some good Poor Law hospitals in the provincial towns. The patients of Glossop Workhouse Infirmary were accommodated in self-contained wards, equipped with a bathroom, a closet and wash-basin. Bathing regulations were displayed. Walls were painted and floors polished. The inspector found that 'all lockers are clean and contain no food, but brush and comb and a few small articles of clothing'. The patients slept in iron-framed beds with straw mattresses.[6] Sheffield Infirmary was equipped with an operating theatre costing £500 and several other institutions possessed expensive electrical equipment and Röntgen Ray apparatus.[7] When the new workhouse infirmary at Halifax was opened in 1900, a visiting ear, nose and throat 'specialist' was appointed at a salary of £60

---

[1] *Royal Commission on Poor Laws 1905–9*, Vol. XIV, Cd 4573, J. C. McVail, *Report to the Royal Commission . . . on Poor Law Medical Relief in Certain Unions in England and Wales*, p. 305, HMSO, 1909. The oldest part of Camberwell Infirmary was built in 1875 and further extensions were added in 1885 and 1903. It is still in use under the NHS as St Giles Hospital (413 beds).

[2] ibid.

[3] ibid., p. 305

[4] ibid., p. 306

[5] ibid.

[6] ibid., p. 262. Glossop Workhouse Infirmary was built in 1897 and is now the Shire Hill Hospital (82 beds).

[7] ibid., p. 243

per annum.[1] The new building at King's Norton, Birmingham, was so 'handsome and well conducted' that the patients did not show 'the abhorrence of indoor relief which is found in the rural unions'.[2]

By no means all the separate infirmaries had attained such high standards. The Salford Board called their infirmary the 'Hope Hospital' to hide any connection with the Poor Law. But all the cleaning and scrubbing was done by widows 'who would be paupers but for such occupation'. They worked from 7 a.m. to 1 p.m. and received two shillings daily. A bathman was employed to bathe all the male patients once a week. It is possible that he was not so gentle because there were patients 'who had left the institution definitely on account of the necessity for taking a weekly bath'.[3] The windows of the bathroom opened only a few inches 'owing, it is said, to one or two inmates having committed suicide by jumping out'.

The walls of the infirmary were of poor quality, colour-washed brick. Some of the urinals were 'very bad and foul smelling' and consisted of slate stalls with leaden floors. The rather terrifying operating room had 'rough brick walls painted over, poor light and bad ventilation, not a very good stock of apparatus, no sterilizer, and only a wooden operating table'. Fortunately there had been only twenty-five operations in the previous two years. This hospital was regarded with 'some degree of dislike or suspicion' by the local population. It still had a few admirers among the residents of common lodging houses, one of whom had 'deliberately prevented his ulcers from healing'. As this patient refused to have his legs amputated 'he spends his life in bed at the cost of the rates'.[4]

The growth of 'specialized institutions' was 'one of the most potent factors' contributing to the rising cost of poor relief.[5] In 1904, new hospitals accounted for 44 per cent of the total expenditure on Poor Law building.[6] As the Local Government

[1] *PLOJ*, 26 July 1901, p. 618

[2] *Royal Commission on Poor Law 1905–9;* McVail, *Medical Relief*, p. 278. King's Norton Infirmary was opened in 1897 and is now the Selly Oak Hospital (1,908 beds).

[3] ibid., p. 291. Hope Hospital is still in use under the NHS. Its complement is now 793 beds, including 26 for pay and amenity patients.

[4] ibid., p. 292

[5] *Report of Royal Commission on Poor Laws 1905–9* (Majority), pp. 27–8

[6] ibid., p. 29

Board's own architect explained, Guardians were allowed 'to put in things now which . . . ten or twenty years ago were not invented'.[1] In-maintenance costs had also risen. In 1872 they had amounted to nearly £500,000 for all the Metropolitan institutions.[2] By 1906 the separate infirmaries alone were costing nearly a million pounds.[3] Specialized infirmaries required 'a large number of officials with superior qualifications' and, in London, the annual cost of salaries, wages and superannuation amounted to £187,000.[4] Direct expenditures on patients and staff in the twenty-three London infirmaries of 1897 had averaged £34 14s 8d per patient. By 1906 the same average for twenty-seven infirmaries was £41 0s 3d.[5]

The number of acutely sick patients seeking hospital care steadily increased. Nearly all the urban infirmaries were kept full to overflowing. The Association of Poor Law Unions thought that the term 'pauper' needed to be retained as 'once the disqualifications attending residence in their infirmaries were removed, the demands on accommodation would be such as it would be almost impossible to cope with'.[6] So, far from deterring patients, some of the infirmaries were positively attracting them. There was the case of the patient who refused 'to be transferred to the workhouse of the same union when the course of his illness renders such transference desirable'.[7]

The heavy demand for admission to the well-equipped infirmaries made it necessary for some system of selection of patients to be introduced. The medical superintendents were quite clear about the criteria they wanted to use. They wanted the acute sick. This was the type of patient they had been trained to care for in the teaching hospitals. The more 'acute' the patients who were admitted, the greater was the use that could

[1] ibid., p. 243
[2] *Twelfth Annual Report LGB 1882-3*, pp. xxvii–xxviii
[3] *Royal Commission on Poor Laws 1905-9*, Vol. II, Cd 4684, Appendix XIII(B), p. 426
[4] *Report of Royal Commission on Poor Laws 1905-9* (Majority), p. 242. The annual cost per head had risen from £37 in 1878 to £60 in 1906.
[5] *Royal Commission on Poor Laws 1905-9*, Vol. II, App. XIII(B), pp. 426-32. Variation in direct expenditure on patients and staff ranged from £31 12s 5d at St Pancras South to £62 9s 7d at Blackwall. The yearly cost of provisions per occupied bed was similarly variable, ranging from £9 2s 3d at Wandsworth Infirmary to £16 7s 0d at the City of London.
[6] *Hospital*, Vol. XLIV, 18 July 1908, p. 428
[7] *Royal Commission on Poor Laws 1905-9*, McVail, *Medical Relief*, p. 147

be made of the limited beds. And the more acute the patients, the higher the status of the medical superintendent in the eyes of his professional colleagues.

Acute patients were quite easily acquired in those areas where there was a gross shortage of voluntary hospital beds. In 1909, it could be pointed out that

> ... in some parts of London and in certain provincial districts, e.g. Camberwell, Woolwich, Bedwellty, etc., general hospitals are either non-existent or too inaccessible. Accordingly, when an accident occurs, it is, as a matter of course, removed for treatment to the Poor Law Infirmary. . . . The Poor Law Infirmary here becomes *de facto*, if not *de jure*, a general hospital for the community.[1]

This was by no means only true of the London area:

> Unfortunately there are more beds in the Mill Road Infirmary than in all the voluntary hospitals in Liverpool combined, and these hospitals have no beds at their disposal. The consequence is that the voluntary hospitals are continually refusing cases and sending them to Mill Road. Mill Road has now become a general hospital and is no longer a Poor Law hospital.[2]

In such districts, the interests of the medical superintendent coincided with the wishes of the local population. As a result it was found that 'absolute destitution, as implying an inability to provide the necessary medical or surgical treatment, acquires a new significance, and may, as regards accident cases at least, include within its scope the whole population of the district, rich and poor'.[3]

Thus, the medical superintendents began to operate policies which flagrantly contravened the principles of the Poor Laws. This led them into conflicts not only with Poor Law inspectors but also with the district medical officers and workhouse medical officers. There were disputes over admission policy when super-intendents tried to exclude the aged and infirm from their hospitals. Overworked district medical officers referred their 'burdensome' patients to the workhouse, and the workhouse doctors tried to move their unwanted cases into the infirmaries.

[1] *Report of Royal Commission on Poor Laws 1905–9* (Majority), p. 247
[2] ibid.
[3] ibid.

But the superintendents of the infirmaries usually had the last word; in London they were remarkably successful in keeping out the 'aged and infirm' patients. According to the Poor Law Census of Sick Paupers carried out in 1896, there were only 94 'aged and infirm' patients in the London separate infirmaries.[1] The average length of stay of the patients in London infirmaries varied from 173 days at Blackwall to 113 days at City of London and 32 days at Whitechapel.[2] Maternity cases in London infirmaries stayed on average for 22 days.[3]

Some Guardians used criteria of social merit in distributing patients between the infirmary and the workhouse. At Poplar and Stepney the sick asylum was reserved for the 'resident poor' and patients from 'common lodging houses' were kept in the workhouse with the venereal and infirm cases. Venereal cases were never admitted to the infirmary but a few were sent to the Lock Hospital at a weekly cost of seventeen shillings.[4]

The superintendents took certain risks in this battle over referrals. As one of them explained in 1906, 'There are cases where the diagnosis of the complaint may not be such as would warrant the man's admission, but the man may be suffering from something far worse than that which has been diagnosed.'[5] In such cases, 'the outdoor medical officer is sending the patient to a more suitable place for treatment; if the patient dies on the way to or soon after admission to the infirmary there is less blame attached than if the same result occurred on the patient's leaving the infirmary.'[6]

Mr Spurrell, the secretary of the Society of Medical Superintendents, thought that it would be 'greatly advantageous' to everyone if 'all the medical work in any one Union were performed by a sufficient number of assistant medical officers under the control of the medical superintendent of the infirmary of that Union'.[7] This arrangement would permit a 'better adjustment of the numbers to accommodation, and the question whether any particular case would be better treated in the infirmary

[1] H of C Sessional Paper 371, 1896, BPP, Vol. LXXII, 1896
[2] Royal Commission on Poor Laws 1905–9, Vol. II, App. XIII(B), pp. 426–30
[3] Fortieth Annual Report LGB, 1910–11, Cd 5865, pp. lix–lx, HMSO, 1911
[4] Royal Commission on Poor Laws 1905–9, Vol. II, Cd 4684, Qs. 21508 and 21550 (evidence of Dr Stoneham)
[5] ibid., Q. 15303 (evidence of Dr Briant)
[6] ibid., Q. 23525 (evidence of Mr Spurrell)
[7] ibid., Q. 23303, section 15

workhouse, at his own home, or as an outpatient would be settled by one authority'.[1] Such a scheme had already been adopted by the Camberwell Guardians in order to check the admission of 'moribund' and other unsuitable cases to the infirmary.[2] Mr Spurrell explained with remarkable frankness how such a system ought to work. The workhouse medical officer would become an assistant to the infirmary superintendent. Thus, '. . . the medical officer of the workhouse would be told: "You sent such and such a man to the infirmary yesterday: now that style of man is not to be sent to the infirmary any more," and he would not be sent to the infirmary any more'.[3]

One reason for the superintendents' preference for the acute sick was the hope of participation in the training of doctors. It had been laid down in Section 29 of the Metropolitan Poor Act that the workhouses 'may be used for the purposes of medical instruction'. This clause had been repealed by Section 20 of the Poor Law Amendment Act of 1869.[4] The Society of Medical Superintendents would have liked a medical school to give an improved status to the service.[5] The presence of students would also have lightened the duties of paid assistants. In 1906 the average medical officer of a separate infirmary was responsible for 233 beds.

The introduction of teaching into the infirmaries would have

---

[1] ibid.

[2] ibid., p. 380 (Appendix 1D, table A). The number of such cases admitted to the infirmary had fallen from 78 in 1904 to 47 in 1906.

[3] ibid., Q. 23469

[4] Dr Bridges, the medical inspector for London, stated that he had never been able to find out why this had been done but had been informed 'that a fear was expressed in the course of discussion in Parliament that it might be said that the bodies of the poor people were dissected in workhouses and that that would create a prejudice against Poor Law administration'. (*Select Committee on Poor Relief 1888*, op. cit., para. 5503.) Arthur Pell, a governor of Guy's and a leading member of the COS, argued that 'unless they [non-paying patients] submit their persons to surgical examinations of a very critical nature, which I consider is equivalent to payment in money, the School of Medicine and Surgery could not advance without cases of that nature. They do make some return to society by illustrating medical teaching.' He was therefore in favour of extending the same opportunities to paupers in poor law infirmaries (*Select Committee on Poor Relief 1888*, para. 1465).

[5] *Royal Commission on Poor Laws 1905–9*, Vol. II, Q. 23501. Spurrell went on to admit that teaching involved a 'certain amount of publicity' and that some patients 'do object to it' and came into poor law infirmaries to avoid the attentions of students in the voluntary hospitals (Q. 23561–3).

improved the standard of medical care provided in them. More and better doctors would have been recruited and, together with the students, would have made it possible to obtain better nursing staff. But the concentration on the 'acute' sick which arose from the desire to emulate the voluntary hospitals, particularly the teaching hospitals, changed the whole character of some of the infirmaries. None of this had been envisaged in 1867 when the decision to build infirmaries had been taken.

In practical terms, the introduction of these criteria for selection of infirmary patients meant that some of the really poor were denied access to the most valuable institutions which had been developed to meet their needs. If the acute sick took precedence over the chronic sick and if this criterion were allowed to predominate over income or class, it meant that some of the beds in the infirmaries were given to those who could afford to pay and were, therefore, denied to those for whom the whole service had been created. In one infirmary, it was alleged with 'a good deal of foundation' that 'the ordinary "infirm" cases have been largely driven out and drafted into the workhouse in order to make room for better-off patients'.[1] There was one superintendent who wanted a separate and 'stricter type of infirmary' with male nurses for patients who 'use foul language and misbehave themselves'.[2] In another Union it was claimed that the public was using the infirmary 'as if it were a private nursing home'.[3]

Thus in the urban areas, where there were separate infirmaries, patients were divided into the acute sick who went to the infirmary and the chronic sick who went to the workhouse. In many rural areas, however, patients of all kinds were still cared for in general mixed institutions: in some of them, all the sick were in separate wards; in others, particularly those operated by the small Unions, there had been little classification. Though great improvements were introduced in the new infirmaries particularly in London, many of the workhouses remained in 1905 little better than they had been in 1865.

The major problem of the workhouses continued to be the standard of the nursing services: even enlightened Guardians who were prepared to spend money were unable to introduce

[1] *Report of Royal Commission on Poor Laws 1905–9* (Majority), pp. 244–5
[2] *Royal Commission on Poor Laws 1905–9*, Vol. II, Qs. 23456 and 23461
[3] ibid., Q. 23387

drastic improvements. There were two major obstacles to reform. The first was the system of workhouse administration and the second was the unwillingness of trained nurses to care for cases of chronic sickness.

Workhouses continued to be controlled by unqualified masters who were unwilling to delegate any of their authority to superintendent nurses. Moreover, their wives continued to perform many of the duties which were undertaken by the matron of a voluntary hospital. Few trained nurses were willing to work under autocratic lay administrators – particularly those who were of lower social class than themselves. Nor were they prepared to tolerate interference from their untrained wives. One nurse who took a post in a workhouse resigned because of the 'utter uselessness of nurses fighting for proper administration under untrained management. . . . We stand so often entirely unsupported.'[1] Young nurses inevitably lost enthusiasm when 'there is nobody to approve of their work, to inspect it, to encourage them, and there is a great jealousy on the part of the workhouse matron very often, because the nurse knows more than she does'.[2] There were masters who preferred to use pauper women for nursing work 'as they are wholly dependent on his will and his power over them is despotic'.[3]

Workhouse employment was unattractive to trained nurses for other reasons. Their skills could not be exercised or, if they could, brought little visible reward because the patients were mostly classed as 'chronic' or 'incurable'. The problem was clearly described by a Poor Law inspector in 1902:

. . . in most of the Rural Unions, when a vacancy occurs, the offer of a fair salary rarely attracts more than one or two candidates, and seldom one with any training whatever. And when a trained nurse is by lucky chance obtained, she is rarely willing to stay long in uncongenial surroundings where, since there are very few acute cases or operations, she is likely to lose her skill for want of practice.[4]

Miss Twining formed the Workhouse Nursing Association in the attempt to secure improvements. Girls were selected and

1 Abel-Smith, pp. 47–8
2 *Select Committee on Poor Relief 1888*, para. 3016
3 Abel-Smith, pp. 44–5
4 *Thirty-Second Annual Report LGB, 1902–3*, Cd 1700, p. 101, HMSO, 1903

given scholarships to take nursing training on the condition that they worked in workhouses for an agreed period. Most of them left workhouse work as soon as the period was over. They wrote to Miss Twining complaining of the cramped accommodation and long hours of duty, the wretched diet, the lack of privacy outside working hours and the rigid control of workhouse officials.[1] The Association also tried to act as an employment agency. But in one year, out of forty-one trained nurses who applied to it for posts, only eighteen were considered suitable and only four ultimately accepted posts.[2]

Thus the system of using pauper nurses continued and so did the periodic workhouse scandals. In 1890, at Stockton Workhouse, a female imbecile was beaten unconscious by a pauper nurse. In the workhouse at Christchurch,

A man, aged sixty, suffering from heart disease, was allowed to lie ill and groaning, cared for only by other inmates in the 'old men's ward' of the workhouse, without proper food and attention, from Saturday night to Monday morning. He was then carried on the porter's back to the infirmary, where he died almost immediately.[3]

In 1890 the sick wards of Bethnal Green Workhouse were described as being a 'crying and a notorious evil'.[4] This opinion was shared by the workhouse medical officer. He described how he had to call in a friendly general practitioner to assist with amputations.[5] There were 590 sick paupers crowded into wards for 495 patients. They were cared for by eleven nurses, only two of whom had received hospital training. The bulk of the nursing was carried out by eighty paupers and it was 'utterly impossible' to keep up discipline. These paupers were 'anything but efficient' and some of them were aged sixty-five and over.[6] The clerk to the Guardians agreed that 'it is a very unfortunate

[1] Abel-Smith, pp. 47–8
[2] ibid.
[3] WINA Tract, 'Nursing in Workhouses and Workhouse Infirmaries', paper read to meeting of Hospital Association, 10 December 1890, by Mrs Wilson, honorary secretary of WINA, p. 14 (British Museum Library, CUP 401, g. 12, No. IV)
[4] *Select Committee on Metropolitan Hospitals 1890–3*, Second Report, para. 24127 (evidence of Dr Knox)
[5] ibid., para. 24132. The amputations were done 'underhanded' as 'it takes three men to get a leg off properly' (para. 24134).
[6] ibid., paras. 24082, 24093, 24126

state of things' but explained that 'it is not their [the Guardians'] fault' and they had found it difficult to obtain a new site for the past ten years.[1] They eventually found one in 1896.

In 1895–6, Mr Ernest Hart, who had been a member of the original *Lancet* Commission, supervised a survey of provincial workhouses and was shocked to find that in many cases conditions were as bad as those he had witnessed in 1866. In one workhouse he found that the sick were

> lying on plank beds with chaff mattresses about three inches thick between their weary bodies and the hard uneven planks. One paralysed woman had a spring bed with a chaff mattress over the springs. . . . Some idiots and imbeciles share the wards with these patients. The infants occupy a dark stone-paved room, bare of furniture with no rug for the babies to crawl or lie upon and no responsible person to see to their feeding and cleanliness.[2]

At Plymouth Workhouse there were only two trained nurses in charge of 164 patients. The sick wards were inadequately ventilated, and had neither running water nor slop sinks.[3]

A census of sick paupers was undertaken in 1896.[4] It was found that the majority of the sick were still accommodated in general mixed workhouses. Over 36,000 patients were accommodated in this way compared with about 22,000 who were in separate infirmaries.[5] At this time there were still 3,443 paupers 'assisting

[1] ibid., paras. 24729, 24705–6 (evidence of Mr Howard)

[2] E. Hart, *The Sick Poor in Workhouses* (Reports on the Nursing and Administration of Provincial Workhouses by a Special Commission of the *British Medical Journal*), 1st Series, p. 36, London, 1894

[3] These wards were still being used in 1905 and remained 'quite inadequate for the cases requiring admission' (*Thirty-Fourth Annual Report LGB, 1904–5*, Cd 2661, p. 219, HMSO, 1905). A medical inspector, who had visited every workhouse in England and Wales, selected the Infirmary at Eye, Suffolk, as being 'if not the worst, one of the worst in the country'. When *The Hospital* challenged this claim by describing a near-by workhouse where patients slept upon the floor, the inspector replied that 'I would rather sleep upon the floor at Ipswich Workhouse than in a bed at Eye Infirmary' (*Hospital*, Vol. LIII, 8 February 1913, p. 500).

[4] *H of C 371*, 1896, pp. 6–43. These returns were made during the summer (1 July 1896) and therefore understate the mean number of sick persons in Poor Law establishments. For further details on this and later censuses see Vol. 2 of this study.

[5] The term 'separate infirmary' was used for institutions ranging in size from a Birmingham infirmary with 1,300 beds to a building in Church Stretton containing 4 infirm patients.

in the personal care of the sick'. Of this total, 1,374 were convalescent patients. At least 600 patients in the smallest establishments were without the services of even one paid nurse and the number denied the benefits of trained nursing was far greater.[1] As Miss Twining said in 1890, 'It is hardly an exaggeration to say that there is, as a rule, no night nursing of the sick throughout the smaller workhouses of the country, but that of paupers.'[2]

In 1897 the Local Government Board issued an Order which contained a stricter limitation of the nursing role of 'pauper inmates'. They were no longer to 'perform the duties of a nurse' – but they could be employed as attendants if they worked under the supervision of a paid officer and were approved by the medical officer. The only qualification required of paid nurses was some 'practical experience in nursing'. But the 1897 Order made one very important stipulation. 'Superintendent Nurses' were to be appointed in every workhouse having a nursing staff of three or more persons. Only nurses with at least three years' training in a recognized school were to be eligible for these posts.[3]

The status of a superintendent nurse was not, however, clearly defined. In practice, she remained subordinate to the workhouse matron.[4] It was not possible to make the post of superintendent nurse effective and attractive without disturbing established hierarchies. This was not seriously attempted until 1900 when an Order was issued to the Basingstoke and Farnham Unions, providing

> ... that the duty of making morning and nightly visits to the sick and lying-in wards of the workhouse should cease to be part of the duties of the master and matron of the workhouse, and that it should be the duty of the superintendent nurse to visit each of these wards daily to see that all proper arrangements for the care of the inmates both by day and by night are made.[5]

[1] *H of C 371*, 1896, p. 43
[2] *Hospital*, Vol. VIII, 2 August 1890, pp. 270–71
[3] *Twenty-Seventh Annual Report LGB, 1897–8*, C 8978, Appendix, pp. 27–9 (Order dated 6 August 1897), HMSO, 1898
[4] WINA Tract, Mrs Wilson, 'Nursing in Workhouses ...', p. 15. 'In some Unions the *Master* as well as the Matron consider it part of their duty to go round with the Doctor when he visits the patients.'
[5] *Thirtieth Annual Report LGB, 1900–01*, Cd 746, p. cvii, HMSO, 1901. This Order was issued on 24 October 1900.

Similar Orders were issued to other Unions between 1900 and 1905 but the conflicts between workhouse matrons and trained nurses continued – and so did the shortage of superintendent nurses. Their position was 'exposed to continual vexation arising out of the relations between this functionary and the master and mistress of the workhouse. Were the matron herself the superintendent, an excellent position would be thrown open to capable nurses.'[1] But the Guardians were more interested in 'the obvious convenience of having a married couple as master and matron'. These joint appointments often meant that 'the best has to be made of one or other of this pair, and since an indifferent master is a serious danger to the discipline of the establishment, naturally the wife of a good master stands an excellent chance of getting the post of matron'.[2] There were few aspects of Poor Law medical care where the principles of deterrence and treatment did not come into conflict.

The 1897 nursing order did not put an end to the use of paupers as nurses.[3] In many cases there was no one else to do the work. The Webbs estimated some ten years later that the 10,000 patients in 'country workhouses' were looked after by only 654 nurses and 105 probationers.[4] Conditions in these rural workhouses continued to be sadly inadequate. Arrangements at Newent Workhouse were particularly bad. Sick paupers slept in the ordinary wards and the bathrooms were without running water. The lavatory for the two venereal wards had rotten woodwork. There was one untrained resident nurse for the eleven sick and five imbecile patients. In the lying-in ward, 'an old lady aged seventy-four, who is troubled with bronchitis' was waiting to act as wardswoman to an expectant mother. Labour was to take place on a bed fifteen inches in height.[5]

In 1905 as in 1865, the medical supervision of workhouse patients came from local general practitioners who were employed on a part-time basis. One workhouse doctor with thirty years' service was only paid £70 per annum. In some years

---

[1] *Hospital,* Vol. XLIII, 11 January 1908, p. 405
[2] ibid.
[3] *Report of Royal Commission on Poor Laws 1905–9* (Minority), p. 861
[4] Sidney and Beatrice Webb, *The State and the Doctor,* p. 100, London, 1912
[5] *Royal Commission on Poor Laws 1905–9;* McVail, *Medical Relief,* pp. 196–7

he 'spent as much as £25 in medicines, from his stipend'.[1] In such cases the medical officer could not afford to prescribe up-to-date drugs. One medical inspector argued that such a system 'may cost the life of an inmate of a workhouse'.[2] It is not surprising that workhouse doctors were not always conscientious in the performance of their duties. An inspector who studied the amount of time given to workhouse duties by one of these medical officers found that 'frequently he has only been in the workhouse for a few minutes and that he has rarely been in the workhouse for half an hour'.[3]

Thus in 1905, though a number of good infirmaries had been built, the majority of the sick were still housed in unclassified institutions, some of which were no better than those which had been condemned forty years earlier. Many patients were still being nursed by aged convalescent and feeble-minded paupers in buildings which had never been designed for hospital purposes. Their medical attendance came from exploited general practitioners who made perfunctory visits and had to pay for any drugs which they prescribed out of their own salaries. At the other end of the scale there were modern, purpose-built infirmaries with salaried medical staffs, trained nurses and all the latest apparatus of a hospital. Such hospitals were ceasing to be regarded as a Poor Law service. It was no longer necessary to drive patients into these institutions: on the contrary, the problem was to ration these limited facilities among the different types of patients seeking care.

If the authorities had really wanted to improve the standard of care provided in mixed institutions, they could have done so

[1] *Report of Royal Commission on Poor Laws 1905–9* (Minority), p. 859

[2] ibid., p. 860

[3] *Royal Commission on Poor Laws 1905–9*, Vol. I, Q. 9316 (evidence of Mr Fleming): 'I have in several unions within the last three or four years taken from the porter's book the length of time that the medical officer has been in the workhouse. I have found that frequently he has only been in the workhouse for a few minutes, and that he has rarely been in the workhouse for half an hour. When you consider that the entry in the porter's book of the time of admission . . . is when the medical officer first goes into the house, that he has then to find his way to the sick wards – very likely saying "How Do You Do?" to the master and matron on his way up – and may have other things besides the sick wards to look after . . . then if he has only been in the house for ten minutes . . . time after time, and week after week, it is very evident that he cannot examine the bodily condition of the patients . . . in the way in which I think it ought to be done.'

effectively but expensively by substituting accommodation in separate infirmaries. But the latter were raising problems of a different kind. They conflicted both in theory and in practice with the concept of 'less eligibility'. Already they were attracting patients above the pauper class and, if the practice were to be given formal sanction, what was left of the principles of 1834? And what was to be the relationship between public hospitals and voluntary hospitals? How could the public be expected to pay rates to support one type of hospital and pay voluntary subscriptions to support another? And if the standards of public hospitals were deliberately kept low to deter prospective patients, how could this be reconciled with the principle of prevention which was strongly championed by so many medical officers? No answers to these questions could be found by studying the precedents of the Local Government Board. The time was ripe for a public inquiry.

CHAPTER 14

The Royal Commission of 1909

TWO separate types of hospital – those owned by public authorities and those owned by independent charitable bodies – had developed separately to provide services for those who could not afford to buy their own. By 1900 there were, in both sectors, persistent complaints about 'abuse'. Patients had been attracted who could afford to pay at least some part of the cost of their treatment.

Both types of hospital had developed in an age when the hospital could do little for the patient. Hospitals were feared and were used only as a last resort. In addition, the use of the Poor Law hospitals was limited by all the stigmas which had been deliberately laid upon applicants for relief. But gradually the barriers which were shielding the hospitals from 'abuse' began to break down. The lower middle classes were increasing rapidly in number and they made it increasingly difficult for the government to make sharp distinctions between 'rich' and 'poor' in its social policies. Many people who could not be considered 'poor' by the standards of the day were seeking access to hospital as progress in medicine and nursing had led to great improvements in the comfort of hospital life and the potentialities of hospital treatment. These changes which came first to the voluntary hospitals were spreading to the public sector. A new era of medical practice and of English social history lay ahead.

As regards payment and electoral rights, the medical services were a morass of anomalies. In many areas, the poor or nearly all the poor were denied care outside the hospital from the public services. Between the district medical officer and the patient there stood the grim figure of the relieving officer. There was, however, an exception in the case of schoolchildren looked after by education authorities. A free consultation could be obtained by any poor person who cared to go and wait in the out-patient department of a voluntary hospital. This indiscriminate system was said to make nonsense of attempts of other voluntary agencies and some Boards of Guardians to encourage the working class to join provident clubs. Nevertheless, some seven million persons were members of clubs, most of which provided, in return for contributions, both 'free' medicine and some choice of doctor.

Patients in the general ward of a voluntary hospital were selected for admission because they were likely to respond to treatment and to stay only for a short period. They made no payment. The role of subscribers' letters had been greatly reduced by 1906 and the medical staff had 'practically unlimited power to admit or reject patients'.[1] This was the culmination of the shift in power which had started early in the nineteenth century. The status of the medical staff had changed from employee to honorary. St Thomas' and Guy's Hospitals still paid their doctors the nominal sum of £50 a year but this payment was now called 'carriage hire'. The doctors were no longer even technically under contract of service. The result was that 'the managers of many hospitals do not control the medical staff because it is held that they render such enormous services without payment'.[2] Burdett said that this was 'the underlying principle of the whole system'.[3]

Patients with infectious diseases were also usually treated free in many of the hospitals provided by sanitary authorities. Some authorities charged them but were not empowered to ask a relative to make payments on their behalf, except in the case of patients who had been admitted through the Poor Law machinery. A tuberculosis patient might be treated free by a sanitary authority or at cost by a Poor Law authority. In theory, patients and their relatives were responsible for paying the maintenance costs in the Poor Law infirmaries and workhouse wards. In practice, the enforcement of this law depended on how the particular presiding barrister concerned chose to interpret it. Thus, whether some payment was extracted depended more on the category of institution in which a patient happened to be treated than on income or social class.

These arrangements satisfied no one. Patients resented paying

[1] *Hospital*, Vol. XLI, 10 November 1906, p. 97

[2] KEHF: *Report of the Committee appointed to Enquire into the Financial Relations between Hospitals and Medical Schools in London*, para. 820 (evidence of Mr Burdett), London, February 1905

[3] ibid.

when they were asked to do so. The British Medical Association resented the loss of paying patients when free care was unnecessarily provided. The voluntary hospitals lacked an adequate and regular income. And the Local Government Board lacked any clear philosophy to guide it in its work.

In 1905 'an energetic man' (J. S. Davy), whom Sidney and Beatrice Webb[1] thought was 'intent on reaction',[2] was appointed chief inspector of the Board. There was also a new president (G. W. Balfour) whom the Webbs described as a 'philosopher who recognized the public advantage of a precise discrimination between opposing principles'.[3] At the close of the parliamentary session of 1905, the Prime Minister rose to 'announce in reply to an evidently prearranged question . . . that the Government had come to the conclusion that the time had come for a full inquiry into the whole question' of poor relief.[4] Shortly afterwards, on the very day the Government resigned, a Royal Commission[5] was appointed to investigate the working of the Poor Laws and to advise on any 'changes in their administration or fresh legislation' which it thought necessary.[6]

[1] Sidney Webb (1859–1947) and Beatrice Webb (1858–1943) – or Miss Potter as she was until her marriage in 1892 – devoted their lives to social reform, politics and the writing of social history. They were early members of the Fabian Society and helped to found the London School of Economics and Political Science (1895), the Technical Education Board of London (1892), the Imperial College of Science and Technology (1903). Sidney was closely associated with the early Labour Party and became a member of the first two Labour Governments. Beatrice sat on the Royal Commission on the Poor Laws, 1905–9: the minority report was written jointly by them. Their writings include a history of trades unions and a voluminous history of local government.

[2] Sidney and Beatrice Webb, *English Local Government: English Poor Law History, Pt II, The Last Hundred Years*, Vol. II, p. 470, Private Subscription Edition, March 1929

[3] ibid.

[4] ibid.

[5] The Royal Commission on the Poor Laws and the Relief of Distress was composed of five Poor Law Guardians, including two members of the COS; three Permanent Heads of the LGB; one Senior Medical Inspector of the LGB; another four members of the COS, including its general secretary, C. S. Loch; Professor W. Smart, a political economist of known 'orthodox' views; two ministers of the Church; Charles Booth, the sociologist, and Mrs Beatrice Webb. Its chairman was Lord George Hamilton, a former Conservative Cabinet Minister. Only George Lansbury, Francis Chandler and Mrs Webb were known as active critics of the Poor Law.

[6] *Report of Royal Commission on Poor Laws 1905–9*, (Majority), p. 1

In his evidence to the Royal Commission Davy showed that he was muddled about the future of his medical services. Significantly he selected the Metropolitan Poor Act of 1867 as the 'beginning of a change in the administration of the Poor Law . . . which has not yet come to an end'.[1] The Act had been an attempt to accommodate within one system of administration two separate services with fundamentally different aims. It sought to lay down a new principle – that the condition of sick paupers should *not* be made 'less eligible', in order that the daily life of able-bodied paupers could be made *more* 'less eligible' than ever before. Davy confessed that the aims of the two services were contradictory. He denounced the Act of 1867 and all the ameliorations that had followed it – not because the sick and the aged ought not to receive adequate care – but because the whole process had undermined the principles of the Poor Laws. He reluctantly conceded that it was now impossible to discriminate clearly between the destitute and the non-destitute sick.

> To be quite honest, I have done my best to find reasons against it because I do not like it. I am afraid there must be some mischief in it which I do not see. But logically, I cannot avoid the conclusion that the time has come when the whole question of institutional relief for the sick at the cost of the rates must be reconsidered; and the point of disenfranchisement would, of course, be an important question . . . possibly the solution of it may be found in the abandonment of the whole problem as one which is outside the scope of the ordinary pauper relief . . . namely, by frankly admitting that in a populous urban community there is a class for whom charity cannot provide, and for whom perhaps the state should provide.[2]

He ended by warning the Commission that, 'If you do that (and you may have to do it), you will in my judgement stop any further provision of charity hospitals all over the country.'[3]

Davy was one of the most important witnesses and a stern believer in a strict Poor Law. There is no record of Mrs Webb changing his opinions – and we would probably have been told if she had done so. Davy favoured the removal of the sick from the Poor Laws as he saw it as the only way of reverting to a wholly deterrent policy for the able-bodied. He wanted to introduce

[1] *Royal Commission on Poor Laws 1905–9*, Vol. I, Cd 4625, para. 3290
[2] ibid., paras. 2866 and 2891
[3] ibid., para. 2891

corn-grinding, flint-crushing and cross-cut sawing. 'The unemployed man,' he told the Commission, 'must stand by his
accidents' and 'suffer for the good of the body politic.'

Thus Davy wanted to be rid of the sick so as to salvage the
principles on which his department was meant to be operating.
There were, however, positive reasons which could be given for
taking the sick out of the scope of the Poor Laws. The Act of 1867
and the legislation which followed had eventually accepted the
preventive principle for patients with infectious diseases.
Beatrice Webb saw early on that this principle had wider applications and she wanted them ruthlessly applied.

> In listening to the evidence brought by the COS members in
> favour of restricting medical relief to the technically destitute, it
> suddenly flashed across my mind that what we had to do was to
> adopt the exactly contrary attitude and make medical inspection
> and medical treatment compulsory on all sick persons – to treat
> illness, in fact, as a public nuisance to be suppressed in the interests
> of the community.[1]

Compulsory treatment for the whole population or a large section
of the population was to replace the 'compulsory' institutional-
ization of the indigent.

The Royal Commission heard a number of witnesses who
supported the preventive approach but with less vehemence. Dr
Nathan Raw believed that no man should be punished because
he is attacked by sickness or accident: 'It is economic to give the
best treatment.'[2] Dr Raw explained how he had studied a
sample of 4,000 tuberculous paupers and concluded that
'nearly 60 per cent were paupers because they were consumptives and not consumptives because they were paupers'.[3]
Throughout the country there were 'over 200,000 men affected
with tubercle . . . the majority of whom will ultimately have to
resort to the workhouse unless relieved by death'.[4] Dr Andrew
Fuller, the provincial medical inspector, described how a
deterrent Poor Law assisted them in dying. Tuberculous
patients were often deterred from seeking treatment until they

---

[1] S. and B. Webb, *Our Partnership*, p. 342
[2] *Royal Commission on Poor Laws 1905–9*, Vol. IV, Cd 4835, Q. 37927. Dr
Raw was medical superintendent of Brownlow Hill Infirmary.
[3] *Report of Royal Commission on Poor Laws 1905–9* (Majority), p. 371
[4] ibid.

were completely destitute – by which time they were also incurable. He was therefore in favour of removing this single group from the Poor Law and placing them under Public Health.[1] He thought this necessary because, 'If we conceded the principle that the Poor Law were to provide for the treatment of phthisis cases in the first stage, we were conceding the principle that the Poor Law should provide for all cases of acute illness amongst . . . the working classes.'[2]

Dr Fuller agreed that the country was drifting towards 'a more socialistic and wider dealing with illness' but disagreed 'with the principle of it'.[3] He feared that the Poor Law hospitals would soon be taking 'all classes of patients irrespective of the Poor Law'.[4] Some members of the Commission began to share his concern. Five of them held a surreptitious consultation with Dr Raw, hoping to persuade him 'to make out a list of diseases that might be "de-pauperized", leaving all the rest in the Poor Law'.[5] It was, however, extremely difficult to see where the line should be drawn.[6]

The Commission appointed a special investigator, Dr McVail,[7] to inquire into the 'methods and results' of the existing Poor Law services. He found that 'Poor Law relief, both urban and rural, is a cripple supported by two crutches – the general hospital on one side and gratuitous medical work on the other'.[8] The service itself was inadequate for dealing with 'the most important medical problems of our time, the healthy bringing-up

[1] *Royal Commission on Poor Laws 1905–9*, Vol. I, Cd 4625, Q. 10220
[2] ibid., Q. 10249
[3] ibid., Q. 10252
[4] ibid., Q. 10234
[5] S. and B. Webb, *Our Partnership*, p. 384
[6] An intriguing exchange took place between Dr Fuller, Mr Lansbury and Mr Bentham on the question of what constituted a suitable case for disfranchisement. Dr Fuller stated that hopeless cases ought not to be disfranchised but he admitted that 'the problem bristled with difficulties'. He conceded 'purely from a medical point of view' that it was wrong to disfranchise the sick. He then qualified this remark by drawing a distinction between 'the case of phthisis and the case of a broken leg' which were 'two different questions altogether' from 'an administrative point of view'. Finally he said that he was not in favour of disfranchising infectious and phthisical cases, but beyond that he was not prepared to go (*Royal Commission on Poor Laws 1905–9*, Vol. I, Cd 4625, Qs. 10312–6, 10475–89).
[7] ibid., Vol. XIV, Cd 4573; McVail, *Medical Relief*
[8] ibid., p. 148

of children, the control of phthisis, and the early prevention of disease'.[1]

With the exception of the separate infirmaries, there was scarcely a single aspect of the service that, in his opinion, did not require radical improvement. He favoured the creation of 'a higher class of local authorities' to take over all medical services at present managed by Boards of Guardians.[2] As Dr McVail believed that 'almost every disease' could be treated 'from the standpoint of prevention',[3] he advised a union of the public health and Poor Law medical services under a new health authority.[4] The inspectors had conceded that the Poor Law could never become a truly deterrent system until the sick were removed from its care. Many other witnesses had explained why a deterrent medical service was prejudicial to the nation's health. The Guardians were shown once again to be either unable or unwilling to provide adequate medical services. The worst scandal of all was the plight of the patients with tuberculosis. Only two Boards of Guardians had built sanatoria by 1906.[5] It was no longer true that 'indoor medical relief', however good in quality, would by its very nature always be a deterrent.[6] But there was still no evidence it would ever become adequate if left under the Poor Laws.

By December 1907 the Commissioners were agreed that the Poor Law services should be drastically reformed, although they had not yet decided upon the type of service that ought to take its place. Mrs Webb later claimed that the entire Commission had accepted her scheme for transferring the Poor Law services to county and county borough councils along with the 'principle of curative and preventive treatment'. The majority of them, however, rejected her plan for redistributing the services among county council committees under the control of 'a stipendiary officer for the administration of out relief'. She therefore insisted

[1] ibid.
[2] ibid., p. 155, para. 9
[3] ibid., p. 154, para. 6
[4] ibid., pp. 153–4
[5] Liverpool and Bradford Guardians had each built a small sanatorium. The Sheffield Board were using a converted house and three other Boards had purchased beds in a private sanatorium. *Thirty-Fourth Annual Report LGB, 1905–6*, op. cit.; Supplement, *Report of the Medical Officer for 1905–6*, Cd 3657, p. 263
[6] *Report of Royal Commission on Poor Laws 1905–9* (Minority), p. 846

that a vote be taken on 'the crucial question of a Poor Law
statutory committee of the county council *versus* a distribution
of services between the education committee, the health committee etc.' Only Lansbury and Chandler voted with her
against having a single statutory committee. Mrs Webb thereupon insisted on their right to prepare 'a great report of my own'.[1]

The Royal Commission's majority and minority reports were
published in 1909. Although the two reports were based on
fundamentally different principles, their schemes for administrative reform had striking similarities. The majority were
'unhesitatingly opposed to a free medical service' because it
would be impossible to limit such a service to the very poor.[2] In
this event, 'Either the accommodation would be inadequate . . .
or else the State would be obliged to provide gratuitous medical
treatment for practically the whole population.'[3] Any such
development must 'inevitably kill all the existing voluntary
organizations . . . and friendly societies'.[4] There were also the
interests of the medical profession which merited protection
from 'excessive socialism'.[5]

> We cannot contemplate with equanimity the extinction of an in-
> dependent medical profession, which may not only serve as a
> recruiting ground for the more responsible posts in a public service,
> but will also by its originality and independence of criticism,
> preserve that service from excessive officialdom.[6]

The combined opposition of all vested interest – the medical
profession, the voluntary hospitals, the friendly societies and the
ratepayers – made the realization of such a scheme 'quite
impossible'. Finally its cost would be 'prohibitive'.

It was for these reasons that the majority were so reluctant to

[1] In her own account of this famous disagreement Mrs Webb's action
appears somewhat precipitate. She seemed determined to split the Commission. As she explained at the time, freedom to publish a separate report
was 'exactly the position which I prefer'. She was 'thoroughly complacent
with having dragged the whole Commission so far in my direction whilst
preserving my freedom for a Minority Report'. S. and B. Webb, *Our Partnership*, pp. 397–8

[2] *Report of Royal Commission on Poor Laws 1905–9* (Majority), p. 290
[3] ibid., p. 290
[4] ibid.
[5] ibid., p. 291
[6] ibid., p. 291

make a clean break with the concept of 'deterrence' and to substitute for it the principle of 'prevention'. They were therefore opposed to the transfer of Poor Law medical services to Public Health. Through 'propaganda, persuasion and forethought', it was the duty of sanitary authorities 'to make . . . [their] . . . services attractive to all classes of the community, irrespective of their economic condition'.[1] It would therefore be against the tradition of these authorities 'to rigorously enforce a system of contributions according to the patient's ability'.[2] Most sanitary authorities had in fact stopped trying to recover the costs of treatment. The only 'foundation' for a public medical service was the means test,[3] which was 'absolutely necessary to prevent the well-to-do from abusing the system'.[4]

A solution had therefore to be found that did not entail the 'supervision and treatment of every human being from the cradle to the grave'.[5] The majority report explained that although good health was a matter of the 'greatest importance', it was not 'the sole aim in life', and 'a complete defence against illness does not at present exist even for the millionaire'.[6] Nonetheless, 'medical treatment should be more readily accessible to all who are in need of it'.[7] They therefore recommended that in future a sick pauper should see the doctor before the relieving officer. 'Investigation should follow treatment.'[8] Secondly, all sick paupers should be accommodated in separate institutions. Thirdly, there should be no disfranchisement of the sick.

As regards outdoor relief, they planned to abandon the policy of driving the sick into institutions by the denial of outdoor relief.[9] Instead, the sick were to be driven into provident dispensaries. They wanted a system which would be constantly 'stimulating and educating those who, though sick, ought to

[1] ibid., p. 292
[2] ibid.
[3] ibid. The Commissioners also argued that handing over the medical services to the 1,800 sanitary authorities would mean a reversion to the small area system that existed before 1834 (p. 376). It was in anticipation of this argument that Dr McVail had proposed a merging of the local sanitary authorities into larger administrative units.
[4] ibid., p. 385
[5] ibid., p. 293
[6] ibid.
[7] ibid., p. 368
[8] ibid., p. 298
[9] Though compulsory removal was to be allowed in certain cases.

have themselves made provision against sickness'.[1] Sickness was to be used as a special opportunity for a lesson in thrift. Those who could have joined a provident scheme were to pay the cost of their treatment in instalments, but there was to be 'discretion to remit the payment of any or all of such instalments upon proof that the recipient of the assistance had joined a provident dispensary'.[2] The aged and the widows already receiving public assistance were to be enrolled in provident dispensaries with their fees paid for them.[3] It was hoped that eventually the district medical officer's job would virtually cease to exist and these officers would get work at the dispensaries.

A dispensary was to be organized in each district and patients were to have a free choice of doctor. This system was to be available for patients up to an income limit agreed with the British Medical Association and the doctor was to be remunerated on a scale agreed with the Association. Patients who were members of the dispensary would be able to go to public hospitals or voluntary hospitals, with whom contractual arrangements had been made, without further cost.[4]

The organization of this plan and the administration of the Poor Law hospitals were to be the responsibility of public assistance authorities with powers over the areas of counties or county boroughs. The administrative arm of the public assistance authority for these services was to be a medical assistance committee which would have representatives from the British Medical Association and the health committee of the local authority. Persons were also to be co-opted from local hospitals, nursing associations, dispensaries and friendly societies. It was hoped 'to organize schemes of co-operation between public assistance institutions and voluntary hospitals'.[5]

While there was to be control over 'unnecessary expenditure in separate infirmaries', there were to be increases in medical and nursing staff, an introduction of teaching 'under suitable safeguards' and a proper system of inspectors. It was believed that as the new medical committees were to operate separately from

---

[1] *Report of Royal Commission on Poor Laws 1905–9* (Majority), p. 295

[2] ibid., p. 298

[3] ibid., p. 302. This proposal is an interesting forerunner to that introduced by Senator Forand and his associates in the United States fifty years later.

[4] ibid., pp. 301–2

[5] ibid., p. 300

A general view

St Thomas' Hospital

THE NEW ST THOMAS' HOSPITAL

Queen Victoria at the opening ceremony, 21 June 1871

St Thomas' Hospital

St Thomas' H

THE LOCK HOSPITAL, Hyde Park Corner

MILLER HOSPITAL AND ROYAL KENT DISPENSARY, 1903

Wellcome Historical Medical L

'pauperizing tribunals', the respectable poor would not be deterred from seeking their help.[1] But the majority were not inclined 'to make medical assistance so attractive that it may become a species of honourable and gratuitous self-indulgence instead of a somewhat unpleasant necessity resorted to because restoration to health is otherwise impossible'.[2] 'A race of hypochondriacs would be as useless to the state as a race of other degenerates.'[3]

The majority hoped that these changes might result in reforming the outpatient departments of the voluntary hospitals, which would now cater for fewer pauper patients. Moreover, there were two types of patient which were possibly better dealt with by the assistance service. The majority felt that persons with chronic ailments, and persons whose home conditions would not allow them to repay any commensurate benefit from such treatment, should be assistance cases. They also wanted the voluntary hospitals to work more energetically to exclude patients who could pay their own doctors or at least join provident institutions. If this failed, 'any endeavour to reform the system of public medical assistance will be locally thwarted'.[4]

Suggestions for remedying the abuses of the outpatient departments have been laid before us by many witnesses, but by none more fully than the representatives of the British Medical Association. We are convinced with them that a strenuous effort should be made to circumscribe the work of the outpatient departments. They should be used exclusively for:
(1) Casualties
(2) Consultations
(3) Cases requiring expensive equipment for the treatment of special diseases and defects.
To this end the 'letter' system should be thoroughly reformed or abolished, and, except for casualties, the recommendation of a medical officer or private practitioner substituted.[5]

These proposals were heavily criticized by the minority of the

[1] ibid., p. 212. There were also to be voluntary aid committees working with the statutory bodies so that more 'agreeable' forms of aid could be offered to the 'deserving'.
[2] ibid., pp. 294–5
[3] ibid., p. 293
[4] ibid., p. 285
[5] ibid.

Commission. They condemned all the existing agencies providing general practitioner care – the outpatient departments, the friendly societies, the private medical clubs and the medical missions. The outpatient departments with their herds of cooped-up patients awaiting perfunctory examination were 'positive dangers to the public health'.[1] The medical missions were seeking to attract persons to religious services by the bait of 'cheap doctoring' without being under responsible and specialized medical supervision.[2] The private clubs were selective and unco-ordinated with other medical services. The friendly societies did not 'provide medical assistance for any women, whether married or single, or for children, for "bad lives", for persons suffering from "constitutional defects", "incipient disease", "venereal disease" or the "results of alcoholic excess". Taken together, these excluded classes must amount to more than three-fourths of the population.'[3]

The minority were militantly opposed to any system which allowed free choice of doctor:

To give either public encouragement or public aid to any system of medical attendance among the poor that was based on a free choice of doctors, and on their remuneration according to the number of patients that they severally attracted, could not fail, in our opinion, to perpetuate and intensify the popular superstition as to the value of medicine and the popular reluctance to adopt hygienic methods of life; and – as we fear we must add – could not fail also to foster the injurious 'medical demagogy' to which, in the stress of competition, these popular feelings already give occasion.[4]

The Webbs had no faith in medicines: 'in the twentieth century we have ceased to believe in the bottle of medicine.'[5]

To expect this freely chosen doctor to give, not the 'strong medicine' beloved by the poor, but the stern advice about the habits of life on which recovery really depends – to look to him to speak plainly about excessive drinking and the unwise eating

[1] ibid., (Minority), p. 869
[2] ibid., p. 870
[3] ibid., p. 870
[4] ibid., (Minority), p. 873
[5] ibid., p. 851

which cause two-thirds of the ill-health of the poor . . . would clearly be chimerical.[1]

The role of the doctor should be to 'inculcate better methods of living among his patients, to advise as to personal and domestic hygiene . . . to insist on the necessity of greater regularity of conduct' and 'to abandon the evil courses which may have led to his ill-health'.[2]

The introduction of provident dispensaries, the minority argued, was no solution. If the poor had their contributions paid for them and they gained a free choice of doctor, then 'one of the strongest inducements at present to join a medical club or otherwise to pay for one's own doctoring'[3] would be removed. 'It is difficult to see why anybody should be at the pains of contributing at all.'[4] And it would be quite 'impracticable' to make the contributions compulsory. It would be an impossible task 'to extract any weekly contribution'. Such a contribution would really be 'in the nature of a poll tax; and England has not had a poll tax since 1381'.[5]

The minority wanted a unified medical service, combining the Poor Law and the sanitary services, run by health committees of the county and county borough councils. The aim of the new service was to be 'the discovery and early treatment' of incipient disease, accompanied by 'remedial changes of regimen and removal of injurious conditions' wherever necessary.[6] While domiciliary care could be appropriately provided in some cases

it ought to be withheld:
 (i)   where proper treatment in the home is impracticable;
 (ii) where the patient persistently malingers or refuses to conform to the prescribed regimen; or
 (iii) where the patient is a source of danger for others.[7]

The public health principle would lead to 'searching out disease, securing the earliest possible diagnosis, taking hold of the

[1] ibid., p. 874
[2] ibid., p. 853
[3] ibid., p. 873
[4] ibid.
[5] ibid., p. 874
[6] ibid., p. 889
[7] ibid.

incipient case, removing injurious conditions, applying specialized treatment, enforcing healthy surroundings and personal
hygiene, and aiming always at preventing either recurrence or
spread of diseases'.[1] In short, Mrs Webb wanted to create a
medical autocracy with wide powers to improve people with
or without their consent.

Treatment was to come first, and only afterwards would a
separate local functionary assess on a statutory scale 'the charge
to be made on individuals liable to pay any part of the cost of the
service rendered to them or their dependants or other relations,
according to their means'[2] and to recover the amount due. The
decisions of the official might be subject to appeal. The report
does not indicate in any detail how all these proposals would
have affected the voluntary hospitals. Their 'inestimable services'[3] were given due recognition.

> We think that many more suitable cases than at present might, on
> proper arrangements as to payment, be transferred from rate-
> maintained to voluntary institutions. But it is clear that such
> institutions provide only for a small fraction of the need, and that
> they leave untouched whole districts for some cases; and whole
> classes of cases everywhere, which there is no prospect of their being
> able or willing to undertake.[4]

It was suggested that the voluntary hospital might make use
of the new machinery for collecting charges to stop 'abuse'.

The publication of two separate reports misleadingly implied
that the Commissioners were in complete disagreement on every
point. Both parties wanted the public hospitals organized on the
basis of counties and county boroughs but the majority refused
to accept the full implications of preventive services for the poor
upon which the minority rested their case. The experts had
failed to agree and their separate reports lacked the authority
of a single pronouncement. A number of important social
reforms, enacted between 1905 and 1929, stemmed directly

[1] ibid., p. 890
[2] ibid., p. 1013
[3] ibid., p. 890
[4] ibid. Mrs Webb wrote in 1910 that the nationalization or municipalization of the voluntary hospitals was 'so remote from practical politics that we
need not discuss it' (*The Coming of a Unified Medical Service and how it will affect
the Voluntary Hospitals*, p. 6, Glasgow, 1910).

from the findings of the Royal Commission. Nevertheless, the Government was given an excuse to do very little about the hospitals. Radical reform of Poor Law institutional services was delayed for another twenty years.

The inspectors had worked for the gradual improvement of Poor Law hospitals only to see the growing popularity of these institutions subvert their 'principles'. Since 1867 the central authority had fought unsuccessfully to limit the use of its infirmaries to the 'destitute': but it could not hold out against the growing number of better-off citizens who could not all be accommodated in the voluntary hospitals either because certain diseases were excluded or because they lived in a region not served by such a hospital. The problem of 'abuse' loomed large. It seems probable that the officials of the Local Government Board were prepared to give up their medical services in order to restore a truly deterrent system for the able-bodied poor.

But Chief Inspector Davy could see, as could the majority of the Royal Commission, the consequence of transforming the Poor Law medical service into a full-blooded public service, free to the very poor and with charges adjusted to the means of those who could afford to pay. It meant the ultimate death of the voluntary hospitals and the medical benefits of the sick clubs. It meant also the organization of a large section of the medical profession by public authorities. Finally it meant much higher taxes. In short, it meant a national health service with charges collected from those who could pay them.

Mrs Webb and her supporters were prepared to go as far as this and even to enforce proper utilization of such a service. The majority of her colleagues wanted instead to drive people into private insurance schemes. But for the Poor Law hospitals the majority of the Commission could find no new rationale. They neither wanted to go back to deterrent hospitals nor forward to preventive hospitals. They wanted improvements where they were obviously needed and they saw that larger authorities were more likely to bring them about, but they did not want 'extravagance'. On the exact relation between public and voluntary hospitals, they were silent. Apparently the two systems were to run parallel and not to duplicate each other's work. It was hoped that the role of the two systems could be settled by local discussion.

As Mrs Webb worked on her minority report, it did seem

possible that it might be immediately accepted by the Government.[1] And if she had carried the Government with her at this stage in Britain's social history, if her proposed test of means could have been administered with equity and without excessive cost, and if poor patients had not protested at the despotic role of the doctors chosen for them, the principle of 'a universal free service' might never have been introduced. But the fact that the Commission was divided, and the general inertia of the Government led to the postponement of the whole question. Had she reached some compromise with her colleagues on the Commission, the Government might have taken some resolute action earlier than it did. Though it was impossible to foresee it at the time, her intransigence had the effect of leaving with the Poor Law officials that part of their service which they were willing to discard.

[1] S. and B. Webb, *Our Partnership*, pp. 402, 414, 421

CHAPTER 15

National Insurance

THE Royal Commission had produced two separate plans for the reform of the public medical services. There were, however, greater similarities between the two schemes than either side was willing to concede: the differences were more philosophical than administrative. But there was no one plan which had the full backing of public opinion. If the Government wanted an excuse for piecemeal action, or no action at all, the apparently sharp split in the Commission provided it.

The unco-ordinated and haphazard development of hospital facilities had been commented on in both reports. The need for larger areas of co-ordinated action was beyond dispute. But each plan bristled with political difficulties, and each plan challenged the vested interests of the Boards of Guardians on which sat the leaders of local political opinion. As Lloyd George told a meeting of the BMA in 1911, 'the local authorities may not be willing to allow infirmaries to be taken out of their hands'.[1]

While both Asquith and Churchill had at various times said that they favoured the proposals of the minority report,[2] the Government took no drastic action on the main recommendations of the Royal Commission. John Burns was allowed to continue as President of the Local Government Board. He had no great interest in medical problems and refused to sponsor any sweeping reform of his own department. He was certainly not prepared to antagonize the Guardians by sweeping them away. Instead he decided to duck the fundamental problems raised by the Royal Commission and to try and improve the Poor Law hospital service by administrative action. Thus by new orders and close inspection, the attempt was made to secure a more

[1] *BMJ Supplement*, 31 May 1911, p. 358
[2] S. and B. Webb, *Our Partnership*, pp. 402, 437

liberal but selective distribution of outdoor relief,[1] a better classification of inmates, the replacement of unsuitable accommodation, the combination of Unions, an increase in the nursing services and a general improvement in the administration of hospital authorities. In the case of tuberculosis a further inquiry was set up to ascertain the facts.

The Poor Law hospital service was encouraged to develop rapidly. More separate infirmaries were constructed in the provinces. Inspectors put pressure on reluctant Guardians. Thus it was reported in 1907–8 that there were many Labour Boards in Wales who remained content with buildings 'totally unsuitable, ill adapted and inconvenient'.[2] Their object was 'to escape the capital outlay and save the rates, which they are prodigal enough with in illegal outdoor relief'.[3] Three years later it was reported that Guardians were 'more ready to erect separate buildings, for the sick',[4] though there remained some who preferred to 'patch and tinker with old structures'.[5] In Yorkshire twelve new workhouse hospitals were erected in ten years.[6] In the Midlands four were opened in one year.[7]

The Local Government Board had powers under existing legislation to combine Unions 'for any purpose connected with the administration of the relief of the poor'.[8] There were some who argued that these powers should be used to create *ad hoc* Poor Law authorities on a district basis.[9] While the Local Government Board encouraged combination, it refused to compel Unions to act together. There were, however, some voluntary combinations. The Birmingham Guardians combined for all purposes and three Liverpool Unions combined to provide a hospital for consumptives.[10]

Classification of institutions was growing rapidly and with

[1] 'It is the plain duty of the Guardians to take precautions to ensure that the relief is adequate.' *Thirty-Ninth Annual Report LGB, 1909–10*, Cd 5260, p. xix, HMSO, 1910

[2] *Thirty-Seventh Annual Report LGB 1907–8*, Cd 4347, p. 354, HMSO, 1908

[3] ibid., p. 353

[4] *Fortieth Annual Report LGB 1910–11*, Cd 5865, p. 105, HMSO, 1911

[5] ibid.

[6] *Thirty-Ninth Annual Report LGB 1909–10*, p. 84

[7] *Thirty-Seventh Annual Report LGB 1907–8*, p. 338

[8] *Poor Law Act 1879*, 42 & 43 Vict. C. 54, Section 8

[9] Charles Booth and Sir Arthur Downes (S. and B. Webb, *Our Partnership*, pp. 327–8)

[10] ibid., pp. 542–3

it came the partial replacement of pauper staff by paid staff. An
inspector from the North of England reported that

> with regard to the purely rural workhouses, these are becoming
> more and more places where only the old and helpless, the mentally
> deficient, and deserted women with children are to be found, and
> the complaints of the Masters and Matrons of these institutions is
> that they have now no able-bodied persons who can do the
> necessary work of the institutions.[1]

In London, infirmary superintendents copied the policies of the
voluntary hospitals and began to classify their patients not only
by type of disease but by acuteness of disease. Thus the Bow
Institution was used to take male adults from all over London
'who were not sufficiently sick to require the elaborate treatment
of an infirmary, but needed more skilled care than is available
in the ordinary wards of a workhouse'.[2]

The nursing services were steadily improving. Gradually
power was being switched from untrained workhouse matrons to
superintendent nurses. Thus in 1909–10 orders were issued
'transferring the duty of daily visitation of the sick and lying-in
wards of the workhouses of the Bakewell and Worcester Unions
from the Master and Matron to the Superintendent Nurse'.[3]
Similar orders were made in later years to six Unions simul-
taneously.[4] Each year 400 probationers completed their three-
year course in London infirmaries alone.[5] In the twenty years
from 1893 to 1913 the number of nurses employed in Poor Law
institutions increased from under 3,000 to 7,652.[6] It was, however, very hard to get and retain nurses in rural areas. As one
inspector of the Local Government Board complained, 'neither
the conditions of life, the prospects, nor the class of case in a Poor
Law institution are likely to attract a trained nurse who has an
ambition to excel in her profession'.[7]

In January 1911 a departmental committee consisting wholly

[1] *Forty-Third Annual Report LGB, 1913–14*, Pt. I, Cd 7444, p. 60, HMSO, 1914
[2] *Forty-First Annual Report 1911–12*, op. cit., Pt. I, Cd 6327, p. 59
[3] *Thirty-Ninth Annual Report LGB 1909–10*, p. lxiv
[4] *Forty-First Annual Report LGB 1911–12*, p. lix and *Forty-Second Annual Report LGB 1912–13*, Cd 6980, p. lxviii, HMSO, 1913
[5] *Forty-Second Annual Report LGB 1912–13*, p. lvi
[6] ibid., p. lv
[7] *Forty-Third Annual Report LGB 1913–14*, pp. 31–2

of senior Poor Law administrators was set up to examine all the
existing instructions which had been issued to Poor Law
authorities, and to produce amended and consolidated orders.
On the basis of the report of the committee[1] new orders were
issued at the end of December 1913.[2]

It was specifically laid down that 'suitable and separate
accommodation'[3] was to be provided for each separate class of
inmate. In the hope of securing more efficient administration,
house committees were to be appointed. Such committees were
to be subordinate to the Guardians and to report to them.[4]
Inmates were to be given the fullest opportunity to make
applications or complaints.[5]

The new nursing order applied generally the policy which had
already been imposed in many individual instances. The superintendent nurse was to exercise in the sick wards the authority
which had previously been exercised by the matron. If an
existing matron was untrained, she was to act under the direction
of the medical officer in matters relating to the treatment and
nursing of the sick. Skilled nursing attendance was to be made
available for the inmates of every institution. The employment
of any inmate in the nursing of the sick was expressly prohibited.[6] Soon after the new orders were issued, the Local
Government Board was able to report that, 'It is gratifying to
find a general desire to carry out the orders both in the letter and
the spirit.'[7]

Fewer criticisms of the 'extravagance' of infirmary buildings
were made after the Royal Commission than before it. It became
accepted at the Local Government Board that the standards of
the infirmaries should be comparable to those of the voluntary
hospitals and that they would inevitably attract more patients.
By 1912–13 all inspectors were reporting a steady increase in the
sick and infirm in their districts as the standards of Poor Law

[1] Cd 6968, HMSO, January 1913
[2] The Poor Law Institutions Order, 1913, and the Poor Law Institutions
(Nursing) Order, 1913, transmitted in Circular of 31 December 1913
[3] Forty-Third Annual Report LGB 1913–14, Pt. I. pp. xxxix–xli
[4] This Order was eventually deleted as the result of strong pressure from
Guardians (S. and B. Webb, English Poor Law History, Part II, Vol. II, op. cit.,
p. 735).
[5] Forty-Third Annual Report LGB 1913–14, Pt. I, pp. xxxix–xli
[6] ibid.
[7] ibid., p. 66

hospital care improved.[1] In the East and West Ridings it was
reported that the Poor Law was really supplementing 'the work
of the public general hospitals which do not increase in size very
rapidly'.[2] A patient would enter the infirmary because the local
voluntary hospital had too long a waiting list.[3] In this area,
there were over seven thousand Poor Law beds and less than
half that number of voluntary hospital beds.[4]

Thus the Poor Law hospital service was allowed to grow and
develop under the administrative structure which had been
condemned. Increasingly the service was running parallel to the
voluntary hospitals, filling in the gaps which they had left. The
major recommendations of the Royal Commission in this field
had been shelved. But before war broke out in 1914 two sectors
of the medical services of the nation were selected for drastic
change – the general practitioner service and the tuberculosis
services. The initiative came from Lloyd George, the Chancellor
of the Exchequer, and his plans were well advanced before he
even looked at the scheme for invalidity insurance set out in the
majority report.[5] He had become fascinated with the national
insurance scheme of Germany and saw the introduction of compulsory insurance in Britain as a means of taking a substantial
section of the population out of the Poor Law without heavy
expenditure from the Exchequer. The new social service for the
working classes was to be paid for largely by the working classes.
After a gap of 440 years a limited poll tax was to be re-introduced
in Britain.

Tuberculosis was a major health hazard and the arrangements
made for it by the multitude of public and private hospital
agencies were grossly inadequate. In the case of the outdoor
relief agencies both majority and minority reports of the Royal
Commission had implicitly accepted that a policy of restricting
outdoor relief was undesirable. Better means were needed to look
after the sick poor in their own homes. The solution favoured by
the Majority Report was to drive as many people as possible into
sick or provident clubs which paid doctors' fees, and to provide a
residual service for those who could not afford such premiums.

[1] *Forty-Second Annual Report LGB 1912–13*, p. 24
[2] *Forty-Third Annual Report LGB 1913–14*, Pt. I, pp. 71–2
[3] ibid.
[4] ibid.
[5] Bruce, *The Coming of the Welfare State*, p. 180

The solution favoured by the minority report was an increase in dispensaries with salaried doctors on similar lines to those envisaged by Goschen forty years earlier, before the 'crusade' against outdoor relief.

A full account of the reasons which led Lloyd George to favour a scheme of compulsory insurance lies outside the scope of this study. So do the detailed negotiations with the friendly societies, the insurance companies and the medical profession. The scheme did, however, have important consequences for the voluntary hospitals. The effect of the new measure was to hurry on many trends which were already at work – in particular the use of hospitals for consultative purposes.

Under the National Insurance Act manual workers and all others with incomes of under £160 a year were required to pay contributions of fourpence per week to an approved society. Their employers were required to pay threepence and the state twopence. In return for these contributions insured persons became entitled to a limited cash benefit in sickness, to the services of a general practitioner and to pharmaceutical benefits. There were optional additional benefits which approved societies were entitled to provide. The principle of free choice of doctor was enshrined under the Act despite the opposition of the Webbs. Instead of the working classes being driven to join some provident system of obtaining general practitioner services by vigilant examination on a case-by-case basis, as suggested by the majority report of the Royal Commission, they were to have 'thrift' imposed on them by Act of Parliament.

Wage-earners, but not their families, obtained a general practitioner service. General practitioners obtained a regular and reliable source of income at a not ungenerous rate. In addition, general practitioners obtained by vehement action emancipation from the lay control of friendly societies. Beyond this the Act did not materially alter the organization of general practice from the pattern which had developed during the crusade against outdoor relief. General practitioners were in-dividual contractors operating from their own premises. Their prescriptions were largely dispensed by separate chemist establishments. There was no incentive for general practice to be conducted in dispensaries as envisaged in both reports on the Poor Laws.

The Act included plans to provide better care for tuberculosis patients. Lloyd George's father had died of this complaint and he had been very impressed by the sanatoria he had seen in Germany.[1] The tuberculosis scheme was to operate partly through the national insurance scheme and partly through grants from the central Government. Initially the Government made available the sum of one-and-a-half million pounds for the construction of new accommodation. Local authorities who built sanatoria were granted three-fifths of the cost of approved schemes; local authorities who built tuberculosis dispensaries were given four-fifths of the cost.[2] In the case of insured persons, a sum of a million pounds was set aside in the insurance fund to be spent by insurance committees on sanatorium benefit. In the case of the dependants of the insured persons and other non-insured persons, local authorities could obtain half the cost of treatment from the Local Government Board.[3] By June 1914, over nine thousand beds had been approved for the treatment of tuberculosis; over half the beds were in voluntary hospitals.[4] The *British Medical Journal* saw in the scheme the embryo of the maintenance or municipalization of hospitals, and indeed the establishment of an extensive state service of doctors.[5] The *Hospital Gazette* also noted that 'the hospitals for consumption are likely to be the first to engage the attention of the state'.[6]

Apart from these provisions for tuberculosis patients, one section of the National Insurance Act permitted the approved societies which were to operate the scheme to make grants to the voluntary hospitals. Beyond this, the Act did not directly affect the position of the hospitals. But as soon as the Bill was published fears were expressed that the scheme would have serious indirect consequences. The *British Medical Journal* feared that there would be a reduction of subscriptions to the voluntary hospitals.

The hospitals will sooner or later become rate- or state-supported institutions – almost one and the same thing. . . . It is true that the Bill proposes to confer specific powers on friendly societies to make contributions to hospitals; but this hardly improves the outlook.

[1] Bruce, p. 184
[2] *Hospital Gazette*, January 1913, pp. 79–80
[3] ibid.
[4] *Forty-Third Annual Report LGB 1913–14*, Pt. III, Cd 7611, p. xx, HMSO, 1914
[5] *BMJ*, 24 February 1912, pp. 448–50
[6] *Hospital Gazette*, October 1912, p. 1

One would anticipate that if the authorities of a hospital had to choose between living on the rates or depending on the chance subscriptions of a friendly society, coupled, as they surely would be with a demand for a share in the management, they would prefer the former alternative.[1]

The fears expressed by the *British Medical Journal* were shared by the hospital managers, though not unanimously.[2] It was feared that there would be a sharp fall in subscriptions particularly from working men and from employers who used the hospitals for the treatment of their employees.[3] It was, however, suggested that there might be a reduction in outpatient attendances. Even this was not agreed by all parties. As one speaker pointed out: 'In the outpatient department pains had hitherto been taken to exclude patients who could be treated by a local medical practitioner, but if the Bill became law, the interests of the profession would lie in the opposite direction.'[4] From all sides fears were expressed of state control or municipalization.

In June 1911, the British Hospitals Association[5] held a meeting at St George's Hospital attended by representatives of over two hundred hospitals. At the meeting it was pointed out that the hospitals would not only lose subscriptions as a result of the Bill, they would also have to pay contributions for their own employees. It was suggested that the insurance fund might be required to pay for the services provided to insured persons by voluntary hospitals. This proposition led to a warning from several doctors that medical staffs would object to hospitals being paid by the state for their work. The meeting ended by passing a woolly resolution hoping that the Bill would be so amended that the usefulness of the voluntary hospitals would be continued and their efficiency unimpaired.[6]

[1] *BMJ*, 13 May 1911, p. 1131
[2] Those who differed from the majority view included the Chairman of the London Hospital (*Hospital*, Vol. LI, 6 January 1912, p. 348) and Mr Michelli of the Dreadnought Hospital (*Hospital*, Vol. LI, 20 January 1912, p. 412).
[3] *Hospital*, Vol. L, 20 May 1911, p. 193
[4] Sir Alfred Pearce Gould at the Governors' Meeting of the Middlesex Hospital, reported in *BMJ Supplement*, 3 June 1911, p. 351
[5] The Hospitals Association had been formed in 1883 by Burdett 'to promote the best interests of hospitals and institutions and of all those who are engaged in their administration' (*Hospital*, Vol. XXVII, 26 October 1889, p. 51).
[6] *BMJ Supplement*, June 1911, p. 419

The suggestion that the hospitals should be paid for work done for insured persons gained the support of such diverse bodies as the Charity Organization Society,[1] the Hospital Saturday Fund[2] and the British Medical Association.[3] It was persistently advocated in *The Hospital* by Burdett, who thought that the payment should include some sum to defray the cost of medical attendance.[4] Both *The Hospital* and the *British Medical Journal* agreed that the clause in the Bill allowing approved societies to make donations to the hospitals should be deleted. It would mean 'that for a relatively insignificant payment its members would consider themselves entitled to demand and to have all their hospital care without further payment each year'.[5]

Lloyd George received a joint deputation of the British Hospitals Association, the Central Hospital Council for London[6] and the Hospital Saturday Fund for London. He argued from the experience of Germany that after the momentary agitation had passed, people would do their duty to the hospitals as they had in the past:

> The hospitals of this country were an essential part of the machinery of civilization. Though he did not wish to indicate at the present moment what would have to be done, he was perfectly clear in his own mind that no country could possibly allow a hospital to be closed because it was short of money.[7]

The Government had not legislated for the hospitals because 'they believed in the voluntary system and wanted it to continue. If they legislated for the hospitals there would be bound to be a certain amount of Government control over their work.'[8]

Lloyd George did, however, make some concessions. Because hospitals paid their employees sick pay, there could be a

[1] *Hospital*, Vol. L, 22 July 1911, pp. 423–4
[2] *BMJ Supplement*, 22 July 1911, p. 186
[3] ibid.
[4] *Hospital*, Vol. L, 8 July 1911, pp. 355–6
[5] *BMJ Supplement*, 22 July 1911, p. 186
[6] This body represented 15 general hospitals and 5 special hospitals. Fourteen of the 33 members of the Council were doctors. It acted largely as the mouthpiece of the London teaching hospitals which had held themselves aloof from the British Hospitals Association. See *Hospital*, Vol. XLI, 2 March 1907, p. 394.
[7] *BMJ*, 29 July 1911, pp. 240–1
[8] ibid.

reduction in the rate of the contributions the hospitals had to pay as employers. Because the hospitals provided medical care for their employees, they could receive the appropriate sum from the insurance fund for this service. In cases where insured persons had no dependants, hospitals could by agreement receive their cash benefit.[1] These provisions did not satisfy the hospitals. A joint conference was held by the BMA and the British Hospitals Association on 4 August 1911 and it was agreed to demand that hospitals should be paid for their services. A second delegation was received by Lloyd George and given the same reply as the first.[2] The BHA held a conference at Manchester in September attended by representatives of two hundred hospitals at which no new points were made.[3] At a further conference in London in November it was agreed to petition local Members of Parliament.[4] And yet another meeting in December was attended by representatives of nearly all the hospitals in the United Kingdom. By this time Burdett was saying that, owing to the loss of income, half the hospital provision of the country would be destroyed.[5]

At the Seventy-Ninth Annual Meeting of the BMA the new role which the voluntary hospitals should play after the National Insurance Act was in operation was discussed. It was recognized that the fact that every insured person could have a general practitioner created a new situation. Dr Lauriston Shaw, a physician to Guy's Hospital, suggested the insured person should be dealt with 'on a consultative basis in co-operation with his insurance doctor'.[6] This was desirable from both a professional and a social point of view:

> To deal entirely on independent lines with another man's patient, even in the sacred name of charity, can hardly be tolerated in the altered circumstances created by the Bill . . . the transformation . . . of voluntary hospitals into truly consultative institutions, taking no independent part in the treatment or investigation of disease, but co-operating always with institutions or private practitioners . . . would provide them with a new lease of useful life.[7]

[1] *Hospital*, Vol. L, 5 August 1911, p. 470
[2] *BMJ Supplement*, 12 August 1911, pp. 298–9
[3] ibid., 7 October 1911, pp. 386–7
[4] ibid., 11 November 1911, p. 449
[5] ibid., 9 December 1911, p. 594
[6] *BMJ*, 19 August 1911, p. 370
[7] ibid., p. 371

Radio Times Hulton Picture Library

SIR JOHN SIMON
(1816–1904)

Wellcome Historical Medical Library

SIR HENRY BURDETT
(1847–1920)

BEATRICE WEBB
(1858–1943)

Passfield Trustees

ANEURIN BEVAN
(1897–1960)

Radio Times Hulton Picture Library

Central Middlesex Ho

A WARD IN WILLESDEN PARISH INFIRMARY, 1903

THE SURGERY AT ST BARTHOLOMEW'S HOSPITAL, C. 1900

Wellcome Historical Medical L

The Bill would make more apparent the distinction between ordinary and special medical attendants.[1]

Another speaker, J. Courtney Buchanan (Secretary of the Metropolitan Hospital), came to the same conclusion:

> For some time the tendency has been for hospitals to perform the function of consultants to the poorer classes, but in future I believe they will be forced to do work solely of this character. . . . Trivial cases need no longer be treated at the hospitals. . . . Voluntary hospitals would bear the same relation to provident institutions and other medical services provided for the general use of the poorer classes which consultants bear to general practitioners in the case of the well-to-do.[2]

In February 1912 the council of the British Hospitals Association passed a resolution which would have hastened the development envisaged by the far-sighted spokesmen at the BMA Conference:

> Insured persons, except for accident or sudden emergency, should no longer be received in the outpatient or casualty departments unless accompanied by a certificate or introduced personally by the medical practitioner who is in attendance, and in such a case, after consultation, he should be referred back to the same medical attendant, with an expression of opinion of the hospital physician or surgeon on the case.[3]

A similar resolution was passed at the meeting of representatives of twenty-nine Midlands hospitals held in May 1912.[4]

Meanwhile Burdett tried to incite the hospitals to militant action. They should call a great meeting and tell the Government that they would only take insurance patients if payments were made, including an addition of ten per cent for the medical staff.[5] 'Will the British people consent to the . . . degradation of charitable aid forced on them by the Government whenever they are so grievously ill as to require hospital treatment?'[6] As

[1] ibid., p. 371
[2] ibid., pp. 371–2
[3] *BMJ Supplement*, 3 February 1912, p. 134
[4] ibid., 18 May 1912, p. 240
[5] *Hospital*, Vol. LIII, 9 November 1912, p. 144
[6] ibid., 23 November 1912, p. 201

the day approached when the Act was to come into force, his editorials became more and more shrill. And failing to get any change out of Lloyd George, he wrote a series of letters to John Burns enclosing copies of the desired amendment. He publicly denounced the British Hospitals Association for inactivity. In early December 1912, a battery of questions was asked in Parliament. The line of the Government was unchanged. If the voluntary hospitals wanted grants, then the whole question of state control would be raised.[1] Lloyd George received a deputation of chairmen of the larger London hospitals and rubbed the point home. The Government wanted to avoid any steps that would imperil the voluntary nature of the great hospitals of this country. He understood that the hospital authorities were greatly desirous of continuing the voluntary system.[2] It was a cunning and effective answer.

The BHA met at the end of December 1912 and considered the Chancellor's statement. It passed resolutions to treat insured persons as outpatients, on a referral basis, but to send a list of such persons to the local insurance committees. In the case of inpatients it was decided to treat insured persons, to keep a list of them and to note the approved society to which they belonged. Rather than risk state control, the hospitals decided not to refuse to treat insured persons. Burdett, who had approved the policy, commented that

> voluntary hospital managers have shown great public spirit, and have raised themselves immeasurably in public estimation, by accepting the position and agreeing to make the best of it during the present year, so that the precise effect of National Insurance may be made clear.[3]

Hospital managers had 'saved the Act'.[4]

When the Act came into force in January 1913, there were many hospitals which refused to treat insured persons (other than emergencies) unless they were referred by their insurance doctors. When St Bartholomew's implemented this policy it was hailed by certain Liberal newspapers as a 'boycott' of insured persons. Contributors to the Saturday Fund were indignant

[1] ibid., 14 December 1912, p. 295
[2] ibid., 21 December 1912, p. 324
[3] ibid., 11 January 1913, p. 389
[4] ibid., 29 March 1913, p. 679

when they were referred to their panel doctors.[1] The executive of the Fund reported 'a constant stream of complaints from the honorary collectors of the Fund',[2] because the voluntary hospitals were returning insured patients with minor ailments to their panel doctors. Owing to the 'indignation and ill feeling' of patients, a period of grace was asked for to enable insured persons to recognize the changed conditions. Burdett accused panel doctors of shirking their duty.[3] Some hospitals granted the period of grace.

There had thus occurred a major change in the role of the voluntary hospital. Services were being refused to the class of persons the hospitals were set up to serve. This had important consequences for teaching. The voluntary hospitals provided students with almost all their clinical material. It was suggested by the *Hospital Gazette* that the hospitals should not be reserved exclusively for consultation cases 'until arrangements were made to give students their elementary clinical instruction elsewhere'.[4]

The *British Medical Journal* welcomed the new role of the outpatient department. It noted that King Edward's Hospital Fund for London had produced a report on outpatient departments which recommended the abolition of subscribers' letters and the system of payment by outpatients. Outpatient reform had been one of the main interests of the BMA since 1853. A gloss was now put on these activities. The aim of the BMA had been 'to elevate the outpatient department from its present position as a mere dumping-ground ... to its proper place in the organized medical service of the nation'.[5] The BMA had had many policies for limiting the role of outpatient departments but only as late as 1909 had the consultative role of outpatient departments become a major feature in the policy of the Association.

The extreme fears about the effects of the National Insurance Act on the finances of the hospitals proved to be unfounded. Lloyd George's prophecy proved to be correct: the public continued to subscribe. Some of the smaller hospitals – particularly in the poorer parts of the country – did have financial

[1] *BMJ*, 22 March 1913, p. 626
[2] *Hospital*, Vol. LIII, 22 February 1913, p. 561
[3] ibid.
[4] *Hospital Gazette*, January 1913, pp. 61–2
[5] *BMJ*, 22 February 1913, p. 603

difficulties, though how far the National Insurance Act contributed to these difficulties it is not possible to establish. Even
Burdett, whose prophecies had been most extreme, had to
concede in his Yearbook for 1915 that the 'greater London
hospitals ... have fortunately been in a position up to the present
to bear the burden of National Insurance without grievous
injury'.[1] There was a large reduction in the number of outpatients – particularly in those hospitals which enforced a
'referral' system. At St Bartholomew's Hospital there were
120,834 outpatient attendances in 1912 and only 78,783 in
1913.[2]

Though the National Insurance Act had made no serious
impact on the finances of the voluntary hospitals, it had many
important consequences. For the first time in its history the
voluntary hospital movement had taken concerted action. Just
as the Act made the BMA into a fighting force, so the Act made
the British Hospitals Association into a body which acted as
spokesman for the hospitals.

Under the impact of changed needs and of fears of financial
insolvency the hospitals drastically altered the role of their outpatient departments. In the case of insured persons, the term
'outpatient abuse' was given a new meaning. Trivial cases were
to be kept away from the hospital. The new role of the outpatient department was to complement that of the general
practitioner by providing a specialist or consultative service.

That this change affected teaching has been mentioned above.
Medical students had to learn the general practitioner's work
from such cases as arrived in the casualty department as emergencies or alleged emergencies. As few women and no children
were counted among insured persons the hospital could continue
to give them a general practitioner service, but the men of
working age who came to the casualty department were hardly
representative of the problems the medical student would
encounter later on in general practice. The voluntary hospitals
had for many years selected their inpatients on medical criteria,
now a similar selection was introduced for outpatients. This had
important consequences for the long-run development of
medical education.

The introduction of the National Insurance Act came at a

---

[1] *Burdett's Hospitals and Charities 1915*, pp. 96–8, London, 1915
[2] MacCurrich, *The Treatment of the Sick Poor of this Country*, p.20

time when the advantages of hospital care, for all except the very rich, were increasingly appreciated by general practitioners. Moreover, the capitation system of paying panel doctors provided them with no special incentive to look after patients with serious illnesses in their own homes. If an operation were done in the patient's home, the panel doctor would have to pay the anaesthetist from his own pocket. There was thus every incentive for the doctor to move to hospital any seriously ill patient.

The Act therefore reversed previous incentives. Patients had learnt that to be sick at home meant paying the doctor; a visit to the hospital was free and so was admission to a bed. It had been, however, in the interest of the general practitioner to treat patients at home: the patient who went to the hospital might never be seen again. For this reason there had been constant criticism by general practitioners of hospitals for taking patients who could afford to pay them even though they could not afford to pay for the more costly services provided by the hospital. Now it paid the general practitioner to hand over his most worrying male patients to the hospitals, and the patient had to balance his fear of hospitals and his natural disinclination to leave his home against the advantage of free maintenance in a hospital bed.

There seems little reason to doubt that the National Insurance Act led doctors to make greater use of the inpatient departments of hospitals. This fact coupled with the underlying development of types of treatment which could only be provided for the poorer patient away from home encouraged the divorce between general practice and hospital practice in urban areas. While the rural practitioner retained the cottage hospital in which he could still attempt surgery, the urban practitioner handed his male surgical patients over to the hospital. No sooner had the Act come into force than it was suggested by one of the divisional chairmen of the BMA (Dr Harding H. Tompkins) that small hospitals should be scattered throughout urban districts open to every general practitioner where he could continue to attend his patient. 'The man in the outskirts of the large town rusts because of the hospital habit.'[1]

General practice had always been divorced from the urban hospitals. This was not a problem while hospitals and general practitioners catered for different segments of the population. Continuity of care was not disturbed. The general practitioner,

[1] *BMJ Supplement*, 20 September 1913, p. 258

aided occasionally by a consultant, supervised *all* the treatment in the patient's home. The hospital in its turn provided all the treatment for some poor persons – both general practitioner and specialist services. The juniors examined the outpatients and referred the cases requiring further care to their seniors and then continued to look after these cases in the wards under the consultant's supervision. Thus though medical care was provided without knowledge of the patient's home circumstances, continuity of care could be provided during any one illness. When the 'poor' obtained general practitioners under the Act, continuity of care was disturbed: the notes which passed between the general practitioner and the hospital were a weak link in the lengthened chain of medical care. On the other hand, many patients who had previously 'shopped around' obtained the services of one general practitioner. And it was now more difficult to go 'gadding round' the outpatient departments.

As a result of the Act, the insured person saw himself as receiving 'free' medical care more as a right and less as charity. This was particularly true of tuberculosis patients who were explicitly receiving an insurance benefit. Possibly hospital managers also tacitly accepted that they were not only 'giving' but 'serving'. For whatever the reason, it is at least worthy of note that virtually the first expression of the patient's own viewpoint is to be found in 1913. Patients began to complain. In tuberculosis hospitals they actually went on strike against monotonous, badly-cooked food and the burden of domestic work. In the other hospitals complaints covered not only food but noise and early waking.[1] One patient wrote to say that 'the treatment of the sick is sometimes too "professional" . . . not enough allowance is always made for the human element'.[2]

In the crisis created for the voluntary hospitals by their fears about the Act, many long-cherished assumptions about the conduct of voluntary hospitals were hastily re-examined. Under the threat of financial insolvency, the hospitals decided to press for a large-scale development of pay beds or, to be more exact, pre-payment beds. Nearly half their patients had become insured persons and they demanded payment for the cost of looking after them. This demand was supported by the British

---

[1] See *BMJ*, 28 September 1912, p. 812; *Hospital*, Vol. LIV, 19 July 1913, p. 477, 16 August 1913, p. 589, and Vol. LV, 7 March 1914, p. 619.

[2] *Hospital*, Vol. LV, 1 November 1913, p. 118

Medical Association, provided the honoraries were paid for their work. And while the Association had always insisted in the past that any patient in a pay bed should have a free choice of doctor, there was no demand that this principle should be introduced for insured persons. Nor did the Association press that the attendance of insured persons in hospital should be undertaken by their own general practitioners. If free choice of doctor was important in general practice and pay beds, was it not also important for other inpatients? The point was not raised by the British Medical Association. What was totally unacceptable before National Insurance was tacitly accepted in the new situation.

The widespread fear that the National Insurance Act would have drastic consequences on the finances of the voluntary hospitals led to a spate of public discussion in articles and lectures of alternative means of raising money. Under the assumed threat of extinction traditional attitudes were re-examined and old prejudices were momentarily cast aside.

A small minority of the medical profession advocated a full public health service. The proposal was by no means new[1] but there were more voices raised in favour of 'the nationalization of the whole medical profession' than earlier.[2] At the Eighty-First Annual Meeting of the BMA, Professor Benjamin Moore argued the case for

> . . . a properly co-ordinated system with local public control . . . unified nationally by a public health authority . . . veterans of the voluntary movement feared the new control which State support might involve, but they would be surprised at how little it would change the spirit of things, and at seeing hereafter the same men sitting on the boards and committees, only sent by other electorates in other capacities. There need be no dislocation, no removal of old and faithful workers of the voluntary movement. . . . It was an absurdity to argue that human nature would change or deteriorate because the State as a whole recognized the performance of its duties towards a national problem. . . . Charity, as we now understand hospital charity, must be rigorously excluded. . . .[3]

Professor Moore was far in advance of his time. The more

[1] See, for example, *BMJ*, 15 December 1906, p. 1732.
[2] *BMJ Supplement*, 27 September 1913, p. 273
[3] *Hospital*, Vol. LIV, 2 August 1913, pp. 529–30

generally held view was that it was essential at any cost to
protect the hospitals from 'the stifling control of the State'.[1]
Britain had to 'avoid the terrible evils we know to exist in other
lands where machine-made public charity takes the place of the
sweet and gracious gift of our voluntary hospitals'.[2]

The most obvious source of larger income for the hospitals was
the patient. For forty years Burdett had suggested a variety of
different ways of arranging for the patient to pay but no scheme
had been adopted. Each hospital continued to rely on such
methods of finance as were available to it. No patients had a
legal right to treatment in a voluntary hospital under any
system of insurance. There remained some hospitals which could
rely on income from endowments as the principal source of
income on current account. But most hospitals had to rely on
legacies and adopt 'the ordinary stereotyped methods of
advertising their needs by means of public appeal, adding, from
time to time, the questionable profits arising from such ex-
traneous agencies as balls, bazaars, banquets, and other amuse-
ment attractions'.[3]

In total the role of patients' payments was small though it had
been increasing over the years and had extended to every type of
hospital. In 1910 general hospitals received about $2\frac{1}{2}$ per cent of
their income from paying patients, while the special hospitals
received 12 per cent in London and 17 per cent in the provinces.[4]
There was no organized or uniform system of patients' payments
either for separate pay beds or for beds in the open wards. In the
case of the former, some charges included medical attendance,
others did not: some aimed at a profit, others at covering costs,
and others at partial payment.[5]

Although the payments made by patients did not bring in
much money, not all the voluntary hospitals were principally
paid for by the well-to-do. It is true that in London only 1·7
per cent of the total income of general hospitals could be
identified as workmen's contributions, but there were some
general hospitals outside London where the contributions of
workmen provided over half the income. 'In 1910 at Stoke-on-

[1] *Hospital Gazette*, December 1912, pp. 43–4
[2] ibid.
[3] *Hospital Gazette*, January 1913, pp. 76–8
[4] *Hospital*, Vol. LIII, 28 December 1912, p. 343
[5] *Hospital Gazette*, December 1912, p. 41

Trent the workpeople contributed 63 per cent of the total ordinary income of the North Staffs. Infirmary, at Sunderland Royal Infirmary 61 per cent, at Newcastle-on-Tyne (Royal Victoria Infirmary) 56 per cent.'[1] As Burdett concluded, it was a misapprehension to assume 'that the best of the working classes throughout the country prior to the passing of the Insurance Act, have been dependent upon charity'.[2]

After some hesitation, those responsible for the voluntary hospitals had reacted to the National Insurance Bill by demanding *pro rata* payments from the Insurance funds: once this step had been taken, the hospitals were well on the way to demanding *pro rata* payments from their patients. Under the threat of 'bankruptcy', it became generally agreed that working-class patients should not only pay the new compulsory contributions but make good themselves the fall in hospital contributions which was expected to follow the Act.

In practice the hospitals were able to manage after the Act much as they had managed before it. And the outbreak of war a year later was to transform bare solvency into relative affluence. But when the financial crisis came, as it did in 1920, the method chosen for augmenting income was the method contemplated seven years earlier. The Act had not only forced hospital authorities to abandon outdated methods of thought, it had unobtrusively shifted one of the major obstacles to demanding payments from patients. The general practitioner had now an assured income from insured persons and he did not protest if part of this work fell on his unpaid colleague in the voluntary hospital.

---

[1] *Hospital*, Vol. LIII, 28 December 1912, p. 344
[2] ibid.

CHAPTER 16

The First World War

The First Phase

ALTHOUGH the outlook and policies of the voluntary hospitals were affected by the National Insurance Act, nothing had been done to bring about co-operation either among the voluntary hospitals or between voluntary and public hospitals. The Royal Commission on the Poor Laws had expressed a unanimous desire for a better co-ordinated hospital system. But no action was taken. The British hospital 'system' remained as haphazard in 1914 as it had ever been and it was this 'system' which was about to face a challenge of tremendous dimensions – the challenge of the First World War.

The principal medical resources of the nation at the outbreak of war can be simply summarized. There were about 24,000 available doctors for a population of about 36 million and about half that number of practising nurses with recognized training. There were about 45,000 beds in some 800 voluntary hospitals, approximately another 40,000 beds in military, fever and smallpox hospitals run by public authorities, and about 120,000 in some 700 Poor Law institutions – though few of them were suitable for patients who were acutely sick.[1]

From 1903 onwards plans had been made for a possible war. But no one expected a war of long duration or with heavy casualties.[2] The armed forces were estimated to require 50,000 hospital beds.[3] By 1914, the number of beds in military hospitals amounted to only 9,000, of which 2,000 were occupied and 2,000 were not actually equipped. At one extreme there were ten

---

[1] For the source of the figures in this paragraph, see Vol. 2.

[2] Major-General Sir W. G. MacPherson, *History of the Great War, Medical Services, General History*, Vol. I, p. 2, HMSO, 1921

[3] *Hospital*, Vol. LVII, 10 October 1914, pp. 23 and 33, and 17 October 1914, p. 69

hospitals with between 200 and 600 beds while at the other extreme there were ninety hospitals with less than ten beds.[1] Arrangements had been made, however, to take over certain schools, asylums and a few voluntary hospitals and to make use of some of the beds in a large number of other voluntary hospitals. By this means accommodation could be acquired for a further 12,000 patients in what were called 'territorial force general hospitals'.[2]

The larger military and territorial hospitals were intended to serve as reception and distribution centres for a secondary group of smaller establishments.[3] But plans for obtaining these extra beds were not worked out in any detail. The military and territorial hospitals were to be expanded by a further 8,000 beds and an additional 10,000 beds were to be obtained from other civilian hospitals.[4] As regards the remaining beds, the War Office 'made the very optimistic assumption that a contract made on the outbreak of hostilities would secure in a few weeks the erection of as many huts as might be required to provide temporary accommodation . . .'[5] It was hoped that a further 11,000 beds could be obtained in this way.

Thus at the outbreak of war only about 20,000 beds were actually ready for the use of the armed forces, and the War Office started issuing appeals for additional accommodation. The voluntary hospitals and private persons responded generously. In total, throughout the war, some 5,000 buildings were offered for use as hospitals, ranging from Lambeth Palace to a variety of stately and less stately homes.[6] The War Office accepted about 1,600 of these offers. It asked the Red Cross to investigate and advise on all offers of accommodation, and to act as co-ordinating agency for these 'auxiliary hospital units'.

This assignment of duties did not bring about the co-

[1] MacPherson, p. 72
[2] ibid., pp. 71–2
[3] ibid., pp. 96–7
[4] ibid., p. 71
[5] Meanwhile, 'In the armies of Europe the planning and equipment of public buildings and barracks as hospitals in the event of war had been thoroughly considered and scheduled.' ibid., pp. 17–18
[6] *Reports by the Joint War Committee and the Joint War Finance Committee of the British Red Cross Society and the Order of St John of Jerusalem in England on Voluntary Aid Rendered to the Sick and Wounded at home and abroad and to British Prisoners of War 1914–19* (Red Cross History), p. 211, HMSO, 1921

ordination which was hoped for. The Red Cross was only one of several voluntary organizations which wanted to play a part in the wartime medical services, and a bitter rivalry existed between them. The War Office had hoped that the voluntary organizations would work together in a joint committee which was to be the 'medium of official communication between the War Office and voluntary aid societies'[1] but the British Red Cross Society had 'deemed it wiser' not only to act apart from other voluntary organizations but even to function outside the scope of military jurisdiction in direct contravention of the Geneva Convention.[2]

The Order of St John and the Soldiers and Sailors Help Society claimed equal status with the Red Cross. They even went so far as to collect their own separate lists of auxiliary hospitals and convalescent homes which they refused to submit to Red Cross inspection.[3] The SSHS was particularly successful in its endeavours. By August 1914 it had collected from private donors offers amounting to over 8,000 beds. The War Office had to recognize the position by allowing it to operate its own Central Convalescent Home Registry.[4]

The result of all the unco-ordinated activity was a chaotic dispersal and waste of scarce resources. Lord Rothschild, the chairman of the BRCS, described the situation after two weeks of war in a letter to *The Times*:

> ... private houses are being turned into hospitals and convalescent homes without reference to any organizing body and without regard to any rational scheme. Nurses are engaged who may never be required in the particular place allotted to them, while worst of all, stores of surgical material are being hoarded up in scores of homes to such an extent that the market is being seriously depleted.[5]

Worse still, parties of surgeons and nurses were actually going to

[1] MacPherson, p. 210

[2] 'Both designation and emblem are the distinctive sign of the medical services of armies, and no person is at liberty to use them under the articles of the Geneva Convention, either in time of peace or in war, unless employed in medical units and establishments of armies and subject to military laws and regulations.' ibid., p. 211

[3] ibid., p. 214

[4] ibid., p. 88

[5] *The Times*, 15 August 1914, p. 8

the front without definite orders. A party of ten surgeons, ten dressers and twenty nurses actually got to the front in August 1914 and were left behind in the Mons retreat. 'They found themselves in the midst of German troops. They were suspected of espionage, and it was some time before they were recognized as members of a Red Cross Society.'[1]

The War Office had to intervene. It informed the British Red Cross and the Orders of St John and St Andrew that they were all equal members of the Red Cross organization. Each body then issued a circular letter to its members advising them that 'all past differences should be forgotten and laid aside . . .'.[2] On 20 October, a Joint War Committee was formed under the chairmanship of Sir Arthur Stanley. The choice was a wise one. Sir Arthur was not only a man of tact but also a governor of St Thomas' Hospital.

Although the decision of the War Office to hand over the control of auxiliary hospital accommodation to the voluntary organizations had serious drawbacks, it also had advantages. It was cheap. The Red Cross was able to raise large funds by appeals to the public to meet needs which would have had to be met partly if not wholly from public funds. During the war the Red Cross raised and spent £21 million.[3]

The Society also drew support from some of the leading members of the community who also ran the voluntary hospitals. This helped in the process of co-ordination and planning. As the *Hospital Gazette* explained, 'The persons chiefly interested in the Society are usually those who are the main supporters of the hospitals and it will be very quickly spread about that the institution is placing obstacles in the way of those desirous of doing some work for the wounded soldiers.'[4] The British Red Cross was fashionable and influential. From the start, voluntary services were 'used by some as a means of gaining notoriety or social advantage'.[5] Red Cross clothing was advertised in shop windows as being 'very smart for present wear'.[6]

Thus, within a few months of the start of war, the War Office

[1] MacPherson, p. 214
[2] ibid., pp. 214–15
[3] *Red Cross History*, p. 43
[4] *Hospital Gazette*, December 1914, p. 30
[5] MacPherson, p. 208
[6] ibid., p. 217

had acquired, on paper at least, roughly the number of beds that it thought it would need. Many of them, however, were in small scattered units hardly suited for the care of the acute sick. The extra nursing staff was found from volunteers who joined Voluntary Aid Detachments. This scheme of recruiting nursing staff for war service had originated in 1909 and formed an integral part of the Territorial Force. At the outbreak of war, its 80,000 members were 'controlled and directed by the Territorial Force County Associations'.[1]

The VADs included among their numbers the daughters of the social *élite*. They were usually unpaid and usually untrained by the standards currently accepted in the nursing profession. Short courses were, however, hastily arranged – much to the disgust of many of the professionally conscious trained nurses who complained that these young women with their cursory training were being called and treated as nurses by medical men and society people. The Countess of Warwick thought it 'intolerable' that 'any girl of good family who assumes a uniform she has not won the right to wear should pose as the representative of a sisterhood she is not worthy to associate with, of whose traditions she is ignorant, of whose high discipline and complete restraint she is intolerant'.[2] When twenty leading members of the Camberwell Red Cross were given permission to attend the infirmary 'to gain practical acquaintance with hospital methods and routine', the matron resigned in protest.[3]

The VADs worked in military hospitals and in the voluntary and auxiliary hospitals. Some of them found their way to the bedsides of the wounded soldiers on the Continent, leaving behind them 'the injured feelings of the many trained nurses' who were eager to go.[4] It was suggested by the *Hospital Gazette* that the infirmaries offered 'a much more extensive . . . ground for the activities of Red Cross workers'.[5]

Many doctors left their civilian practices to join the armed forces and to work in military hospitals. The British Medical Association was made responsible for co-ordinating the arrangements for the recruitment of doctors. Those working in hospitals

[1] MacPherson, p. 212
[2] *Hospital Gazette*, July 1915, p. 140
[3] *PLOJ*, 12 March 1915, p. 321
[4] Abel-Smith, op. cit., p. 86
[5] December 1914, p. 30

caring for members of the armed forces were given ranks in the armed forces. The ranks granted were in accordance with the professional standing and social status of the different categories of doctors as interpreted by the War Office. The fading distinctions of the 'old orders' were crystallized in the military hierarchy. Thus general practitioners, district medical officers and housemen became lieutenants. Medical superintendents became captains or occasionally majors.[1] Consulting physicians and surgeons became colonels.[2] There were salaries which accorded with all these ranks.

The full-time employees of asylums and infirmaries and the junior salaried medical staff of voluntary hospitals were also readily absorbed by military establishments. Thus the chief administrators of the voluntary hospitals were nearly always given commissioned ranks[3] while the chief administrators in the Poor Law who came from a lower social background became quartermasters or warrant officers.[4] The honorary medical staffs of the voluntary hospitals presented special difficulties. They had previously been unpaid for their hospital work which they combined with private practice. Moreover, as in most cases only part of voluntary hospitals was used for military patients, the honoraries needed still to look after civilian patients. In most cases the honoraries were given full salaries and in addition were allowed to engage in private practice. In the case of the outlying auxiliary hospitals, local general practitioners were paid twopence or threepence a day for each occupied bed under their supervision, once they had found out that such grants were authorized and had applied for them.[5]

There were a few voluntary hospitals which gave their services freely throughout the war[6] but within a few weeks of the outbreak of war some of them applied for grants from the War

[1] *Hospital*, Vol. LXII, 21 April 1917, p. 41
[2] MacPherson, p. 49
[3] *Hospital Gazette*, January 1915, pp. 49–50. A list of 14 serving secretaries, honorary secretaries and assistant secretaries is given here. Only 2 were NCOs and one of these was a sergeant in the Hon. Artillery Company.
[4] *PLOJ*, 26 November 1915, p. 1371. The workhouse master of Amersham 'said he would like to apply for a quartermaster's commission at once, several workhouse masters having been granted quartermasterships recently'.
[5] *The Times*, 12 May 1917, p. 70
[6] A. J. Cleveland, *A History of the Norfolk and Norwich Hospital*, p. 32, Norwich, 1948

Office. The system of *pro rata* payments which had been denied the voluntary hospitals for insured patients before the war, despite frequent and persistent demands, was granted to the voluntary hospitals for the care of military patients under the stress of war. Each hospital had to be dealt with separately.[1] The auxiliary hospitals organized by the Red Cross also demanded payment. On 18 August, the War Office sanctioned a flat rate capitation grant of two shillings per day for each occupied bed.[2] This was increased in November 1914 to three shillings per day 'where necessary',[3] and even higher figures were paid in special cases. Thus the scale of payment for ordinary cases ranged from three shillings a day at Brighton to four shillings at Liverpool.[4] Acutely infectious servicemen were being sent to civil isolation hospitals where daily grants of six shillings and 'in special cases a maximum of seven shillings was allowed'.[5] From March 1915, capitation payments of two shillings a day were paid to private convalescent homes. The British Hospitals Association appealed unsuccessfully for a uniform scale of payments. Despite Lloyd George's prophecies before the war, the receipt of these grants did little to limit the independence of action of the voluntary hospitals.

The arrangements made for the hospital care of the armed forces in the early days of the war aimed at economy rather than co-ordination. Medical resources were acquired in such a way as would impose the minimum cost on the Exchequer and the maximum cost on charitable funds. The best use was not made of scarce resources. Everyone concurred in giving priority to the needs of the military over the needs of the civilian sick. In theory the organization did not look too bad. There were military hospitals for regulars directly under the War Office and territorial hospitals for territorials under the Red Cross, and at the fringe of these two nuclei of acute beds were the auxiliary hospitals and convalescent homes controlled by the SSHS. But the faults of the system were nakedly revealed under its first real test.

Early in November 1914, 57 trainloads of wounded soldiers

---

[1] MacPherson, pp. 86–8
[2] ibid., pp. 85–6
[3] ibid.
[4] *Hospital Gazette,* January 1915, p. 63
[5] MacPherson, p. 83

arrived in London from Ypres.[1] Immediately there were signs that 'the reserve line of beds is now being drawn on. . . '.[2] And the casualty lists from Flanders mounted rapidly. By the end of the year, 73,000 wounded officers and men had arrived in England.[3] The War Office had to revise its original estimate of 50,000 beds and begin looking hastily for extra accommodation.

Huts were hurriedly erected in military hospitals and territorial hospitals. Spaces between beds were reduced and extra beds set up wherever possible. But these measures were not adequate to meet the demand. More buildings had to be taken over from the civilian sick and even more from the sick in Poor Law institutions and mental hospitals. Selection for requisition had to be done by the War Office itself. While the Red Cross could browbeat voluntary hospitals it was less able to handle the self-important elected local authorities. There were many Boards of Guardians who refused to allow 'the Red Cross Society . . . to take over control in Poor Law institutions'.[4]

While a voluntary hospital could allocate part of its accommodation to military purposes, it was much more difficult to arrange for accommodation in Poor Law premises to be divided between civilian and military use. Attitudes to the Poor Law deliberately instilled by the ruling class over several generations could not be suddenly altered to suit the needs of the war emergency. Public opinion would 'not tolerate the association of the wounded with the evil reputation'[5] of the Poor Law. Thus it was the practice 'to remove from the infirmaries taken over all notices or other indications of their former connection with the Poor Law'.[6]

During November 1914 several Poor Law institutions were taken over for the use of the armed forces. The War Office negotiated directly with local Boards of Guardians. The Brighton Board was among the first to find out what the War Office meant by 'negotiation'.

A positive bombshell burst among the Brighton Guardians on Tuesday. Without the slightest warning or preparation of any kind

---

[1] *Hospital*, Vol. LVII, 9 November 1914, p. 123
[2] ibid.
[3] MacPherson, p. 390
[4] *PLOJ*, 20 November 1914, p. 1473
[5] *Hospital*, Vol. LVIII, 17 April 1915, p. 46
[6] ibid.

they were informed that the War Office wanted the workhouse as a hospital for Indians. A deputation from the War Office waited on the Board in the morning to prepare them and in the afternoon the whole matter was settled.[1]

All contracts with Guardians were arranged so that 'while no extra expense will fall upon the poor rates, no profit will be made out of the transaction'.[2]

When Poor Law institutions were taken over, extra medical staff were brought in to work in them. Thus senior consultants were in contact with the Poor Law medical services for the first time. The institutions which were taken over were 'carefully selected and only those known to be well-equipped as judged by Poor Law standards were chosen'.[3] Nonetheless, the top doctors found the facilities sadly inadequate. Stocks of 'surgical instruments, of X-ray apparatus, of appliances for bacteriological and pathological work, and for more specialized methods of clinical examination and treatment had to be very considerably increased'.[4]

There were serious deficiencies in staffing ratios. 'In the Poor Law institutions with training schools in England and Wales, there was one trained nurse for forty-four beds.'[5] This ratio had now to be brought into line with the normal military hospital requirement of one trained nurse for nineteen beds.[6] The average Poor Law infirmary of 500 beds had a peace-time medical staff of one superintendent and, at the most, three junior medical officers. When such buildings became war hospitals the RAMC increased their staffs to one superintendent, one registrar, four full-time and six half-time assistants, a radiographer, an anaesthetist, a pathologist, an ophthalmic surgeon and a dental surgeon.[7]

Throughout the winter and spring of 1915 more and more civilian beds were handed over to the military authorities. The voluntary movement had given nearly 16,000 beds 'immediately

[1] *Brighton Herald & Hove Chronicle*, 28 November 1914, p. 10
[2] *PLOJ*, 9 April 1915, p. 439
[3] *Hospital*, Vol. LIX, 25 March 1916, p. 569
[4] ibid.
[5] Abel-Smith, p. 85
[6] ibid.
[7] *Hospital*, Vol. LIX, 25 March 1916, p. 569

after war was declared'.[1] By January 1915 the Red Cross had approved nearly 20,000 beds in 686 auxiliary units.[2] The Poor Law was providing 'no less than 30,000 beds'[3] as well as accommodation for 5,000 fit soldiers and over 17,000 Belgian refugees.[4] At the end of the first year of war just over 90,000 hospital beds were reserved for wounded servicemen throughout the United Kingdom. Nearly 70,000 were occupied.[5] The major voluntary hospitals of the Metropolis increased their number of beds from 9,766 in 1913 to 11,406 in 1916. One in four of the beds which had previously been at the disposal of civilian sick were used for service patients.[6]

The war was making serious inroads on the accommodation available for the civilian sick. When Brighton Workhouse was handed over to Indian soldiers 'to meet the pleasure of the King' the Guardians had to find alternative accommodation for over 1,000 sick paupers.[7] They did so in spite of the local population for 'there was not a single occasion on which they had not to fight for possession' of local boarding houses.[8] When a few sick paupers were lodged in 'well-appointed hotels' the local parish council 'passed a resolution of horror at this profanation of their stately neighbourhood'.[9] Elsewhere the evicted paupers did not do so well. At Bradford they were lodged in requisitioned schools;[10] in Bagthorpe they were transferred to 'the mental wards and test-house'.[11] Six hundred infirm paupers were turned out of Tooting Home for the Aged and sent to Mitcham Workhouse where they had to wear 'a distinctive dress on which is conspicuously stamped to whom it belongs'. This peremptory

[1] MacPherson, p. 83

[2] *Hospital*, Vol. LVII, 30 January 1915, p. 395

[3] *PLOJ*, 2 July 1915, p. 783

[4] ibid., and 9 July 1915, p. 805. The MAB was made responsible for the care of these Belgian refugees. 12,000 were accommodated at Alexandra Palace and the 'War Refugees Camp', Earls Court. The remainder were sent to St Anne's Home, Streatham; Endell Street Home; and the Poland Street Refuge. In addition, the MAB provided some 6,500 beds in three of its fever hospitals.

[5] MacPherson, p. 94, approximate returns for 1 August 1915

[6] *Hospital*, Vol. LXIII, 3 November 1917, p. 96

[7] *PLOJ*, 4 December 1914, p. 1530

[8] ibid., 1 January 1915, p. 19

[9] *Brighton Herald & Hove Chronicle*, 5 December 1914

[10] *PLOJ*, 22 October 1915, p. 1228

[11] *Hospital*, Vol. LVII, 20 March 1915, p. 552

evacuation sometimes had grave effects. One of the aged male paupers who had lived fourteen years at the Home drowned himself in the Thames.[1]

The unrequisitioned workhouses became seriously over-crowded. Even the Guardians expressed concern. The medical officer at Brampton Workhouse had to reassure his Board that 'if the windows were kept open the children would be all right'.[2] The stricter Unions upheld their pre-war reputations. At Atcham, where the Guardians had abolished out-relief, reductions were made in the paupers' meat ration.[3] The Local Government Board encouraged such policies and issued a circular to all Unions stressing 'the urgent need for strict economy. . . .'[4]

Most Boards of Guardians did their best to maintain a minimum standard of care for all their sick. They were, indeed, legally bound to do so. The voluntary hospitals were under no such obligations. Most of them welcomed the wounded soldiers with 'exceeding great warmth'. They even extended their welcome to uninteresting cases 'that were quite unsuitable on ordinary medical or surgical grounds'.[5] As the number of students declined, teaching requirements took second place 'to cases of frostbite and minor ailments'.[6] The London Hospital had admitted over 1,300 wounded soldiers by the end of November 1914, a fact which it stressed in its Christmas Appeal.[7] The Norfolk and Norwich Hospital provided 250 of its 350 beds.[8] In Wales, where the shortage of hospital accommodation amounted to a national scandal, the chairman of the Swansea Hospital offered to 'treble' his original offer of fifty beds.[9]

Many doctors and nurses had left their posts to care for

---

[1] ibid., Vol. LVIII, 12 June 1915, p. 221

[2] *PLOJ*, 27 August 1915, p. 1001

[3] ibid., 13 August 1915, p. 952. As one of the Guardians explained, 'If every public body in the country could save $1d$ in the £, it would make a big difference.'

[4] ibid., 20 August 1915, p. 973

[5] *Hospital Gazette*, November 1914, pp. 17–18

[6] *Hospital*, Vol. LVII, 13 March 1915, p. 526

[7] ibid., 19 December 1914, Christmas Appeal Number, p. 11

[8] ibid., 1 May 1915, p. 100

[9] ibid., 20 March 1915, p. 548. Three years later the chairman admitted that there was a 'serious question of a growing waiting list' of about 200 civilians (*Hospital*, Vol. LXII, 16 June 1917, p. 200).

wounded servicemen.[1] As a result there were many voluntary hospitals which had to close their outpatient departments and civilian wards.[2] Operations were being delayed for days at Manchester Royal Infirmary because of the shortage of surgeons.[3] A hospital for women and children at Plaistow faced closure because of the lack of doctors.[4] Many voluntary hospital patients were turned out to 'homes which were frequently unfit to receive those in the early stages of convalescence'.[5]

Sir Henry Burdett, as he had become, was outspokenly critical of the neglect of the civilian sick. In the first months of the war he had warned against the coming 'invasion' of the voluntary hospitals.[6] During 1915 he again spoke out for 'the dispossessed sufferers' who were 'forgotten by the War Office ...'. And he scorned the 'sleek and self-congratulatory phrases'[7] with which the members of the Hospital Saturday Fund complimented each other. ... Sir Henry described how the policy of admitting so many wounded soldiers 'was pleasing to the subscribers to the Hospital Fund, and in some quarters ... was judged good business, as a means of getting new subscribers'.[8]

Shortages of trained staff in civilian hospitals grew more acute as the war progressed. Military service became compulsory in January 1916 and the Joint War Committee of the British Medical Association began planning for 'the complete mobilization of the medical profession'. But the War Office was not prepared to wait while the doctors sorted out their various grades of exemption. Call-up papers were summarily issued to every doctor in the country under forty-one years of age. The BMA protested vigorously and it was finally agreed that the professional committees alone would call up doctors 'according to the numbers required from time to time by the Director-General of the Army Medical Services'.[9]

Even middle-class civilian patients suffered hardships. When the local cottage hospital at Wimborne was requisitioned, the

[1] ibid., 23 October 1915, p. 89
[2] ibid.
[3] *Hospital Gazette*, July 1915, p. 146
[4] ibid., October 1915, p. 6
[5] *Hospital*, Vol. LIX, 12 February 1916, pp. 423–4
[6] *Hospital*, Vol. LVI, 22 August 1914, p. 561
[7] ibid., 29 May 1915, p. 178
[8] ibid., p. 177
[9] MacPherson, p. 146

patients were transferred to the local Poor Law infirmary. The Local Government Board ordered that they should be dealt with in exactly the same way as other 'destitute' persons and refused to provide a separate operating theatre. Their own private doctors were also denied access.[1]

Under the impact of the war, there was a rapid growth of hospitals for the middle classes. It was much more difficult for nursing to be provided within the family circle and domestic help was harder to obtain. At Leicester, Highfield Hospital was converted into a paying home to meet the growing demand for private medical care.[2] Horsham Cottage Hospital also became a pay hospital and the experiment was so successful that the managers were able to finance improvements at a time when capital expenditure in the public hospital sector had virtually ceased.[3]

In so far as the armed forces were making use of the vast number of hospital beds it had borrowed and requisitioned for urgent cases, there was some justification for the priority given to the military over the civilian. Many of them were volunteers. When resources are strictly limited, there is a case for giving preference to patients who are likely to return to a full and productive life over those with a less fortunate prognosis, especially if it also means helping to win a war. But by delegating such extensive duties to voluntary bodies and by leaving such a wide measure of independence to them, the War Office was not in a position to enforce an efficient use of medical resources.

The policy of the department was openly stated to be to 'give preference in the matter of patients to those institutions to which no payment was being made'.[4] This further reduced the control of the military authorities. It meant that if there was any temporary leeway between patients and available beds, the empty beds appeared in the hospitals under its direct control rather than in those over which its power could be less directly exercised. Beds in military and territorial hospitals which had the highest staffing ratios and the best equipment were left empty 'in order to fill auxiliary hospitals'.[5] Local deputy

---

[1] *PLOJ*, 28 May 1915, p. 638
[2] *Hospital*, Vol. LVII, 13 March 1915, p. 526
[3] ibid., 17 April 1915, p. 51
[4] *Hospital*, Vol. LVII, 20 March 1915, p. 546
[5] MacPherson, p. 98

directors at their Command Depots were ordered to resolve the conflicting claims between the military and auxiliary hospitals. At the same time they were instructed to send wounded soldiers direct from embarkation points to 'suitable' auxiliary hospitals. The War Office urged them to allot 'the larger share to those receiving a lesser capitation grant . . .'.[1]

Within two months the army had regretted handing over to the SSHS responsibility for convalescent homes. Officers and men were not returning from them to their units on time. The SSHS and its central registry were abandoned and local army commands began to provide their own convalescent homes. The term 'convalescent home' was abolished in September 1915 and thereafter all auxiliary hospitals were classified as either Class A or Class B.[2] The latter received smaller capitation payments. Only convalescent officers remained under the care of the Red Cross. It became a 'coveted distinction' for a hospital to attain Class A status by one means or another.[3] 'Local influences were often brought to bear on a Deputy Director Medical Superintendent to grant the authority to unsuitable hospitals.'[4]

Thus the convalescence of other ranks was brought under closer supervision of the army but control over auxiliary hospitals remained remote. Moreover, as capitation grants were only paid for occupied beds, the auxiliary hospitals were tempted to hold on to recovered patients and admit patients with minor injuries. Many hospitals yielded to these temptations. It is possible that what the War Office was saving on the daily rate paid to the auxiliary hospitals it was losing in the long period for which it had to pay it and in the long absence of soldiers from the front.

In the spring of 1916 there was a lull on the Western Front. Thousands of beds reserved for wounded soldiers in the voluntary hospitals fell vacant. And they remained empty while the civilian poor went unattended.[5] The War Office ordered the return of the remaining service patients to empty military hospitals. The order was greeted with protests from the voluntary hospitals. Governors complained 'that they were faced with the loss of present revenue . . . which is on a capitation basis for

[1] ibid.
[2] ibid., p. 89
[3] ibid., p. 98
[4] ibid.
[5] *Hospital*, Vol. LIX, 12 February 1916, pp. 423−4

occupied beds'.[1] The War Office did not enforce its order. Instead it decided to make a payment of sixpence to the voluntary hospitals for each unoccupied bed.

The arrangements which the War Office had made had been for a short war and for a relatively small casualty rate. The organization of the medical services did not allow the planned allocation of scarce resources to conflicting needs. The consequences were to become even more apparent as the war progressed.

[1] ibid. See also *Hospital Gazette*, February 1916, pp. 65-6.

CHAPTER 17

The First World War

The Second Phase

THE fall in the flow of army casualties from the front line
early in 1916 did not last for long. The first battle of the
Somme began in June of that year. During July and August the
number of beds occupied increased by over 70,000. The number
of maimed and injured continued to grow for the rest of the
year.

During 1917 the great battles of Arras and Ypres were fought
to a stalemate. After the first few hours of the battle of Passchen-
daele there were 13,000 casualties, of whom some 4,000 died after
one day's fighting.[1] Fresh appeals were made and more hospital
beds were handed over, constructed or adapted for the use of the
armed forces. By August 1917, the total number of beds for
servicemen in the United Kingdom had risen to 317,075 – a
figure which dwarfed the 50,000 originally planned in 1914.
During the year nearly 700,000 wounded officers and men[2] were
transported from the barren battlefields to a country where the
autumn fashion shows were advertised as 'amongst the most
fabulous in generations'.[3]

Records which would have explained exactly how this vast
total of accommodation was provided are not available. However, the military hospitals which existed at the outbreak of war
are known to have expanded from 9,000 beds to nearly 30,000
beds and new military hospitals to have provided another
47,500 beds. About 22,000 of these were in huts. In addition to
these 77,500 military beds, there were in England and Wales well
over 20,000 beds in voluntary hospitals, about 29,000 in lunatic
asylums, about 35,000 in infirmaries and workhouses and about

[1] L. Wolff, *In Flanders Fields*, p. 183, London, 1963
[2] MacPherson, p. 390
[3] L. Wolff, pp. 14–16

4,000 in hospitals run by the Metropolitan Asylums' Board and public health authorities. The remainder of the beds, amounting to well over 100,000, were provided in buildings not previously used for hospital purposes – schools, universities, town halls and a large number of private houses.

Doctors and nurses were not only in drastically short supply, but also badly distributed. By delegating responsibility to so many different authorities, the War Office had little effective control. Although there was a great increase in the number of girls taking the full nurses' training during the war, the biggest contribution to the nursing services came from the VADs who had started the war 80,000 strong and increased their number to 120,000 by its conclusion. Of these 12,000 were working in military hospitals and 60,000 in auxiliary hospitals.[1] In June 1918, there were said to be as many as 200 auxiliary hospitals 'unable to obtain the help they need'.[2] Even pauper orderlies were used to help with the war effort. When the Mile End Infirmary was taken over, the colonel arranged with the master to keep on the thirty aged pauper orderlies: instead of their traditional tobacco allowance, they were paid 2s 6d per week.[3]

In September 1916 the War Office set up a committee to ascertain 'the resources of the country in trained nurses and those partially trained in nursing, so as to enable it to suggest the most economical method of utilizing their services for civil and military purposes'.[4] It found that

> ... military hospitals at home were employing nearly 8,000 nurses to staff about 126,000 beds. In addition, there were a further number of nearly 4,000 trained nurses manning about 93,000 beds in hospitals abroad. There were also about 800 beds for officers under private management, staffed by about 192 trained nurses. In total, therefore, they collected information covering about 220,000 beds staffed by about 12,000 trained nurses.[5]

The committee's only recommendation was that 'an appeal might be made [to the officers' hospitals] to reduce the present

[1] Abel-Smith, p. 85–6
[2] *Hospital*, Vol. LXIV, 1 June 1918, p. 188
[3] *PLOJ*, 13 August 1915, p. 951
[4] Abel-Smith, p. 84
[5] ibid., p. 85

proportion of trained nurses from one to four to that of one to six.'[1]

No attempt was made to standardize the pay of nursing staff – whether or not they worked for the armed forces. VAD members working in military hospitals received salaries and allowances of £20–30 a year plus extra allowances for board, lodging and travelling expenses. There were also grants of £5 for uniforms.[2] VAD nurses in voluntary hospitals were nominally unpaid but full-time workers were able to claim expense allowances, a fact which was not widely known. Matrons in military hospitals received starting salaries of £75 per annum rising by annual increments to £150. Sisters' salaries ranged from £50 to £65. There was additional 'charge' pay for matrons and sisters, ranging from £15 per annum in hospitals of between 100 and 199 equipped beds to £30 in hospitals of 300 or more beds. Staff nurses were paid from £40 to £45 per annum.[3]

The relatively high pay in military hospitals led the Local Government Board to introduce a revised scale of pay for nursing staff working in institutions taken over for war purposes. The new rates averaged 'some 30 per cent higher than the salaries generally paid to fully trained nurses in Poor Law institutions'.[4] Voluntary hospitals and Poor Law institutions caring for the civilian sick found that they had also to increase their salary scales substantially if they were to keep their nursing staff. At Sheffield Royal Infirmary the annual wages of probationers were gradually raised from £5 in 1914 to £30 in 1918. Salaries of sisters were increased from £30 to a new scale ranging between £40 and £50 a year.[5] The Southwark Guardians who were reluctant to move with the times soon found themselves left with three head nurses out of a pre-war staff of twelve. In an effort to check the resignations, the Guardians placed their head nurses on the same scale as trained nurses in military hospitals.[6] The variety of policies which were thus permitted did not promote a more rational distribution of staff and there were severe and indeed dangerous nursing shortages in many

[1] ibid.
[2] *Hospital*, Vol. LXIV, 1 June 1918, p. 188
[3] *PLOJ*, 4 June 1915, p. 670
[4] ibid., and *LGB Memorandum of 18 May 1915*
[5] *Hospital*, Vol. LXIV, 25 May 1918, p. 166
[6] ibid., Vol. LVIII, 11 September 1915, p. 499

hospitals throughout the war – particularly in those for the civilian sick.

The British Medical Association had the responsibility of adjusting medical personnel to current needs. The War Office had granted the top doctors full-time salaries while allowing them to retain their private practices. This unpublished arrangement came in for criticism when it leaked out in 1917. It emerged that six part-time consultants were being paid £5,000 each a year for services rendered at the Royal Naval Hospital. After protests in the House of Commons the Admiralty terminated their contracts and then re-engaged them as Surgeons-General at annual salaries of £1,300.[1] In August 1917, the War Office followed this example and 'abruptly notified' part-time doctors working in military hospitals that their services were no longer required.[2] Their places were taken by doctors from the United States, many of whom were said to have orthopaedic training.[3]

The practice of employing part-time consultants continued, however, in hospitals which were not controlled by the armed forces. The system became 'progressively unsatisfactory as the war went on'. A War Office committee which reported in August 1917 condemned the system of 'staffing the territorial force general hospitals with *à la suite* officers of high local standing'.[4] No action followed. In August 1918, a second committee set up by the Ministry of National Service found that the top doctors were still holding on to their part-time posts. The committee pointed out that throughout the war these consultants had held 'an unfair advantage over their colleagues . . . because they held a commission and although doing in many instances very little military work, were in full enjoyment of their private practice and of army pay'. The average daily attendance of many of these consultants 'had been less than one hour'. It was suggested that they 'might be made available for service . . . overseas or as whole-time officers elsewhere'.[5]

The Army Medical Advisory Council decided to act on the committee's recommendations. Plans were made to enforce a minimum daily attendance of three hours on all territorial

[1] *Hansard* (H of C), Vol. LXXII, 23 June 1915, col. 1153
[2] *Hospital*, Vol. LXII, 22 August 1917, p. 499
[3] ibid., 29 September 1917, p. 520
[4] MacPherson, p. 151
[5] ibid., p. 152

hospital consultants and specialists. Surplus staff were to be demobilized.[1] But the war ended before the new regulations could be enforced.

While the Government had been willing to pay generously throughout the war for the very limited services of the top doctors, it was much less generous with humble general practitioners. In 1917 Burdett criticized the secretiveness of the arrangements for paying doctors and accused the military authorities of obtaining free medical services under false pretences. He explained how

> ... it has leaked out, in spite of official evasiveness ... excessive even for the War Office, that the military authorities have the potential right to make certain payments to the medical officers of the VAD hospitals. . . . One of the conditions was that personal application should be made and there was something more than a hint that the transaction should be a strictly private one, the recipient being bound in honour not to betray his luck to his less well-informed colleagues.[2]

After the exposure the Government had to accept the principle of paying all doctors and negotiate about the appropriate salaries. The rate of payment was not settled until February 1918, when it was agreed that doctors should be paid fourpence a day for each bed occupied by a patient from overseas. For all other war patients they were to receive threepence a day. Limits of 17s 6d and 12s 6d were laid down for overseas and home cases respectively.[3] Doctors treating service patients in voluntary hospitals were paid 9d for each occupied bed per day. These contracts with voluntary staff were backdated to 1 October 1917.[4]

The standard of accommodation available for servicemen varied widely. At one extreme were well-equipped units staffed with top doctors and a high ratio of nursing staff: and at the other were lunatic asylums and workhouses brought into service as war hospitals, and staffed by nurses and doctors in inadequate numbers and with limited experience. Standards of comfort

[1] ibid.
[2] *Hospital*, Vol. LXII, 11 August 1917, p. 367
[3] MacPherson, p. 86
[4] *Army Council Instruction*, 10 February 1918, and *Hospital*, Vol. LXIII, 9 February 1918, p. 386

varied from the luxury of country houses to the rigours of temporary huts.

The few soldiers who were lucky enough to be sent to voluntary hospitals were generously cared for. The wounded soldiers were allowed to smoke in the wards – a practice which *The Hospital* hoped would not be extended to 'hospital patients generally' and would 'lapse with the war'.[1] Visiting hours were relaxed and relatives allowed to call daily. Alcohol was smuggled into the wards.[2] Local residents provided car rides and other forms of entertainment. Discipline in the voluntary hospitals was generally relaxed in spite of War Office directives that 'patients marked "up" will shave, wash and dress before breakfast'. NCOs were ordered to wear their chevrons at all times and 'if confined to bed, their chevrons will be hung over their beds'.[3] Few of the patients seemed to concern themselves unduly with such regulations.

The other ranks who were accommodated in the hutted hospitals 'designed upon the open-air principle' were much less comfortable. In some huts there was 'no gap in the continuous line of windows all down each side of the ward' and the windows were kept open 'throughout the entire summer and generally . . . in winter also . . .'[4] In others, the walls opened out like a series of stable doors. At first 'no heating whatever was provided' but later it was found necessary to provide 'a few open fires . . . for the appearance of comfort'. They were also useful for the nurses as a 'means of warming their hands previous to changing dressings etc.'[5] As one enthusiast explained, 'The raindrops may rattle a shade noisily on the roofs, the asbestos lining may be devoid of ornamentation', but the patient still had the advantage of 'indoor comfort plus an outdoor atmosphere'.[6] By the end of the war there were 47,500 beds in these hutted camps, of which only 372 were reserved for officers.

The allocation of places in this sporadic hospital service took account of rank, nationality and colour, quite apart from the degree of medical need. On the whole, the officers had the pick

[1] *Hospital*, Vol. LVIII, 24 April 1915, p. 82
[2] ibid., 29 May 1915, p. 185
[3] *Red Cross History*, op. cit., p. 214
[4] *Hospital*, Vol. LXII, 9 June 1917, p. 188
[5] *Hospital Gazette*, January 1916, p. 59
[6] *Hospital*, Vol. LXII, 9 June 1917, p. 188

of what was available. There were many private donors who
offered accommodation only for officers. Many appeal funds for
officers were over-subscribed.[1] The surplus money was spent on
equipping new hospitals and purchasing extra amenities. At the
Kensington Officers' Home there were two bathrooms on every
floor and most of the accommodation was in single rooms. The
thirty-five patients were cared for by a resident medical officer, a
matron, three trained nurses and three probationers.[2] There
was on average in all the private officers' hospitals 'one trained
nurse for every four beds'.[3] However, there were some officers'
hospitals which found it difficult to make ends meet. One of these
advertised in *The Times* that it was 'feeling financial strain' and
would 'give important post to any lady giving liberal support to
same'.[4]

In August 1917 there were only about 1,170 officers in former
Poor Law establishments, asylums and huts. There were
1,545 officers in military convalescent hospitals, and a further
4,794 were cared for in territorial hospitals. Nearly two-thirds of
the total number of officers' beds were in the military, voluntary
and other auxiliary hospitals where the highest staffing ratios
were maintained.[5] The Red Cross provided generously for the
comfort of convalescent officers. It rented many furnished
houses so that officers' families could be near the convalescent
homes. In such cases, 'an allowance was always made for house-
hold expenses and the wages of a servant paid for periods varying
from one to six months'. Many officers, accompanied by their
wives, were sent to Harrogate, Bath and the Riviera resorts. All
these services were paid for out of charitable funds.[6] Nearly
4,000 officers who had contracted tuberculosis were placed in
English sanatoria and 'every available bed was booked . . .'.
Others were sent to the Swiss resorts. These 'particularly high'
expenses were met out of charitable funds.[7]

The behaviour of such officers who were out of the control of
military discipline was not always exemplary. Stern action had
to be taken against 'a minority' who 'unfortunately regarded this

1 *Hospital*, Vol. LXI, 3 March 1917, p. 435
2 ibid., Vol. LVII, 16 January 1915, p. 345
3 Abel-Smith, p. 85
4 *The Times*, 22 September 1917
5 MacPherson, pp. 74–8 and 80–2
6 *Red Cross History*, pp. 58–9
7 ibid., p. 233

liberty as an excuse for drunkenness and worse forms of debauchery'.[1] These officers were refused home leave and spent their convalescence under strict supervision in the former Great Central Hotel, Marylebone. Even teetotal officers had to be restrained from self-indulgence. The War Office had to issue 'stringent orders' against 'excessive milk-drinking' in officers' messes and hospitals.[2] In some hospitals for other ranks, on the other hand, patients who were admitted after the daily diet sheets had been dispatched received nothing but milk for forty-eight hours. 'Healthy surgical cases' became 'ferocious with hunger' and 'inspectors never came round when the patients were stealing each other's food and when the thermometers were at freezing point'.[3]

Many Dominion and colonial troops were cared for in hutted camps except the Canadians who were given a modern MAB fever hospital and the 'five leading hotels' in Buxton.[4] Sick and wounded prisoners of war were guarded in Poor Law institutions and asylums.[5] This practice outraged some patriotic Guardians. At Mile End they refused to admit any wounded Germans.[6] The Withington Board accepted 1,700 and then turned away another 1,000 from 'one of the best equipped institutions in the Kingdom [while] so many of our men are being treated in converted schools'.[7]

The way in which the accommodation was graded according to the class of casualty was revealed with particular poignancy when there was a change in the nationality of the casualties. One workhouse was 'transformed' to meet the needs of wounded Indians, but when British soldiers had to be admitted later on it was necessary to spend 'further large sums of money'.[8] Even more extensive improvements were thought necessary for American servicemen.

The army did not believe in pampering its sick and wounded.

[1] *Hospital*, Vol. LXI, 3 March 1917, p. 435
[2] ibid., Vol. LXIII, 9 March 1918, p. 478
[3] ibid., 29 September 1917, p. 522
[4] Sir A. Powell (compil.), *The Metropolitan Asylums' Board and Its Work 1867-1930*, p. 92, London, 1930
[5] MacPherson, pp. 80-1
[6] *Hospital*, Vol. LXI, 23 December 1916, p. 239
[7] ibid., Vol. LXII, 11 August 1917, pp. 369-70
[8] ibid., Vol. LXIV, 25 May 1918, p. 155, and *Hospital Gazette*, February 1916, p. 73

Service patients were entirely dependent upon voluntary aid for
such 'comforts' as 'bedjackets, bedsocks, dressing gowns,
hospital bags, pyjamas, slings, felt slippers, sphagnum moss
dressings, operation swabs, specially prepared bandages and so
on'. Official ordnance depots were not authorized to supply any
of these articles.[1] Nearly 400,000 voluntary workers had to be
organized into about 3,000 local 'comforts' associations under
the Director-General of Voluntary Organizations.[2] The army
did issue a ward dress to wounded soldiers. It consisted of a
'Reckitts Blue uniform whose outer skin is of flannelette'. The
garment was not popular as it shrank 'at a different rate from
the lining' when washed. There was a second choice of flannel
suiting which was equally unpopular with the wounded, who
resented walking around in 'bright blue trousers and dark blue
coats'.[3] Officers received personal clothing allowances.

While the military authorities tried to make proper arrangements for soldiers who recovered from their wounds and could
return to the front, arrangements for those who could wage war
no longer were far from satisfactory. Disabled soldiers and
sailors were being discharged at the rate of roughly 1,000 a
month. By December 1915, there were nearly 16,000 of them.[4]
The Government was sharply criticized for allowing the War
Office to discharge disabled other ranks 'before everything that
medical and surgical care can do for them has been done'.
Lloyd George explained that 'the matter was receiving sym-
pathetic attention'[5] and that a civil organization was being set
up. But it was still being alleged in 1917 that 'the discharged
soldier, technically capable of work, but really incapacitated
and thrown aside with a trifling pension, [was] once more
knocking at the infirmary's doors'.[6] Local war pensions committees were sending their cases to the workhouses.[7]

Attempts to organize a rehabilitation service did not begin
until October 1917. Negotiations between the Ministry of

[1] MacPherson, p. 184
[2] ibid., p. 221
[3] *Hansard* (H of C), Vol. XXXVI, 24 October 1916, cols. 970–1. As the
Minister explained, it was 'not possible to consult individual tastes' in this
matter.
[4] *PLOJ*, 14 May 1915, p. 581
[5] *Hansard* (H of C), Vol. LXXXVI, 17 October 1916, cols. 387–8
[6] *Hospital*, Vol. LXII, 9 June 1917, p. 180
[7] ibid., 9 July 1917, p. 267; also *PLOJ*, 22 October 1915, p. 1229

Pensions and the British Hospitals Association lasted for nearly four months. Finally the voluntary hospitals agreed to give inpatient care at charges rising to a maximum of 7s per day and outpatient care at sums ranging from 1s to 2s per attendance.[1] Complaints continued. In 1918 the Lambeth Guardians had to apologize for discharging, without crutches, a patient whose leg had been amputated. They added by way of explanation that neither the patient nor his wife had asked for such an appliance.[2]

The dependants of servicemen were left to the care of charity and the Poor Law. Over two million pounds had been collected by September 1914 through the National Relief of Distress Fund. It was distributed by local committees which 'consisted virtually of members of the Charity Organization Society and Guilds of Help'.[3] Voluntary organizations were also helping to distribute statutory army allowances.[4] Guardians were instructed by the Local Government Board to remove from the records all the names of soldiers' dependants receiving poor relief. Local Boards were thus unable to advise the COS officials whether the husbands of applicants held good pre-war working records. Hundreds of wives and children waited hours in long queues for their 'National Relief' while the charity officials patiently sorted the deserving from the undeserving. As one journal commented, 'what would be said of the Poor Law if it compelled a woman to walk eight miles and wait long hours for three days in succession to register her needs for relief? And then . . . to travel eight miles each week and wait for hours at a pay station to receive from four to five shillings?'[5]

The problem of auxiliary hospitals holding on to convalescent servicemen longer than was absolutely necessary continued throughout the war. A further cause of absenteeism from active service which worried the War Office was the high wastage rate of officers and men who contracted venereal disease. Between 1914 and 1918 approximately 400,000 military cases of venereal disease were treated in Britain and France. The army tried to solve the problem in two ways – both of which failed. A system

---

[1] *Hospital*, Vol. LXIII, 2 February 1918, p. 384
[2] ibid., Vol. LXIV, 28 September 1918, p. 451
[3] *PLOJ*, 4 September 1914, p. 1163
[4] *Hospital*, Vol. LVI, 19 September 1914, p. 663, and *LGB Circular*, 3 September 1914
[5] *PLOJ*, 4 September 1914, p. 1163

of *maisons de tolérance* was set up at French embarkation ports which worked very successfully until it had to be abandoned out of 'deference to strong public opinion in the United Kingdom'.[1] The second method involved charging venereal patients for their treatment. 'Stoppages' of 2s 6d a day for officers and sevenpence a day for other ranks were imposed.[2] This meant that private soldiers 'who had to go into hospital through their own fault' actually left the hospital in debt.[3]

Although these regulations were sharply criticized, the War Office refused to alter them. In 1917 the Army Council tried to impose twelve months' forfeiture of leave on all venereal patients.[4] This new penalty could not be enforced because such a high proportion of soldiers were returning home as sick and wounded within the twelve months' period. The authorities resorted to drastic measures. Medical officers were instructed to speed up treatment by injecting full doses of '606' at intervals of less than two weeks. Unfortunately, a 'proportion' of the cases treated in this way died with 'severe cerebral symptoms' or 'severe dermatitis'.[5]

Voluntary hospitals did not seem eager to receive venereal patients and by November 1918 the Army had opened twenty of its own venereal disease hospitals with accommodation for 11,000.[6] The growing prevalence of venereal disease was a threat to both civilians and military personnel. A Royal Commission which had been appointed in 1914 to investigate the subject reported in 1916. The Government acted swiftly and passed the Venereal Diseases Act. This Act provided for free and confidential treatment for every citizen and authorized 75 per cent exchequer grants to co-operating local health authorities.[7]

[1] MacPherson, p. 125 (Vol. II). One street of licensed brothels in Le Havre received 171,000 British soldiers in 57 weeks. Only 243 cases of infection were reported.

[2] ibid., p. 123. In the pre-war army, all sick soldiers were subjected to such 'stoppages' unless they were 'field cases'. These stoppages were abolished in 1914 − except for venereal cases. In addition, field allowances and proficiency pay could also be forfeited subject to the discretion of COs.

[3] *Hansard* (H of C), Vol. LXXXVII, 21 November 1916, col. 1206

[4] *Army Council Order of 27 January 1917* and MacPherson, p. 123

[5] MacPherson, p. 138 (Vol. II)

[6] ibid., p. 130

[7] *Forty-Fifth Annual Report LGB 1915–16*, Part III, Cd 8332, pp. 10–11, HMSO, 1916; *Hospital Gazette*, April 1919, p. 107; *Forty-Sixth Annual Report LGB 1916–17*, Cd 8697, pp. 31–2, HMSO, 1917

Although there were gaps in the provisions for the armed forces and although not all the military sick were given comfortable accommodation or adequate medical care, it remains true that the war led to a serious decline in the standards of care given to the ordinary civilian sick. Over half the general practitioners had been taken for the armed forces and the bulk of the trained nurses were caring for wounded servicemen at home and abroad. By the addition of huts and by overcrowding, the capacity of civilian hospitals had been greatly expanded but, judged by pre-war capacity, the armed forces had taken over a third of the accommodation in voluntary hospitals and in Poor Law infirmaries and workhouses. Nearly a third of mental hospital accommodation had also been requisitioned. And additional strains were thrown on the Poor Law mental and public health services by the need to accommodate refugees and prisoners of war.

In the struggle to retain doctors for the civilian sick, the hospitals were forced greatly to increase the pay of junior medical staff and to set aside certain of their prejudices about doctors whom they were reluctant to employ. Thus in October 1914, the St Pancras Guardians failed to obtain a senior assistant medical superintendent after raising the salary from £175 to £225.[1] The new amount was equal to the starting pay of a junior lieutenant in the RAMC.[2] The Bristol Royal Infirmary tried to attract junior medical staff in October 1915 by offering £120 a year to young doctors awaiting call-up.[3] Voluntary hospitals began appointing women house surgeons and physicians in December 1914.[4] Charing Cross Hospital admitted women students for the first time during 1915, making it clear that they were 'of a subordinate order and carry no prospect of accession to the full staff'.[5] Even general practitioners were asked to take appointments.[6] By 1917 the situation was so grave that Indian, Egyptian and Chinese doctors were working for voluntary hospitals, Boards of Guardians and local insurance

[1] *Hospital*, Vol. LVII, 31 October 1914, p. 101

[2] ibid., Vol. LIX, 23 October 1915, p. 83

[3] ibid.

[4] ibid., Vol. LVIII, 24 July 1915, p. 342; also Vol. LXII, 8 September 1917, pp. 455–6: 'There was a vigorous press campaign to popularize the profession as a means of livelihood for women.'

[5] ibid., Vol. LVII, 12 December 1914, p. 232

[6] ibid., Vol. LVIII, 3 July 1915, p. 281

committees.[1] But many voluntary hospitals had to make do with fifth-year students and other unqualified men.[2] Meanwhile the War Office added to the difficulties by offering combatant commissions to junior medical students.[3]

By 1 January 1917 more than half of the medical profession had been called up for military service. The official statistics for January 1918 showed that 12,720 doctors had been called up, leaving 11,482 in civil practice.[4] As the Joint War Committee explained, the supply of civilian doctors was 'practically exhausted'.[5] The Insurance Commissioners were finding it impossible to maintain pre-war standards of medical services. The London Insurance Committee reduced the number of tuberculosis beds from 932 to under 500 and in October 1917 confessed that it could no longer fulfil its obligations to insured consumptives.[6] Similar breakdowns of civilian medical services were occurring throughout the country.[7] Meanwhile, doctors were returning to their practices after serving a one-year contract commission 'with tales of having had little to do'.[8]

The last year of the war strained the medical services of the nation to their limit. The entry of the United States into the war brought some modest relief to the military hospitals in the form of about 1,500 American doctors and about 1,000 trained nurses.[9] Faced with the heavy casualty lists which followed the final assault on the Hindenburg Line in June 1918, the War Office made peremptory demands for more civilian hospital beds. The patriotism of the hospital governors had reached its limit. When the War Office suddenly demanded 'the entire surrender' of St George's Hospital for wounded officers the governors refused to yield. The army council blustered and threatened to invoke its powers under the Defence of the Realm

[1] ibid., Vol. LXII, 26 May 1917, p. 144
[2] ibid., Vol. LVIII, 7 August 1915, p. 384, and Vol. LXIII, 10 November 1917, p. 106
[3] ibid., Vol. LVIII, 11 September 1915, p. 497
[4] MacPherson, p. 147 (Vol. I)
[5] *Hospital*, Vol. LXII, 18 August 1917, p. 388
[6] *Hospital*, Vol. LXIII, 20 October 1917, p. 47
[7] ibid., Vol. LVIII, 4 September 1915, p. 466; Vol. LIX, 8 January 1916, p. 312; Vol. LXIII, 20 October 1917, p. 47, and Vol. LXIII, 9 February 1918, pp. 389–90
[8] MacPherson, p. 150
[9] ibid.

Act. The governors replied that they would not commit what they termed 'a breach of trust' to their public. They offered 200 of their 340 beds. A few days later the War Office withdrew its demands altogether.[1]

By August 1918 'many Poor Law infirmaries [were] crowded out with children' and 'a large proportion of these [were] from well-to-do homes'.[2] The Lord Mayor's Council on Health denounced the medical arrangements of the Poor Law: it reported that 'cases are discharged too soon, that babies in particular often came out worse than they went in; that there is a lack of care and cleanliness . . . indifferent nursing and medical treatment'. Babies were being left 'to lie alone for hours in their cots with feeding bottles fastened to the cribs within reach'.[3] The medical officer of health for Liverpool described how 'tuberculous civilians' were 'compelled to remain at home' and 'consumptive soldiers . . . actually have to go back to houses scheduled unfit for human habitation'. The army had requisitioned the local sanatorium and converted the children's wing into a boot store.[4]

In the summer of 1918 the first of the great influenza epidemics struck hard at a tired and neglected civil population. It was impossible to provide adequate medical care for the victims. There were reports that 'all over the country' people were being 'allowed to die for want of institutional treatment'.[5] Burdett again denounced the War Office for its 'invasion of our voluntary hospitals' and for failing to 'organize proper facilities of its own'. His strongest criticism was directed at the 'managers of the hospitals' who were still holding on to 'a large proportion of soldiers' who did not 'in the least need hospital treatment'.[6] By December 1918 the number of deaths from influenza in London alone totalled over 10,000.[7] As the war ended the civilian population began making its own contribution to the casualty lists.

Britain had muddled through. With only a moderate questioning of its policies the War Office had been reprieved. The number

1 *Hospital*, Vol. LXIV, 29 June 1918, p. 275
2 ibid., 31 August 1918, p. 477
3 ibid.
4 ibid., 21 September 1918, p. 531
5 *Hospital*, Vol. LXV, 25 January 1919, p. 349
6 ibid., 2 November 1918, p. 84
7 ibid., 28 December 1918, p. 269

of equipped beds for wounded servicemen in the United Kingdom reached a peak figure of 364,133 in November 1918. Roughly 318,000 of these beds were occupied. There are no statistics indicating how many civilian sick were also receiving hospital accommodation, though it is unlikely that the total was less than 200,000. It seems likely that never before or since had so many patients been accommodated in the hospitals of Britain.

The services for tuberculosis which had been developed just before the war by the National Insurance Act were crippled almost as soon as they were set up. The death-rate from tuberculosis rose throughout the war. But the war emergency had undoubtedly hastened action on one group of diseases for which provision had been noticeably inadequate for many years. Grants-in-aid had been made available by the central Government for the treatment of venereal diseases.

The services taken over from the civilian sick had not even been effectively utilized. Throughout the war there were beds kept empty for the armed forces while some civilian sick who needed hospital care had to stay at home. The percentage of unoccupied auxiliary beds during 1915 had risen to 38 per cent of the total stock. Between 1916 and 1918 the number of auxiliary hospitals with less than 25 beds was reduced from 251 to 130. The percentage of unoccupied beds fell temporarily to 16.58 per cent during 1917[1] after the War Office ordered the closure of all establishments with less than ten beds.[2] Thereafter the percentage steadily increased again until it reached an average of 22·43 per cent for the last year of the war. The explanation of the Red Cross was that so many wards had to be closed 'for cleaning or because of scarcity of patients'.[3]

In no respect had the burdens of war been fairly shared. While many of the younger doctors had been called up for service abroad and had on their return to build up again the goodwill of their practice, many of the top doctors were allowed to retain their private patients throughout the whole war. In addition they were paid generous salaries for services which in some cases were little more than nominal. General practitioners helping out in their local hospitals were much less generously treated. There was little effective attempt to prevent profiteering

[1] *Red Cross History*, p. 226
[2] ibid., p. 218
[3] ibid., pp. 226–7

even at the expense of the sick and wounded. Some private nursing home proprietors in London were accused of enriching themselves by contracting to treat military patients and engaging voluntary staff.[1] The cost of certain drugs increased by twelve or even fifteen times when supplies from Germany were finally cut off.[2] 'Middlemen' were accused of war-profiteering as they held back existing stocks in order to push up prices still further.[3]

The voluntary hospitals which were not considered vital for the war effort fell into financial difficulties. By Christmas 1917 the Chelsea Hospital for Women was advertising deficits on their new building of £16,000 and on their maintenance account of £5,500. The City of London Lying-in announced a debt of £1,500 while the East London Hospital for Children claimed especial attention from the public as it was 'to the children that we look for our future armies and the future mothers of our race'.[4]

The War Office paid about £880,000 to the voluntary hospitals between 1914 and 1919 for the care of the sick and wounded.[5] It was claimed, however, that 'the aggregate War Office payments to the London hospitals alone fell short of the total cost of maintaining and treating the military patients by £530,000'.[6] Nonetheless, wounded soldiers made excellent appeal copy and the 'purse-strings' of the charitable public were 'unloosened as they have perhaps never been before'.[7] The total surplus income of all the charitable organizations sending their statistics to Burdett between 1915 and 1919 amounted to just over £7 million.[8] Throughout the war the charities 'collected more than they expended' and were able to place 'substantial amounts to their reserve funds'.[9]

The price of these unco-ordinated policies was paid by the

[1] *Hospital*, Vol. LXI, 14 October 1916, p. 23
[2] ibid., Vol. LVIII, 7 August 1915, p. 384
[3] *Hospital Gazette*, December 1915, p. 35
[4] *Hospital*, Vol. LXIII, 15 December 1917, p. 237
[5] *Hospital Gazette*, September 1921, p. 188
[6] Ministry of Health, Voluntary Hospitals Committee (the Cave Committee), *Final Report*, Cmd 1335, p. 34, HMSO, 1921
[7] *Hospital*, Vol. LIX, 15 January 1916, p. 347
[8] *Burdett's Hospitals and Charities 1922-3*, p. 4, London. Owing to the various accounting practices of certain voluntary hospitals it is not possible to obtain exact figures.
[9] ibid.

civilians who lost half their supply of doctors and roughly a third of their already inadequate stock of hospital beds. Nevertheless no one had suffered as much as the soldiers at the front – many of them volunteers. Five years before war was declared, both the Majority and the Minority Reports had recommended that a co-ordinated hospital service was essential for the less extensive needs of peace-time. Even under the stress of war, no attempt was made to unite the medical services of the nation. Throughout the whole war the needs of officers had been given priority over the needs of other ranks and the needs of the armed forces over the needs of the civilian sick. In the crisis of war young active males came before women, children and old people. Relatively minor conditions suffered by members of the armed forces took precedence over the scourge of tuberculosis which threatened the health of the whole population, both military and civilian. It was total war.

CHAPTER 18

The Lost Opportunity

THE war had revealed deficiencies in the organization of the nation's health services. It had also revealed failings in the health of the people. The high proportion of men rejected for active service had established the need for better preventive and promotive services. The case for an integrated approach to the nation's health which had been canvassed by a minority of 'experts' before the war became widely accepted in the national crisis. No longer was ill health dismissed as part of the wider problem of poverty. The health of the nation merited separate consideration and specific remedies.

The war had provided a severe test for the administration of the country, both central and local, and the machinery of government had been found wanting. After 1909 no new functions were given to the Boards of Guardians. Instead, many supplementary units of local administration were created – the Insurance Committee, the Employment Exchange, the Old Age Pensions Committee, and the Local War Pensions Committee. The general growth of public responsibilities during the war made the reform of the machinery of local administration more urgent than ever before.

Thus the reform of local government was one of the matters to be given early attention when plans for post-war reconstruction were considered. Early in 1917, Lloyd George set up a reconstruction committee and one of its sub-committees, on which sat both Beatrice Webb and Lord George Hamilton, examined the whole system of local government. Beatrice Webb offered to try and secure some agreement between the Majority and Minority of the Poor Law Commission and the Local Government Board. The latter, seeing itself stripped of functions and by-passed by the creation of other departments, had already come to accept the need for reform and even Lord George Hamilton, while serving on the Venereal Disease Commission,[1]

[1] Margaret I. Cole, *Beatrice Webb's Diaries 1912–24*, p. 99, London, 1952

had been persuaded that the Poor Law should be broken up. Thus the committee[1] under the chairmanship of Sir Donald Maclean was able to report unanimously at the end of 1917 that the Guardians should be abolished and that with some exceptions their functions should be transferred to the county and county borough councils.[2] All arrangements for the sick and infirm were to be made through the public health committees.[3] Another committee of the council was to be responsible for making inquiries into the economic circumstances of applicants for services.[4] The committee did not, however, specify which services were to be free and which were to be subject to a test of means.

'We may confidently say,' commented the *Hospital Gazette*, 'that the Poor Law as it stands today is doomed. . . . The Poor Law has in fact remained for many years an anachronism, though the difficulty of suggesting a practical alternative has given the system an extended lease of life.'[5] The journal was, however, quick to point out the problem which would remain – co-ordination with the voluntary hospitals:

> The voluntary institutions have considered themselves free to transfer to the Poor Law all cases of 'chronics' which could not be properly nursed at home. On the other hand, the infirmaries have not regarded themselves as under any obligation to transfer to the hospital such of their cases as might specially require consultant treatment. Thus there has been no sort of co-operation between the two classes of institution, and an atmosphere of aloofness, if not of antagonism, has been prejudicial to the sick poor. We hope that under the new régime such a regrettable state of affairs will be impossible. . . .[6]

There were, however, rumours that the Government was intending to deal with this problem also. It was reported in the popular press that Lord Rhondda, as President of the Local

[1] By this time the original reconstruction committee had been merged into a Ministry of Reconstruction.
[2] Ministry of Reconstruction, Local Government Committee: *Report on the Transfer of Functions of Poor Law Authorities in England and Wales* (Maclean Report), Cd 8917, p. 5, HMSO, 1926
[3] ibid.
[4] ibid., p. 6
[5] *Hospital Gazette*, February 1918, p. 53
[6] ibid.

Government Board, was preparing a '... scheme which would throw the whole medical system of the country in the melting pot' and involve the taking over by the state of the established voluntary and Poor Law hospitals. The scheme aimed at 'nothing less than the nationalization of the medical profession, involving free medical attendance for all without any element of charity'.[1] The Cabinet did not, however, accept this proposal.

Meanwhile Mrs Webb had been busy planning with her colleagues in the Labour Party. An advisory committee on public health had been set up and a statement of policy was published in 1918.[2] The report assumed the creation of a Ministry of Health and of a National Health Service under democratic control centrally and locally. There were to be local health areas which were to receive substantial grants from the central government. The service was to be free as only the rich could afford proper health services and it was important that disease should be treated in its earliest possible stages. Any discrimination by means would be inefficient and unpopular.

The service was to be run from the hospitals to which, where possible, the public health services were to be transferred, 'so as to encourage co-operation between preventive and curative medicine'.[3] At these 'health centres',[4] the nurses, midwives, school health services, maternity and child welfare services, and general practitioner services were to be based. There were, however, to be two separate teams – preventive and curative. In addition, there were to be at least 1,000 whole-time medical officers employed in preventive and early diagnostic work in industry. General practitioners were to work in the health centres in groups of from four to twenty but none of them were to have more than 3,500 patients in urban areas and 2,000 patients in rural areas. Patients were to have free choice of doctor, and doctors were to be free to decide whether they joined the service or not. It was implied that most of the doctors would be full-time salaried officers.

[1] ibid., pp. 61–2
[2] The Labour Party, *The Organization of the Preventive & Curative Medical Services & Hospital & Laboratory Systems under a Ministry of Health*, London, 1918
[3] ibid., p. 5
[4] The origin of the term 'health centre' is not easy to establish. It was certainly being used in the United States before the First World War. See M. M. Davis, *Dispensaries: their Management and Development*, p. 318, New York, 1918.

The inpatients in the health centre were to be looked after by general practitioners with the help of visiting consultants. Cases needing specialist care were to be referred to county hospitals or national hospitals. It was envisaged that the existing voluntary hospitals would be merged with this system, as two types of hospital would cause waste and overlapping and, as hospital care should be regarded as the right of every citizen, not left for private charity.

These recommendations of the advisory committee did not constitute the policy of the Labour Party, as Sidney Webb hastened to point out in a letter to the *British Medical Journal* in August 1918. Fears had been expressed of a state salaried medical service on the lines of the army medical service. In his carefully worded and conciliatory letter, Webb argued that the Party had never committed itself to a whole-time salaried service. What it wanted to do was to 'give the medical profession more effective opportunities than it is now allowed for rendering its services to all who need them'. The possibilities were to extend to either the National Insurance Acts or the local government services or both. He could not

> . . . imagine any practical politician dreaming that . . . both the machinery of the National Insurance Acts and that of the all-powerful local governing bodies could simultaneously be superseded by any State army of salaried clinicians operating, like the RAMC, from a central headquarters, and working in conjunction with an array of State hospitals and sanatoriums, administered, like the prisons, by a Government department in Whitehall. . . . It must be plain that . . . it would be quite impracticable . . . to engage the medical practitioners in a whole-time salaried clinical service as such a service would have no doctors available for the fee-paying part of the population.[1]

The olive branch was graciously accepted. Dr Brackenbury, of the BMA, wrote to say how 'gratified' he was to find how closely the Labour Party's views were in agreement 'on this occasion' with those of the Council of the Association. 'Where so much that is basic is agreed upon we need not despair of carrying Mr Webb and the Labour Party with us the whole way.'[2]

Radical thinking was not only to be found in Labour Party

[1] *BMJ*, 17 August 1918, pp. 175–6
[2] ibid., 24 August 1918, p. 203

circles. There were others who wanted to learn from the lessons of the war in their planning for peace-time services. On 4 July 1918 a striking lecture on the future of the medical profession was given by Dr Bernard Dawson, then a major-general in the army. He was convinced that the medical services must have some kind of state aid and central control. What was needed was co-ordinated effort – 'team work' – in specially equipped institutions, which were designed for diagnosis and treatment. Moreover, curative and preventive medicine could no longer be separated. Regarding general practitioner services he asked, 'Why, then, if you want to be restored to health, should you not go to a hospital? Why is a room in a dwelling made to suffice?'[1] Though he avoided the term, he, like the Labour Party, was advocating health centres.

Dawson suggested that all professional and technical questions must be determined alone by medical men. Administrative questions must be determined by a health board composed of both lay and professional members – partly elected, partly *ex officio*. Central policy was to be determined by a Minister with medical advisers who were to have direct access to him 'in contrast to the baneful tradition of the Local Government Board whereby the Medical Officer can only advise the Minister through the intermediacy of a lay official'.[2] Dr Dawson was attempting to apply the lessons learnt in the war to the peace-time health services. There needed to be a rational system of casualty clearing stations to treat minor injuries, supported by major hospitals to which more serious cases could be referred. Dr Dawson was to have the opportunity to develop his ideas further when he later became chairman of an official committee set up to make plans for the nation's health services.

All this radical thinking did not go unnoticed by the leaders of the voluntary hospital movement. A well-attended meeting of the British Hospitals Association was held at St Thomas' to discuss the position of the voluntary hospitals in relation to the proposed Ministry of Health. It was unanimously resolved

that the British Hospitals Association welcomes the proposal to form a Ministry of Health; but is strongly of the opinion that the interests of the patients and of the community as a whole, the

[1] *BMJ*, 13 July 1918, p. 24
[2] ibid., p. 26

progressive education and training of doctors and nurses and the prosecution and advance of scientific research, will be best served and provided for in the scheme by the retention of the voluntary hospital system.[1]

There were, however, many speakers at the conference who were prepared to accept grants-in-aid from public authorities. In addition, Sir Henry Burdett was prepared to accept the principle of payment of medical staffs.[2]

Soon after the war ended, Lloyd George went to the country and was returned with a handsome majority for his Coalition Government. The Government was pledged not only to 'hang the Kaiser' and build 'homes for heroes' but also to implement the Maclean Report and establish a Ministry of Health. The election manifesto pledged that 'all services relating to the care and treatment of the sick and infirm should not be administered as part of the Poor Law but should be made a part of the general health services of the country'.[3] The Ministry of Health was set up in the spring of 1919, taking over functions from the Board of Control, the Insurance Commissioners, the Privy Council, the Board of Education and the Local Government Board. The first Minister was Dr Addison – the only doctor ever to hold the office. He had been Minister of Reconstruction in the earlier administration and was therefore fully acquainted with the plans produced by the Maclean Committee for the reform of the Poor Laws.

Under the Act which set up the Ministry, the Minister was empowered to establish consultative councils. This power was used to set up a Council on Medical and Administrative Services. The chairman was Sir Bernard Dawson. The appointment was welcomed by the *British Medical Journal* – 'a better selection, we venture to say, could not have been made'.[4] Within a few weeks the Council was asked by the Minister to consider 'the scheme or schemes requisite for the systematized provision of such forms of medical and allied services as should, in the opinion of the Council, be available for the inhabitants of a given area'.

[1] *Hospital Gazette*, November 1918, p. 23
[2] ibid.
[3] quoted in R. F. Minney, *Viscount Addison: Leader of the Lords*, p. 166, London, 1958
[4] *BMJ*, 4 October 1919, p. 446

In view of the assumed urgency of the matter,[1] a preliminary report was issued in the middle of 1920. It was a revolutionary document. It bore remarkable similarities to the statement produced by the Labour Party's advisory council two years earlier. The report largely ignored the whole history of the development of medical care in Britain, its underlying philosophies and the existing framework of services. The Council started from first principles and then looked to see whether any of the existing medical institutions could be incorporated in its plan.

It had come to the conclusion that the organization of the medical services was insufficient to bring the advantages of medical knowledge adequately within reach of the people. This was more apparent 'with the increasing conviction that the best means of maintaining health and curing disease should be made available to all citizens'.[2] It determined that preventive and curative services 'must be brought together in close co-ordination. . . . They must likewise be both brought within the sphere of the general practitioner whose duties should embrace the work of communal as well as individual medicine.'[3] Thus the Council favoured the development of health centres, where various medical services, preventive and curative, could be brought together so as to form one organization.

There were to be primary health centres and secondary health centres – the former providing the simple health services, the latter the more specialized services. The primary health centre was to be staffed by general practitioners with the aid of visiting consultants. It was to include sixteen, thirty-two or more hospital beds and was to be the headquarters of the local preventive services. More difficult cases, or cases requiring more specialized treatment, were to be passed on to the secondary health centre, which was to be mainly staffed by consultants and specialists. Some secondary health centres were to be teaching hospitals. Up to this point the scheme was almost identical with that of the Labour Party.

While the Labour Party envisaged that doctors would be

---

[1] No final report was ever published.

[2] Ministry of Health, Consultative Council on Medical and Allied Services, *Interim Report on the Future Provision of Medical and Allied Services* (the Dawson Report), Cmd 693, p. 5, HMSO, 1920

[3] ibid.

entirely based on the health centres, the Dawson Report envisaged that the custom of practitioners having their surgeries in their own homes would continue, though in certain circumstances accommodation at the health centre might be tried if local medical opinion favoured it. Dentists, on the other hand, were to practise wholly in the centres. The centre was, however, intended to be the home of the intellectual life of the general practitioner. Instead of being isolated, doctors would be brought together and into contact with consultants and specialists. The Council was opposed to a full-time salaried service 'which would tend, by its machinery, to discourage initiative, to diminish the sense of responsibility, and to encourage mediocrity'.[1] Consultants were to be paid on a time basis with extra fees for special visits – leaving them free for their private consulting practice.[2]

The Council was divided on the question of patients' payments. Some favoured a free service but the majority thought that this would impose a heavy burden on public funds. Even the majority did not favour more than a contribution being made by patients towards the cost, as 'efficient treatment will often be beyond the means of most citizens to provide in its entirety'.[3] And by efficient treatment the Council meant a very wide range of services. There were to be laboratory services, dental services and recuperative centres. In the twenty-page report, one and a half pages were devoted to the question of physical culture.

The report described in detail the exact function of health centres and an appendix was included showing architectural plans for three different types of centre. It is worthy of note that, while one plan showed two wards with twelve patients in each and smaller wards for private patients, in both the other plans patients were all accommodated in wards for two or three patients.

The Council thought that in some cases existing buildings such as Poor Law infirmaries or cottage hospitals could be adapted as health centres 'at any rate as a beginning'. 'On the other hand,' the report continued,

it would be important to guard against making expensive alterations to buildings which, from their positions or structures, could

[1] ibid., p. 11
[2] ibid., p. 13
[3] ibid., p. 14

U

only be makeshifts. Health centres and hospitals require adequate ground, so as to provide not only for future expansion, but also for open-air clinics, convalescent treatment, physical culture and such like services.[1]

Clearly a massive construction programme was envisaged. The Council attempted no estimates of cost.

On the future of the voluntary hospitals the report was rather 'cagey'. They were to be given grants-in-aid for work carried out. The assistance of existing voluntary hospitals would be welcomed

> both in the provision of beds and equipment, and in the accumulated experience of its medical staff and management, which would be valuable to any Health Authority. The benefits they would receive under the scheme would be in proportion to the extent of their co-operation and their readiness to come into co-ordination with the general plan.[2]

The Council did not, however, state the exact administrative framework of the whole plan or the exact relationship between the plan and hospitals ready 'to come into co-ordination'. Some thought that the health authority might be a statutory committee of an existing local authority, while others favoured an *ad hoc* independent body. Whichever course was decided upon, the Council favoured representation of the medical profession in the health authority, and the association with the authority of a local medical advisory council.[3]

These radical proposals were not in advance of public opinion at the time when they appeared. The report was given a good press. Although *The Times* and the *Morning Post* pointed out that the scheme was too expensive to be carried out immediately as a whole, the latter thought the scheme 'ideal' and the *Daily Telegraph* said that it 'foreshadowed a very remarkable development in the national health policy'. Both the *Daily News* and the *Manchester Guardian* went so far as to criticize the rejection of the principle of a full-time salaried service. The *Yorkshire Post* conceded that the scheme was 'admirably logical' but feared 'a new bureaucracy intimately affecting the life of every

[1] ibid., p. 10
[2] ibid., p. 16
[3] ibid., p. 17

individual'.[1] The *British Medical Journal* had no fundamental criticisms to make. It remarked without criticism that the 'recommendations would have a profound effect on the future of medicine in England'. *The Lancet* was cautious. It recommended 'trial along many lines to see how far it furnishes a practical solution of public and professional difficulties'.[2]

The thinking of the Dawson Report was in one respect in line with the current thinking of the British Medical Association. The Ministry of Health committee of that body had reported in March 1920 in favour of primary hospitals staffed by general practitioners where patients should pay an agreed sum to the hospital for maintenance while paying their doctor separately. Provision of accommodation for this purpose could be met to a large extent by utilizing present voluntary hospitals and poor law infirmaries.[3] A month later Dr Brackenbury was saying that general practitioner hospitals were 'the most urgent matter required'.[4] There ought to be at least one general practitioner on the staff of every teaching hospital. Those general practitioners who did not undertake surgery could get it done for them by others who did.

In the following month, Lord Dawson,[5] as he had now become, spoke to several divisions of the BMA about his report, which was 'unanimously adopted'.[6] But by November criticism was being voiced in the *British Medical Journal*. There were doctors who 'resented any interference with their present work and only wanted to be left alone'.[7] There were general practitioners who would rather have sent their cases right away to a secondary health centre just as they were then sending them to hospitals.[8] There were fears of the health centres. 'Who is going to pay the GP for these services? The buildings . . . will be State buildings. . . . Is it likely that any patient will consent to pay his doctor's fees in buildings of this kind?'[9] If the state

---

[1] A summary of press reports is to be found in *The Hospital*, Vol. LXVIII, 5 June 1920, p. 253.

[2] *Lancet*, 29 May 1920, p. 1175

[3] *BMJ Supplement*, 20 March 1920, p. 81

[4] ibid., 15 May 1920, p. 156

[5] as from April 1920

[6] *BMJ*, 12 June 1920, p. 800, and 13 November 1920, p. 750

[7] ibid., 13 November 1920, p. 768

[8] ibid.

[9] ibid., 27 November 1920, p. 842

paid, it would probably give two guineas instead of twenty guineas for an appendicitis operation. 'If this scheme is carried through, we shall not only become servants of the State but most of us would be paupers.'[1]

While Dawson's grandiose scheme for a complete remodelling of the nation's health services was under discussion, the Minister of Health was faced with more mundane problems which required urgent decision. One sector of the existing health services appeared to be perilously near to collapse – the voluntary hospitals. They were faced with graver financial problems than ever before. This was true, despite a substantial income from public authorities.

As the number of wounded servicemen in hospital fell, the voluntary hospitals lost the *per diem* payments that went with them. In July 1920 there were still, however, 15,000 war pensioners receiving treatment in civil hospitals.[2] In May 1920 the British Hospitals Association managed to negotiate fairly generous payments for their maintenance from the Ministry of Pensions. The rate varied between seven and eleven shillings according to the character and equipment of the hospitals.[3]

There were, moreover, other permanent sources of income from public authorities. The National Insurance scheme for tuberculosis had been seriously disorganized by the war. Deaths and notifications had risen steadily and the need for care was not confined to insured persons. An interdepartmental committee reported in 1919 that the number of beds available for the treatment of the disease was seriously inadequate and should be increased immediately. The Treasury agreed to make capital grants for the construction of new accommodation at the rate of £180 per bed, subject to a maximum of three-fifths of the total cost.[4] The National Insurance Act was amended in 1920 and sanatorium benefit was removed from the scheme; the provision of inpatient care for all tuberculosis cases was made the responsibility of county and county borough councils.[5] Many

[1] ibid.
[2] *Hospital Gazette*, July 1920, p. 142
[3] *BMJ Supplement*, 29 May 1920, p. 170
[4] *Hospital Gazette*, November 1919, p. 24
[5] *Second Annual Report Ministry of Health 1920–1*, Cmd 1446, p. 5, HMSO, 1921

councils made grants to voluntary hospitals for provision in this field. Half the cost was covered by the Exchequer.

During the war the treatment of venereal diseases had brought a new source of grant to the voluntary hospitals and the scheme had come swiftly into operation. In 1916–17 'between 140 and 150 hospitals in England and Wales ... expressed their willingness to participate in the plans of local authorities'.[1] A year later it was reported that 121 treatment centres were in operation – the large majority in general hospitals.[2] Three years later there were 191 centres; during the year 1920–21 St Thomas' Hospital and the London Hospital opened centres.[3] Three-quarters of approved expenditure fell upon the Exchequer and one-quarter on local authorities.

In 1920 the voluntary hospitals in England and Wales (excluding London) had an income of roughly £2 million. It was estimated that about a quarter of this income came from public authorities. The Ministry of Pensions, the War Office and the Admiralty paid over £300,000, another £117,000 was paid under the legislation concerning venereal diseases and most of the remainder came for the care of tuberculosis patients and school-children.[4] Despite all these large payments from public authorities, the hospitals could not make ends meet. The inflationary spiral generated by the war continued for two years after it. And the voluntary hospitals had continued to expand rapidly. The number of beds increased from about 43,000 in 1911 to about 57,000 in 1921.[5] In this last year there were 86 more general hospitals and 90 more special hospitals – mainly for tuberculosis. It was hard to raise the money needed to maintain all these extra beds despite the grants from public authorities.

Many hospitals had to abandon their traditions of not charging patients. It was announced in March 1920, a month before the death of Sir Henry Burdett, that the London Hospital was going

[1] *Forty-Sixth Annual Report LGB 1916–17*, Cd 8697, p. 32, HMSO, 1917

[2] *Forty-Seventh Annual Report LGB 1917–18*, Cd 9157, p. 10, HMSO, 1918

[3] *Second Annual Report MoH*, pp. 14–15

[4] Sir Napier Burnett, *Report on the Financial Position of the Hospitals in England & Wales (excluding London) for the Year 1920*, quoted in The Trades Union Congress and The Labour Party, *The Labour Movement and the Hospital Crisis*, p. 11

[5] See Vol. 2 of this study.

to charge inpatients ten shillings per week.[1] A few months later the ten shillings was found to be 'not worth the trouble of collection'. The charge was raised to twenty-one shillings, except for children and persons with a written certificate from a responsible person of inability to pay. Except for accident and emergency cases, two weeks' payment in advance was required.[2] The Hospital embarked on a large money-raising campaign. It was even arranged for school-children to march to the Hospital to drop pennies into a milk churn to help to pay the milk bill. According to *The Hospital*, this was 'a real object lesson in the art of making it interesting to give'.[3] Despite these efforts the position of the London Hospital became so desperate that the chairman, Lord Knutsford, committed himself to a policy of state aid. He suggested that the government should provide one-third of the cost of approved hospitals. He was soundly scolded by *The Hospital* for this suggestion.[4]

All over the country charging schemes were introduced and extended. At the Royal Northern Hospital, patients in the general wards were required to pay from five shillings to one guinea per week. In the cubicle wards charges ranged from one guinea to four guineas per week.[5] At the Royal Portsmouth Hospital the charge for adults was fifteen shillings per week and it was said that the committee compelled patients to give more than they said they were able to give.[6] Hospitals in industrial areas, however, found that 'since the men contribute while they are well, they will take it ill to be asked to contribute when they are sick'.[7] At the Norfolk and Norwich Hospital patients were required to pay one guinea per week unless they could not afford it or had contributed to the Saturday Fund.[8]

At King's College Hospital outpatients were charged the basic sum of sixpence with extras for special treatment. The role of the almoner was reversed. While previously it had been her task to see patients who, it was thought, could pay, now it was her task to see patients who claimed they could not pay. In-

[1] *BMJ*, 13 March 1920, p. 372
[2] *Hospital*, Vol. LXVIII, 3 July 1920, p. 353
[3] ibid., 10 July 1920, p. 394
[4] ibid., 10 April 1920, p. 27
[5] ibid., 17 July 1920, p. 418
[6] ibid., 18 September 1920, p. 618
[7] ibid., 3 April 1920, p. 2
[8] *Hospital Gazette*, April 1921, p. 106

patients were told what the hospitals cost and asked to pledge what they could afford. It was the task of the almoner to get them to pledge more when circumstances warranted it. On average 10s 6d per bed per week was received. Lord Hambleden said the scheme worked smoothly and satisfactorily throughout.[1] At Wigan, however, it was found impossible to introduce a system of almoners. As a correspondent explained: 'the working man will not have it.'[2]

There was no co-ordination of the various pay schemes adopted by the different hospitals. As Mr Morris, the house governor of the London Hospital, put it, the voluntary hospitals worked

> as isolated units, almost as rival tradesmen. . . . We suddenly start charging patients a guinea a week without saying a word to you about it. One result is that we are receiving as a consequence a new income of £20,000 a year. Another result is that certain hospitals complain that a great many of our patients are crowding to them, blocking their outpatient departments and swelling their waiting lists.[3]

Despite the fact that these different schemes of charging patients were growing so rapidly that by the end of 1920 'practically all hospitals [in London] had either already adopted a system of payment by patients, or were considering the advisability of doing so',[4] the position of some hospitals was desperate. It was said that the Manchester Royal Infirmary needed £9,000 extra each year to restore the finances of the hospital.[5] In the middle of 1920, it was reported that the London Fever Hospital would be closing and that the National Hospital, Queen Square, was already in the process of discharging all its patients.[6] Notices were being displayed everywhere saying: 'Help us to keep open.'[7]

The Minister of Health was busy searching for sources of money. After discussions held with the King's Fund it was announced that an immediate distribution of £250,000 would

---

[1] ibid., January 1921, pp. 54–5
[2] *BMJ*, 8 January 1921, p. 66
[3] *Hospital Gazette*, January 1921, pp. 51–3
[4] ibid., January 1921, pp. 54–5
[5] ibid., July 1920, p. 139
[6] *Hospital*, Vol. LXVIII, 10 July 1920, p. 377
[7] *Hospital Gazette*, July 1920, p. 141

be made.[1] This sum was taken from reserve funds so that 'time might by this means be secured for the reorganization of hospital finances'. The Fund considered that 'any repetition of such a drain on the invested funds and on permanent income would be disastrous to the Fund and to the Hospitals'.[2] The National Hospital was enabled to re-open a month after it had closed.[3] The National Relief Fund also appropriated a grant of £700,000 towards meeting the war deficits of the voluntary hospitals. Of this sum £560,000 was allocated to England and Wales, £200,000 being allocated to London and £360,000 to the provincial hospitals.[4]

These measures postponed the crisis without any grants being made from the Exchequer. For the economic crisis was not only affecting the voluntary hospitals. Practising ruthlessly the dogmas of traditionalist public finance, the Government had reacted to the economic situation of 1920 by rigid economy of public expenditure. The policy of retrenchment was applied to all public services. The Ministry of Health implanted in the minds of all concerned 'a new and restricted conception of the immediate possibilities of securing improvement in the health of the people by measures involving a call upon the public purse'.[5] There was a general cut back in plans to open new sanatoria 'in view of the general financial astringency'.[6] Local authorities were deterred from constructing new isolation hospitals 'although there are many parts of the country in which improved isolation hospital accommodation is urgently needed'.[7] In spite of the importance of removing children over three years of age from Poor Law institutions, in no case was authority given to build a new children's home.[8]

This was the climate of opinion when the recommendations of the Dawson Report were considered by the Government. Whatever actions Dr Addison might have wished to take, he was a member of a Government which now clearly would not enter into the heavy financial commitment which the plan entailed.

[1] ibid., p. 142
[2] Viscount Long, *Memories*, p. 40, London, 1923
[3] *Hospital*, Vol. LXVIII, 14 August 1920, p. 500
[4] *Second Annual Report MoH*, p. 46
[5] ibid., p. 1
[6] ibid., p. 12
[7] ibid., p. 19
[8] ibid., p. 127

The Government was, however, pledged to implement the Maclean Report of 1917, and it could be argued that the transfer of hospitals from one authority to another need not necessarily cost money. But if all hospitals had been immediately transferred as envisaged by the Maclean Report, the major local authorities would have *demanded* an Exchequer grant. A measure which made possible a gradual transfer was not open to this objection. Whether for this reason or because of divergent views within the Cabinet the course decided on was one of piecemeal reform.

In August 1920, the Minister gave his approval to the proposal of the Bradford Borough Council to take over the local infirmary from the Guardians and create a municipal hospital.[1] The step was taken under Section 121 of the Public Health Act of 1875 which enabled local authorities to provide hospitals. There was, however, some doubt about whether the Act could in fact be used for this purpose.[2] To clarify the situation, Dr Addison tagged on to a Bill,[3] which primarily concerned housing, certain clauses concerning hospitals. It gave power to county and county borough councils to take over and maintain any hospital or infirmary owned by a Poor Law authority, either by agreement or by the direction of the Minister. The councils were to have powers to borrow money for new construction and to recover costs from patients. Finally, the councils were to be allowed to subscribe to voluntary hospitals.

The last proposal led to considerable anxieties. The medical profession objected to these proposals as they did not 'face the need for providing means by which the medical profession, as such, shall be able to express – and in some measure to enforce – its opinion'.[4]

The managers of the voluntary hospitals were also suspicious: they did not trust local government and feared that the hospitals were being surreptitiously put on the rates. *The Hospital* expressed the position in no uncertain terms:

. . . The voluntary hospitals will become the sport of parochial politics, into whose vortex they will have to plunge as the price of

[1] *BMJ*, 28 August 1920, p. 331
[2] *Hansard* (H of C), Vol. 134, 4 November 1920, col. 629
[3] Ministry of Health (Miscellaneous Provisions) Bill, presented to the House of Commons on 16 August 1920
[4] *BMJ*, 28 August 1920, p. 327

continued existence. Their fate will be settled by chance aggregations of county councillors, profoundly ignorant for the most part of what hospitals do and of what they need.[1]

No new principle was, however, being introduced. From 1916 onwards, various authorities had taken powers under Private Bills to subscribe to local hospitals.[2]

The views of the medical profession began to emerge clearly. A meeting was called at Bradford at which the local doctors condemned the 'the high-handed action of the Health Committee in settling a matter of so much importance without consultation with the medical profession of Bradford – and indeed behind its back and without its knowledge'.[3] The profession wanted to be assured that patients would not be allowed 'to attend the hospital for such treatment as they could receive from their own medical attendant, panel or private'.[4] They demanded the removal of the requirement that a member of the staff of the municipal hospital should hold no other hospital appointment. They asked for a consultative or advisory medical committee to be set up 'to advise the Health Committee upon the appointments to the staff or on any other points affecting the professional work in connection with the health of the city'.[5]

One problem which had to be faced was the relation between the municipal hospital and the old-established voluntary hospital – the Bradford Royal Infirmary. It was agreed on all sides that the two hospitals ought to 'co-operate'. But the medical superintendent of the municipal hospital complained about what some intended to be the nature of the co-operation. They wanted his hospital 'with its splendid wards and equipment' to be converted

... into a dump, on to which the infirmary could shoot its patients after giving them the more exciting portions of their surgical treatment. This would make less risky than it is at present the well-known procedure by which has been attained the new boast: '*There is at present no waiting list at the infirmary.*'[6]

[1] *Hospital*, Vol. LXVIII, 21 August 1920, p. 517
[2] *Hansard* (H of C), Vol. 134, 4 November 1920, col. 626
[3] ibid., 13 November 1920, p. 753
[4] ibid., p. 754
[5] ibid.
[6] ibid., 29 January 1921, pp. 171–2

While the Bradford dispute continued, Dr Addison introduced his Bill. He said that he had no wish to place the voluntary hospitals on the rates.[1] He assured the House that the BMA had no objection to the principle of municipal hospitals; it had only raised questions of detail. A local medical body was to be set up with which the Council could discuss questions in future.[2]

When the Bill was given its second reading fears were expressed in Parliament that, if public money were given to the voluntary hospitals, the public would refuse to subscribe at all.[3] The Bill would 'torpedo the marvellous voluntary work which has been done in hospitals in the past'.[4] 'So long as the voluntary hospitals are voluntary, they propose to manage themselves. They do not propose to be managed by the State nor to be managed by the British Medical Association.'[5]

The proposal to create municipal hospitals was attacked from every angle. Conservative speakers saw it as a big step along the road to socialism and likely to lead to expenditure which the country could not afford.[6] Labour speakers argued the case for Exchequer finance and 'free' hospitals.[7] In general, the House did not like this major reform tucked away at the end of a small Bill.[8] The Bill scraped through the Commons at the end of an acrimonious all-night sitting, only to be defeated in the Lords.[9]

When the Bill was re-introduced, the clauses referring to hospital reform were dropped. The only concrete result of the Bill was the undertaking given by Dr Addison in the middle of the debate that he would set on foot an inquiry into the financial position of the voluntary hospitals. And in January a committee was set up under the chairmanship of Viscount Cave.

The reports of both the Maclean Committee and the Dawson Council had been tacitly dropped by the Government. A few months afterwards, Addison himself, who had played a principal part in sponsoring both projects, was ignominiously discarded by

[1] *Hansard* (H of C), Vol. 134, 4 November 1920, col. 624
[2] ibid., col. 630
[3] ibid., col. 641 (Winterton)
[4] ibid., 9 November 1920, col. 1044 (Sir G. Collins)
[5] ibid., 4 November 1920, col. 642 (Winterton)
[6] ibid., cols. 660–1 (Lord Cecil)
[7] ibid., col. 668 (Charles Edwards)
[8] ibid., 9 November 1920, col. 1090 (Mr Lyle); see also col. 1111 (Mr Briant)
[9] ibid. (H of L), Vol. XLIII, 14 December 1920, col. 148

Lloyd George to placate the more conservative elements in his Coalition. The lessons learned in the war were comfortably forgotten. The mood of purposive reform which had infected doctors, Ministers and public opinion alike, was over. The Poor Law hospitals, said to be doomed in 1918, were to survive – some for ten years, others until a similar drive for reform generated by a second world war led to their dissolution thirty years later.

CHAPTER 19

The New Role of the Voluntary Hospital

THE Government's half-hearted attempt at hospital reform
had had one concrete result. A committee had been set up
to consider the financial problems of the voluntary hospitals.
Voluntary contributions could no longer be their principal
source of income. Either the system of patients' payments had to
be extended or substantial aid had to come from government
(central or local). And a solution had to be found at a time when
the role of the hospital in the British system of medical care was
changing rapidly.

During the war, hospitals had catered for all social classes.
There had been hospitals for officers as well as hospitals for other
ranks. Persons from the upper middle classes had learnt to value
the comfort and safety of care away from home when they were
ill, and few of them could afford the domestic staff needed to
give the sick adequate care at home. The trend which had been
at work since about the beginning of the century had advanced
rapidly in war-time circumstances. There were now many well-
to-do patients who expected to enter hospital when seriously ill.
This important change was reflected in the Dawson Report and
was not lost on the leaders of the medical profession. A general
practitioner without access to hospital beds would lose his
middle-class patients at the time when they most needed medical
services and were most willing to pay for them. For these reasons,
among others, the BMA began pressing vigorously for beds under
the control of general practitioners.

In many areas of the country there were neither nursing
homes nor voluntary hospitals offering accommodation for
paying patients. Thus some of the latter began to be admitted
to Poor Law infirmaries. By the middle of 1920 all the Manchester Poor Law hospitals were said to admit private patients,
but under a ruling of the Minister of Health these patients could
only be attended 'by the doctor who happened to be in charge

of that institution'.[1] The Council of the BMA took the view that there should be free access for any doctor whether on the staff of the hospital or not.[2]

In Sheffield the local division of the BMA approached the Guardians asking for pay beds.[3] In Barnet the Guardians on their own initiative 'set aside some wards for persons unable to obtain admission to voluntary hospitals, but who were able to pay for medical care, treatment and nursing'.[4] This initiative brought the Guardians into conflict with the local medical profession which complained that they had not been consulted and demanded free access for all practitioners in the area. The Guardians refused to grant this and the BMA took up the matter with the Minister.

The Minister told the Guardians that they had no legal authority to 'hold themselves out as prepared to receive patients without investigation of their circumstances, in consideration of an undertaking to pay a fixed weekly sum; to recover more or less than the cost of the relief provided; or to differentiate between patients merely on the ground that repayment was being obtained.'[5] Despite the legal objection, the practice continued. The BMA was determined to enforce on reluctant Guardians the principle of free access which was not to be found in many of the larger voluntary hospitals. A deputation from the BMA asked the new Minister of Health (Sir Alfred Mond) in April 1921 to ensure that infirmary patients should only be accepted as a general rule on the recommendation of a private practitioner and that private practitioners should have the right of entry. The Minister expressed sympathy with this point of view.

In July 1921 the Manchester Guardians gave way to pressure from the local profession. In future any doctor was to be entitled to treat his own patient and any tariffs or fees were to be arranged by the medical association. Patients were to be admitted on the recommendation of the medical practitioner, subject to the final approval of the medical superintendent of the hospital.[6]

1 *BMJ Supplement*, 10 July 1920, p. 35
2 ibid., 24 April 1920, p. 122
3 *BMJ*, 17 July 1920, p. 93
4 *BMJ Supplement*, 26 March 1921, p. 81
5 ibid., 9 April 1921, p. 94
6 ibid., 16 July 1921, p. 26

At the West Middlesex Hospital, however, local doctors were not allowed to attend their own patients.[1] And the West Derby Board of Guardians were accused by a speaker at the annual meeting of the BMA in 1921 of 'practically setting up as a medical corporation and without any of the restraints of medical etiquette'.[2] They were charging an inclusive fee for accommodation and treatment and were advertising freely. Salaried doctors were looking after paying patients without any reference to general practitioners. The general meeting voted its support for the Council's policy. General practitioners had to be allowed into the infirmaries to attend their patients and to send any bill for the service they thought appropriate.

The profession found no difficulty in forming a united front on the question of payment for services in Poor Law infirmaries. There were to be two distinct classes of patient – non-paying patients cared for by the staff of the infirmary, and paying patients who should be cared for by doctors from outside. The problem of the voluntary hospitals proved more difficult. There were a number of intermediate classes of patient such as those paid for by public agencies and those who were themselves paying part of the cost of their maintenance. Should the medical staff be paid for looking after these?

As long ago as 1910, the representative body of the British Medical Association had instructed the Council to consider whether the medical staffs of voluntary hospitals should be paid for their services. In 1913, it was decided that medical staffs should remain unpaid.[3] However, this was a broad decision to which important exceptions were made. Payment for patients maintained by public funds had been accepted in 1909 and in subsequent years the Association made clear its expectation of a share of any *pro rata* payments paid by the Government for insured persons. A figure of 10 per cent was widely accepted. After the war it decided to extend this policy to cover discharged and disabled soldiers and sailors maintained in voluntary hospitals at public expense. The hospitals committee of the Association demanded that medical staffs should be 'adequately remunerated' for this work. It was decided in February 1920 that the remuneration should represent an addition of not less than

---

[1] ibid., 30 July 1921, p. 72
[2] ibid., p. 73
[3] See *BMJ Supplement*, 21 June 1919, pp. 74–5.

25 per cent of the costs falling on the hospital. The additional sum was to be placed at the disposal of the medical staff.[1]

When a decision on payments to hospitals for service patients was reached in May 1920, the doctors were dissatisfied and sent a deputation to the Minister of Pensions. They were told that the Minister had made a contract with the hospitals and could not deal with the profession direct.[2] When the BMA thereupon approached the British Hospitals Association, the latter agreed to advise voluntary hospitals to allocate one-fifth of the payments from the Ministry of Pensions to the medical staff. The hospitals committee of the BMA had acted resolutely so that 'the principle of paying medical staffs of voluntary hospitals should be firmly established in view of the probable extension of such work in connection with the treatment of other patients for whom the state or some local authority is responsible'.[3]

The next logical step was to extend this practice to *all* payments from public bodies. In many areas of the country, hospital staffs met and resolved to claim a fifth of such payments.[4] The staff of the Lock Hospital were an exception: they preferred 'to maintain the honorary tradition'.[5] There was a move to go further. A motion passed at the 1920 representative meeting said that 'the decision to demand contributions in aid of their maintenance from the patients fundamentally alters the basis of the relationship hitherto existing between the honorary medical staff and the subscribers'.[6] The question was referred to the Council for consideration.

Thus the medical profession was adjusting its policies to the use of the hospitals by all social classes. It had attempted to control local authority policies by making sure that private practitioners did not lose money, when paying patients were admitted to private beds in Poor Law infirmaries. It had also attempted to make sure that the medical profession as a whole did not lose money when patients who could have afforded to pay at least something to their general practitioners, if they had been sick at home, were admitted to the voluntary hospitals.

[1] ibid., 20 February 1920, p. 45
[2] ibid., 29 May 1920, p. 170
[3] ibid., 12 June 1920, p. 187
[4] ibid., 31 July 1920, pp. 50, 55; 9 October 1920, p. 89
[5] ibid., 31 July 1920, p. 62
[6] ibid., 10 July 1920, p. 35

Further, they had laid it down that hospital doctors should be paid for patients supported at public expense.

Though the profession had no power to thrust its decisions on voluntary hospital managements and though most hospitals chose to ignore the profession's claims, new policies had nevertheless been developed. And it was not slow to see the importance to its own interests of the appointment of the Cave Committee. A conference of hospital medical staffs was immediately called. This was attended by physicians and surgeons from 27 London and 71 provincial hospitals. Voluntary hospitals were advised not to receive general subsidies from local authorities, to continue to give free treatment to necessitous persons but to extract a contribution towards the cost of maintenance from others 'unless the contributory method of subscription, regarded as essential in industrial areas, is adopted'.[1] In this case the rates of contribution should be materially increased, in line with rising costs. The payments for professional services made by patients in 'full-pay' beds should be arranged privately with the doctor in each case. When payments were made by or on behalf of other patients, a percentage of them was 'to be passed into a fund which can be allocated in any manner which the honorary medical staff may determine'.[2] This last decision was not taken unanimously. One speaker at the conference said that, with all the payments received by the hospitals, they were ceasing to be voluntary. 'If staffs insisted on receiving their cut, they too would cease to be honorary!'[3] The chairman replied that 'no one could contest the proposition that such a sum was not a payment but an honorarium'.

The Cave Committee reported within a few months of its appointment. After a careful analysis of the finances of the voluntary hospitals, it found that while some had surpluses the majority had deficits and the deficits greatly exceeded the surpluses. The present crisis had arisen from rising costs rather than from falling income[4] and was unlikely to be overcome by larger voluntary contributions 'while taxation continues at its present level'.[5] The committee noted, on the other hand, that

[1] ibid., 1 January 1921, p. 6
[2] ibid.
[3] Sir Hamilton Ballance of the Norfolk and Norwich Hospital. ibid.
[4] Cave Committee, *Final Report*, op. cit., pp. 6–7
[5] ibid., p. 18

the role of patients' contributions and collections from wage-earners was increasing and saw great potentialities in this source of income. While it thought that the approved societies owed the hospitals a large measure of support, it held that they were not under any obligation to pay the whole cost of the maintenance and treatment of their members.[1] It was, however, strongly of the opinion that they should pay a substantial part of their surpluses to the hospitals, towards the cost of maintaining their members.

The Committee rejected the possibility of permanent support for the hospitals from public funds as this would mean the end of the voluntary hospitals. The system had to be helped to continue partly because of its important educational work and partly because of the advantages of mobilizing voluntary service. 'The personal relation between the patient and the doctor and nurse . . . would be difficult to reproduce under an official régime.'[2] And the 'infinite care and time which is given to the management and support of voluntary hospitals by Boards of Management, Hospital Aid Societies and other bodies could hardly be reproduced under a State system'.[3]

The Committee favoured temporary support to save the hospitals from 'immediate disaster' but the 'assistance should be temporary only and . . . it should be clearly understood that it will not be continued beyond a limited period, which may be fixed at two years'.[4] Moreover, support should be given only to hospitals which showed that they were taking every step to re-establish their financial position. A special agency on the model of the University Grants Committee was to be created to administer the temporary grants which would work through specially constituted local agencies. The King's Fund could be used as such an agency in London but elsewhere there needed to be new bodies: the regional committees of the British Hospitals Association did not seem to be appropriate for this work because it was difficult for them to enforce their views upon their constituent members.[5]

It was hoped that this new structure of committees would use its financial powers to create some order in the hospital world.

[1] ibid., p. 29
[2] ibid., p. 9
[3] ibid.
[4] ibid., p. 11
[5] ibid., p. 12

The committee was impressed by the lack of co-ordination, which led to both inefficiency and unnecessary expense.[1] Thus it hoped that the committees would co-ordinate appeals, standardize accounts, develop corporate prescribing schemes and even go so far as to grade hospitals and act as a clearing house for patients requiring accommodation.[2] The temporary grants were to be used to secure changes which the Lords Committee had recognized to be needed some thirty years earlier in London.

The committee recommended Parliament to allot £1 million for these purposes. The Government responded by giving only half this sum. Even this was to depend on the hospitals raising an equivalent amount. It was made abundantly clear that this was to be the state's final contribution.[3] After that, the hospitals would have to manage as best they could. When the Bishop of Birmingham accused the Minister of 'inhumanity', Sir Arthur Mond replied that any continuing grant would have led to the disintegration of the voluntary hospital movement.[4]

The Cave Committee did not overstate the gravity of the crisis which faced some hospitals in 1921. Full particulars became available later, showing the income and expenditure of 152 hospitals in England and Wales during this year. They spent nearly £5 million[5] on current account and obtained an income of only about £4½ million.[6] But they had received also endowments of about another £1 million[7] which they had hidden away in their capital accounts. Nevertheless some of the large teaching hospitals (Middlesex, St George's, the Royal Free and the Royal Infirmaries at Sheffield and Bristol) could only finance out of current income two-thirds of their current expenditure. Such was the final outcome of the year's operations, despite an increase in the contribution of patients' payments in London teaching hospitals from 10 per cent of current income in 1920 to 25 per cent in 1921.

In the course of its report, the Cave Committee made some remarks about payments to medical staff which were not in line

[1] ibid., p. 13
[2] ibid., p. 14
[3] *Hospital Gazette*, August 1921, p. 113
[4] *Hospital*, January 1922, p. 106
[5] *Burdett's Hospitals and Charities 1922–3*, p. 62, London
[6] ibid., p. 40. These figures exclude 'extraordinary' income and expenditure.
[7] ibid., p. 31

with the views of the British Medical Association. It pointed out that there were already some hospitals which were allocating some 10 or 20 per cent of their payments from public authorities to a fund controlled by the medical staff. While in some hospitals the fund was used for such purposes as 'the purchase of expensive apparatus or books, and the support of young practitioners taking up special branches of work, in others the fund was divided out among the staff'. The Committee had been told by two distinguished physicians that, if the medical staff became subsidized to any substantial extent, 'the bottom would drop out of the voluntary system'. 'It should be remembered also,' the Committee continued,

> that although the services of the staff are honorary, they obtain a valuable return in the form of medical and surgical experience and the enhanced reputation which accrues to the member of the visiting staff of a great hospital. If the system of carrying a percentage to a staff fund is confined to cases where the full cost of maintenance and treatment is paid by or on behalf of the patient, not much objection can (we think) be taken to it; but any extension of the practice beyond these limits appears to us to endanger the future of the voluntary hospitals.[1]

At the annual representative meeting of 1921, a motion was passed disagreeing with the comments which the Cave Committee had made on staff funds and endorsing the evidence previously given to the Committee. The meeting asserted that 'the essence of the voluntary hospital system is the independent and voluntary management and that this is in no way related to the conditions of service of the medical staff'.[2] The views of the Association were reported to all the secretaries and senior honorary medical officers of all the voluntary hospitals. The honorary staffs were to establish the principle

> firmly and once for all. . . . The Boards of all voluntary hospitals should insist on the position of their staffs being recognized in any arrangements which are made for dealing with patients who cannot properly be regarded as recipients of charity and should see that some payment is made, if only an acknowledgement, into the staff fund.[3]

[1] *BMJ Supplement*, 20 July 1921, p. 72
[2] ibid., 26 July 1921, p. 72
[3] ibid., 20 August 1921, p. 103

In November 1921 the BMA organized a further meeting of the staffs of voluntary hospitals. Many of the representatives thought it wrong that the medical staff should receive a cut when the patients themselves were paying what they could afford for hospital care. The doctors from King's College Hospital felt that to take such a proportion would be 'to do away with the last shred of voluntary treatment'.[1] Dr Couzens of Stratford ridiculed the suggestion: Were medical staffs to ask for a share of the three-pences and sixpences paid by outpatients? 'Why should not the honorary medical staff then resign and seek re-election on a non-honorary basis if they wanted percentages from patients' maintenance?'[2] On the question of taking a share of part-payments made by patients themselves, the meeting was evenly divided. But the vast majority was prepared to vote that the agreed percentage should be deducted from a payment made from a public body, employer, insurance company, friendly society or under a contributory scheme.

By November 1921 contributory schemes did not refer only to the rather casual system of workmen's contributions through the Hospital Saturday Fund or to the industrial schemes which played an important role in the North of England. A new and more formal contributory mechanism was growing up in the South to complicate still further the network of payments which were buttressing the voluntary hospitals. By 1921 it was clear that the hospitals could look to no permanent support either from the rates or from the central government except in return for specified services. The Cave Committee had suggested that the friendly societies might give their surpluses to the hospitals as a contribution towards the treatment of insured persons. No immediate payment could, however, be expected from this source as the societies decided to devote their immediate surpluses to additional cash payments to members,[3] and post-pone consideration of grants to hospitals until their next valuation.

In 1921 a provident scheme was started in Brighton by Dr Gordon Dill and a group of local consultants, which gave patients in return for their contributions the right to pre-paid care in a number of co-operating hospitals. The plan was

[1] ibid., 26 November 1921, p. 196
[2] ibid., p. 195
[3] *Hospital Gazette*, May 1921, p. 114

considered and rejected by the 1921 annual meeting of the BMA. Nevertheless, some three hundred members of the public were enrolled within half an hour of the representative meeting turning it down.[1] The honorary secretary of the Eastbourne division of the BMA wrote to the *British Medical Journal* to protest against this 'contempt for the representative body'.[2] He said the scheme was controlled by 'a small section of class practitioners' – 'a Brighton caucus'.[3] He claimed that the scheme would 'jeopardize the maintenance of voluntary hospitals on a charitable basis', push out 'those impecunious cases for whose benefit voluntary hospitals were originally founded' and deprive the local consultants and specialists of their fees if they stayed outside the scheme.[4]

Despite this opposition, a similar scheme was planned and started in London. Three hospitals participated (the London, St Thomas' and the Royal Free) in a scheme which provided not only inpatient care but outpatient consultations, home nursing services and domiciliary consultations. Those joining it were not, however, to take precedence over more urgent cases for admission to hospital.[5]

The BMA watched these developments closely. It was not opposed to all types of contributory scheme. It did, however, want to make sure that such schemes developed in a manner which it thought appropriate. Indeed, the whole concept of a class of contributory patients strongly influenced its report on the organization of voluntary hospitals which was prepared during the winter of 1921–2.[6] The report skirted the controversial issue of part-pay patients by suggesting that patients should be divided into three classes – free patients certified as unable to pay, private patients in special accommodation, and tariff patients who did not pay directly themselves (including members of contributory schemes). Payments for the latter class of patient were to include a percentage for treatment which was to be passed into the staff fund. Income limits were laid down for these 'tariff' patients, varying from £250 to £350 according to family

[1] *BMJ Supplement*, 22 October 1921, p. 155
[2] ibid., p. 156
[3] ibid.
[4] ibid.
[5] *Hospital Gazette*, October 1921, p. 9
[6] *BMJ Supplement*, 22 February 1922, p. 45

responsibilities. A tariff patient was only to be admitted to hospital on the recommendation of his own practitioner.

Private patients were to have free choice of doctor. And as the number of tariff patients increased 'so should the medical staffs, giving more opportunities for eligible practitioners'. All private practitioners 'who possess the necessary qualifications and experience to participate in the work of voluntary hospitals' should be given full opportunities to participate. On boards of management, 'representation should be distributed so as to secure the representation of each interest in the hospital so that no single interest should be in a majority'.

Referring to the report, Dr Alfred Cox said that

the main question for Harley Street is, What is going to be the relation of the hospital staffs of the voluntary hospitals when the majority of the patients in those hospitals are, to a greater or lesser extent, paying patients, or when the hospitals are financed mainly by contributions from people who expect a quick *quid pro quo*? . . . The tendency for Harley Street up to the present has been rather to bury its head in the sand and wait for something to turn up. Nothing will turn up but confusion, unless our Association can work out an acceptable policy. Nobody is tackling the question. I have seen no attempt by the Royal Colleges to give a lead.[1]

The report was presented to a third meeting of representatives of the medical staffs of voluntary hospitals. There was a lot of opposition to the proposal to allow outside practitioners to come in and attend their own patients in private wings of voluntary hospitals. A speaker from St Bartholomew's thought it 'a very retrograde step',[2] and others said that doctors might be admitted 'whose method of work and practice might not commend themselves to the more honourable members of the profession and this would create friction'.[3] An outsider might damage the X-ray machine. Either for these reasons which were expressed or because of the effect on the private practice enjoyed by existing consultants, the appropriate clause was deleted from the statement.

Two further paragraphs were also voted out by the conference. The representatives did not agree that 'full opportunity should

[1] ibid., 18 March 1922, p. 72
[2] ibid., April 1922, p. 88
[3] ibid.

be given to private practitioners who possess the necessary skill and experience to participate in the work of voluntary hospitals'.[1] Nor did they agree that 'when the number of tariff patients of voluntary hospitals increases, the medical staffs of such hospitals should be increased'.[2] The rest of the statement was approved. The hospital doctors had voted both for honoraria and for exclusive rights of hospital practice.

The report of the conference was not unanimously welcomed by the Council of the BMA. Dr Brackenbury complained that:

> One proposal of great importance was rejected – namely, that nursing home annexes should be established in connection with hospitals, and that patients therein should be at liberty to choose their own private practitioners. That, in his view, was an essential part of the hospital scheme, without which he was not prepared to accept the scheme at all. If the free choice of doctor was going to be denied in the case of voluntary hospitals, while it remained a part of the scheme for municipal hospitals, then he preferred the latter.[3]

When the report on hospital policy finally came before the annual representative meeting of 1922, there was yet another debate about the payment of hospital staffs. One speaker favoured full payment because there might be a Labour Government which would come and ask the doctors what their services were worth. The doctors would say, 'Nothing,' and that is what they would be paid. The majority, however, argued that if doctors were paid it would 'only be smoothing the way for hospitals to be placed under the State'.[4] It was decided that the hospital doctors should not be remunerated for their services. But the proper role of honoraria remained unclear. A motion that honoraria should be collected on payments from public authorities and any other full cost payments to hospitals failed to get the two-thirds majority necessary to carry it.[5]

The meeting stuck rigidly to the principle that the primary role of the outpatient department should be for consultations. Only such treatment was to be given 'as cannot consistently be properly undertaken by a general practitioner of ordinary

[1] ibid., p. 91
[2] ibid.
[3] ibid., 13 May 1922, p. 166
[4] ibid., 24 July 1922, p. 53
[5] ibid., p. 54

professional competence and skill'. One participant asked whether an exception might be made in the case of patients referred for long treatment by their own medical attendant, on the grounds that it might be in the best interest of an uninsured woman or child who required prolonged treatment not to be allowed to run up a doctor's bill of £10 or £20, but to be admitted to the hospital. The meeting voted against this exception.[1]

The profession had shown itself to be far from unanimous in its views. In many of the smaller hospitals, the doctors were glad to have a share of the income of the hospitals in which they were working. In the high prestige teaching hospitals of London, however, there was a reluctance on the part of the medical staff to imperil their honorary position for the relatively modest sums which were at stake. A meeting of the medical staff of two London teaching hospitals was held in September 1922. It was resolved unanimously that where patients contribute not more than the cost of their maintenance, no payment should be made to the medical staff. On the question of payments made by public bodies, the staff were divided. The doctors of Guy's Hospital would not accept payment in any circumstances.[2]

Meanwhile, plans were being prepared for a different kind of contributory scheme in London. King Edward's Hospital Fund for London was the prime mover though it decided itself not to administer any such scheme. At a special council meeting held in the House of Lords on 8 March 1922, the Fund revealed its plan. The scheme was to be available for persons earning less than £4 to £6 a week, depending on family size, 'to avoid abuse by those who can afford to pay for treatment outside the hospital'.[3] Free hospital care was to be offered in return for 3d per week or 12s per year. The scheme was called 'The Hospital Saving Association'.

In November 1922, the Metropolitan Counties branch of the BMA called a conference of medical staffs of voluntary hospitals to consider the scheme. Violent opposition was expressed. First, there had been no consultation with the medical staffs of the hospitals nor any provision for representation of the medical staff on the management. Secondly, there was no requirement that the contributor should see his own doctor before applying

[1] ibid., p. 62
[2] *Hospital*, Vol. LXXI, September 1922, p. 345
[3] *Hospital Gazette*, April 1922, p. 93

for hospital benefit. Thirdly, there was no indication that a payment was to be included for medical treatment. Fourthly, there was a risk that outpatient departments would be flooded with trivial cases and that 'those who at present make their own arrangements for specialist services will be diverted to the special departments of hospitals'.[1]

These objections were put to the Hospital Saving Association, which replied that it was pledged not to interfere with the hospitals. Questions of admissions procedure, both inpatient and outpatient, were in the hands of individual hospitals, as was also the question of the payment of medical staff. This was reported to a further meeting of hospital staffs at the end of January 1923, and it was resolved that the HSA scheme was unsatisfactory and in particular that outpatient benefit should be excluded under the scheme.[2]

At a further meeting in May 1923, the HSA scheme was again firmly rejected. It was resolved to be 'unsatisfactory from the point of view of the general practitioner and the staffs of hospitals, and, moreover, [did] not conform to the policy of the BMA'.[3] Dr Brackenbury hoped that the hospital doctors themselves would take up 'an antagonistic attitude' so that the scheme would break down.[4] One speaker suggested that if the general practitioners boycotted the co-operating hospitals, the hospital staff 'who depended on private practitioners to send them cases for consultation' would soon change their attitude.[5]

At the 1923 representative meeting the whole policy of the Council in supporting any type of contributory scheme came under fire. The Council was accused of trying to dovetail contributory schemes into the voluntary system. The attempt to get payments for doctors was also criticized. It was said that the public would stop subscribing if they got to know that the doctors were being paid. Thus the contributory schemes would tend to squeeze out the patients for whom the hospitals came into existence.[6] Some doctors were strongly opposed to any form of payment.

---

[1] *BMJ Supplement*, 9 December 1922, p. 211
[2] ibid., 10 February 1923, p. 46
[3] ibid., 9 June 1923, pp. 230–1
[4] ibid., p. 230
[5] ibid.
[6] ibid., 28 July 1923, pp. 47–51

Not until the 1924 representative meeting did the Council of the BMA get its way. The principle of payments to medical staffs by or on behalf of patients was thus accepted by a two-thirds majority. The definition of contributory payments was very broad. The wording of the resolution was as follows:

> Where the Board of Management of a voluntary hospital accepts contributions for patients from an approved society, insurance company, contributory scheme, employer of labour and/or by mass or periodic payments by employees, the members of the visiting medical staff should receive recognition of their services either in the form of an agreed honorarium or in the form of a percentage of all such payments being passed into a fund. Such honorarium or fund can be allocated in any manner which the visiting staff may determine.[1]

In a separate resolution it was decided that there should be a similar levy on payments made by individual patients.[2] Even though many hospitals continued to ignore the views of the Association, the latter's policy had been finally settled.

The development of contributory schemes and patients' payments seemed the only way in which the voluntary hospitals could solve their financial problems. Failing continuous Exchequer grants, it seemed the only means by which they could continue to operate. Nevertheless it involved a fundamental alteration in the role of the voluntary hospital movement which both the trade union movement and the Labour Party hastened to point out. In 1922, a joint statement of policy was published which was wholly devoted to 'the hospital crisis'. It severely criticized the system of patients' payments. There was 'naturally a bias on the part of the management to admit those who can pay in preference to those who cannot, and if the fee varies with the patients' means, to select those who pay most. Hence the purse becomes the criterion of admission, instead of medical and surgical necessity, which is a bad principle.'[3] Moreover, it was 'very difficult for the administration and the nursing staff not to show some slight difference in favour of "pay-patients" '.[4]

[1] ibid., 28 July 1924, pp. 47–9
[2] ibid., p. 53
[3] Trades Union Congress and Labour Party, *The Labour Movement and the Hospital Crisis: A Statement of Policy with regard to Hospitals*, p. 9, London, 1922
[4] ibid.

And the patient had to be cross-questioned: it was his 'unpleasant task to prove his inability to pay'.[1]

The Labour Party objected to contributory schemes, as they were 'sure to result in the exclusion from hospitals of many of the poorer citizens, who cannot afford the luxury of insurance and for whom the hospitals were originally founded'.[2] It quoted the organizing secretary of such a scheme as asking co-operating hospitals 'to give such a measure of privacy and priority to the members of the scheme as may be found possible without prejudice to the work of the hospitals or to the needs of more urgent cases'.[3] To this request there had been 'a generous response'.[4]

The Labour Party castigated the system of honorary medical and surgical staffs for all the anomalies and abuses it created. As honorary appointments had a monopoly value, the number of such appointments was 'jealously guarded'.[5] As a result all big hospitals were 'badly understaffed'.[6] The price was paid by the patients in the long hours of waiting in outpatient departments. Patients who had a letter from a general practitioner got preferential treatment; they tended to see the consultant in person, to be seen earlier, and to secure preferential admission. 'What with lay managements desiring to keep on good terms with large subscribers and the consultants with general practitioners, all the available beds are too often fully occupied, leaving no room for those who have no influence to assist them in gaining admission.'[7]

There was a further system of 'queue-barging':

A general practitioner will send a patient to see a consultant privately with a note saying that the patient can only afford a consultation fee, and, therefore, should an operation or special treatment be necessary, would he take him into hospital. Under these circumstances, the consultant feels himself under some obligation, not only to the general practitioner, but in a way to the patient himself, and he therefore secures his admission to hospital

[1] ibid.
[2] ibid., p. 8
[3] ibid.
[4] ibid.
[5] ibid., p. 4
[6] ibid.
[7] ibid.

at the earliest moment. Indeed, the 'man in the street' is beginning to realize that a consultation with a member of a hospital staff will generally secure to him early admission to hospital, should it be necessary, and he pays the fee willingly for the privilege it carries.[1]

The ideal plan for hospitals envisaged by the Labour Party was

... a completely organized hospital service, with receiving stations, cottage hospitals, county hospitals and national hospitals, ramifying throughout the length and breadth of the country, all working together for the speedy cure of individual sufferers and for raising the standard of the health of the whole nation. Each hospital should become the 'Health Centre' of the district which it serves, and all medical activities should be gathered together within its walls. The hospital system would be but part of an organized public medical service, controlled and inspired by the Ministry of Health, but administered by enlarged and reorganized local health authorities. It considers that the public medical service, including the hospital service, should be financed by the local health authorities, assisted by substantial grants-in-aid from the Ministry of Health, and should be free and open to all. Those who enjoy the blessings of good health would contribute through the rates towards those afflicted with ill-health or disease.[2]

The plan envisaged a much more important role for general practitioners. The separation of the latter from the hospital was considered to be both bad for the patient who suffered discontinuity of care and bad for the practitioner who lost 'all interest in the case'.[3] Ideally, general practitioners should 'take an active share of the responsibility for the care of their cases as a recognized part of the honorary hospital staff'. This would give them not only interest in their work but they could be 'kept abreast of the times by daily contact with consultants and specialists and with hospital methods'.[4] They should have 'beds under their own control for the treatment of such of their cases as do not require the services of a specialist, and where there is no local or cottage hospital certain wards in the larger general hospitals should be set aside for this purpose'.[5]

[1] ibid.
[2] ibid., pp. 12–13
[3] ibid., p. 2
[4] ibid.
[5] ibid.

The Labour Party stressed that its plan would not mean the end of voluntary work or the end of charity. 'It is surely as noble and satisfying to give to the community as a whole for the benefit of all as to give to a charitable institution reserved in theory for but one section of the community.'[1] There would be a need for 'men and women of experience on many a committee, and for the personal service of lay-visitors to the patients in the wards'.[2]

The Labour Party did not intend to introduce its ideal plan all at once. The first step was to hand the Poor Law infirmaries over to the local health authorities as the nucleus of a public hospital service for the use of all citizens. The local authorities should then give the voluntary hospitals the choice of being taken over root and branch, remaining independent, or receiving grants with public representation on the governing body proportionate to the grant received.[3]

The *Hospital Gazette* hastened to point out that the specific proposals of the Labour Party's pamphlet left no future for the voluntary hospitals. The hospitals would have to ask for grants, and when they received them, voluntary subscriptions would certainly decline. And as the subscriptions declined, the grants would have to increase, thus augmenting the power of the local authorities over the hospitals until eventually they were all 'owned, controlled and managed by public bodies'.[4] It denied some of the specific allegations of the Labour Party: in particular, contributors were not given any preference in admission to hospital – the criteria were medical and not financial. It went on to ask: 'Why should those who can afford to pay the full cost of maintenance and medical treatment not be permitted to avail themselves of the perfected organization of these institutions?'[5] Attitudes had changed considerably from the time when the question of hospital 'abuse' was discussed thirty years earlier.

In April 1924, the Labour Party held a conference on state aid for hospitals. The views of the Party were presented by Mr Somerville Hastings, MD, FRCS. He stressed the shortage of hospital beds: he thought that $2\frac{1}{2}$ general beds per thousand

[1] ibid., p. 15
[2] ibid.
[3] ibid., p. 18
[4] *Hospital Gazette*, May 1922, p. 103
[5] ibid., June 1922, p. 115

population were needed and the voluntary hospitals only provided a third of that number. He said that the system of workmen's contributions was almost a compulsory levy. 'Surely a rate
or a tax which all would have to pay would be a much more
equitable arrangement?'[1] With the growth of all the contributory schemes there was a danger of the voluntary hospitals
becoming 'nursing homes for the middle classes'.[2]

The case for the voluntary hospitals was put by Lord Knutsford. The hospitals were not understaffed so far as inpatients
were concerned and only partly understaffed so far as outpatients were concerned. He denied that patients who could pay
were given any preference in admission to hospital. The doctors
and not the management were responsible for admitting patients.
Lord Knutsford proposed that all voluntary hospitals and Poor
Law infirmaries in each district should be placed under one
management. The voluntary hospital would act as a mother
hospital and the infirmaries would act as annexes to it. The
Minister of Health should make large grants to the mother
hospital and he must therefore 'be given the power to nominate
on to its management representatives of the state and of the
district served'.[3] Lord Knutsford had anticipated by a quarter of
a century the essence of the solution which was eventually to
be adopted.

The representatives of the King's Fund confined themselves to
producing statistics to show that the voluntary hospitals were far
from being on the decline. The representatives of the BMA
wanted some less far-reaching scheme of co-ordination than that
proposed by Lord Knutsford. And a Manchester trade union
secretary quoted instances in which his members paid for a
private consultation to buy themselves into their local hospital.
The conference concluded by passing resolutions favouring an
increase in hospital accommodation, the better co-ordination of
individual hospitals and the introduction of grants from public
authorities.

Though the conference was held while the Labour Party was
enjoying its first brief spell of power, no action was taken. The
Party did not have a majority in the House of Commons and
depended upon the support of the Liberal Party. Though it held

[1] *BMJ Supplement*, 3 May 1924, p. 214
[2] ibid.
[3] ibid., p. 216

radical views, it could do nothing to put them into effect. Even the reform of the Poor Law hospitals which might have commanded a majority of the House was not brought before Parliament.

It was clear that by the early twenties the voluntary hospitals had taken on a completely new role. A high proportion of their patients made some payment and some of their medical staff received payments. At the annual representative meeting of the BMA in 1921 an innocuous motion expressing belief in the voluntary method of administration was passed. One speaker suggested that from the point of view of finance the municipal system was distinctly better. Another countered this by arguing that 'the determining factor in the management of the hospitals of Boards of Guardians was fear of the poll. What the medical profession wanted was the good of the patients, not fear of the poll.'[1] It was pointed out also that 'the advantage of voluntary hospital committees was that they were imbued with a finer spirit through the influence of their medical members'.[2]

Yet some of the committee members of voluntary hospitals were not really volunteers. 'In Leicester and other industrial areas, certain trade union representatives were paid by their trade unions for the time they gave to service on hospital committees.'[3] And the medical staff of St Bartholomew's had always been paid. By 1924 no distinguishing characteristic of a voluntary hospital could be found. But whatever a voluntary hospital was, it still enjoyed a wide measure of esteem among the leaders of British society.

At the 1924 representative meeting of the British Medical Association a motion was proposed that 'inasmuch as voluntary hospitals were established primarily for . . . [the sick poor], these cases should in all circumstances receive priority of consideration'.[4] The mover pointed out that he was only asking 'that poor persons should receive priority of consideration, not necessarily priority of admission'.[5] The motion was defeated.

[1] ibid., 30 July 1921, p. 67
[2] ibid.
[3] ibid., 1 April 1922, p. 86
[4] ibid., 26 July 1924, p. 60
[5] ibid.

CHAPTER 20

Contributory Schemes and the 'Abuse' of Hospitals

THE post-war financial crisis had forced the voluntary hospitals to introduce drastic changes. Patients were asked to pay what they could afford and as a result there had developed much more formal contributory schemes. In addition, the central government had promised a once-and-for-all payment of £500,000 to restore the position of hospitals worst hit by the crisis.

Soon afterwards, there came a general fall in prices and no longer did hospitals have to match rising expenditure with rising income. Legacies, gifts and interest on endowments increased in value. Helped by the new sources of income, nearly all the hospitals were able to maintain their services.

A Commission was set up under the chairmanship of Lord Onslow to carry out the functions envisaged by the Cave Committee. Although it had only half the money to distribute which had been originally asked for, the need for subsidies was smaller than had been anticipated. The Commission set up local committees in each county area to help with the distribution of the grant and to try and secure co-ordinated action. The task of acting as the local committee of London was entrusted to the King's Fund: in other areas, committees were set up consisting of representatives from the major local authorities, the hospitals, the local doctors and five persons appointed by the Commission.[1] Combined appeals were organized. In London about half a million pounds was raised by a combined effort in 1922. Every stunt was used: three hundred Guy's students were out with barrel-organs; there were lorry-loads of concert parties and jazz-bands; there were pageants, carnivals, dances,

[1] Ministry of Health, *Voluntary Hospitals Commission* (Onslow Commission), Interim Report, p. 7, HMSO, 1923

bazaars, dinners, boxing matches, tattoos and processions.[1]

The half-million pounds provided by the Government was found more than adequate to meet the 1921 deficits. The Commission required hospitals to keep their accounts in a standard form as a condition of receiving a grant. When hospital accounts were standardized and 'free' legacies (legacies without conditions attached) were treated as part of current income and not hidden away as capital receipts, it was found that many hospitals had no deficit at all. The Commission decided to allocate £225,000 to London hospitals and £275,000 for the rest of Great Britain.[2] By the end of December 1922, £372,013 had been distributed.[3] The work of the Commission caused no friction with the hospitals. It avoided any interference with the workings of hospitals and determined 'to maintain the voluntary system intact'.[4] It pointed out that there had been virtually no increase in voluntary hospital accommodation since the war. 'The provision of additional accommodation is essential if the success of the voluntary system in the future is to be secured.'[5]

The hospitals received considerable help on capital account from grants totalling £1,360,000 out of the surplus war funds of the British Red Cross Society. Grants were given to meet the cost of repairs and for general schemes of improvement – nurses' homes, X-ray rooms, remodelled kitchens, etc. A grant was never given for more than half the cost of a scheme.[6]

A further and growing source of income for the hospitals came from the approved societies. About £200,000 per year was set aside for payments to hospitals. It was not easy to arrange the distribution of this sum. Each patient who belonged to an approved society was supposed to report the name of his society when treated in hospital. The relevant particulars were then forwarded to the society. Not only was this system cumbrous but insured persons were reluctant to reveal that they belonged to approved societies lest they might lose sickness benefit as a result.[7] Moreover, some hospitals were reluctant to take payments

[1] *Hospital*, Vol. 2, November 1922, p. 22 and February 1923, p. 101
[2] Onslow Commission, *Interim Report*, p. 10
[3] ibid.
[4] ibid., p. 15
[5] ibid., p. 14
[6] F. N. K. Menzies, *The Voluntary Hospitals In Great Britain* (British Red Cross Society, Fifth Annual Report for the Year 1923), pp. 100–01
[7] *Hospital*, Vol. 2, June 1923, p. 233

of this kind lest it should militate against payments under mass contribution schemes.[1] The administrative problems were in time overcome and insured persons were reassured that they could not lose any sick pay by being in hospital. By 1929 a sum of over £270,000 was being allocated to hospitals.[2]

A form of indirect assistance to the voluntary hospitals was provided under Section 20 of the 1922 Finance Act. A person (and, in certain circumstances, a company) who covenanted to make payments (yearly or half-yearly) to a charity for over six years was able to secure relief of income tax on the payments made.[3] In effect, the Inland Revenue was 'subsidizing' covenanted donations to charities. The arrangement greatly helped the voluntary hospitals.

The voluntary hospitals received further indirect aid under the Road Traffic Act of 1930.[4] Insurance companies were compelled by this statute to make payments to hospitals for the treatment of road accident cases. This step had been recommended both by the Voluntary Hospital Commission and by the BMA. The latter had held in 1925 that it was wrong for accident cases to be treated gratuitously.[5] It had, however, been very difficult for hospitals to recover any costs because they had no right of action against the insurance company and their right of action against the victim of the accident could not easily be exercised. Very soon after the Act was passed, the BMA wrote to hospital medical staffs saying that they should 'insist' on one quarter of the sum paid by the insurance being credited to the staff fund.[6]

Meanwhile the Voluntary Hospitals Commission continued its work. It calculated the extent of the shortage of hospital beds: an additional 10,000 beds were required 'to ensure a reasonable standard of adequacy' and suggested that some further state aid might be made available for the purpose. The Government was not willing to make any funds available. The annual report of the Ministry of Health states that 'after careful consideration of the Report, the Minister very reluctantly came to the

[1] Onslow Commission, *Interim Report*, pp. 12–13
[2] Newsholme, Vol. III, op. cit., p. 136
[3] *Hospital*, Vol. 27, September 1931, p. 212
[4] Clause 36 (2) of Part II
[5] *BMJ Supplement*, 19 December 1925, p. 211
[6] ibid., 31 January 1931, p. 25

conclusion that in the present financial situation it would be impracticable at this stage to consider the proposal for an Exchequer grant'.[1]

Despite the absence of a building grant from the Exchequer the voluntary hospitals expanded. Between the end of 1924 and the end of 1926, 3,829 more beds were opened and a further 2,964 beds were in course of construction at the second date. By 1928 the Commission had distributed all its money and prepared its final report. Reluctantly the Commission disbanded. In the words of the annual report of the Ministry of Health, 'the Government had found themselves unable to make any further grants in aid of the capital cost of hospital extensions' and thus agreed that the Commission 'should bring their work to a close'.[2]

The Minister could draw attention to the much healthier position of the finances of the hospitals. In 1920 the returns to the Cave Committee had indicated a deficit of about £280,000 for 452 provincial hospitals and of nearly £370,000 for 113 Metropolitan hospitals.[3] By 1923 the accounts of 624 provincial hospitals showed a total surplus of nearly £270,000 and the accounts of 116 Metropolitan hospitals showed a total surplus of nearly £230,000.[4]

By continued begging the hospitals managed to collect more money in subscriptions and donations. At each opportunity there were 'balls, masquerades, dances, bazaars and lotteries'.[5] There were more joint appeals: in some cases there were secret agreements between hospitals on the proportions which each should receive.[6] The Temple Fête and Gala Agency of Nottingham advertised that it offered 'all classes of stage performances and sensational attractions'. Fête, Carnival, Bazaar Organizers offered 100 profitable 'Fayre' games on hire.[7] A Kensington firm offered a 100-page illustrated catalogue showing the items

[1] *Seventh Annual Report Ministry of Health 1925–6*, Cmd 2724, pp. 40–41, HMSO, 1926

[2] *Ninth Annual Report Ministry of Health 1927–8*, Cmd 3185, p. 6, HMSO, 1928

[3] *Sixth Annual Report Ministry of Health 1924–5*, Cmd 2450, p. 35, HMSO, 1925

[4] ibid.

[5] R. W. Chalmers, *Hospitals and the State*, p. v, London, 1928

[6] ibid., p. 110

[7] *Hospital*, Vol. 27, March 1931, p. 74

it had on hire, including a revolving horse, a haunted house, swings, flags, marquees and scenic bazaar stalls.[1]

Though more money was collected from the public, the finances of the voluntary hospitals were rescued not so much by the charitable public or by the Government as by the patients themselves. The contributory schemes grew rapidly. The largest was the Hospital Saving Association. In 1924 about 62,000 contributors subscribed £22,397; in 1929 about 650,000 contributors paid about £320,000.[2] This scheme which had been sponsored by King Edward's Hospital Fund and assisted with an initial grant of £10,000 operated largely in London. In return for threepence per week the contributor and his dependants could receive *as a privilege, not a right*, general hospital care without further payment or test of means. If attendance was at a non-affiliated or public hospital, reimbursement at a maximum rate was paid for up to ten weeks of treatment.[3] In some cases workers' contributions were collected by employers through the pay roll.[4]

The Hospital Savings Association was the largest scheme but there were many others. A scheme had been started at Sheffield as early as 1919 by a Joint Hospital Council, consisting of representatives of the hospitals, contributors, employers, workers, the City and the University. The income of the scheme rose from about £62,000 in 1919 to £163,000 in 1929.[5] By the last year the scheme was producing about 60 per cent of the income of the four voluntary hospitals. Contributions of a penny in the pound were deducted at source by employers who added one-third to their employees' contributions.[6] The Birmingham scheme started in 1927 and incorporated the local Saturday Fund. It was run by a joint committee of the Saturday Fund, the hospitals and the Chamber of Commerce.[7]

By 1930 there were over 300 different schemes in existence in different parts of the country.[8] Their total income greatly exceeded that of the old Sunday Fund and Saturday Fund. The

[1] ibid., July 1931, p. 175
[2] ibid., Vol. 26, March 1930, p. 43
[3] Newsholme, Vol. III, pp. 72–3
[4] ibid., p. 76
[5] *Hospital*, Vol. 26, September 1930, pp. 226–7
[6] Newsholme, Vol. III, pp. 64–70
[7] ibid., pp. 77–8
[8] *Hospital*, Vol. 26, July 1930, p. 150

former received less than £300,000 in 1926 and the latter less than £110,000 in the same year. In 1931 it was reported that there were at least 132 contributory schemes run by the hospitals and a further 80 run by outside organizations. Rates of contribution were 1d, 2d, 3d or more per week.[1]

The growth of contributory schemes represented a potential challenge to the position of the general practitioner. There were fears that members might obtain a *right* to attend hospital either as inpatients or as outpatients. Hospitals might be prepared to accept patients for whom payment would be obtained, without being too scrupulous in verifying that they had been referred from a general practitioner. If these things happened on any scale, private practice would suffer as badly as it was believed to have done in the old days of hospital 'abuse'. One solution to the problem of 'abuse' had been to use an almoner to keep out patients who could afford to pay a doctor. But members of contributory schemes had purchased freedom from almoners' inquiries. And it was now beneficial for hospitals which were short of funds to take pre-paid outpatients in preference to the sick poor.

While it was a breach of good medical principles and medical ethics, as they were currently understood, for a patient to go direct to a hospital, in the case of insured persons such lapses involved no loss of income for the general practitioner. But little more than a third of the population was covered by panel practice. There remained the wives and families of the insured, the aged, the long-term unemployed, and those whose incomes were too high for them to be admitted to the national health insurance scheme.

Right from the start the BMA had tried to impose income limits for the new contributory schemes but without much success. Indeed, one scheme had actually been organized to provide pre-insurance for those above the poorer classes – the British Provident Association. Mr Bishop Harman, the chairman of the hospitals committee of the BMA, made it clear that he disapproved of the provisions of this scheme. There was nothing to prevent a man with an income of £1,000 taking advantage of the benefits.[2] Income limits were not, however, the only means of controlling contributory schemes. Dr Brackenbury said it was

[1] *BMJ Supplement*, 18 July 1931, p. 45
[2] ibid., 21 March 1924, p. 121

more important for there to be 'some arrangement that would ensure that nobody would be allowed to have treatment at the hospital without first seeing a practitioner and obtaining his recommendation'.[1] Indeed, it was clear that if this last provision were enforced, the scheme, so far from damaging private practice, would actually stimulate it.

The BMA tried to press the principle of referral on to the Hospital Saving Association. The HSA argued in reply that it could hardly penalize *its* members by insisting on a letter while other patients attended hospitals without them. Moreover, some practitioners refused to supply letters.[2] The Council decided that both the public and general practitioners needed further education in these matters. The hospitals committee decided in 1927 to undertake a comprehensive survey into contributory schemes which were 'springing up in all parts of the country'.[3] There needed to be 'an active campaign among the hospital staffs in the hope that the principles already enunciated may be actively enforced before irremediable harm has been done'.[4] The committee was 'seriously concerned at the apathy shown in many quarters in this connection'.[5]

The BMA was concerned not only to see that there were income limits and that medical staff were paid, but also anxious to have contributory schemes controlled by external bodies rather than by the hospitals themselves. This would reduce the incentive for hospitals to give preference to contributory patients and to grant a right to treatment. There was a danger that 'the primary consideration in the admission of a patient – namely, the suitability of the case on medical grounds – would be prejudiced'.[6] In other words, patients should not go to the hospital for services which could be provided by general practitioners.

The 1927 representative meeting asked medical staffs of hospitals to claim payments in accordance with the hospital policy of the Association. 'Any laxity in securing such recognition is detrimental to medical work of all kinds and ultimately

[1] ibid.
[2] ibid., 30 April 1927, p. 167
[3] ibid., 26 November 1927, p. 205
[4] ibid.
[5] ibid.
[6] ibid., 19 December 1925, p. 210

to the general public.'[1] At the same meeting the Association expressed its fears for the future of general practice as a whole. A resolution was carried which stated:

> That the Representative Body, viewing with considerable concern the insidious inroads continually being made on private medical practice under the auspices of the State, voluntary bodies, and others, and being of the opinion that this is not only detrimental to the interests of the individual members of the medical profession but ultimately to all classes of the community, instructs the Council to watch all such developments and actively to interest itself in safeguarding private practice amongst all groups in the medical profession and to develop throughout the Branches and divisions closer co-operation with the local medical profession for that purpose.[2]

The speeches on this resolution produced many examples of the 'inroads' on private practice. Not only were public authorities developing salaried services but rival professions were taking over doctors' functions: dentists were doing anaesthetics; opticians were claiming recognition; midwives were supervising deliveries. As one doctor put it, 'In thousands of rural areas the general work of the practice supplies the bread and butter, but the midwifery is looked to to put the jam on it. The jam is becoming less and less.'[3] Last but not least the voluntary hospitals were making inroads with their contributory schemes.

In 1929 the Council of the BMA produced a report on contributory schemes. Local practitioners regarded them as potentially dangerous. Their members were beginning to imagine that they had a *right* to the service of the hospital. The promoters of the schemes were 'much more concerned with the effect of the scheme on the finances of the hospital than with the effect on the finances of the doctors whose living depends on private practice'.[4] The report continued:

> People who in the past would have expected to get their attendance from their own doctor or who would have raised the

---

[1] ibid., 30 July 1927, p. 74
[2] ibid., p. 63
[3] ibid., p. 64
[4] ibid., 20 April 1929, p. 135

modest fee for a consultant, now are inclined to go to the hospital as a matter of course. There can be little doubt that the widespread diffusion of these schemes, unless safeguarded in accordance with the policy of the Association, is bound to divert more and more practice into the hospitals to the detriment of those practitioners . . . who are competent to perform the services privately. . . . There are still many consultants and specialists whose practice may be seriously affected thereby because they are not on the staff of the particular hospital. The introduction of the National Health Insurance system should have led to a considerable decrease if not in the number of outpatients, certainly in the number of outpatient attendances. . . . Unfortunately there is a body of testimony from members of the staffs of large hospitals that considerable numbers of insured and contract patients are sent to hospital outpatient departments for services well within the competence of the practitioners sending them; not for the purpose of getting a second opinion so much as in the hope that the patient will be taken off the doctor's hands. The duty of the members of the staff to refer such cases promptly back to their own doctor cannot be emphasized too strongly.[1]

This outpatient question is a crucial test of the *desire* of the profession to prevent hospitals from encroaching on the sphere of private practice. If it can be shown that a large number of patients who are able to afford to pay for appropriate treatment by a private practitioner or for whom some doctor is under contract to provide, are allowed without protest to go to the outpatient departments or are even sent there direct by the practitioners under whose care they are, it is little use for the doctors on or off the staff, or for the Association on their behalf, to complain that the outpatient departments encroach on the sphere of private practice. . . . Even when hospitals do insist upon having a medical recommendation this is capable of great abuse. In more than one important area where it is necessary for the patient to produce a medical recommendation, it is said that if the usual doctor will not give such a recommendation, the patients have no difficulty in getting another doctor who is more complaisant . . . it is a misuse of the subscribers' money to utilize the resources of the hospital for people who can afford to get treatment elsewhere, and an imposition on the charity of the honorary staff to utilize their services for people who might be private patients of some doctor (perhaps themselves), or to employ them in treating minor cases which could and ought to be dealt with elsewhere.[2]

[1] ibid., p. 134
[2] ibid.

The Association therefore suggested compliance with the following paragraph of its policy:

> Where arrangements for consultations or specialist services for tariff patients are made under some contributory scheme or otherwise, such arrangement should provide that these services shall be given so far as is possible and consistent with the best interests of the patient by a private practitioner at his consulting rooms or at the patient's own home and not at the outpatient department of the voluntary hospital.[1]

The Council knew of no contributory scheme which had attempted to put this arrangement into operation. It was thought to be particularly important that contributory schemes for the middle classes should contain this proviso. The only possible solution for the working classes was to extend the national health insurance Acts to include consultant and specialist services.

A year later the Association published results of an inquiry undertaken to ascertain how far the principles laid down by the Association were actually being practised. It appeared that schemes were in operation at 352 hospitals. There was found to be a definite income limit in operation in 237 instances although the limit was not always stated in terms of money. Thus in some cases the scheme was limited to 'working people' or 'fishermen' or 'insured persons'. In 267 hospitals a doctor's letter was necessary to secure admission to hospital though this was less frequently the rule in London than in the provinces. Only 66 schemes gave financial recognition to the services of medical staffs.[2]

A further inquiry published in 1931 showed that out of 212 hospitals answering a questionnaire, 78 objected to the idea of giving their doctors a share of money received from contributory schemes, 32 accepted the principle, and 102 expressed no opinion. The method used to calculate the honoraria for medical staff varied widely:

> In some cases 5 per cent was taken for the honoraries, in one case 20 per cent of the first thousand pounds, 17 per cent of the next £500 and 15 per cent of the remainder. Another plan followed in some

[1] ibid., p. 135
[2] ibid., 19 April 1930, p. 142

instances was to allocate one-third of any surplus after paying full hospital costs. Another was to allocate one-sixth of the contributions for non-insurance patients. In a number of schemes the contribution was intended only to meet the hospital costs, and the medical staff were allowed to charge fees to all patients whether contributors or not.[1]

The Hospital was opposed to the principle of payments to medical staff in cases where the patient was within the hospital's income limits. In such cases the hospital was entitled 'to the whole of the contribution provided that it does not exceed the cost and neither the patient nor the contributory association can afford more'.[2] The journal did, however, recognize that owing to the increased use of outpatient departments all over the country, 'the position of the honorary staff required especial attention, either by reducing the income limits as compared with inpatients or establishing clinics where consultations can be obtained by appointment and where reduced fees would be paid and the amount handed over to the medical staff after the deduction of a small percentage for working expenses'.[3]

Meanwhile, early in 1931, the BMA had produced a new report on 'the problem of the outpatient'. As a result of the National Insurance Act the number of outpatients fell until 1920, but then started to increase until more outpatients were treated than in 1911. The report repeated the long established view of the Association that outpatient departments should be used for consultations and should undertake such treatments

as cannot, in the best interests of the patient, be obtained elsewhere under the usual arrangements as between private practitioner and private patient. . . . All patients not accepted for treatment should be referred to a private medical practitioner (or an insurance practitioner if the person is an insured person), to the Public Medical Service, to a Provident dispensary, or to the Public Assistance Officer of a Local Authority.[4]

This policy was to be 'rigorously applied'. There were few persons, except those of the pauper class, who had 'any real

[1] ibid., 18 July 1931, p. 45
[2] *Hospital*, Vol. 27, December 1931, p. 272
[3] ibid.
[4] *BMJ Supplement*, 21 February 1931, p. 53

excuse for not having established family doctor relations with some practitioner'.[1]

The voluntary hospitals remained as divided on the question of outpatients as they had always been. At a conference of the British Hospitals Association held in July 1931, Mr Orde of the Bureau of Hospital Administration 'sounded a trumpet call to action'. He called for joint action between hospital managements and medical staffs. He suggested that the first step was to impose a lower income limit for outpatients than inpatients: 'especially since the HSA, contrary to the expressed decision of the BMA, has persuaded a certain number of hospitals to raise the income limits from £300 to £400 a year.'[2]

At the same conference, however, Colonel Parkes, the secretary of St Mary's Hospital, London, said the abuse was 'comparatively small'. He could not see that 'any person would willingly submit to the intolerable delays and muddles [in outpatient departments] if, for a reasonable fee, he could obtain a similar opinion and services in a private consulting room'.[3] There was no financial gain for the hospitals out of outpatient departments. The average payment per patient was sixpence, while an attendance cost the hospital in the region of two shillings. He thought that a considerable proportion of the medical profession were opposed to restricting outpatient departments to 'persons in possession of a doctor's letter'. Poor people also valued 'second opinions'. None of the London teaching hospitals insisted on a doctor's letter though privileges were often given to those who had them.[4]

Thus the position was unchanged. The teaching hospitals wanted to continue to receive 'walk in' patients as some of them proved useful for teaching purposes. Selected patients were seen at the formal outpatient sessions while the casuals were seen at the casualty or at what St Thomas' Hospital bluntly called the 'sorting room'.[5] Inevitably the system meant some loss of income to private doctors.

Thus the historic conflict between the general practitioners and the voluntary hospitals, after a temporary lull following the

[1] ibid.
[2] *Hospital*, Vol. 27, July 1931, p. 150
[3] ibid., p. 159
[4] ibid., p. 164
[5] The phrase remains in use at the present day (1964).

1911 Insurance Act, was revived, fanned by the new potential challenge of the contributory schemes. The BMA, representing faithfully, as it always had, the financial interests of its members, fought hard to have these schemes conducted in a manner which made no inroads on private practice.

This 'trade union' behaviour of a professional association came in for sharp criticism in left-wing circles. At a meeting of the Fabian Society in 1927, Mr W. A. Robson (later Professor of Public Administration at the London School of Economics) said that the BMA was incredibly selfish and lacking in public spirit:

> Whenever you see a statement on public policy by the BMA, you always know that they are considering the private pockets of the doctors who are their members, and are never in the slightest degree interested in the public welfare. I do not think that there is a single exception where for a quarter or half a second the BMA has ever put aside the pecuniary interests of its members for the sake of an improvement in public health.[1]

Though the growth of contributory schemes reawakened fears among the doctors of a loss of income, voluntary hospitals were given a new lease of life. They were able to make ends meet. And their governors improved the amenities provided for their patients. Though it was carefully pointed out that the patient who had paid his contributions had not obtained a 'right' to hospital treatment, at least the patient had more of a right to complain about discomfort than the patient who was wholly a recipient of charity.

Hospital life, as seen from the patient's point of view, was rarely discussed in the hospital or medical journals before the National Insurance Act; the question was given growing attention throughout the twenties. In 1920 there were reports of 'experiments' in allowing patients to smoke in wards between the hours of 5 and 7 p.m. in Cardiff, Wigan and Edinburgh.[2] It was pointed out to the more cautious that patients had been allowed to smoke in the Dreadnought Hospital 'in bed and in the wards' for a hundred years.[3]

In 1922 *The Hospital* reported that it was being asserted 'in the

---

[1] *BMJ Supplement*, 5 March 1927, pp. 80–81
[2] *Hospital*, Vol. LXVIII, 3 April 1920, p. 5, and 17 April 1920, p. 64
[3] ibid.

interests of paying patients of one kind or another' that various details of hospital life bore 'the stamp, in the derogatory sense, of charity; that the bread is served too thick, that the mugs are too coarse and the like'.[1] *The Hospital* confessed that food was often made 'unappetizing through want of care in serving it'.[2] Then there was the 'classic objection to the early hour at which the patients are roused. . . . It will be interesting to see what changes paying patients bring to details like this.'[3]

Hospitals answered the criticisms of bad food by complaining that they could not get good cooks. Inefficient people were asking for exorbitant wages and having to be dismissed when their inefficiency became too patently obvious.[4] *The Hospital* thought that some part of the difficulty was due to the 'post-war dislike of hard work, even when combined with good pay'.[5] It was suggested that the hospitals might band themselves together to establish a hospital school of cookery. By 1930 the introduction of trained dieticians was being advocated, following American practice.[6]

Protest against the practice of early waking in hospitals was being organized through the trade unions and the Labour Party. It was reported in the *Daily Herald* that some patients were woken as early as 3 a.m.[7] A resolution was submitted to the National Labour Party Women's Conference affirming that the practice of early waking had 'grave results on the health of the patients' and declaring that 'the first and main purpose of a hospital is the restoration to health of the patient, and feels therefore that no consideration of the convenience of doctors or nurses should be allowed to supersede the primary object'.[8]

The Central Bureau of Hospital Information undertook an inquiry into the subject which revealed that in more than two-thirds of the 63 hospitals about which information was given 'the work begins at 6 o'clock and the interval for breakfast is at any time between that hour and 8.30'.[9] It was suggested by

---

[1] ibid., Vol. 1, June 1922, p. 264
[2] ibid.
[3] ibid.
[4] ibid., Vol. 3, December 1924, p. 363
[5] ibid., p. 364
[6] ibid., Vol. 26, April 1930, p. 78
[7] quoted ibid., p. 68
[8] ibid.
[9] ibid., June 1930, p. 116

the Middlesex Hospital that a solution might be a later hour for breakfast.[1] The King's Fund undertook an investigation of the subject in 1931 and concluded that the difficulties in the way of leaving patients to sleep until 6.45 or 7 a.m. were 'insuperable'.[2] It therefore suggested that patients should be wakened at 6 a.m. at the earliest and should be given either tea or breakfast before being washed. The problem was to get everything done in time for the consultant's round or the start of operations. As *The Hospital* commented, the argument looked 'suspiciously like making the patients' interests subservient to those of the staff'.[3]

The question of outpatient waiting-time was given increasing attention in the twenties. The London Hospital attempted to introduce an appointment system but had later to abandon it.[4] Other hospitals such as the King George's Hospital at Ilford were more successful.[5] It was pointed out that a teaching hospital would find it more difficult to run such a system as it needed 'abundant and comprehensive clinical material'.[6] Though little action followed, at least the patient's point of view began to be expressed.[7]

Such were the important changes in attitude in which the introduction of the contributory system played a part. The patient had become 'more critical and exacting'.[8] Voluntary hospital managements began to pay closer attention to the preferences of their patients. The concept of a community service was beginning to replace that of a charity.

---

[1] ibid.

[2] King Edward's Hospital Fund, *Patients' Waking Hours in London Voluntary Hospitals*, p. 5, London, 1931

[3] *Hospital*, Vol. 27, July 1931, p. 175

[4] ibid., Vol. 26, October 1930, p. 240

[5] ibid., Vol. 27, January 1931, p. 14

[6] ibid.

[7] One patient wrote to *The Hospital* to complain about 'the long and dreary vigil', the nurses who took 'curtness to the point of incivility', the 'hard wooden forms', 'the corridors which have no windows at all' and the cake and 'unpalatable fluid at the buffet which may cost one one's place in the order of waiting'. *Hospital*, Vol. 27, February 1931, p. 44.

[8] *Hospital Gazette*, January 1928, p. 6

CHAPTER 21

Private Patients

THROUGHOUT the 1920's more well-to-do patients were admitted to nursing homes and hospitals when they were sick. As medical procedures became more complex, everyone became more conscious of the limitations of treatments provided at home. Doctors attempting to provide comprehensive care for private patients had to have access to hospital beds. Hospital work was no longer just a stepping stone to consultant practice: it became an integral part of successful private practice.

One response of the voluntary hospitals to the financial crisis of 1920 had been to increase the number of pay beds. Hospitals which had previously hesitated to combine trade with charity opened up private wards or built private wings such as the Chester Royal Infirmary and the North Lonsdale Hospital in 1921,[1] the Royal Sussex County Hospital in 1923,[2] and the Burton-on-Trent General Infirmary in 1924.[3] The charges varied from three to seven guineas per week. In general the beds were intended for those who could not afford nursing home fees. Thus the beds at the Queen Victoria Infirmary, Preston, were intended for the 'black-coated fraternity' and the 'new poor'.[4] In some hospitals the full cost was charged, in others a modest profit was earned. In some hospitals, patients with incomes above a stated limit were ineligible for admission, in others any patient could be admitted who could pay the charges. And while in some hospitals the private patient could bring in any doctor to treat him, in others the right to attend patients

---

[1] R. H. P. Orde, *The Voluntary Hospitals in Great Britain (excluding London)*, (Seventh Annual Report for the Year 1925, Jt. Council of Order of St John and British Red Cross Soc.), pp. 104 and 107, London, 1926

[2] ibid., p. 103

[3] ibid., pp. 107–8

[4] ibid., p. 105

in private beds was a monopoly of the hospital staff. By 1929 there were over 1,000 pay beds in London.[1]

The main reasons for the increase in the demand for private accommodation can be found in changes in medical techniques and in changes in social and economic conditions. The growth of contributory schemes deliberately designed to cater for private patients was beginning to play a part. The British Provident Association, as mentioned in Chapter 20,[2] had no income limit. For a charge of one guinea a year, it offered to pay up to £4 a week for a three-week stay in a hospital or nursing home, to meet consultation fees up to three guineas, and to cover the cost of radium treatment and certain other services. For a further premium, insurance could be effected to cover the cost of the surgeon's fee for major operations.[3]

In 1929 there were only 2,500 members of the British Provident Association, largely consisting of single women with relatively low incomes.[4] The Association estimated, however, that there were 2½ million middle-class and professional people in London out of a total population of 8½ million. It calculated from these figures that six to seven thousand beds were required for paying patients.

In addition to more than 1,000 private beds in London voluntary hospitals there were an increasing number of nursing homes. It is not possible from such statistics as are available to make a reliable subdivision between convalescent homes and nursing homes for 1911, but it appears that the combined total of beds in these institutions in England and Wales was about 13,000. By 1921, this total had become about 40,000, of which about 26,000 were beds in nursing homes.[5] Very few of the latter were able to offer facilities comparable with the large voluntary hospitals. In some of them conditions were as deplorable as when the first Bill for the registration of nursing homes had been rejected by Parliament some twenty years earlier.

Parliament had granted the power to register to a few local authorities, under special local Acts. The London County Council, as vigilant as ever to safeguard the morals of its popu-

---

[1] *Hospital Gazette*, February 1929, pp. 21–2
[2] See above, p. 328.
[3] *BMJ Supplement*, 15 December 1928, p. 257
[4] *Hospital Gazette*, February 1929, pp. 21–2
[5] See Vol. 2 of this study.

lace, thought that its powers to control massage establishments were still inadequate. 'There are women in several of these establishments,' it complained,

> who are improperly dressed. There are women who are known to associate with prostitutes or other bad characters. We cannot bring a charge against them. There are persons who after being registered exercise no supervision over the establishment but leave the management entirely to young women assistants. There are women who advertise their registered establishments in a certain way, namely, as English, French or Scottish masseuses, or give Christian names in order to attract people to the establishments who do not want to go there for purposes of massage. . . . Nearly all the clients are men, and we know from the way in which the girls dress and where their evenings are passed that they must spend a considerable amount of money, which, obviously, they do not receive for their occupation at massage work.[1]

A Bill to register all nursing homes was laid before the House of Commons in the spring of 1925. The Council of the BMA hastened to define its position. It was particularly worried about the question of doctors who accommodated patients in their own private residences. It thought that accommodation provided in such circumstances should be excluded from the Bill. It was pointed out that 'hundreds of doctors would be affected'.[2]

Applications to accommodate patients might be refused because the doctor was himself thought to be unsuitable or because someone he employed was unsuitable or unqualified or because the premises, equipment or staff were thought unsuitable. Doctors should be exempt from interference of this kind.

It was argued that the Bill involved 'further invasion by the State of our professional secrecy'.[3] Drastic amendment was needed. Undesirable homes should be closed down but this could be accomplished by other means. Doctors were urged to write to their MPs pressing that the Bill should be read 'on this day six months'.[4] The Bill was withdrawn, 'under promise that a committee should be formed to go into the whole question and

---

[1] quoted in *Hospital*, Vol. LXVIII, 15 May 1920, p. 179
[2] *BMJ Supplement*, 4 April 1925, p. 133
[3] ibid., 16 May 1925, p. 207
[4] ibid., 13 June 1925, p. 263

decide what, if anything, should be brought up at a later date'.[1]

In March 1926, a Select Committee was appointed:

> ... to consider and enquire into the question of the inspection and supervision of Nursing Homes, and to report what legislation, if any, is necessary or desirable for this purpose.[2]

The Society of Medical Officers told the committee that 'privately managed nursing homes form the source of constant complaints to medical officers of health all over the country'.[3] The Ministry of Health, on the other hand, said that they were not aware of any conditions which would make it advisable to interfere, by means of control or supervision, with what may be regarded as a legitimate industry.[4]

The most vigorous proponent of registration was the College of Nurses. The register of nurses, set up under the 1919 Act, had not been in existence for long. The nurses had pressed for registration to enable the public to protect itself from unqualified nurses and also to protect trained nurses from unqualified competition. The Act had not, however, prevented unregistered nurses from working as nurses. They concentrated in nursing homes where women could gain sufficient nursing experience to be able to go into private practice posing as trained nurses. Proprietors of nursing homes employing trained staff had to compete with proprietors employing untrained staff. The College of Nursing presented to the Select Committee a long list of signatures from matrons and owners of nursing homes demanding a minimum proportion of registered nurses in every home.

The College of Nursing made sure that the committee learned of the worst abuses. Its evidence described overcrowded and often insanitary buildings[5] and the extreme neglect of patients.[6] Some people who were totally unqualified were 'carrying on the nursing home as a main or subsidiary business proposition'.[7]

---

[1] ibid., 1 August 1925, pp. 54–5

[2] *Report of Select Committee on Nursing Homes (Registration)*, 1926, p. iii

[3] ibid., p. vi

[4] ibid., p. v

[5] ibid.

[6] ibid., Qs. 725–80 (quoted in Caroline Woodroffe and P. Townsend, *Nursing Homes in England & Wales, A Study of Public Responsibility*, p. 10, National Corporation for the Care of Old People, 1961)

[7] ibid., p. v

'Patients are frequently quite unaware that the uniformed individuals in charge of them are in many cases quite unqualified girls with no real training.'[1] Some homes actually combined the taking in of patients with the letting of rooms to lodgers.[2] The committee was convinced that 'abuses do exist and are sufficiently prevalent, particularly in the cheaper class of home and the home catering for senile chronic cases, to render some form of supervision and inspection essential'.[3]

The British Medical Association, on the other hand, claimed to be 'ignorant of widespread abuses'.[4] This was surprising in view of the fact that the arrangements for admission were made in most cases by general practitioners. The Association stated that it would only agree to registration if the registering authorities were to delegate their powers to a committee including nurses and doctors, if nursing homes run by doctors were to be exempt from inspection and if no medical records in nursing homes could be inspected by the representative of any 'lay body'.[5]

The committee met the wishes of the doctors only on the last point. And though it recommended registration and inspection it regarded this only as a partial and temporary expedient. The real problem was the 'senile and chronic sick' among the class of persons who did not desire to incur the stigma of a Poor Law institution.[6] For this group the committee recommended 'the provision of proper paying accommodation by the local authorities'.

In 1927, the Nursing Homes Registration Act was passed. Homes had to be run by a 'fit' person in 'fit' premises and have some qualified person on the staff. In the same year the BMA decided to formulate a middle class hospital policy,[7] and the King's Fund set up a committee to inquire into the question of hospital pay beds.[8] The question which needed to be solved was the same as had been raised fifty years earlier: was development for paying patients to be in separate hospitals or attached to the existing voluntary hospitals?

[1] ibid., p. xiii
[2] ibid., p. v
[3] ibid., p. ix
[4] ibid., p. v
[5] ibid., p. vi
[6] ibid., p. ix
[7] *BMJ Supplement*, 30 July 1927, p. 74
[8] ibid., 22 October 1927, p. 159

More information was collected on the quality of nursing homes. It was estimated that there were some three or four thousand nursing home beds in London compared to about a thousand pay beds in the voluntary hospitals. One-third of the former had no operating theatre; less than a quarter were served by a lift. In nearly every case there was no X-ray apparatus, no laboratory and no resident doctor.[1] Nursing homes were grossly inadequate. Either they had to be expanded into large paying hospitals, or the voluntary hospitals had to expand to serve the class now using nursing homes.

The development of efficient pay hospitals in a situation where local authorities were already employing consultant staff could offer a dangerous challenge to the position of the voluntary hospitals. If the Poor Law hospitals were placed under the major authorities

> ... a voluntary hospital might find itself between a large municipal hospital, with well paid consultants and residents and a large pay hospital, providing institutional treatment for all those who can afford more than maintenance. Those that are friendly to the voluntary system could not view such a contingency without misgiving.[2]

The poor would be well cared for in the municipal hospital and supporters of the voluntary hospitals 'harassed by increasing taxation' would feel relieved of further responsibility for their care 'while by their failure to provide within their walls for those who can afford to pay for treatment, they would have lost a golden opportunity of attaching subscribers to their fortunes by new and more personal bonds'.[3]

The position of the teaching hospitals in particular depended upon their power to attract 'picked men to their staff'. The Dean of St Mary's Medical School found that this power might be

> ... impaired if these men can acquire the experience in municipal and paying hospitals without the long hours and years of unremunerative, or at any rate not directly remunerative, toil. ...

---

[1] ibid., 17 March 1928, p. 85, C. M. Wilson, 'Pay Beds and the Future of the Voluntary Hospitals'. Dr Wilson, later Lord Moran, was Dean of the Medical School at St Mary's Hospital.

[2] ibid.

[3] ibid.

It is ... of some importance to the future of medicine that consulting physicians and surgeons should continue to look to the teaching hospitals as the direct avenues to practice. Plainly the growth of large paying hospitals, altogether independent of the teaching hospitals, with the opportunities they offer of acquiring practice without the intervention of the general practitioner, together with the creation of the municipal hospitals paying considerable salaries to their consultants, offer an alternative to the method by which consulting practice has hitherto been built up . . . an alternative that must be jealously scrutinized if the standards of practice are to be preserved. . . .[1]

There were, however, many other equally difficult problems which made it difficult for voluntary hospitals to increase their pay beds. There were patients treated free by medical staffs, patients for whom some percentage of payments received by the hospital were paid into a staff fund, and patients whom the medical staff charged what they thought appropriate. Practices varied from one hospital to another and medical opinion was by no means unanimous on the principles which ought to be applied.

Moreover, general practitioners might not send patients to pay beds if they were not allowed to play their part in treatment. Many hospitals were unwilling to admit general practitioners. The hospital staffs took the view that additional years of study were needed to acquire the standards of hospital practice. If even a few general practitioners were allowed to attend patients in pay wards, they would come to

. . . occupy in the eyes of the public much the same position as that of the medical consultant. Presently, without the additional years of study and without the unproductive hours in the outpatient department they will reap the same advantages as the consulting staff. This is a state of affairs which is inequitable, and if it came to pass it would not level up but level down the whole standard of medical treatment.[2]

The BMA sent out a questionnaire to 813 voluntary hospitals to ascertain the facts about pay beds.[3] About 80 per cent of them sent replies; all the provincial teaching hospitals responded but

[1] ibid., pp. 85-6
[2] ibid., p. 87
[3] ibid., 19 April 1930, p. 141

only eight of the twelve London teaching hospitals sent a reply. While 60 per cent of the small provincial hospitals admitted private patients, there were private beds in only a quarter of the remainder. Three-quarters of the hospitals replying had restricted staffs. Only in the small hospitals were general practitioners allowed to treat private patients. Doctors were remunerated for treating public ward patients in less than half these hospitals and the practice was much more common in the provinces than in London.

In the 169 unrestricted staff hospitals, in no case was the financial recognition of the practitioners' services based upon a scale of fees agreed with the Board of Management whether the patients were treated in (a) private wards, (b) private rooms or cubicles, or (c) special paying blocks or annexes. Whatever financial recognition there was took the form of arrangements between practitioner and patient. This obtained (a) in 50% of the hospitals where the patients were treated in private wards (81 hospitals); (b) in some 70% where the patients were treated in private rooms or cubicles (115 hospitals); and (c) in only 4 hospitals where the patients were treated in special paying blocks or annexes. ... Similarly, in the 479 restricted staff hospitals whatever financial arrangement there was took the form of arrangements between practitioner and patient. This obtained (a) in some 35% where patients were treated in private wards (169 hospitals); (b) in 43% (206 hospitals) where patients were treated in private rooms or cubicles, and (c) in 6% (27 hospitals) where patients were treated in special paying blocks or annexes.[1]

The BMA settled its policy for the middle classes at the 1929 representative meeting. The Council reported that patients were being admitted to pay beds in voluntary hospitals who could well pay for private nursing home treatment under the care of private doctors.[2] Secondly, the Council acknowledged the fact that the governing bodies of many hospitals wanted patients to be treated only by members of their staff[3] and this privileged position could not be taken away from them. On the other hand there was a strong feeling that the general practitioner should 'be in closer touch with and have a larger share in the treatment

[1] ibid.
[2] ibid., 20 April 1929, p. 135
[3] ibid.

of his private patients when they were in a hospital of any class'.[1] It was therefore decided to try and bring in the general practitioner *as well as* the consultant. Thus in hospitals with consultant staff which did not allow general practitioners to treat their own patients, it was resolved that 'the patient should be under the responsible care of a member of the visiting staff in association with the private practitioner of the patient who should have free access to the patient and have such share of responsibility and treatment of the patient as may be agreed upon between the member of the visiting staff and the private practitioner'.[2] Thus the private patient would obtain greater continuity of care. The cost of this arrangement, however, would be two bills instead of one.

Thus the BMA reached a compromise on the question of pay beds in voluntary hospitals. But this was only one leg of its middle-class hospital policy. Sir Richard Luce, who had taken over from Mr Bishop Harman as Chairman of the Hospitals sub-committee, argued that 'the provision of separate institutions for pay beds would go a long way to solve the difficulty which at present existed in that private practitioners were, generally speaking, excluded from the pay beds at hospitals'.[3] He argued that patients should have free choice of doctor subject to proof of special skills on the part of the general practitioner where these particular skills were needed.[4] The Council endorsed the policy and urged the King's Fund

> ... to encourage the establishment of institutions of sufficient size for paying patients to permit of the patients therein deriving the benefits to be obtained from a large and efficiently administered hospital with ancillary services, in which they could remain under the medical charge of their own practitioner with free choice of consultant.[5]

The policy was endorsed at the 1929 representative meeting.[6]

Six months later, it was reported that the foundation stone of such a hospital had been laid by the Duchess of Atholl. The

[1] ibid., 27 July 1929, p. 40
[2] ibid., 27 July 1929, p. 43
[3] ibid., 22 December 1928, pp. 266–7
[4] ibid.
[5] ibid.
[6] ibid., 27 July 1929, pp. 46–7

London Clinic and Nursing Home was to provide accommodation for 'about 200 patients, each in a separate room, and the
latest equipment for the treatment of any kind of complaint'.[1]
The project was to cost about £300,000. It was laid down that
any registered practitioner could use the Home for his patients,
treating them himself or calling in the services of any consultant.
The use of the operating theatre was, however, reserved for
surgeons on the staffs of recognized hospitals.[2] Two years later
it was announced that a group of London business men had
been down to Brighton to select a site on the seafront for a
100-bedded nursing home which was to cost £250,000.[3] The
project was, however, never carried out.

The compromise reached over the question of pay beds in
the voluntary hospitals did not satisfy all the general practitioners. There were some who tried to widen their right to
'closed list' voluntary hospitals at the 1930 representative
meeting. According to Dr Fothergill it was

> . . . a fly-blown bogey – still used to frighten old women on the
> governing body of hospitals – that the general practitioner, if
> admitted to use the hospitals, will be found running about with
> rusty scalpels and distorted forceps, crying out 'Who can I try my
> skill on?'[4]

It was another bogey that the admission of general practitioners
to hospitals would 'result, in a town with, say, 150 general
practitioners, in probably 130 clamouring next morning at the
portals'.[5] At a hospital at Ilford, where the board of management
had decided to allow general practitioners to be appointed as
assistants in certain departments, the medical committee turned
down the recommendation. One member told the board that
the hospital would become 'a laughing stock' if such appointments were made.[6] Attention was drawn to the invidious position
facing doctors when they had to hand over their cases 'to another
man who might be a rival, or not on friendly terms'.[7]

[1] *Hospital*, Vol. 26, January 1930, p. 4
[2] ibid., Vol. 29, January 1933, pp. 23–4
[3] ibid., Vol. 28, May 1932, p. 116
[4] *BMJ Supplement*, 5 July 1930, p. 5
[5] ibid.
[6] ibid.
[7] ibid., 26 July 1930, p. 54

The Council managed to beat off the extremists and the hospital policy was agreed. It was decided to organize a campaign of meetings and conferences throughout the country among the visiting staff of hospitals to forward the policy.[1] The Association had gone as far as it could to ensure that general practitioners gained a share of the medical fees when private patients were admitted to hospital.

In this same year, 1930, the BMA published its *Proposals for a General Medical Service for the Nation*. Despite its imposing title, it was far from being a revolutionary document in the sense in which the adjective can be applied to the Dawson Report or the reports of the Labour Party. As the preface made clear, it was 'a record of proposals which the Association is making as to the way in which the medical services of the nation should develop'.[2] The document was little more than an attempt to string together into a coherent, if not a consistent, whole the different streams of policy which the Association had gradually developed over thirty years of pressure on public and private authorities. The Association thought its scheme had 'the advantage which a great many schemes, from time to time presented to the public, conspicuously lack, namely, that it is in accordance with the beliefs and traditions of the medical profession and would have its whole-hearted support'.[3]

Essentially the policy expressed the Association's approval of the principle of the National Health Insurance Scheme. It argued for the extension of the scheme to cover the dependants of insured persons and for persons using the Poor Law domiciliary services. It was hoped that most of the latter could be included under some system of local contract, and thus gain the advantage of a service without the intervention of a third party. 'The Association pleads on behalf of the poorer sections of the community that they should have the same consideration in the matter as is demanded as a matter of course by the more wealthy sections of the community.'[4] The insurance scheme itself was to be extended to include maternity services and consultant services, and the optional additional benefits under the existing

[1] ibid., 22 November 1930, p. 230
[2] *BMA, Proposals for a General Medical Service for the Nation*, p. 2, London, 1929
[3] ibid., p. 8
[4] ibid., pp. 17-18

scheme were to be made statutory. In general there was to be an
income limit for membership of the scheme of £250 per annum.

The Association did not recommend that hospital treatment
should be available as a benefit to insured persons. Such a
proposal was held to be impracticable, first because of the cost,
secondly because of the impossibility of guaranteeing that enough
accommodation would be available and thirdly as 'it would be
inequitable to exact contributions from a large number of
citizens if the benefits of the institutions were available (as they
must necessarily be on medical and humanitarian grounds) for
those who had not contributed'.[1] It was not suggested that the
control of the voluntary hospitals should be altered in any way
nor that free hospital services should be provided. A growth of
voluntary pre-payment schemes was, however, anticipated,[2]
and it was pointed out that most of them would require radical
alteration 'because at present few make provision for payment
for the medical treatment received'.[3]

There were to be three classes of hospital patients – those who
paid directly, those who insured themselves and 'those for whom
the community must provide. To none of these sections of the
public can the medical staff be expected to give their services
as a charity, whether in a voluntary or council hospital. The
staffs must be paid in both.'[4] It was argued that if doctors were
paid for their hospital work, fees charged by these doctors for
their other work would tend to fall.[5]

In addition to the existing large hospitals, there were to be
many more cottage hospitals (called Home Hospitals) to keep
the doctor, after qualification, in close touch with the hospital.
It was 'a great loss to the profession and the community' that the
majority of doctors in general practice rarely got a chance of
'partaking in the educational experience of hospital work'.[6]
Some of the accommodation for this purpose was to be provided
by opening the doors of more of the hospitals to all local practitioners, thus giving every doctor the opportunity to 'put under
hospital conditions such of his cases as he could treat better if

[1] ibid., p. 27
[2] ibid., pp. 26–7
[3] ibid., p. 28
[4] ibid., pp. 33–4
[5] ibid.
[6] ibid.

they were in a hospital'.[1] Other home hospital units were to be provided in separate blocks or annexes of existing hospitals. The *maintenance* costs of these patients were to be paid by the patients themselves – either directly or by pre-insurance. The bills of those who could not pay should be met by the public authorities. In every case there should be separate payments for medical treatment.

All the services were to pivot round the family doctor. He would have links with every hospital in his area and with every medical service. This, said the report, would achieve 'complete co-ordination of the whole medical service for the community'.[2] The report contributed no new thoughts on the relationship between voluntary and council hospitals. The problems of rationalizing hospital provision which had worried the Lords Committee of 1892, the Royal Commission of 1909, the Dawson Committee and the Labour Party were totally ignored.

The profession was advocating a scheme which gave full payment to doctors for all services but preserved their position as independent entrepreneurs responsible only to their professional code of honour. One great advantage claimed for the National Health Insurance system was that the discipline of the doctors had been increasingly entrusted to the profession itself.[3] There was no reason 'why any third party should come between the patient and his medical adviser'.[4] The BMA did not, however, recommend the tight hierarchy of professional control to be found in many religious organizations.

The profession wanted also to preserve the voluntary hospitals. The reason for this was stated by Sir Richard Luce some years earlier.

> State bureaucratic control kills freedom and initiative, damps scientific ardour and is fatal to medical advance . . . is extravagant medicine . . . has no incentive to economy and creates an army of officials . . . would remove that healthy rivalry and competition between individual hospitals which does so much to maintain their standard of efficiency and progress . . . would deprive the nation of that object of sympathetic sentiment and altruistic service

[1] ibid., p. 29
[2] ibid., p. 40
[3] ibid., p. 18
[4] ibid.

which the hospitals afford them to-day, and the patients the advantages which that sympathy and service brings them.[1]

The profession expected the voluntary hospitals to give full remuneration to medical staffs out of payments from public grants and contributory schemes while exercising no more supervision over their work than when they had been working as totally unpaid volunteers. The profession was demanding the best of both worlds. It was to continue to demand it with only one brief intermission for the next twenty years.

[1] *BMJ Supplement,* 10 March 1928, p. 78

CHAPTER 22

Poor Law Reform

A FTER the demise of the Miscellaneous Provisions Bill at the end of 1920, no new attempt was made to implement the main recommendations of the Royal Commission of 1909 and of the Maclean Committee of 1917. Economy continued to be the watchword of the Government. Ministers of Health were appointed and replaced in remarkably quick succession.[1] The lack of resolute leadership from the centre did not, however, inhibit all action from the numerous public authorities responsible for health services.

Provisions for maternal and child health were stimulated by the availability of a 50 per cent grant for approved expenditure under the legislation passed in 1918. The value of maternity hospitals became increasingly recognized. On 1 July 1920 there were 88 maternity homes with 1,145 beds recorded by the department. These figures excluded beds in Poor Law institutions and general hospitals.[2] By the end of December 2,561 beds in 158 institutions had been recognized for grant purposes. About half of these were run by local authorities and half by voluntary bodies.[3] Many wards in isolation hospitals were also being made available for maternity purposes. Grant aided beds were originally intended for women requiring hospitalization for medical or social reasons but the use of the homes extended to admit women who preferred institutional confinement.[4]

Accommodation for tuberculosis patients also increased greatly. In 1911 there had been about 1,300 beds in public sanatoria and another 4,200 in private and voluntary institutions.

[1] In one period of two months there were no less than 4 different Ministers of Health, as pointed out in *Hospital*, Vol. 2, October 1923, p. 355.

[2] *Third Annual Report Ministry of Health 1921–2*, Cmd 1713, p. 16, HMSO, 1922

[3] *Eleventh Annual Report Ministry of Health 1929–30*, Cmd 3667, p. 68, HMSO, 1930

[4] Newsholme, Vol. III, p. 157

By 1929 there were 22,500 beds excluding those in voluntary *general* hospitals; about 15,000 of these beds were provided by local authorities.[1] By the end of 1934 there was a total of 28,900 beds.[2] Increasing stress had been laid on early treatment. In November 1921, local authorities were reminded not to allow their system of charges to deter persons who were in need of treatment. In March 1924, local authorities were told not to charge unless they were satisfied that the patient could provide proper and adequate maintenance for himself and his family.[3]

While these two services (maternity and tuberculosis) which were aided by the Exchequer on a percentage grant basis developed rapidly in the twenties, they were not the only hospital services provided by local authorities to make progress. The authorities which had 'lent' institutions to the armed forces found, when they were returned to them, that considerable improvements had been made. Facilities thought adequate for the sick poor had been found to be unsatisfactory for the use of wounded servicemen. Valuable additions were made to the accommodation and equipment and 'greatly improved facilities for treatment became available'.[4]

The total accommodation for the sick in public institutions increased from about 154,000 beds in 1911 to 172,000 beds in 1921.[5] The number of beds in separate Poor Law infirmaries decreased slightly by about 3,000 between these years: the major increases were in specialized institutions. There were about 10,000 more beds for general cases of infectious disease and about 5,000 more beds for tuberculosis cases. There was little overall change in the number of chronic and unclassified beds. Nevertheless the general trend towards better classification was continuing as far as was possible within the existing legislative framework. Thus at Bristol acute cases were concentrated in one of the three institutions, leaving one institution for adult mental cases and another for the aged, infirm and able-bodied.[6] A concentrated unit for 100 venereal disease cases was established at one

[1] ibid., p. 226
[2] *Sixteenth Annual Report Ministry of Health 1934–5*, Cmd 4978, p. 8, HMSO, 1935
[3] *Fifth Annual Report Ministry of Health 1923–4*, Cmd 2218, pp. 2–3, HMSO, 1924
[4] *Lancet*, 28 January 1922, p. 188
[5] See Vol. 2 of this study.
[6] *Second Annual Report Ministry of Health 1920–1*

Manchester infirmary.[1] And certain Unions went so far as to pool their institutions to secure better classification and increased specialization. This happened both in the West Riding of Yorkshire and in Lancashire.[2] Orders were issued to various infirmaries to 'place the medical rather than the lay officers of the Guardians in charge of the entire administration of the institution'.[3] By all these means, more institutions catering for the sick came under professional control. The Ministry was, however, well aware that 'adequate specialization' within the area of a single Union was 'rarely possible'.[4]

In the best separate infirmaries, a staff of consultants began to be employed on a part-time basis. By the end of March 1921, there were ten Metropolitan infirmaries and seven institutions under the Metropolitan Asylums' Board which employed consultants. A 'visiting staff' was also to be found in numerous infirmaries in the provinces.[5] The Ministry of Health had, however, to report that the system had not yet won 'the entire confidence of certain of the institutional medical officers'.[6] Arrangements were also made for the instruction of medical students 'under more detailed safeguards'.[7] This arrangement often followed the introduction of consultants. Clinical demonstrations could only be given with the consent of the patient which was 'usually found to be readily accorded'.[8]

By 1928 there were 93 separately administered Poor Law institutions, of which at least 19 were used solely for mental cases. The total number of 'inmates' in all these institutions on 11 February 1928 was 35,864 and there were 5,125 vacant beds.[9] The Ministry noted 'an increasing willingness on the part of patients needing surgical or medical care in an institution to look to the nature of the treatment open to them rather than

[1] ibid.
[2] *Lancet*, 28 January 1922, p. 188
[3] *Second Annual Report Ministry of Health*, p. 131
[4] ibid., p. 131
[5] *Lancet*, 28 January 1922, p. 188
[6] *Second Annual Report Ministry of Health*, pp. 129-30
[7] ibid.
[8] ibid.
[9] *Ninth Annual Report Ministry of Health 1927-8*, Cmd 3185, p. 165, HMSO, 1928. There were 60 infirmaries which were administered 'under separate regulations' and 33 others which were 'separately administered' though not 'under separate regulations'.

the ownership of the institution in which it is given'.[1] Guardians
in urban areas found themselves 'more and more catering for
patients who had formerly been treated at home or in the
voluntary hospitals'.[2]

Thus the number of patients in local authority and Poor Law
accommodation increased as the facilities for treatment were
extended or improved. Guardians were, however, more willing
to grant outdoor relief than before the First World War – even
to the able-bodied: the latter were usually subjected to a labour
test rather than a workhouse test;[3] by the end of the twenties
such a test had become 'practically obsolete'.[4] The sick were also
able to obtain outdoor relief and the services of the district
medical officer in minor illnesses.

There was no change in the domiciliary services under the
Poor Law. There were in 1930 over 3,400 district medical
officers: the post was nearly always held by a part-time practitioner who was paid a salary varying from a few pounds to
£100 or more.[5] The post carried a pension and security of
tenure: the District Medical Officer could only be removed
from office by the Ministry of Health after an inquiry. Some
Guardians used whole-time officers to do this work. The work
was planned on the same basis as had been suggested by a
medical superintendent to the Royal Commission of 1909.[6] A
medical officer based on the infirmary was made responsible
for the care of the sick in their own homes. This practice, which
was to be found in several London Unions and in Cardiff, was
strongly opposed by the British Medical Association which was
keen to avoid the precedent of salaried doctors in the general
practitioner services.[7] It was thus hard to find doctors willing
to take on this work.[8]

While thirty years earlier, Guardians had put pressure on the
sick poor to enter the institution by inadequate levels of outdoor
relief, in the twenties the task of the DMO was regarded by

---

[1] *Eighth Annual Report Ministry of Health 1926–7*, Cmd 2938, p. xxii,
HMSO, 1927
[2] ibid.
[3] *Ninth Annual Report Ministry of Health*, p. 145
[4] *Eleventh Annual Report Ministry of Health*, p. 185
[5] Newsholme, Vol. III, pp. 93–5
[6] See Chapter 13, p. 207–8
[7] Newsholme, Vol. III, pp. 93–5. See also *BMJ*, 24 July 1920, pp. 140–41.
[8] N. Wilson, *Public Health Services*, pp. 115–17, Glasgow, 1938

many Unions as being to protect the infirmary against the admission of patients who could satisfactorily be treated at home.[1] There were, however, some Guardians in urban areas who allowed general practitioners to send their patients to the infirmary without any examination by the staff of the Poor Law services until the patient arrived. The system led to complaints by medical superintendents of the 'abuse' of the facilities they were offering. They said that their wards were overcrowded with dying patients and patients who would have been much better treated at home and that patients were being sent without proper notification of the treatment they had received or with seriously incorrect diagnoses.[2] They were concerned at 'the appalling inefficiency of some panel doctors in a poor locality'.[3] Other Guardians insisted that all patients had to be examined by an infirmary assistant medical officer before they were admitted.[4]

Though many infirmaries were providing higher standards of care and although procedures for admission were simplified in some cases, the stigma of the Poor Law still remained. It was still necessary for every patient to obtain an admission order signed by the relieving officer. As the *Hospital Gazette* remarked in 1928, people had a natural 'distaste for approaching this official: whose very designation smacks of the parochial, the patronizing, the humiliating.'[5]

The admission of private paying patients to Poor Law infirmaries created further difficulties and anomalies. An old age pensioner was admitted to a Barnet infirmary as a private patient with the cost borne by his relatives. The pension was taken away as the pensioner was 'an inmate of a Poor Law institution'.[6] A year later a well-to-do Guardian who also entered a Poor Law institution as a private patient found himself 'stripped of his office and his vote' on the board.[7] *The Hospital* concluded that there was 'no solution but for the Ministry, the Guardians, the electorate and public opinion to press unremit-

[1] Newsholme, Vol. III, pp. 94–5
[2] ibid., pp. 103–5
[3] ibid., p. 105
[4] ibid., p. 104
[5] *Hospital Gazette*, November 1928, p. 223
[6] *Hospital*, Vol. 2, October 1922, p. 377
[7] ibid., October 1923, p. 377

tingly for the alteration of the law'.[1] It was resolved at a conference of Poor Law Guardians that 'the disqualifications and
disabilities to which paying patients in voluntary hospitals are
not subject should no longer continue to afflict paying patients
in Poor Law infirmaries'.[2] The British Medical Association in its
turn protested that the system 'tended to operate against the
utilization of Poor Law beds for suitable private persons'.[3]

Although some infirmaries were attracting patients of the
voluntary hospital class and some had private wards which
well-to-do Guardians were prepared to use themselves, much
infirmary accommodation was of a low standard. Some of the
London infirmaries were reported in 1927 to be 'old and
inconvenient'. Space was 'strictly limited by a circumscribed
site or existing buildings'.[4]

Quite apart from the 32,567 inmates of separate infirmaries,
there were still in February 1928 no less than 35,864 sick inmates
in general mixed workhouses.[5] In East Anglia some Poor Law
buildings which had been constructed before 1834 were still
in use. It was held to be out of the question for financial reasons
to destroy and rebuild these old country workhouses.[6] Equally
old buildings were to be found in the West of England where
many Guardians were unwilling to incur expenditure to improve the conditions of the inmates.[7] It was reported in 1927
that:

... in 25 institutions there is still no fully trained nurse in charge of
the sick, and in 10 institutions there is normally no nurse or
attendant on night duty in the sick wards. . . . Such obvious
desiderata have been refused as a sufficiency of baths, the appointment of a paid attendant to take charge of the infants, or the
substitution of available electric light for dangerous oil lamps in
mental wards.[8]

The problem of finding nursing staff for the mixed institution
remained unsolved and there was also the problem of recruiting

[1] ibid., November 1923, p. 406
[2] ibid., Vol. 3, April 1924, p. 108
[3] *BMJ Supplement*, 12 April 1924, p. 161
[4] *Eighth Annual Report Ministry of Health*, p. 235
[5] *Ninth Annual Report Ministry of Health*, p. 164
[6] *Eighth Annual Report Ministry of Health*, p. 235
[7] ibid., p. 240
[8] ibid.

suitable medical staff. *The Hospital* advised doctors to beware of the 'non-separated infirmary' under the administration of a workhouse master.[1]

The best use was not made of the accommodation for the sick in both the Poor Law and voluntary hospital sectors. On neither side was 'the acid test applied – what is best for the patient'.[2] Owing to reluctance to enter a Poor Law institution, patients in London waited months to enter a voluntary hospital even though accommodation with appropriate facilities was available in the Poor Law sector. While voluntary hospitals refused chronic patients or referred them to the Poor Law hospitals, it was rare for a voluntary hospital to be offered a patient from a Poor Law institution even in cases where the voluntary hospital had the better facilities for meeting the patient's needs. The doctors in the Poor Law institution did not wish to restrict their work to elementary medicine and surgery and the doctors in the voluntary hospitals had 'quite sufficient material already at hand to keep their beds filled'.[3]

The case for the reform of the Poor Law was as strong as it had ever been, and at the end of 1924, Lord George Hamilton wrote to *The Times*, reminding readers of the recommendations of his Royal Commission which had reported fifteen years earlier.[4] In the following year plans were being prepared by the Ministry. A Royal Commission on Local Government was set up in 1923 and given wider terms of reference in 1926. The reform contemplated was not just the modest change attempted five years earlier. The plan was for a major piece of legislation altering the whole finance and functions of all levels of local government. A Minister had arrived who intended to grasp the nettle. It was Mr Neville Chamberlain.

The ground was carefully prepared. Chamberlain went and saw local government for himself,[5] and in January 1926 sent provisional proposals for Poor Law reform to Boards of Guardians.[6] He then discussed his ideas with all the representative associations of local bodies.[7] He was particularly anxious to

[1] *Hospital*, Vol. LXVIII, 4 September 1920, p. 571
[2] *Hospital Gazette*, November 1928, pp. 223–4
[3] ibid.
[4] *Hospital*, Vol. 3, December 1924, p. 362
[5] K. Feiling, *The Life of Neville Chamberlain*, pp. 135–6, London, 1946
[6] *Eighth Annual Report Ministry of Health*, pp. xxii–xxiii
[7] Feiling, p. 138

substitute block grants for percentage grants 'which in his view
forced the State to contribute automatically to local expenditure,
good or bad, and consequently, in self-defence, to intervene
overmuch in detail'.[1] Revised proposals were published in June
1927,[2] and the following months were occupied with disagree-
ments with his Ministerial colleagues. Winston Churchill made
derating a condition for his support of Chamberlain's proposals.[3]
The Prime Minister, Stanley Baldwin, was continually 'getting
cold feet', harping 'continually on the danger of alienating our
supporters in the rural districts'.[4]

Chamberlain was well aware that the transfer of the public
hospitals to the major authorities would lead not only to further
improvements in the standards of these services but to greater
use by persons far above the pauper class. With the removal of
the last vestiges of the stigma of the Poor Law, the public hospitals
would inevitably challenge the position of the voluntary
hospitals. How would it be possible to delineate the functions of
the two sectors? How would it be possible to co-ordinate them?
Early in 1928 the Minister asked the views of the BMA on these
questions. A sub-committee was appointed which came to the
conclusion that hospitals in each area should be grouped round a
parent or primary hospital which would 'generally be one of the
bigger voluntary general hospitals'.[5] Where a voluntary hospital
already had a leading position, this position should be maintained. Possibly a central bureau for co-ordinating the distribution of cases was required.[6]

The sub-committee thought that voluntary hospital staffs
would be able to undertake responsibility for cases in public
hospitals. But it stressed that this work must be paid for either
by a fixed salary or an honorarium for definite services and
responsibilities. The Association insisted that this visiting staff
should be given direct access to the governing body of the
hospital.[7]

When the report of the sub-committee came up for ratification
at the 1928 representative meeting, it was not approved

[1] ibid.
[2] *Eighth Annual Report Ministry of Health*, p. xxiii
[3] Feiling, pp. 144–5
[4] ibid.
[5] *BMJ Supplement*, 25 February 1928, p. 61
[6] ibid., p. 62
[7] ibid.

unanimously. One speaker (Mr E. W. D. Masterman) said that the public authority would never accept a voluntary hospital as a base hospital. It was 'a consultants' scheme, pure and simple', to make the public hospitals into 'a kind of annexe to the voluntary hospitals'.[1] Some speakers protested that the right persons to care for the patients in the public hospitals were the local general practitioners.

Despite these objections the draft statement was approved by a large majority and forwarded to the Minister. It was hardly a helpful document. It was far from clear how the Minister was to secure the continued supremacy of the voluntary hospitals upon which the plan depended. Nor was it likely that a Minister who believed in the maximum autonomy for local government would wish to check at birth the development of the municipal hospitals which he had decided to create.

Not until November 1928 did Chamberlain present his Bill to the House of Commons, a month after the recommendations of the Royal Commission on Local Government were published.[2] The functions of the Boards of Guardians were to be handed over to the major authorities and the duties of the Metropolitan Asylums' Board were to be handed over to the London County Council. The new health authorities were not, however, required to treat all the sick outside the ambit of the Poor Law. They were free to take what action they thought fit. Even in hospitals run under the health committee it was the duty of the local authority to recover from an inpatient such part of the cost of maintenance as the inmate could afford: the only exception to this rule was in the case of infectious diseases (including tuberculosis). In future, there were to be no percentage grants for health services. Instead, a new block grant would assist the authorities to provide these services. If a minimum standard of service were not attained, the block grant would be withheld in whole or in part.

In presenting these proposals, Chamberlain stressed the present overlapping functions of local authorities,[3] and reminded the House that the transfer of responsibility to the major authorities was no new suggestion. It had been advocated not

---

[1] ibid., 4 August 1928, p. 78
[2] *Second Report of the Royal Commission on Local Government*, Cmd 343, HMSO, 1928
[3] *Hansard* (H of C), Vol. 223, 26 November 1928, col. 71

only by the Maclean Committee of 1917 but by Joseph Chamberlain in 1888.[1] 'The whole trend . . . in modern medicine,' he pointed out, 'is towards . . . treatment . . . in institutions.' The Bill was creating 'one single health authority in each area whose duty and function it will be to survey the whole institutional needs of that area'.[2] It would be the duty of that authority to decide which institutions remained under the Poor Law and which came under other committees of the council. He was not prepared to compel all the sick to be taken out of the Poor Law, for two reasons. First, 'local authorities take the strongest exception to having inserted in an Act of Parliament not merely what they ought to do, but also how they are to do it'.[3] Secondly, 'in many cases the councils have not sufficient institutions to be able to break up the Poor Law'.[4] The function of the Poor Law could be exercised by a public assistance committee of which one-third of the committee members could be co-opted.[5]

Chamberlain explained at length his financial proposals. Central government money would have to be spent on these services, but it would be 'the apotheosis of bureaucracy' to place them in the hands of central government. He did not favour 'the creation of a new horde of officials from one end of the country to another'.[6] Nor was he prepared to allow the continuation of percentage grants which would mean the perpetuation of the circumstances which had led to some areas being so much better off than others.[7] He argued that the block grant system which he was proposing would make it possible to 'withdraw all those irritating examinations of small details' and give local authorities 'that independence and initiative which I think they value above all things'.[8] He stressed that the Minister was to have the power, 'such as he has never had before, to take away the grant, or that portion of the grant which he may think right, from any local authority which is not keeping up this service to an adequate extent'.[9]

[1] ibid., col. 72
[2] ibid., col. 74
[3] ibid., col. 75
[4] ibid.
[5] ibid., col. 76
[6] ibid., col. 92
[7] ibid., cols. 93–4
[8] ibid., col. 105
[9] ibid., col. 29

The Labour Party opposed the Bill with a reasoned amendment arguing that

> . . . whilst amending the Law relating to poor relief, [it] perpetuates the evils of the Poor Law system and extends the vicious practice of unrepresentative persons being nominated to membership of elected bodies, makes no provision for the prevention of destitution, fails to make unemployment a national responsibility, and will not appreciably relieve the financial position of necessitous areas; will arrest the normal and steady development of local health services by the establishment of fixed block grants from the Exchequer and the imposition of a charge for treatment in hospitals, especially maternity hospitals, a proposal calculated to increase the already high mortality amongst mothers; inaugurates a system of rating relief that will be unfair in its incidence; and, by failing adequately to reimburse local authorities for loss of revenue will add to the burdens of shopkeepers, householders and other ratepayers.[1]

The Labour Party opposed co-option because it feared that the system made it possible for reactionary Guardians to continue to work in Poor Law administration.[2] And in general it was argued – particularly by Lansbury – that local authorities should be compelled, not just enabled, to take the hospitals out of the Poor Law.[3] But the principal opposition was concentrated on two key issues: the block grant and the formal requirement that patients should be required to pay where they were able to do so.

The block grant was dubbed by Greenwood 'a Treasury device for saving the money of the taxpayer'.[4] A grant fixed in advance for five years was certain to impede the development of the health services.[5] The maternity services which had previously enjoyed a percentage grant were said to be certain to suffer most. Sidney Webb was able to quote the report of the Chief Medical Officer (Sir George Newman) with considerable effect. 'There can be no doubt that the percentage Exchequer grants in aid of health have been of the highest possible

[1] ibid., col. 107
[2] ibid., col. 118 (Mr Greenwood)
[3] ibid., 17 December 1928, col. 2649
[4] ibid., 26 November 1928, col. 114
[5] ibid., col. 115

value . . . in getting special medical services in operation and in guiding their direction.'[1]

It was argued that the means test system was going to be fastened more securely on local government. The energies of the public health services and medical officers of health would be directed 'from their right job to the job of debt collector'. Expectant mothers and cancer patients had as much need for free treatment as cases of infectious disease.[2] The immoral man who contracted 'a foul loathsome disease' would now get free treatment while the virtuous woman would be forced by the courts to pay for her confinement.[3] Webb suggested that the reason why the Minister favoured charges was to protect the voluntary hospitals: the public hospitals would be so good that if they were free no one would go to the voluntary hospitals.[4]

The Government pushed its Bill through the Commons. In the House of Lords an amendment was accepted as a result of pressure from the British Medical Association. The doctors were in favour of the main principle of unified public services[5] but feared that the local authorities would be inefficient and bureaucratic hospital managers.[6] They wanted hospital committees on to which medical practitioners and suitably experienced lay persons would be co-opted. The Government were not prepared to go as far as this but they did concede that local authorities, when proposing schemes for hospital accommodation, should be required to consult a committee or such other body as they consider to represent both the governing bodies and the medical and surgical staffs of the voluntary hospitals.

This amendment was greeted with scorn when it was debated in the House of Commons. 'Has the Conservative Party now turned Syndicalist,' asked Arthur Greenwood, '. . . that public authorities have to call into consultation, whether they like it or not, the employees of the voluntary hospitals? . . . It looks suspicious to me, and it seems to me that a body like the BMA will oppose any arrangements which do not harmonize with their own professional interest.'[7]

[1] ibid., col. 453
[2] ibid.
[3] ibid., cols. 462–3
[4] ibid., 28 November 1928, col. 462
[5] ibid., 26 November 1928, col. 190
[6] *BMJ Supplement*, 20 April 1929, p. 117
[7] *Hansard* (H of C), Vol. 226, 22 March 1929, cols. 1990–1

Despite the opposition of the Labour Party, the Local Government Act reached the statute book shortly before the 1929 General Election. And it fell upon the shoulders of the second Labour Government to implement the new legislation. Fears were expressed that the new government would deliberately try and undermine the voluntary hospitals. It might 'create an atmosphere of uncertainty which would divert the fount of philanthropy to other channels'.[1] If the Labour Party encouraged the local authorities to create first-class public hospitals, they would attract the majority of patients. If they engaged at good salaries first-class young physicians and surgeons, 'they would starve the voluntary hospitals of the personnel upon which their reputations depend'.[2]

The challenge to the position of the voluntary hospitals was recognized in many quarters. The *Hospital Gazette* calculated that the voluntary hospitals provided only 14 per cent of the hospital beds in Britain. The idea that the voluntary hospitals were

> . . . the prevalent system of hospitals was not supported by the facts. . . . It is common knowledge that the number of beds in the voluntary hospitals is totally inadequate to meet existing demands for accommodation. Hospitals in London and in the larger industrial centres have long waiting lists for admission, and generally it is only found possible to admit cases requiring active surgical treatment and acute medical cases, together with cases of special scientific interest, and some of value for teaching purposes. This deficiency of beds is aggravated by lack of organization and by a faulty distribution of hospital accommodation, deficiencies which not only detract from the efficiency of the hospitals, but which result in increased expenditure.[3]

A doctor, expressing a view to which few doctors would have subscribed, wrote in *The Lancet*:

> . . . far from our hospitals being, as they once were, the envy of other nations, the great majority are years behind the times, and lack of funds compels the hospitals of our Metropolis to carry on their work in the heart of London, with an equipment and in

[1] *Hospital Gazette*, July 1929, pp. 119–20
[2] ibid.
[3] ibid., June 1929, pp. 7–8

surroundings which would not be tolerated in a small provincial town in Sweden.[1]

Somerville Hastings, one of the signatories of the Labour Party's statements of policy, attacked the whole system of voluntary hospitals in an outspoken article in *The Hospital*. He criticized the casual system of visiting staffs and advocated regular payment so that governing bodies could have 'a greater check on the time spent on hospital work, and it would be less easy to pass on duties which ought to be performed by senior officers to men with insufficient experience'.[2] He thought that the contributions expected of wage earners were excessive and that the system of requiring payments from them in hospital made it very uncomfortable for those who could not afford to pay. It was impossible to prevent patients who paid from being treated with more deference than those who did not. And the more the well-to-do were admitted to hospitals, the more the poor would be excluded.

He criticized the indiscriminate setting up of hospitals and pointed out that while public houses and nursing homes

. . . have to be registered and inspected . . . a hospital can be founded anywhere by anyone. What is even more important from the nation's point of view is that any qualified doctor can carry out any operation in this hospital even though he has never performed such an operation before, or even watched it performed. . . . There should be some outside authority, perhaps a hospital planning and development committee of the Ministry of Health, with advisory if not compulsory powers.[3]

Hastings also criticized the BMA scheme for having a central or base hospital around which other municipal or voluntary hospitals should be grouped, as well as their proposal that the central hospital should be one of the larger voluntaries.

In the first place, the standard of work in some of the Voluntary Hospitals, without a medical school, is none too high. Further, it is clear that the authorities controlling a Municipal Hospital will not be willing for their hospitals to take up a place secondary or subservient to a Voluntary Hospital.[4]

[1] *Lancet*, 3 August 1929, p. 244
[2] *Hospital*, Vol. 27, February 1931, p. 34
[3] ibid., p. 36
[4] ibid.

There was strong and increasing pressure from public opinion to make hospitals free. When this happened,

> . . . it seems unlikely that patients will be prepared to pay for treatment in the voluntary hospitals or that generously minded people will continue to subscribe to them. The absorption of the Voluntary Hospitals into a National or Municipal system seems, therefore, certain within a comparatively few years' time.[1]

Sir Harold R. Pink, chairman of the Council of the British Hospitals Association, wrote to attack 'the extreme socialistic policy which aims at abolishing the voluntary hospitals and establishing a state medicine service'. He argued that:

> . . . the *Faith* a patient has in his or her doctor tends as much to recovery or alleviation as the doctor's treatment. If a State Medical Service were to be established this very valuable asset would be lost, as under State Control there would be no choice of doctor and recovery or alleviation would be thereby hindered.[2]

But hospitals could not be run on faith alone. It was easy enough to get money for capital construction but to get the money for maintenance was recognized to be the major problem of the voluntary hospitals. As one correspondent put it:

> . . . With two or three peerages and a few baronetcies at one's disposal, it would be comparatively easy to enlarge all the London hospitals, but where is the money for their maintenance coming from, other than the same source from which Mr Lansbury derives his?[3]

The Council of the British Hospitals Association, imbued with a new sense of urgency, pressed every hospital to join the organization. It wanted to create an active regional organization and an efficient and independent secretariat.[4] The propaganda committee of the King's Fund sent lecturers to the public schools to talk about the voluntary hospitals and arranged for the boys to visit certain institutions.[5] All agreed that combined action

[1] ibid.
[2] ibid., March 1931, p. 68
[3] ibid., May 1931, p. 116
[4] ibid., July 1931, pp. 153 and 156
[5] ibid., May 1931, p. 107

was essential. If no drastic steps were taken, it would mean the eclipse of the voluntary hospital movement.

Many contemporary writers both in the local authority camp and in the voluntary hospital camp tended to overestimate the rate of progress which the counties and county boroughs were likely to achieve. Moreover, the average standard of the separate infirmaries was still considerably below that of the average large voluntary hospital. Nevertheless the local authorities had been given a new opportunity to challenge the supremacy of the voluntary hospitals, if they wished to do so.

CHAPTER 23

Local Government in Action

A T long last the hospital functions of the Poor Law were handed over to the major authorities. It was a vast administrative operation. The areas of 190 out of the 635 Poor Law Unions extended over more than one county or county borough. The transfer of both offices and institutions was to be effected by 1 April 1930.[1] Each authority was free to decide what part of its accommodation for the sick would be taken out of the Poor Law, and run as part of the general public health services.

In London the basis of a municipal hospital service had been built up over sixty years by the creation of separate infirmaries and the expanding operations of the Metropolitan Asylums' Board. Thus the London County Council was able to appropriate 27 institutions as hospitals on 1 April 1931.[2] By 1 April 1932, all the MAB institutions were appropriated and all but twelve of the separate infirmaries.[3] The county boroughs had found themselves able to appropriate as hospitals 76 infirmaries by the same date.[4] The majority of the latter had been separate infirmaries before the appointed day, though one institution was wholly appropriated as a hospital which had previously been a mixed workhouse. In nine cases, part of a mixed institution was appropriated as a hospital. It was, however, found impossible to appropriate part of an institution where 'the resulting separation of the two units would have been unreal and administratively inconvenient'.[5]

The progress of the county councils was inevitably much slower as there had only been nine separately administered

1 *Eleventh Annual Report Ministry of Health, 1929–30*, p. 152
2 *Twelfth Annual Report Ministry of Health, 1930–1*, Cmd 3927, p. 50, HMSO, 1931
3 *Thirteenth Annual Report Ministry of Health 1931–2*, Cmd 4113, p. 39, HMSO, 1932
4 ibid., p. 40
5 *Twelfth Annual Report Ministry of Health*, p. 51

'hospitals' in these areas before the appointed day. The majority of the institutions inherited by the counties were of a mixed type which were hard to break up.[1] The Minister decided to undertake surveys to ascertain the progress being made and ensure that the local authorities were discharging their obligation satisfactorily. In the course of these surveys a number of points were raised, 'the remedy of which' in the words of the Minister's report, 'ought not as a rule to be beyond the competence of an authority interested in the maintenance of its health services'. Apart from criticisms of inadequate co-ordination and insufficient provisions in certain specified fields, the survey drew attention to the failure of some authorities to make adequate use of their opportunities to appropriate institutions.[2] The main offenders were the county councils. By 1 April 1934, only one county council outside London (Salop) had transferred an institution as a public health hospital.[3] It was found by the Ministry that there were a number of counties 'in which there were one or more institutions or parts of institutions suitable for appropriation'.[4]

The reason for the inadequate progress made, particularly in county areas, was not solely the unsuitable nature of the institutions which they had inherited. The fears which the Labour Party had expressed in the debate on the Bill, about the role of reactionary Guardians and particularly co-opted Guardians, proved to be justified. It was found that:

. . . public assistance committees tended to attract those members of the Council who had previously served as Guardians, while the addition of co-opted members often served to strengthen this association between the past and present regimes.

The Public Assistance Committee started, therefore, with a strong inherited interest in the administration of the institutions which many of their members had assisted in building up over a period of years. . . . The thought that the administration of this most constructive aspect of their work should be taken out of their hands and passed over to another Committee has naturally been distasteful, and suggestions for the appropriation of Poor Law infirmaries have in a number of instances clearly started under the

[1] *Thirteenth Annual Report Ministry of Health*, p. 41
[2] ibid., p. 45
[3] *Fifteenth Annual Report Ministry of Health 1935–6*, Cmd 4664, pp. 48–9, HMSO, 1936
[4] ibid.

handicap of considerable disfavour in the eyes of the Public Assistance Committee.[1]

In the county areas powers had been delegated to 'Guardians' Committees'. These committees seemed to the Ministry

... to be more conscious of the need for maintaining provision for the sick within the area for which they function than of that for securing the concentration of such provision in institutions capable of providing the most efficient treatment. In a number of Counties the management of the transferred institutions has been entrusted by the Council to the Guardians' Committees and it may be assumed that the opinions of the Guardians' Committees are generally adverse to appropriation.[2]

The Minister thought that the question of appropriation ought to be considered 'from a somewhat broader point of view than hitherto'.[3]

Some authorities were deterred from appropriation because of the cost of undertaking it. Expenditure on general modernization, on new equipment and additional staff 'deterred councils from a project to be paid out of local funds'.[4] Narrower financial considerations were also obstacles to appropriation. Some authorities feared that they would have 'a more restricted right of recovery of the cost or some part of the cost of treatment under the Local Government Act than if the administration of the institution remained under the Poor Law Act'.[5] The range of relatives from whom recovery could be sought was believed to be narrower under the new legislation. Thus *all* patients were admitted under the Poor Law to make absolutely sure that contributions could be collected from more distant relatives who were liable to pay under the older legislation. A further cheese-paring consideration, which influenced the decisions of some of the authorities, was the absence of the right of recovery under the Public Health Acts from other local authorities for patients whose 'settlement' was in those authorities. Rather than risk that these costs would balance out between authorities, all

[1] ibid., p. 51
[2] ibid., pp. 51–2
[3] ibid.
[4] Wilson, p. 111
[5] *Fifteenth Annual Report Ministry of Health*, p. 50

patients were made to apply for a relieving officer's order.[1]

For all these reasons, progress in implementing the intentions of the Local Government Act was not as great as Ministers had hoped. Local authorities took advantage of the freedom they had been given to act or not to act as they chose. By 1 April 1938, 109 hospitals containing 57,318 beds had been appropriated as *general* hospitals. Of these, 49 belonged to county boroughs, 38 to the London County Council, 6 to the Surrey County Council, 5 to the Middlesex County Council, leaving only 11 for all the other counties.[2] The counties had made less progress than the county boroughs, but even among these only about half had appropriated hospitals.[3] At the end of 1937, the majority of beds for the sick were still operated under the Poor Law.[4]

Even if every authority had made the best use of the buildings it had inherited and had rushed to build new ones where they were required, the Local Government Act had not provided a full solution to all the problems of planning local authority hospitals. Some of the county areas were too small to form the basis of a full hospital service, and the boundaries of authorities did not always follow natural 'catchment areas'. Thus, for example, residents in the new housing estate at Huyton, near Liverpool, found themselves excluded from the Liverpool hospitals. Residents in the area of the former West Derby Union, which included Bootle and part of the county of Lancashire, did on the other hand retain access to Liverpool's public hospitals. This was because this Union had built what had now become the general public hospitals of Liverpool.[5] In the case of specialized hospitals, some authorities were too small to be able to provide units of appropriate size. Thus in Leicestershire and Nottinghamshire the respective counties and county boroughs 'each erected good modern sanatoria, each pair being only 5 miles apart, instead of combining to produce more efficient and larger hospital units'.[6]

[1] ibid., and N. Wilson, *Public Health Services*, p. 110
[2] *Nineteenth Annual Report Ministry of Health 1937-8*, Cmd 5801, pp. 76-7, HMSO, 1938
[3] Wilson, p. 111
[4] *Nineteenth Annual Report Ministry of Health*, pp. 76-7
[5] PEP, *Report on the British Health Services*, p. 255, London, 1937
[6] Nuffield Provincial Hospitals Trust, *The Hospital Surveys*, p. 14, Oxford, 1946

Problems of this kind could have been met by a system of joint boards but this would have been a cumbrous solution. Such a system was, however, frequently used to provide hospitals for infectious diseases. There were no less than 97 joint boards established for this purpose in England and Wales in 1937. Represented on them were county and municipal borough councils, urban and rural district councils, in a variety of different combinations.[1] In the case of tuberculosis services, only about six joint boards were in being at the outbreak of war.[2]

The London County Council ruled over a vast hospital empire. Including beds for the mentally ill, it found in 1932 that it possessed a total of 77,000 beds compared to a total of 14,000 beds in the voluntary hospitals of the county of London.[3] It started with the initial advantage of the good institutions maintained by the Metropolitan Asylums' Board and the well endowed separate infirmaries which several of the London Guardians had provided. It also inherited the good tradition of hospital management built up by the MAB. It was not, however, content merely to maintain existing services: under the forceful leadership of its Medical Officer of Health, Sir Frederick Menzies, it worked energetically to continue the historic progress of up-grading and reclassification. The general hospitals had been developed by separate Boards of Guardians acting each for their own district. What was now needed was the reorganization of all the varied institutions into a co-ordinated hospital service for London.

The gradual evolution since 1867 had produced a situation in which a typical London Board of Guardians possessed one infirmary which enjoyed the financial advantages of the Common Poor Fund, and at least one mixed institution which accommodated the chronic sick and other Poor Law 'inmates'. The separate infirmaries had been purpose-built while the older workhouses were used for those not requiring the facilities of an acute hospital. The historic distinction between the acute sick and the more chronic sick, which had broadly delineated the role of the voluntary and Poor Law hospitals before 1870, had now given way to a new distinction as more and more persons above

---

[1] ibid.

[2] Acton Society Trust, *Hospitals and the State: Background and Blueprint*, p. 11, London, 1955

[3] *BMJ Supplement*, 13 August 1932, p. 119

the pauper class sought care away from home when they were sick. Now the acute sick were divided between the voluntary hospitals and separate infirmaries appropriated as public health service hospitals under the Act. The vast majority of the chronic sick remained in the old mixed institutions of an earlier age.

The London County Council decided to make the best possible use of the facilities it had inherited. It would have contradicted this principle for a place in a better equipped institution to be occupied by a chronic sick patient, while a patient needing specialized active care was sent to the sick ward of a workhouse. Thus, without much critical examination of alternatives, the Council decided to perpetuate the distinction which had arisen, more from chance than conscious design, of separate acute and chronic hospitals. But it did gradually attempt to separate the chronic sick patients from the other categories of person occupying the workhouse ward.

Thus it was announced in August 1932 that chronic sick cases were gradually being concentrated in twelve out of the twenty-nine public assistance institutions.[1] It was, however, impractical to arrange the transfer of 'all sick persons, including expectant unmarried mothers, from public assistance to public health establishments'.[2] The twelve institutions (containing 9,000 to 10,000 beds) were placed under the Public Health Committee. A further institution containing 320 beds was transferred for the exclusive use of the female convalescents and female chronic sick (St Benedict's Hospital).[3] And another hospital at Sidcup was acquired from the Ministry of Pensions for the use of the chronic sick and given the name of Queen Mary's Hospital.[4]

Though some authorities kept their chronic sick in acute hospitals, the concentration of the acute sick in the 'better' institutions was also the policy of many provincial health authorities. In Surrey, the acute sick were put in six institutions and it was decided to build an additional new general hospital.[5] Middlesex concentrated their acute sick in five institutions and

[1] *Sixteenth Annual Report Ministry of Health 1934–5*, Cmd 4978, p. 56, HMSO, 1935
[2] ibid.
[3] ibid., p. 58
[4] ibid.
[5] *Eighteenth Annual Report Ministry of Health 1936–7*, Cmd 5516, p. 83, HMSO, 1937

adapted other accommodation to receive the chronic sick who were displaced.[1] Essex decided to build three new hospitals of 500 beds or over, while Lindsey and Cumberland made arrangements with voluntary hospitals.[2]

One of the tasks of the hospital authorities was to work out and operate systems of charging patients, other than those who were suffering from infectious diseases. The London County Council decided to make no charge for ante- and post-natal attendances, for examination of inpatients after treatment and for first attendances, except for X-ray examinations. The basic charge for outpatients was fixed at 1s 6d.[3] Inpatients other than those belonging to the Hospital Saving Association were required to pay what they could afford. The Council restricted the relatives whom it would hold liable 'for most practical purposes' to husbands in respect of wives and parents in respect of children up to the age of twenty-one.[4] In assessing liable relatives deduction was allowed for insurance benefits, rent, rates and a sum for personal needs. After these deductions, assessments were made at the rate of one-third of the first twenty-four shillings of remaining income and one-half of any income over twenty-four shillings. In the year 1934-5 the LCC collected nearly £200,000 as patients' payments in appropriated hospitals.[5]

While local authorities had a duty to charge in general hospitals, they had no such duty in an isolation hospital. Indeed, there was some doubt about whether a local authority had a right to charge at all. It was decided by the Ministry that authorities had a right to charge, but that the charge could not be levied on the patient if there were a contract of service in the case of a child. Some authorities refrained from doing so, while others collected where they could a substantial part of the cost. The Ministry ascertained after taking legal advice that the term 'infectious disease' included tuberculosis.

The concentration of the acute sick in the better buildings made the best use of such ancillary services as were available. It also made possible improvements in the training schools for

[1] ibid.
[2] ibid.
[3] *Hospital*, Vol. 29 May 1933, p. 130
[4] *BMJ Supplement*, 24 August 1935, p. 121
[5] ibid.

nurses for the general register: 'More acute patients were available for training purposes.'[1] The price of achieving these advantages was to make it less easy to provide proper nursing services for the chronic sick. The chronic sick hospitals were primarily staffed by unqualified nurses, and a number of institutions lacked even enough qualified staff to provide adequate supervision.[2] The number of unqualified nurses at work in the hospitals rose from 15,000 in 1933 to 21,000 in 1937.[3] Faced with the apparently insoluble problem of obtaining enough registered nurses for the chronic sick hospitals, some local authorities started a special course of training for nursing the chronic sick. Despite the opposition of the College of Nursing, a second grade of trained nurse was introduced.[4]

The extension and upgrading of acute hospitals undertaken by the major authorities inevitably required an increase in medical staff. The original infirmaries started under the Poor Law had been staffed almost exclusively by whole-time medical officers. This system was also used in the hospitals for infectious diseases. Such expertise as there was in Britain for the treatment of these diseases was developed by whole-time medical officers working in publicly owned hospitals. The same was virtually true of mental hospitals. These were subjects which were given scant attention by the teachers and clinicians of the great voluntary hospitals.

Whole-time salaried medical staff remained the basic system of staffing the public general hospitals. The career prospects of a doctor who entered this service were not good. There were few posts as medical superintendent or deputy medical superintendent; promotion was slow and depended considerably on length of service. Thus, while in voluntary hospital work or even general practice, there was a chance of both a high income and full clinical responsibility by the age of 35 or 40, some medical officers in the local government service might never gain a senior post or, if they did, would achieve it late in life. And until they reached the rank of medical superintendent they would be subject to interference from higher authority in clinical matters. For all these reasons, there was little competition for posts in

[1] *Fifteenth Annual Report Ministry of Health*, pp. 99–100
[2] ibid., p. 96
[3] Abel-Smith, p. 156
[4] ibid., p. 158

local authority hospitals, and the residents appointed were 'not often the best product of the medical schools'.[1]

Thus, part-time consultants were brought more and more into the local authority hospitals from the voluntary hospitals. Early in the twenties, Guardians who were anxious to improve the standard of care in their infirmaries had started to purchase a few hours of weekly service from the visiting staffs of the voluntary hospitals. Each Board had acted independently. Boards did not seek to combine together to employ one whole-time experienced consultant for their several hospitals. Nor could they have offered either the full facilities for research and practice or the rewards of teaching, both direct and indirect, available in teaching hospitals.

In its reply to the Minister's questions in 1928, the BMA had recommended that the major local authorities should obtain their consultant staff in the same manner as had been the practice of the Poor Law authorities. This decision had been opposed by some general practitioners who sought beds in public hospitals and the question was re-opened at the 1930 representative meeting. It was agreed that in addition to the full-time superintendent and resident staff, there should be employed in council hospitals not only part-time consultants but part-time general practitioners who could either have responsible charge of beds and clinics or act as clinical assistants. In this latter role it was argued that general practitioners could develop specialized work. By this means each area would breed its own consultants and specialists. In general, it was argued by Dr Fothergill, for many years the spokesman of ambitious practitioners, that 'the hospitals belonged to the general practitioner. . . . He had been kept out of them far too long.'[2] Not all general practitioners supported Dr Fothergill. One asked and himself answered a particularly pertinent question: 'If any member of the Association had his wife or daughter or son down with acute abdomen, would they ask a highly trained practitioner to operate? No, they would get the best surgeon they could.'[3]

Though some of the councils did allow visiting practitioners to attend and treat their own cases,[4] the more common practice

---

[1] Nuffield Trust, *The Hospital Surveys*, p. 12
[2] *BMJ Supplement*, 26 July 1930, p. 48
[3] ibid., p. 50
[4] ibid., 7 January 1933, p. 1

was to engage visiting consultants to supplement the work of the resident staff. They tended to be brought in 'to give a second opinion, or to perform specialized surgery on selected cases.'[1] Thus the visiting consultant, 'not having charge of beds, has little real stake or interest in the work of the hospital'.[2] The Ministry advised that the pay offered for such appointments should be such as to attract the very best.[3] And some local authorities were prepared to pay well. Thus Newcastle-upon-Tyne was prepared to pay £500 a year for part-time services on certain days of the week. Such offers did not go unnoticed by the voluntary hospitals. It was feared that young consultants would leave the voluntary hospitals and build their practices on the basis of the council's services.[4]

The London County Council was inevitably the largest purchaser of consultants' services and it decided on a complete reorganization of its arrangements. At the beginning of January 1933, the Council gave notice that it was going to suspend all existing contracts with effect from the end of March. New contracts would then be offered. The dismissed consultants went to the BMA, and a sub-committee was set up which prepared a memorandum to be sent to the Council.[5] This memorandum stressed the importance of co-operation between council and voluntary hospitals, in which the interchange of *part-time* consultants was an essential feature. Part-time employment with opportunities for private practice acted as a great stimulus to professional attainment. Regional grouping would increase efficiency and reduce unnecessary travelling. It was hoped that consultants' committees on a group or hospital basis would be formed.[6]

The Council's new offer was published towards the end of March. There was no demand for full-time service as had apparently been feared, but the proposals caused widespread dissatisfaction among the doctors. It was complained that the Council had taken the BMA minimum scale as its maximum and even gone below it by lengthening the session from two to two-

[1] Nuffield Trust, *The Hospital Surveys*, p. 11
[2] ibid.
[3] *Hospital*, Vol. 27, April 1931, p. 94
[4] ibid., Vol. 26, July 1930, p. 162
[5] *BMJ Supplement*, 25 March 1933, p. 105
[6] ibid.

and-a-half hours. Anaesthetists were to be paid less than other consultants, and furthermore, consultants were to have to pay for a substitute if they took a holiday.[1] For these and other reasons it was resolved at a meeting held on 28 March 1933 to advise members of the profession not to accept service until discussions were held between the profession and the Council.[2] Sir Frederick Menzies, Chief Medical Officer of the Council, dubbed these activities of the BMA as 'a strike campaign'.[3]

Conditions of service were not the only matters in dispute. The BMA demanded the right of consultation before 'proposals seriously affecting the work of the profession' were adopted by the Council. It also was critical of the means of appointing selection committees for consultant appointments. The BMA made no impact on the last question but won concessions on all the other matters in dispute.[4] When the terms of service were revised a year later anaesthetists obtained equality with other consultants.[5] The open breach was at an end. But the Association became no less keen to influence the policy of local authorities. At the 1936 representative meeting it was decided to encourage members to offer themselves for election to local councils as a means of promoting BMA policy.[6]

The British Medical Association watched carefully not only the terms of service of medical staffs in council hospitals but also practices concerning private wards. When one council opened a ward for middle-class patients at $2\frac{1}{2}$ guineas per week with a scale of charges payable to the *council* for services given by the full-time medical staff, the hospitals committee protested vigorously. The hospital was offering services 'at rates seriously to undercut members of the profession in private practice locally'.[7] Moreover, the local authority had an incentive to use the full-time officer 'to the discouragement of men in private practice'.[8] It insisted that a definite income limit should be introduced and a new schedule of charges should be drawn up in collaboration with the practitioners in the area.

[1] ibid.
[2] *Hospital*, Vol. 29, April 1933, p. 85
[3] *BMJ Supplement*, 22 April 1933, p. 142
[4] ibid., 22 July 1933, p. 43
[5] ibid., 16 June 1934, p. 310
[6] ibid., 14 November 1936, p. 258
[7] ibid., 21 October 1933, p. 210
[8] ibid.

The Association undertook an inquiry into arrangements for private beds in appropriated hospitals. Out of thirty hospitals examined, ten admitted private patients. Only in one hospital was the payment of the doctor recognized. In three others it was stated that, 'If the patient makes any arrangement privately with a consultant, the corporation does not interfere.'[1] To prevent 'exploitation' in private wards of council hospitals, the Association decided that terms of service with councils should only cover patients not in private wards. Private patients should make separate arrangements to pay the doctor whether he was on the hospital staff or not.[2]

Another aspect of the work of council hospitals which the BMA watched closely was the work of outpatient departments. The BMA was anxious that outpatient consultations should not expand, and particularly that patients who could afford to pay proper fees should not attend. Backed by the report of the committee on local expenditure (1933) the Ministry decided to invite local authorities to hold separate sessions for patients suffering from venereal diseases at which fees would be charged. This was 'to meet the needs of those persons who would be willing or who desire to pay for treatment provided'.[3] The BMA hospitals committee opposed the scheme.[4]

Though local authorities were not specifically authorized to provide general outpatient departments until 1936,[5] outpatient departments grew with the popularity of council hospitals. By 1935 there were nearly 1½ million outpatient consultations and by 1937 nearly 2 million.[6] Most of the consultations, however, constituted no more than the continuation of treatment of discharged inpatients. Nevertheless, councils were prepared to take more vigorous steps to stop 'outpatient abuse' than voluntary hospitals, as they did not need a crowd of outpatients either for appeal purposes or for the selection of teaching material. Moreover, they had separate services under the Poor Law for those who could not afford general practitioners' fees. For

[1] ibid., 25 April 1936, p. 217
[2] ibid.
[3] *Fourteenth Annual Report Ministry of Health 1932–3*, Cmd 4372, p. 52, HMSO, 1933
[4] *BMJ Supplement*, 4 November 1933, p. 238
[5] PEP, *Report on British Health Services 1937*, p. 253
[6] *Nineteenth Annual Report Ministry of Health*, p. 77

patients who were not referred for special treatment or examination, the LCC introduced a double test. The medical staff
had to satisfy themselves that the patients could not be treated
by the district medical officer or by a general practitioner. The
almoner had to satisfy herself that the patients could not afford
to buy the specialized care for themselves. It was to perform this
function that almoners were introduced into council hospitals.

Despite these precautions, the familiar cry of abuse was raised
by some general practitioners. 'These free clinics,' wrote Dr
Bradlaw of Tooting, 'are usurping the place of the general
practitioner. . . . This is the beginning of a deliberate attack
upon private practice, with the object of depleting it.'[1]

In one respect at least, local government was in fact enhancing
the role of private practice. The skeleton dispensaries under the
Poor Law, which had never played much of a role in the national
system of medical care, and the part-time, salaried district
medical officer under the Poor Law were steadily being replaced
by a new system of providing general practitioner services for
public assistance cases. In 1933, the Newcastle-upon-Tyne
council offered poor patients an 'open' choice of doctor from a
list of practitioners willing to provide such services. The doctor
was paid on a fee-for-service basis from a limited pool and there
was a rapid increase in units of service.[2] The system spread to
many other areas with the warm support of the BMA.[3] The
Association did not like the 'limited pool' system and succeeded
in having remuneration on a capitation system substituted in
a number of areas.[4]

Chamberlain had hoped that the development of council
services would be closely co-ordinated with the work of the
voluntary services. And the House of Lords, which had always
acted as custodian of the interests of the voluntary hospitals,
had amended Chamberlain's Act by requiring local authorities
in each area to consult with bodies representative of the voluntary hospital governors and medical staffs. By 1934, 83 such
committees had been set up out of a possible 146.[5] In London,
there had been a suggestion that the King's Fund should appoint

[1] *BMJ Supplement*, 20 August 1938, p. 157
[2] ibid., 6 April 1935, p. 125
[3] ibid., 16 December 1933, pp. 297–8 and 17 February 1934, p. 65
[4] ibid., 25 April 1936, pp. 208–10
[5] PEP, *Report on British Health Services*, p. 245

the consultative committee but the BMA opposed the idea that this important function should be exercised by a 'lay organizing body'.[1] In the end the British Hospitals Association constituted the committee.[2]

The role of the consultative committees depended on what each local authority wanted to make it. The law required them to consult voluntary hospitals. They had, however, no means of forcing their opinions. Moreover, strictly speaking, the requirement of consultation only extended to Poor Law services; there was no need for a local authority to consult regarding the hospitals appropriated to the public health services[3] – the sector most likely to conflict with the work of voluntary hospitals.

In general, however, local authorities were prepared to consult on all their health services. Co-ordinated action became most effective in areas where there was an overlap of personnel between the two sectors: this was fairly common in the provinces.[4] And in some towns rationalization was developed not only between the voluntary and council sectors but within the voluntary sector itself. The towns with the best co-operation included Birmingham, Liverpool, Plymouth and Bristol.[5] There were, however, other areas where consultations were regarded as 'merely a matter of form'.[6]

In London, the voluntary hospitals regarded the London County Council as unco-operative.[7] While the Council was prepared to pay hospitals to provide services which it wished to have rendered, it saw its first duty as that of keeping its own beds occupied.[8] In a number of instances the Council preferred to develop its own services rather than to help voluntary hospitals to meet the need.[9] One concrete achievement did, however, emerge from the work of the London voluntary hospitals committee. Nineteen council hospitals were linked with undergraduate teaching hospitals for teaching purposes. In addition,

[1] *BMJ Supplement*, 26 July 1928, p. 11
[2] *Hospital*, Vol. 27, July 1931, p. 156
[3] ibid., Vol. 32, June 1936, p. 143
[4] ibid., Vol. 28, April 1932, p. 83
[5] PEP, *Report on British Health Services*, p. 245
[6] *Eighteenth Annual Report Ministry of Health*, p. 85
[7] *Hospital*, Vol. 27, October 1931, p. 226 and Vol. 28, April 1932, pp. 84–5
[8] ibid., Vol. 27, May 1931, pp. 112–13
[9] ibid., June 1931, p. 141 and July 1931, p. 156

students were enabled to reside for a fortnight at municipal hospitals to obtain practical instruction in obstetrics.[1]

Chamberlain's experiment in freedom had produced widely different standards not only of co-operation but of every aspect of hospital management. The wealthier and more progressive authorities had forged ahead, determined to create a service of which the public would be proud. The larger units of administration made possible economies from centralizing purchasing: the achievements of both London and Surrey are notable in this connection.[2] They also made possible the employment of specialist officers to cover the whole area. Not only did the London County Council have a matron-in-chief but also a domestic supervisor whose task it was to supervise all the domestic arrangements including the preparation and service of meals.[3]

How far councils managed to 'humanize' their hospitals after the long and harsh tradition of the Poor Law is hard to establish. Voluntary hospital administrators who visited Lambeth Hospital in 1932 noted 'a sense of exclusiveness, almost of captivity, engendered by locked iron gates and only one small entrance', and 'the lack of that atmosphere of sympathy and assistance which permeates the voluntary hospital'.[4] They regretted the absence of flowers, books and charitable visitors.[5] On the other hand it was claimed by supporters of the public hospitals that patients were not 'patronized' as they were in voluntary hospitals. They were treated less as 'cases' and more as human beings. They could expect redress for any grievances by appealing to the local authorities.[6]

The period between 1921 and 1938 was one of only modest growth in the number of beds for the sick provided by local authorities.[7] The overall total of beds increased from about 172,000 to about 176,000: the number of beds failed to keep pace with the growth of the population. But a much higher proportion of the beds provided were in general acute and specialized hospitals. The number of beds in the mixed institutions dropped

[1] ibid., Vol. 30, August 1934, p. 210
[2] *Fourteenth Annual Report Ministry of Health*, p. 197
[3] *Hospital*, Vol. 29, September 1933, p. 259
[4] ibid., Vol. 28, February 1932, p. 29
[5] ibid.
[6] PEP, *Report on British Health Services*, p. 253
[7] See Vol. 2 of this study.

from about 84,000 to 56,000, while the number of acute general beds increased from about 38,000 to about 53,000. Similarly the number of beds in tuberculosis hospitals increased from about 7,000 to about 16,000 and the number of beds in maternity hospitals increased from about 2,500 to about 6,500.

While some authorities were attempting to provide a service to the public, there were others who made little progress in their health services. There continued to be authorities which failed to remove any part of their new inheritance out of the shadow of the Poor Law. There continued to be what the Ministry described as 'a considerable amount of accommodation at present used for the sick which is not entirely suitable for the purpose'.[1] Indeed, some of them did not provide 'either the physical or mental amenities to be found in even the most ordinary well-conducted domestic dwelling'.[2] Many of the workhouses were very old structures. 'Of twenty-one institutions for the chronic sick existing on the eve of war in South Wales and Monmouthshire, nine were over 100 years old, eight over fifty years, two more than forty years old, while the remaining two were put up in 1904 and 1908.'[3]

Chamberlain had stressed the powers he had taken *for the first time* to withhold some proportion of the block grant from an authority which had 'failed to achieve a reasonable standard of efficiency and progress'.[4] Though a recalcitrant local authority may have been reminded of the existence of this section, it was never used.[5] Much depended on the 'skill and ability of the Medical Officer of Health'.[6] But much also depended on the underlying philosophy which guided the actions of local councillors. The principles of some were those of the nineteenth century; the principles of others were such as to anticipate developments after the Second World War. Such was the price of local independence.

---

[1] *Fifteenth Annual Report Ministry of Health*, p. 64
[2] quoted in R. M. Titmuss, *Problems of Social Policy*, pp. 69–70, London, 1950
[3] ibid., p. 70
[4] *Local Government Act 1929*
[5] Wilson, op cit., pp. 168–9
[6] *Fifteenth Annual Report Ministry of Health*, p. 91

CHAPTER 24

The Growth of Voluntary Insurance

THE creation of municipal hospitals could in time undermine the predominant position of the voluntary hospitals.
If the local authorities provided hospitals of a high standard, they
would eventually attract patients and consultants from the
voluntary sector. And would the charitable public continue to
provide funds for a task which had been so clearly accepted as a
public responsibility? To survive, the voluntary hospitals had
to show themselves to be not just equal to, but superior to, the
public hospitals. This meant that their governors had to obtain
funds not only to continue existing services but to maintain their
lead over the developing municipal sector.

The story of the voluntary hospitals in the thirties was similar
to that in the twenties. Despite valiant efforts[1] they were unable
to increase substantially their income from the charitable public.
Worse still, some of the existing sources of income failed to live
up to expectations. In particular, the right to demand payment
from insurance companies for road accidents brought in much
less revenue than had been hoped. In 1931, only about a tenth
of the cost of treating such cases was estimated to have been paid
by insurance.[2] The grants to hospitals from approved societies,
which had been stimulated by pressure from the Cave Committee, dwindled to less than £100,000 per year.[3] And although
local authorities could have granted up to £12 million for the
general support of the voluntary hospitals, they actually gave
less than £100,000 per year.[4]

But there was one source of revenue which proved to be elastic.
Before the First World War, about 10 per cent of the cost of the

---

[1] The attempt to collect money from patients' visitors occasionally led
to complaints in the press. See *Hospital*, Vol. 28, January 1932, p. 3.

[2] *Hospital*, Vol. 29, July 1933, p. 195

[3] *BMJ Supplement*, 7 August 1937, p. 109

[4] ibid., 20 August 1938, p. 152

hospitals was paid by patients and prospective patients. By 1931, the proportion had risen to 40 per cent[1] and by 1938 to about 50 per cent. There were three categories of patients' payments. First, there were the somewhat casual payments assessed from or donated by persons arriving at the outpatient department or admitted to the general wards. Secondly, there were the full or above cost payments paid by private patients who usually paid separate medical fees. Thirdly, there were the sums received through the various schemes of pre-insurance. It was the last two which increased most rapidly in the thirties.

In 1921 the hospitals reporting to *Burdett's Annual* had a gross income of about £5½ million, if legacies and other 'extraordinary' income are included.[2] By 1938, hospitals reporting to the *Year Book* had a gross income of nearly £14 million.[3] Voluntary contributions (including donations, subscriptions, legacies, collections and income on investments) increased from about £4 million in 1921 to about £6½ million in 1938. Receipts for services (including charges, contributory schemes and payments from public authorities)[4] increased from £1½ million in 1921 to over £7 million in 1938. It was this last elastic source of income, rather than voluntary effort, which made possible rapid growth in the work of the voluntary hospitals. In no other period were so many beds added to the voluntary sector.[5] Between 1921 and 1938, the number of beds increased from about 57,000 to about 87,000. In the twenties and thirties more beds were opened than existed in 1891 or were added between 1891 and 1921. Out of the increase of about 31,000 beds, approximately 21,000 were in teaching and general hospitals and 10,000 were in special hospitals: among the latter the number of maternity hospitals grew from 14 in 1921 to 235 in 1938. In this last year, about 3,600 beds were provided in separate maternity hospitals.

In 1921 the proportion of patients being treated in voluntary hospitals was about 25 per cent: by 1938 this proportion had risen to 36 per cent[6]. The role of the public sector dropped from

[1] *Hospital*, Vol. 28, September 1932, p. 244

[2] *Burdett's Hospitals and Charities 1922–3*, p. 41

[3] *The Hospitals Year Book 1940*, pp. 60–63 and 68, London, 1940

[4] In 1938, receipts from public authorities amounted to about £0.9 million.

[5] For the figures upon which this and the subsequent paragraph are based, see Vol. 2 of this study.

[6] These calculations are based upon the average number of occupied beds in the two sectors.

75 per cent of the patients to 64 per cent. While a spectacular expansion of accommodation was under way in the voluntary sector, there was hardly any increase in the number of beds provided in the public sector: progress in the latter consisted almost wholly of replacement and upgrading. It is not surprising, therefore, that throughout the inter-war period most of those who worked in the voluntary hospitals believed that the voluntary movement had an indefinite future: only a few identified the critical planning problems which were emerging and which the system was failing to resolve.

The key to the rapid development of the voluntary hospitals was to be found primarily in the success of the pre-insurance schemes. They spread rapidly among those working-class people who had regular jobs, wages above the minimum and families of modest size. Development was, however, piecemeal and unco-ordinated. Schemes sprang up in each area with varying sponsorship, varying income limits and with varying levels and systems of contribution. In one district of Yorkshire there were said to be 'more schemes than days in the month, with uniformity neither of benefits nor of contributions'.[1] A contributor who happened to need hospital care while away from his district might find that his scheme would pay to the hospital what was customary in his home district, a special reduced contribution, or nothing at all.[2] There were bitter complaints from such areas as London,[3] Leeds[4] and Merseyside[5] which found themselves treating large numbers of cases referred to them from outside the catchment area of their district contributory scheme. The house governor of St Mary's complained of the lengthy correspondence involved in applying to many different schemes. In some cases he would be given less than a pound and warned not to approach the patient or his employer for any sort of thank-offering. He was told in one case that if he had the 'effrontery to attempt anything of that sort, you may rest assured we shall hear of it'.[6] One scheme which would pay nothing for a patient sent to London advertised itself in the

[1] *BMJ Supplement*, 18 February 1939, p. 75
[2] *Hospital*, Vol. 28, October 1932, p. 272
[3] ibid., Vol. 30, November 1934, p. 290
[4] *BMJ Supplement*, 18 February 1939, p. 74
[5] *Hospital*, Vol. 29, October 1933, pp. 288–9
[6] ibid., Vol. 30, November 1934, p. 290

following terms: 'By paying a regular contribution you meet your emergency in advance. You receive hospital treatment and maintenance free. You preserve your independence and self-respect.'[1]

Except on this question of reciprocal arrangements, all these different schemes were able to operate without any further conflict arising between them, provided there was only one scheme operating in each area. This was not the case in London. While the Hospital Saving Association (HSA) was offering freedom from charges and almoners' inquisitions at a cost of threepence per week, the older and less formal Hospital Saturday Fund (HSF) was prepared to offer the same facilities for a lesser fee. The HSA complained that the HSF was 'certifying as suitable for free hospital treatment persons who had not contributed a sum proportionate to their means'.[2] Thus where the HSF was long-established, the HSA found it difficult to obtain a footing and 'the different practice in regard to a minimum weekly payment is the deciding factor'. Accordingly the HSA threatened to withdraw support from any hospital that dealt with the HSF.[3] The hospitals placed the matter before the regional committee of the British Hospitals Association and one of the parties in turn appealed to the King's Fund.[4] But no agreed decision emerged and each hospital was left to resolve the dispute as best it could.[5]

The HSA was not only prepared to fight its rival in its home territory; it also invaded the provinces in the attempt to become a national organization. The trouble started when some of the railway companies with headquarters in London decided to adopt the HSA for all their employees. It was obviously easier to make payroll deductions for one scheme than to attempt to make different contributions according to the employee's place of residence. And many railwaymen were mobile workers. When the HSA agreed to look after railway workers on a national basis, it was greeted by tough hostility from the provincial schemes. At Wolverhampton, the Royal Hospital took the drastic step of refusing or threatening to refuse to treat

[1] ibid., p. 291
[2] ibid., Vol. 28, January 1932, p. 138
[3] ibid.
[4] ibid., September 1932, p. 245
[5] ibid., Vol. 30, January 1934, p. 15

HSA members in its district. The HSA was accused of selling 'without authority the services of the Royal Hospital and its honorary staff'.[1] The HSA in its turn professed to be shocked that the Royal Hospital should turn away a sick person 'simply because he has been provident enough to save in advance of sickness part of the cost of his treatment'.[2]

The HSA was asked to withdraw its organization and leave 'the affairs of each scheme and hospital to be dealt with by men and women on the spot'.[3] Similar representations came from Ipswich and Hereford,[4] and the hospitals concerned took up the matter with the BHA and asked it to intervene on their behalf. Accordingly, the Council of the BHA resolved that the HSA should 'confine its activities to its own recognized hospital area for which it was established, namely, London'.[5] But the HSA refused to withdraw. It stressed that railwaymen had a very real need for a national scheme and said that, if any hospital did not want to co-operate with the HSA, then their members would be notified accordingly.[6]

As the contributory schemes expanded, the BMA continued its long campaign to win a stake in the proceeds for the medical staff. In April 1932, a joint committee of the BMA and BHA reported signs of 'a reduction in the numbers of consultants and specialists who were in a position to give gratuitous services to the voluntary hospitals'.[7] As more patients were going to the hospital it was said to be harder for consultants and specialists to earn a living from private consulting practice. For these reasons, the joint committee concluded that the ideal contributory scheme was 'one designed to provide a contribution towards the remuneration of the Visiting Medical Staff'.[8] This did not, however, mean that all medical staff got paid. The report was instantly dismissed by Mr J. P. Wetenhall as a 'purely . . . Utopian conception outside the range of practical politics'.[9] Most of the regional committees of the

[1] ibid., Vol. 29, April 1933, p. 95
[2] ibid.
[3] ibid.
[4] ibid., May 1933, p. 135 and June 1933, p. 172
[5] ibid., July 1933, p. 209
[6] ibid., p. 210
[7] *Hospital*, Vol. 28, April 1932, p. 87.
[8] ibid.
[9] ibid.

BHA decided to leave the question for the decision of each hospital.[1]

Not all members of medical staffs were agreed that the making of percentage payments to a staff fund was the right way to handle the problem. Two provincial surgeons wrote to the BMJ to suggest that the pre-payment system should only be used for maintenance; the question of fees should be a matter of private arrangement with the doctor in charge.[2] In an inquiry published in 1935 there were reported to be some fifty-four hospitals which did already work on this system.[3]

Some of the hospital doctors decided on militant action. When, despite three years of pressure from the medical staff, the governors of a hospital at Barrow-in-Furness refused to give their doctors a share of the receipts from the local contributory scheme, the latter decided to resign, in the sense that they refused to 'treat any new patients apart from accidents and emergencies'. The governors responded by threatening to advertise for a full-time doctor.[4] The Mayor of Barrow was called in as arbitrator and the doctors won the right to 1 per cent of workmen's contributions in years when income exceeded expenditure.[5] At Harwich and District Hospital, the medical staff gained 25 per cent of contributory scheme payments in 1933. In 1936 the governing body proposed to reduce this percentage. The medical staff, backed by the BMA, argued for an increase to 45 per cent of payments as the contributory scheme had a high income limit and low subscription rate. The doctors got what they wanted.[6]

In an inquiry conducted in 1935, there were found to be 74 hospitals in England and Wales which allocated some proportion of payments to a medical staff fund.[7] There were, however, only three London hospitals on the list.[8] There remained consultants who did not want the whole question of honorary service to 'pass into the melting pot . . . for the sake of a mere pittance per staff member'. A paid staff 'could not expect to

[1] *BMJ Supplement*, 13 August 1932, p. 119
[2] ibid., 29 April 1933, p. 191
[3] ibid., 12 January 1935, p. 11
[4] ibid., 5 August 1933, p. 94
[5] ibid., 9 September 1933, p. 161
[6] ibid., 5 December 1936, p. 297
[7] ibid., 12 January 1935, p. 11
[8] *Hospital*, Vol. 31, February 1935, p. 41

confer with the responsible hospital authority on the same footing as now exists'.[1]

By 1938 there were 418 contributory schemes listed in the *Hospitals Year Book*. Information on income limits was available for 314 of them. The BMA's recommended limits were used in 68 schemes, there were 126 schemes which had no limits and most of the rest had limits higher than those recommended by the BMA – including a few which were designed to meet the total cost of hospital maintenance.[2] The 114 schemes making returns to the British Hospitals Contributory Schemes Association reported that they had 5,241,000 subscribers in 1935.[3] The BMA estimated that there were about 10 million members of schemes of all types by 1938.[4]

The schemes were unpopular with the profession. It was found hard to assess the incomes of farmers and small tradesmen and 'to secure the elimination of subscribers whose incomes although initially within the limits of the scheme have risen above those limits'.[5] The BMA received complaints of 'the exploitation of staffs by patients who could well afford private treatment', of 'special damage to the private practices of the ear, nose and throat surgeons and of radiologists', of 'abuse of outpatient departments', of 'diversion of minor operations to hospitals', of 'unnecessary retention of casualty cases and failure to refer back'.[6] On the effect of the schemes on the quality of medical care provided for patients, no comments were apparently collected.

Contributory schemes were thus blamed for creating a new abuse of outpatient departments. The number of attendances was increasing rapidly.[7] It was alleged that 'members were encouraged to attend hospital for any and every ailment which they may suffer'.[8] Hospitals were accused of being 'interested in one thing only regarding their outpatient departments and that is in keeping up the numbers of those attending and this is not for any reason connected with the medical welfare of a

[1] ibid., January 1935, p. 17
[2] *BMJ Supplement*, 22 April 1939, pp. 185–6
[3] PEP, *Report on British Health Services*, p. 234
[4] BMA, *A General Medical Service for the Nation*, p. 22, London, 1938
[5] *BMJ Supplement*, 22 April 1939, p. 186
[6] ibid.
[7] ibid., 1 January 1938, p. 1
[8] *Hospital*, Vol. 29, February 1933, p. 50

patient'.[1] And the hospitals in turn blamed general practitioners for sending cases for whom treatment at hospital was 'obviously unnecessary'.[2] The BMA published a special pamphlet on the subject,[3] and issued 300,000 model letters for the use of both general practitioners and hospital medical staffs.[4] Dr Cox complained that hospital medical staffs were 'unduly modest . . . in estimating their usefulness to the hospitals and therefore their legitimate influence on their Boards'.[5]

The dispute between general practitioners and hospitals which was revived in the late twenties, and which continued throughout the thirties, was so old and the arguments employed so familiar that it would be tedious to repeat further illustrations of them. The only new emphasis in the discussion was the greater weight placed on the loss of the private practice earnings of consultants and specialists. Increasingly, the patient was turning to the hospital for consultant services, and members of contributory schemes felt they had a right to a consultant's opinion without further payment. It was suggested that some of the patients who came to the hospital would in an earlier age have gone to the private consulting room.

The HSA attempted to provide an answer to this problem. It arranged that any of its members could get a private consultation on the recommendation of a general practitioner at a special reduced fee of one guinea, and drew up a list of consultants prepared to offer such services. This led the British Medical Association to intervene, pointing out that it could not approve of 'a "closed" or restricted panel being created and controlled by a non-medical authority',[6] and decided instead to maintain a list itself. This was done despite 'certain misgivings'[7] and delay[8] from the Royal College of Physicians. It was thought that the Association had to start a list 'even though it might incur some temporary unpopularity in certain quarters'.[9]

[1] *BMJ Supplement*, 18 June 1932, p. 296
[2] ibid., 3 December 1938, p. 347
[3] ibid., 28 March 1936, pp. 118–20
[4] ibid., 18 June 1938, p. 371
[5] ibid., 8 January 1938, p. 19
[6] ibid., 28 November 1931, p. 289
[7] ibid., 19 December 1931, p. 323
[8] ibid., 6 February 1932, p. 39
[9] ibid.

Whether there actually was a reduction in consultant practice or in the incomes of consultants will probably never be established. Consulting work was certainly very competitive. And under the strain of competition, unethical practices developed including what was called 'fee-splitting': the consultant passed part of his fee back to the general practitioner without the patient's knowledge. The system gave the incentive to the general practitioner to choose not the best consultant but the one who gave the largest commission. The subject had been mentioned in the *British Medical Journal* before the First World War but was believed to be very rare.[1] It was discussed again in 1920 when it was believed to be taking root in England:[2] the practice was, however, roundly condemned by the leaders of the profession.[3] In 1933 it was again reported that the practice had appeared in London, but the *British Medical Journal* stated that there was 'no evidence of its degree or of its extension to the provinces'.[4] Evidence of its extension to the provinces was soon given by a correspondent.[5] It was pointed out that it was a criminal offence[6] and 'highly detrimental to the honour of the medical profession'.[7]

There were some consultants and specialists who found other answers to the loss of private practice caused by the general drift to the hospitals. They persuaded their governing bodies to allow them to see private patients at their hospitals. By 1932, it had become in some hospitals 'one of the privileges of the outpatient staff at the hospital to see private patients on ordinary outpatients' days in a room which the hospital provided, the patients either being picked out by the almoner as those who ought to pay a fee, or being sent by the local practitioners for consultations'.[8] The hospitals committee of the BMA was aware that the system had 'possible abuses'. It was suggested that the room used should not be part of the department and that the time of these sessions should not correspond with usual outpatient hours.[9] By 1939

[1] *BMJ*, 6 December 1913, p. 1506
[2] *Hospital*, Vol. LXVIII, 17 April 1920, p. 61
[3] ibid., 24 April 1920, p. 85
[4] *BMJ*, 11 March 1933, p. 422
[5] ibid., p. 483
[6] ibid., 24 June 1933, p. 112
[7] *BMJ Supplement*, 17 June 1933, p. 267
[8] ibid., 22 October 1932, p. 214
[9] ibid.

it was reported that there was a growing tendency for such private sessions to be held.[1]

One of the 'possible abuses' was what the Labour Party had called 'queue-barging' in its report of 1922. By 1933, it had become a big enough problem to gain discussion in the *British Medical Journal*. The journal was opposed to the system of 'tipping the consultant' to secure priority in admission to the general ward of a voluntary hospital, or to secure admission without going through the proper test of means. According to one young doctor who wrote to the *British Medical Journal* in 1933, some wards were three-quarters full of such special cases 'while other patients, more urgently ill, are awaiting beds which rightfully belong to them'.[2] In 1938 a correspondent described the system as 'very prevalent' and said that the usual 'tip' was three guineas.[3] Sometimes the general practitioner used his influence with consultants to demand such favours.[4] At Hull, the office staff of one hospital reported that 'the majority of the patients whom they would query as suitable for admission from the point of view of financial status came direct from the private consulting rooms of the honorary staff'.[5] It was clear that in such hospitals the charitable nature of the work had undergone a profound change.

Though consultants and specialists may have been losing consultations at their homes, they were treating more private inpatients. More and more pay beds were opened for what were called 'the new poor'. Thus in 1932 the Golden Square Throat, Nose and Ear Hospital was reported to have opened two whole wards with curtained cubicles. The inclusive charge was four guineas a week. The wards were intended to be 'of benefit to the large class of persons who are not eligible for hospital treatment in the ordinary sense but are feeling very severely the effects of the present economic situation'.[6]

There were some charities, however, who encouraged the well-to-do to use their pay beds. An administrator from Kings Cross (Mr Whiteley) defended the practice by pointing out that 'you cannot get the same treatment outside the hospitals' and

[1] ibid., 7 January 1939, p. 5
[2] ibid., 20 May 1933, p. 227
[3] ibid., 1 October 1938, p. 229
[4] ibid., p. 251
[5] ibid.
[6] *Hospital*, Vol. 28, January 1932, p. 24

such patients 'do help to pay for those beds which we get in every hospital which do not pay for themselves'.[1] A Birmingham consultant drew attention to the luxury of private beds in America with individual telephones, cookers and refrigerators.[2] The secretary of the Royal Northern Hospital stressed that in a successful private wing the general equipment should be unlike the ordinary hospital equipment and, as far as circumstances allowed, as much like hotel equipment as possible. 'No private section can be fully successful unless special consideration is shown to the fads and fancies of patients and the provision of facilities for their convenience and comfort is vital.'[3] These features were apparently not so vital for the care of patients in the general wards.

The trend towards pay beds did not proceed without opposition. When the Warneford Hospital devoted its centenary appeal to the erection of a paying patients' block, a workers' representative protested strongly but unsuccessfully.[4] A medical teacher argued for 'strict limitations on the proportion of pay beds allotted to each teaching hospital' as it was not possible to use as teaching subjects patients who were in paid beds.[5] But the major opposition came from the general practitioners who feared that they would not be allowed to treat their patients in the private wards of the voluntary hospitals. Violent statements were made by general practitioners in the correspondence columns of the *British Medical Journal*. It was complained that honorary staff looked upon their beds as 'their own special exclusive province and the GP is anathema there'.[6] According to another general practitioner, these 'monopolies' were 'a flagrant abuse and injustice'.[7]

The question was regularly discussed at the annual meetings of the BMA. The policy of trying to associate the general practitioner with the visiting medical staff who had the control of the care of private patients did not work out very well. It was found in some cases that the patient was prepared to pay the consultant and the resident staff, but did not want to pay the

[1] ibid., Vol. 29, July 1933, p. 180
[2] ibid., Vol. 28, July 1932, p. 192
[3] ibid., Vol. 31, December 1935, p. 323
[4] ibid., Vol. 28, March 1932, p. 57
[5] *BMJ Supplement*, 31 March 1934, p. 126
[6] ibid., 11 February 1933, p. 46
[7] ibid., 25 February 1933, p. 66

general practitioner in addition.[1] The BMA had, however, other strings to its bow. It was resolved in 1932 that 'accommodation should be provided in all districts for the treatment of patients by general medical practitioners'.[2] It was also agreed that the practice of unrestricted staffing should be extended.[3] It was pointed out that as the result of the Nursing Homes Act, 'the authorities had closed most of the smaller and less expensive Nursing Homes as being unsuitable, and that had robbed the urban practitioner of reasonably cheap Nursing Home accommodation'.[4]

While there were general practitioners who regretted the closing of Homes which had been deemed unsuitable, there were other doctors who felt that the Act was not being operated with sufficient stringency. In 1935, a helpless aged cripple was murdered by the unqualified proprietress of an unregistered nursing home. Different standards were being operated by different local authorities so that 'homes which would be refused a registration in one area manage to pass elsewhere'.[5] There was still a certain number of nursing homes which were as yet unregistered and unsupervised, housing 'patients under the care of practitioners and consultants, who, perhaps, do not know whether the home is registered or not'.[6] The deputy medical officer of health of Hastings argued for a clearer definition of 'nursing' and of a 'Nursing Home'.[7] It seems probable that many nursing homes had, as the result of the Act of 1926, changed their titles to 'convalescent home' without any major change in their work. Between 1921 and 1938, the number of beds in nursing homes decreased from about 26,000 to about 22,500,[8] while the number of beds in convalescent homes increased from about 13,000 to about 26,000.

Despite the opposition of general practitioners and workingmen's representatives, the voluntary hospitals continued to open pay beds. There were, however, legal difficulties which a number of hospitals had to overcome. Many of the voluntary hospitals

[1] *Hospital*, Vol. 31, December 1935, p. 327
[2] *BMJ Supplement*, 22 October 1932, pp. 213–14 and 5 August 1933, p. 88
[3] ibid., 29 April 1933, p. 175
[4] ibid., 22 October 1932, p. 214
[5] ibid., 2 July 1938, p. 3
[6] ibid., p. 5
[7] ibid.
[8] See Vol. 2 of this study.

were endowed under charitable trusts, some of which expressly stated that treatment had to be free. Under other trusts the money had to be used for a hospital for 'the sick poor'. Such a trust could hardly be used to provide beds for 'the new poor' let alone 'the sick rich'. In many cases the Charity Commissioners had helped hospitals round these legal difficulties. Thus when the term 'necessitous poor' had been used in the trust it was given a wide interpretation. And when a hospital could show that a number of beds were empty either because of shortage of money or because of a shortage of sick poor patients, the accommodation had been allowed to be used for pay beds for a limited period. The Charity Commissioners 'had been consistently helpful and in favour of the movement'.[1] If a hospital

> had wished to build on trust land a block in which well-to-do people could obtain luxurious accommodation at nursing home prices, they have declined to vary the trusts, but have suggested that the hospital should let the necessary land to a separately constituted body which should manage a block apart from the hospital.[2]

Some hospitals had got round the legal problems by special Acts of Parliament. Thus St George's obtained the right to build pay beds in 1914. Such units had to be self-supporting. The practice became more and more popular in the thirties. In 1933 there were Acts for the Manchester Royal Infirmary, the Cancer Hospital and the Samaritan Free Hospital. Hospitals in Birmingham and Plymouth followed in 1934.[3] St Bartholomew's, which had provided pay beds since 1921 'in the best wards' with the full support of the Charity Commissioners, decided in 1934 to ask Parliament for the right to build on trust land a pay block out of money expressly raised for this purpose. Parliament gave them the power and under the 'doctrine of partial poverty' allowed them to subsidize part-pay beds out of trust funds.

St Bartholomew's hoped to raise £124,000 for this purpose, but only £10,000 was subscribed: complaining that the supply

[1] *BMJ Supplement*, 17 December 1938, p. 374 (article by D. Harcourt-Kitchin, 'Pay Beds in Voluntary Hospitals: the Legal Side')
[2] ibid., p. 374
[3] ibid., p. 375

of benevolent millionaires was exhausted,[1] the governors went back to Parliament and asked for the power to build the block out of trust funds. Parliament would not, however, agree to this. A Select Committee of the House of Lords found itself unable to agree with the treasurer of the hospital 'that nowadays the expression "sick poor" means a man with £1,000 a year and three children'.[2] The scheme would 'risk the trust fund to an unlimited extent, without even the control of the Charity Commissioners, on a commercial adventure'.[3]

Meanwhile, the BHA and the King Edward's Fund had planned a general Act to give all hospitals the right to provide pay beds under proper safeguards. The Bill was introduced, as might have been expected, in the House of Lords. The Bill was greeted by vehement opposition from a few members who feared that the existing provisions for the sick poor would be whittled away.[4] Many doctors were opposed to the Bill though for different reasons. Dr Fothergill thought it 'very unsatisfactory from the point of view of the general practitioner who wanted bed accommodation for other than acute cases needing specialist treatment'.[5] Another general practitioner wrote to the *British Medical Journal* complaining that the Bill would 'render hospitals quite independent of the general practitioners in the area'.[6] In a later letter Dr Fothergill went so far as to say that the visiting medical staff would gain 'a monopoly in institutional medical treatment *for the whole local population* not using a council hospital, as against their professional colleagues in the district'.[7]

The hospitals committee of the BMA refused to be driven into any precipitate action. Dr MacDonald, the chairman, pointed out that it would be both 'futile' and 'a diplomatic mistake' to try and use the Bill 'to promote the access of outside practitioners to hospitals'.[8] There was, however, one clause of the Bill which he thought needed amendment. The Bill had proposed to give hospitals the power not only to charge for maintenance but also for treatment. It needed to be made clear

[1] ibid., 24 December 1938, p. 387
[2] ibid.
[3] ibid.
[4] ibid., p. 377
[5] ibid., 13 April 1935, p. 136
[6] ibid., 18 May 1935, p. 222
[7] ibid., 1 June 1935, pp. 241–2
[8] ibid., 4 May 1935, p. 213

that this only applied to the resident staff and that the system of payment for the attending practitioners was left for independent negotiation. With this amendment, the Bill became law.[1]

The creation of pay beds under the Act was hedged with restrictions. Existing buildings could only be used for this purpose if they could not be used for their original purpose. The cost of new accommodation had to be paid for out of separate funds. The schemes of charges had to be approved by the Charity Commissioners and had to include, where appropriate, arrangements for partial payment with the difference met out of trust funds. Thus the Act gave 'statutory recognition of the class of the "new poor" '.[2] Little use was, however, made of the Act: it appeared that most of the hospitals had already obtained other means to provide pay beds.[3]

Thus pay beds spread throughout the thirties. More and more hospitals issued special appeals in aid of the middle classes. There were more and more complaints from patients who found that they were expected to pay two bills for medical services when they only expected to pay one.[4] And more and more well-to-do patients entered the voluntary hospitals. One children's hospital which charged only three guineas a week found that the wards were not properly filled. When it raised the fee to four-and-a-half guineas per week the wards were immediately filled. 'It appears that our charges were too low and people wondered what was the matter.'[5]

Hospital policy had been based on the assumption that there were two classes of patient – the private patient who paid the whole cost or more than the cost and the ward patient who paid what he could afford. The BMA had fought hard to maintain the distinction: thus it had tried, though with limited success, to ensure that uniform income limits of its own choosing were imposed on members of contributory schemes. Gradually the distinction was becoming less meaningful: provision had to be made for patients above the income limits who were unable to pay the fees commonly charged to private patients. The British Provident Association had pioneered a pre-payment

[1] ibid., 27 June 1935, p. 347
[2] ibid., 17 December 1938, p. 386
[3] ibid.
[4] For example, see *Hospital*, Vol. 32, May 1936, p. 114.
[5] ibid., p. 115

scheme for the middle classes and other schemes were developing on these lines.

At a joint conference of hospital administrators and governors at Liverpool in 1932 it was argued that 'what the middle classes needed now was some form of co-operative scheme analogous to the contributory schemes common among manual workers'.[1] It was held that there must be maximum income limits and free choice of doctor. In May the next year the BMA organized a conference of representatives of hospital provident schemes and a sub-committee was appointed to draft a scheme with appropriate income limits and a schedule of doctors' fees. At the 1934 representative meeting certain principles were approved. It was decided that an association running such a scheme should have medical representation on its governing body and should be linked neither with any particular hospitals nor with any hospital *contributory* scheme. Income limits were to vary between £350 for a single person living in the provinces to £550 for a person living in London with more than one dependant. A single person was to pay £1 18s per year and a member with more than one dependant £3 per year. This would permit an *average* medical payment of £16 per case and a *maximum* payment of 15 guineas to a hospital.[2]

Having worked out these principles, the BMA watched carefully to see that all new provident schemes kept to the rules it had laid down. The Association favoured the setting up of a central co-ordinating body and when an interim committee was set up for this purpose lent £100 to its new protégé.[3] Twenty associations were represented at a conference held in March 1936. Both Oxford and Cambridge had provident associations which broadly followed the BMA model. The Birmingham scheme had three grades of benefit in return for payments of 6s 6d, 9s 9d, or 13s a quarter.[4] The British Provident Association scheme still had no limit of area or income and offered payments not only for hospital care but also for home nurses, consultation fees and for ambulance services.[5]

Thus provident schemes developed under the eagle eye of

[1] ibid., Vol. 28, July 1932, p. 188
[2] *BMJ Supplement*, 6 October 1934, p. 189
[3] ibid., 13 March 1937, p. 130
[4] ibid., 20 February 1937, p. 91
[5] ibid., p. 91

the BMA. The calm was, however, shattered in 1938 when the HSA announced that it proposed to bring into its scheme contributors above the existing income limits of £4–5 per week. While existing contributors paid threepence per week, it was proposed that single persons with between £4 and £5 per week, married couples with between £5 and £7 per week and couples with dependants and incomes of between £6 and £8 per week were to receive benefits on payment of sixpence per week.

The BMA expressed grave concern.[1] It protested both to the HSA and to the Voluntary Hospitals Committee for the County of London.[2] The latter favoured the HSA scheme but agreed to limit outpatient consultations generally and to try and secure that hospitals insisted on members of contributory schemes obtaining the first consultation at a private consulting room. It also expressed the view that medical staffs should receive some financial recognition.[3] In the light of these concessions the BMA hospitals committee was prepared to accept the HSA's new proposals providing this last point was made more definite and included a figure of not less than 20 per cent of the monies received by the hospital and provided also that the London medical staffs were in agreement.[4]

Meanwhile it was known that the King's Fund was preparing a scheme on provident lines. In the jargon of the day, a contributory scheme meant a system of partial pre-payment which did not aim to cover the total cost of hospital care, and a provident scheme was a system which aimed at covering full cost including the cost of medical attendance. Early in 1939 the hospitals committee of the BMA was prepared on certain conditions to see a place for both types of scheme. One of these conditions was the agreement of the medical staffs. This was not forthcoming.

At a meeting of medical staffs on 27 January, it was resolved not to endorse the HSA scheme. Both Dr MacDonald representing the hospitals committee of the BMA and Dr Gray representing the Voluntary Hospitals Committee pointed out that persons with incomes of less than £6 to £8 could not afford to pay the high contribution required for a provident scheme, but the medical staffs were not convinced. The HSA scheme

[1] ibid., 19 March 1938, p. 147
[2] ibid., 18 June 1938, p. 372
[3] ibid., 19 November 1938, p. 317
[4] ibid., 7 January 1939, p. 5

was dubbed 'charity at the expense of the medical profession' and 'an insult to every consultant in London'.[1] Despite warnings from the deputy secretary of the BMA, Dr Charles Hill, the doctors decided that the right way to provide for persons above the present income limits of the HSA was by a provident scheme and they urged the King's Fund to hurry on their draft for such a scheme.[2] The HSA scheme was, however, inaugurated by a few hospitals[3] with the full support of the Voluntary Hospitals Committee which told hospitals that the medical staffs' opposition was based on misconceptions.[4]

By this time the BMA as a whole had decided to back a provident scheme for all above the old HSA income limits and in June 1939 the King's Fund scheme[5] was announced with fitting dignity by the Duke of Kent. The scheme had been prepared by a committee chaired by Sir Bernard Docker, which included representatives of the BMA.[6] Income limits varied from £400 to £700 according to family size and subscriptions were from thirteen shillings per quarter to a guinea per quarter. Payments were to be made for a stay of up to four weeks in hospital. Persons above the income limits could join the scheme on a grant-in-aid basis: the benefits would be paid towards the cost, whatever fees and charges might be settled privately. There was an agreed schedule of payments to consultants and specialists which would not be disclosed to the subscriber or the public. There would be no payments for consultations before treatment in hospital.[7] Soon after the scheme was published, a meeting of medical staffs resolved to try and persuade hospitals who had accepted the new HSA scheme to give the King's Fund scheme a fair trial.[8]

Thus, on the eve of war, a pre-payment scheme was launched for London with Royal Patronage. Anyone was eligible to join. There was provident insurance for the middle and upper classes and contributory schemes for the bulk of the working classes. For the aged, for the unemployed and for all who did not or

[1] ibid., 4 February 1939, p. 57
[2] ibid., 24 June 1939, p. 337
[3] ibid.
[4] ibid., 1 April 1939, p. 137
[5] ibid., 17 June 1939, p. 328
[6] ibid.
[7] ibid.
[8] ibid., 1 July 1939, p. 6

could not make regular payments there remained the right to free hospital care after a test of means. Under the impact of financial pressure and the spread of the hospital habit up the social strata, the voluntary hospitals had become primarily trading concerns and only secondarily charitable institutions.

As the hospitals were used by a wider section of the population, the life of the hospital patient was made more comfortable. The campaign against early waking conducted by the King's Fund gradually bore fruit. The proportion of London hospitals reporting that patients were awakened before 6 a.m. fell from 53 per cent in 1931 to 21 per cent in 1934.[1] The subjects discussed in *The Hospital* extended from hospital food, smoking,[2] and waiting time[3] to include the supply of reading matter,[4] information given to patients' relatives,[5] and noise in wards.[6] A branch of the Hospital Officers' Association even tried the experiment of inviting patients to attend one of their meetings.[7] This experiment was not found to be a success and was soon discontinued.

The beginnings of a revolution in hospital architecture could be detected. No longer were all new hospitals designed with long rows of beds set at right angles to the walls. Beds began to be placed parallel to the windows and arranged in groups separated by glazed screens.[8] This arrangement 'seems first to have been used in the Hertford County Hospital (1929), in the new wing of the Sussex Hospital for Women and Children (1930), and in the Southend Hospital (1932)'.[9] One maternity block even had single rooms for the early period of the hospital stay.[10] General ward patients were given bed lights, bell pushes

[1] *Hospital*, Vol. 30, December 1934, p. 315
[2] ibid., February 1934, p. 5
[3] ibid., Vol. 32, August 1936, p. 196
[4] ibid., October 1936, p. 269
[5] ibid., p. 255
[6] ibid., July 1936, p. 180; May 1936, p. 128
[7] The patients said that the 'rattling of money boxes was overdone', that seriously ill patients ought to have separate accommodation, that the sharp manner of some doctors was 'particularly unkind to people who are ill', and that 'the work of the chaplain might be of greater benefit if younger men and men of a more cheerful disposition were appointed to this post'. *Hospital*, Vol. 35, May 1939, p. 178
[8] ibid., Vol. 32, July 1936, p. 182
[9] Nuffield Provincial Hospitals Trust, *Studies in the Functions and Design of Hospitals*, p. 4, London, 1955
[10] *Hospital*, Vol. 35, May 1939, p. 159

and earphones.[1] Space was provided for convalescent patients in 'solaria'.[2] Hospitals began to be decorated in what were thought gay colours – green and cream, 'at once restful and a delight to the eye'.[3]

Thus, by 1938 there were some hospitals which were consciously attempting to adapt their service, to make it attractive to the public as a whole rather than merely acceptable to recipients of charity. Progress in this respect as in every other respect was, however, very uneven. Much depended on the funds available, on the attitude of the governing body and medical staff, and on the imagination and initiative of the chief administrator. As hospitals became more complex institutions, as the range of professional persons employed by hospitals expanded and the number of specialist departments increased, the task of co-ordination required administrative skill, tact and knowledge of a higher order. No longer could a lay committeeman or an honorary secretary master quickly all the details of running a hospital. Moreover, the hospitals were undergoing rapid change in response to the new demands of the scientific medicine of the 1930's.

While formal training had for many years been instituted for both doctors and nurses, the lay administrator was given a very casual introduction to hospital work. The chief administrator of a hospital (known as secretary, clerk or house governor) was paid about £300 in a small voluntary hospital, about £800–1,000 in a large provincial hospital and between £1,500–2,000 per annum in a London teaching hospital.[4] Entry to the profession was by apprenticeship. Just as the local government service did not attract persons with university or advanced secondary education,[5] so the voluntary hospitals had extremely few administrators who had university degrees. There was no scheme of professional training, and the only diploma which was available was not of a standard to gain the respect of either a voluntary or local authority hospital.[6] Shortly before the war, steps were

[1] ibid., Vol. 32, October 1936, p. 260
[2] ibid., Vol. 33, September 1937, p. 277
[3] ibid., Vol. 32, July 1936, p. 182
[4] See advertisements in *The Hospital*.
[5] Ministry of Health, *Report by the Departmental Committee on Qualifications, Recruitment, Training and Promotion of Local Government Officers*, p. 18, HMSO, 1934
[6] *Hospital*, Vol. 32, April 1936, p. 88

being taken to upgrade the diploma but not until after the war was a formal course in hospital administration started.

In the twenty years between the wars, there had been spectacular developments and drastic changes in the voluntary hospitals. There were more beds and better beds, but funds were not available in all hospitals to meet the growing expense of looking after patients at the standards which doctors were demanding. By 1938 there were some municipal hospitals which had better premises and offered a higher standard of care than the average voluntary hospital. Not until this had actually occurred did the hospitals attempt to take concerted action.

Half the cost of the voluntary hospitals was now paid by the patients, mainly in the form of contributory schemes. No longer was a voluntary hospital just a charitable body attempting to serve the 'sick poor'. A new definition was needed. The King's Fund had in fact produced a new description as early as 1928:

> The voluntary hospital is already becoming a co-operative effort in which all classes of the community, including the hospital patients themselves, combine as their means permit to provide hospital services which produce benefits for all classes; directly for the less wealthy, because without the hospitals the necessary medical treatment cannot be brought within their means, and indirectly for the more wealthy, because without the hospitals the necessary medical treatment would not exist.[1]

---

[1] quoted in *BMJ Supplement*, 25 July 1931, p. 88

CHAPTER 25

The Problem of Planning

THE remarkable growth of the voluntary hospitals during the inter-war period gave confidence to all those associated with them. By introducing contributory schemes, provident schemes and pay beds, the movement appeared to have taken on a new lease of life. Only the most perceptive observers appreciated the challenge which could arise out of the 1929 Act. But the process of growth was itself producing the seeds of destruction. While hospitals were few and small, there was little need for central planning. But many years earlier the experience of London had shown the problems which could come with unco-ordinated expansion. These lessons were forgotten as hospitals grew and spread throughout the country.

The mistakes of London were repeated in the provinces. Some areas had too many hospitals, others had too few. The pattern of provision depended on the donations of the living and the legacies of the dead, rather than on any ascertained need for hospital services. The foundation of new hospitals and the extension of old ones depended 'upon the mere whim or caprice of some person with money to leave – often by Will'.[1] Such persons were parochial. A neighbourhood would thus be saddled with a hospital whose location and function it was in no position to alter. There could be

> congestion in some hospitals with empty beds in others, the building of new minor hospitals without due regard to the requirements of the region as a whole, the attempt of each minor hospital to do the work of a General Hospital in miniature and to waste money in equipping itself for work it should not attempt, and the consequent employment of staffs of consulting and general practitioner grades indifferently on whatever cases may happen to arise in the immediate vicinity.[2]

[1] British Hospitals Association, *Report of the Voluntary Hospitals Commission* (the Sankey Report), para. 51, April, 1937

[2] ibid., para. 52

Britain became littered with small hospitals. Despite the growing concentration of population in the towns, the improvement in transport facilities and the greater complexity of medical care, the number of hospitals was constantly increasing. The village general practitioner who was losing his patients to the town hospitals and to the doctors that staffed them would persuade local benefactors to endow a hospital for local use. At the outbreak of war it was found that 'of about 700 general voluntary hospitals only some seventy-five were equipped with over 200 beds, some 115 provided between 100 and 200 beds, over 500 had less than 100 beds, and more than half of these had less than 30 beds'.[1] Small hospitals were more frequently to be found in the rural areas than in the towns. Thus in 'Berkshire, Buckinghamshire and Oxfordshire there were 75 hospitals of all types (voluntary and municipal), 41 of which had less than 50 beds. In addition, there were 89 private nursing homes with an average of less than 9 beds apiece.'[2]

It was in these small hospitals that some of the really bad medical care was provided. There were general practitioners who were prepared to attempt surgery which was beyond their competence and to attempt it in conditions which denied them the services of skilled and experienced nursing staff or a proper range of equipment. Some of them were 'entirely self-taught'.[3] The annual reports of small hospitals would often contain lists of visiting consultants, but 'the visits of consultants to these small hospitals were relatively infrequent, and some specialists, whose names appeared in the Annual Reports, were never asked to see patients at all'.[4] A general practitioner would often defer 'calling in consultant help because no fees could be offered and it was common for a patient in a general ward to have to wait for a consultant opinion until a private patient also required the advice of a consultant in that particular branch of medicine or surgery'.[5]

Qualified specialists were concentrated in those towns which had enough private work to give them a living. No less than a third were in London.[6] As specialists received the bulk of their

1 Titmuss, *Problems of Social Policy*, p. 67, London, 1950
2 ibid.
3 Nuffield Provincial Hospitals Trust, *The Hospital Surveys*, p. 10
4 Titmuss, p. 67
5 Nuffield Trust, *The Hospital Surveys*, pp. 10–11
6 Acton Society Trust, *Hospitals and the State*, p. 8

income from private work, the staffing of the local hospital tended to be related more to the number of wealthy residents in the area than to the number of patients needing care. And as a hospital appointment was one of the requirements for the more lucrative private work, there was an obvious incentive for existing staff members to prevent any additional appointments being made to the hospital staff or to ensure that the new men who were appointed would not attract much private practice. Thus an increase in the senior staff of a hospital could involve existing incumbents in very real sacrifices. Hospitals, therefore, tended to be understaffed. As the house governor of Hull Royal Infirmary put it, 'the managing body of a hospital cannot, or at any rate is seldom willing to, develop its services if that development is likely to have an adverse effect upon the private interests of its staff'.[1]

As the doctors were 'honoraries', there was 'no direction or control of their activities'.[2] The beds were usually divided out among the consultants which prevented them from being used with maximum economy. There was often a waiting list for one speciality or specialist while there were many empty beds in other parts of the hospital.[3] The occupancy of voluntary hospitals as a whole was not high but there were at least 100,000 persons waiting to get into hospital.[4] Though there were still a few hospitals where the 'letter system' survived,[5] the doctors were nearly everywhere responsible for selecting patients for admission. They admitted the acute sick whenever possible and patients who outstayed their welcome were often transferred to a local authority hospital. During 1935-7, the voluntary hospitals transferred 27,000 patients to general hospitals provided by the London County Council.[6]

These were the principal failings of the voluntary hospitals which led to the demand for 'planning'. In a free market the demands of consumers can be met by a variety of firms each acting independently and without any conscious planning of the system of supply. But voluntary hospitals were not developed

[1] *Hospital*, Vol. 36, May 1940, p. 112
[2] ibid.
[3] Titmuss, p. 71
[4] ibid., p. 73
[5] See *BMJ Supplement*, 26 July 1930, p. 50.
[6] ibid., p. 68

to meet the expressed demands of the market. Nor were they developed to meet what either general practitioners or consultants believed to be the medical needs of the area. The availability of capital for construction had introduced an element of chance into the pattern of hospital services. In this sense there was no hospital 'system'.

In London, the King's Fund had managed to secure modest improvements. It held considerable funds which it could allocate according to its own interpretation of the needs of each hospital. It could use both its influence and financial power to influence the planning of hospitals. Though not a few amalgamations and removals were partly or wholly due to its machinations, much still remained to be done: hospitals were still over-concentrated in the centre of London. The desire of their doctors to be near both the University and the fashionable centres of consulting practice were major obstacles to change. Doctors were 'unwilling to travel long distances to see their patients'.[1] Both the Middlesex and the Westminster Hospitals were rebuilt on central sites and St George's Hospital was planning to do likewise. In 1931 it was calculated that 37 per cent of voluntary hospital patients came from beyond the county boundary to be subjected to 'the endless noise and hubbub of the centre of London and the fog which pollutes the atmosphere'.[2]

Nothing had happened to alter the problem of the special hospitals. A few of them had been absorbed by general hospitals but it was stated that, in 1935, nearly a quarter of the hospitals in Great Britain were special hospitals.[3] Out of 233 of these hospitals, only 67 had over 100 beds and many had less than 50 beds.[4] Though most of them specialized in particular diseases, there were also the hospitals for children, for women, for the clergy, for officers, for gentlewomen. There were no less than six special hospitals for women in the central London area.[5]

There were 600 cottage hospitals containing about 10,000 beds.[6] The smaller hospitals were said by one observer to 'embody many of the worst features of the voluntary system. . . .

---

[1] PEP, *Report on the British Health Services 1937*, p. 261
[2] ibid.
[3] ibid., p. 243
[4] ibid.
[5] ibid.
[6] *Hospital*, Vol. 30, July 1934, p. 171

They are responsible for turning out a great deal of bad surgical work, and I suspect that a similar statement might be truthfully made about their work in medical and special departments.'[1] A general practitioner could hardly be expected to do as good work as a specialist – particularly when he attempted to combine several specialities.

Whilst the King's Fund had had limited success in securing co-ordination in London, in the provinces there was as yet no endowed fund. Moreover, the Onslow Commission with its limited resources had been unable to secure the dramatic changes which the Cave Committee had hoped for. Some co-ordinating arrangements between voluntary hospitals had, however, been instituted in a few areas. In 1933 a committee was set up in Liverpool to inquire into the problems of the voluntary hospitals in that locality. As a result of its report, a Board was set up in 1935 consisting of six representatives of the nine teaching hospitals, three representatives of the Hospital Staffs Association and two representatives of the University of Liverpool. The Board turned its attention to the problems identified by the commission: the amalgamation of the four general hospitals, the plans for rebuilding, the appointment of honorary staffs, the provision of a 24-hour ambulance service, the co-ordination of X-ray services and similar matters. A committee was also set up to secure permanent co-operation with the local authority services.[2] Eventually, on 1 January 1939, the four general hospitals were amalgamated into the Royal Liverpool United Hospital.[3]

The history of Birmingham was similar. The amalgamation of the two general hospitals had been recommended by the Birmingham Hospital Council as far back as 1926. The amalgamation in this case was to be effected by the construction of a new hospital centre with 1,000 beds outside the city. Work began in 1930 and amalgamation was achieved in 1939 by a special Act of Parliament.[4] A Hospitals Council had also been set up at Sheffield in 1919 consisting of no less than 82 members, of which two were representatives of the local press. It was this body which had started the 'penny in the pound' scheme. In

[1] quoted in Newsholme, p. 93
[2] *Sankey Report*, p. 69
[3] *Hospital*, Vol. 36, February 1940, p. 35
[4] ibid.

1936, about £185,000 was collected under the scheme. The Council owned nine ambulances, and in 1936 sent 2,558 cases to approved convalescent homes.[1]

All these schemes attempted to secure co-operation between voluntary hospitals. A joint hospitals board was set up at Manchester with the wider function of co-ordinating voluntary and public hospitals. It consisted of ten representatives of the City Council, eight representatives of the Voluntary Hospitals Council, five of the University and one of the local branch of the British Medical Association. Although the Board was only to act in an advisory capacity, all hospitals agreed to consult with the Board on major issues. The Board was to deal with new construction, medical staffing, education and any other matters. To ensure the fullest co-operation between council and voluntary hospitals, honorary Directors of Service in Medicine, Surgery and Gynaecology were appointed.[2]

These were the main attempts to encourage co-operation, but they covered only a small part of the country. Where there was no co-ordinating body, the voluntary hospitals worked in rivalry with one another. Outside the area covered by the King's Fund, each hospital was free to present its accounts in any manner which it thought appropriate. This made it impossible for a prospective benefactor to ascertain with any accuracy the needs of each charity. Over the majority of the country there was no co-ordination whatsoever.

The British Hospitals Association had been founded in 1884, but not until the negotiations conducted over the National Insurance Act had it attracted a wide measure of support. And even then, it had found itself bypassed by the King's Fund or by the London teaching hospitals. When the temporary grant had been made to the hospitals in 1921, the Cave Committee had not worked through the BHA but had sponsored a separate organizational structure to distribute it. The BHA held regular annual conferences, but by no means every hospital bothered to send representatives. Some governing bodies chose not to belong to the Association at all.[3] Though it was nominally organized in 23 regions, five of these were 'to all intents and purposes inactive'.[4]

[1] ibid., p. 75
[2] ibid., p. 71
[3] *Hospital Gazette*, June 1929, p. 105
[4] *Sankey Report*, p. 15

The Association attempted to be of use to its members by publishing memoranda and information upon matters of interest and importance. It also had a committee which was responsible for all matters concerning parliamentary legislation. But the Association had been able to achieve little. Although in 1936 the voluntary hospitals possessed capital to the value of some £200 million and had an income of some £16½ million, they were only paying £2,000 as membership fees to the Association.[1] Thus the service which it could give its members was strictly limited. Nor did every hospital participate in its work. In particular, the London teaching hospitals had their own means of getting what they wanted. Among their governors were those who were at the apex of the social system. Representations on any issue could more conveniently be made through informal approaches to Ministers or through the effective network of social relationships that ran through the King's Fund, the City, the Royal Colleges and the House of Lords. The teaching hospitals – particularly the London teaching hospitals – were not prepared to throw in their lot with the voluntary hospitals as a whole.

Thus the hospitals lacked a strong central organization which was 'thoroughly representative of the hospitals up and down the country'.[2] The Association was 'a school master without the authority of a cane trying to keep in order one thousand mischievous boys and failing'.[3] It lacked the authority which 'would enable it to speak promptly and confidently regarding the views of its members and with the assurance that all would abide by a majority vote'.[4] Many hospitals were too strongly entrenched in the affections of their local supporters to think of the wider needs of the whole voluntary hospital movement. There was no real corporate sense. As a result, as the Secretary of the BHA (Mr Orde) put it, the hospitals 'consistently shut their eyes to danger patent to all except themselves'.[5]

All this was known by those who were prepared to think of the welfare of the voluntary hospital movement as a whole rather than of the welfare of one particular hospital. But the greatest

[1] ibid.
[2] ibid., p. 16
[3] ibid.
[4] ibid.
[5] *BMJ Supplement*, 20 August 1938, p. 152

weakness of the whole movement was shown by the fact that so little was done about it. Not until six years after the 1929 Act did the Association take a step which had the possibility of changing the *status quo*. And that consisted solely of the establishment of a commission of inquiry. On 1 June 1935, it was resolved at the annual conference of the BHA that a commission should be set up:

> To take into consideration the present position of the Voluntary Hospitals of the country; to enquire whether in view of recent legislative and social developments it is desirable that any steps should be taken to promote their interests, develop their policy and safeguard their future, and to frame such recommendations as may be thought expedient and acceptable.[1]

The chairman of the Commission was The Rt. Hon. Viscount Sankey, PC. Nine other members were appointed, of whom three were medical – Sir Henry Brackenbury of the BMA, and one Fellow each from the Royal Colleges of Physicians and Surgeons. The other members consisted of one nurse, one accountant, two Aldermen and two other laymen. Mr Orde of the BHA acted as secretary. The Commission reported in 1937.

The Report started by paying tribute to the achievements of the voluntary hospital movement. The strength of the system arose from 'the spirit that inspires' and 'the freedom it possesses'. The system had

> . . . enabled all classes to come together in order that the more fortunate should give help and encouragement to their less favoured fellow citizens. . . . It would be a national loss if the country were deprived of this voluntary association of individuals without distinction of class, creed or politics, and if they were no longer to work together to achieve an end for the benefit of humanity.[2]

The freedom of the movement was 'an example of the dislike of over-control and bureaucracy which is inherent in the genius of our race'.[3]

The Commission recognized that

> . . . the rise of the public authority system is affecting and may further affect the position of the voluntary hospitals. . . . While

[1] *Sankey Report*, p. 5
[2] ibid., pp. 7–8
[3] ibid., p. 8

we do not suggest that there is in the public authority system an entire absence of that spirit of voluntary service, which is so prominent a feature of the voluntary system, yet there is always a danger in the former system of too much uniformity with too many regulations and too much bureaucracy in carrying them out.[1]

The Commission recognized that both systems would 'exist side by side . . . for many years to come'.[2] If there was to be co-existence, there had to be co-operation. There also had to be local co-ordination.

The ancient problem of the special hospitals was reviewed once more. The Royal College of Surgeons stated that 'it was infinitely preferable for a General Hospital to have specialist departments to numberless small Special Hospitals being set up independently as they were very often uneconomic and difficult to staff'.[3]

Accordingly, the Commission decided that

> . . . the further establishment of Special Hospitals . . . is, generally speaking, to be deprecated. Such hospitals should be associated with General Hospitals. Special hospitals mean rigidity of accommodation and so may bring about empty beds. Disabilities cannot be cut up into water-tight compartments and patients should have the benefit of consultation and co-operation between various members of the hospital staff in their treatment.[4]

The Commission recommended that hospitals should be graded and that the smaller areas should be 'grouped round'[5] the larger hospitals. There should be central, district and cottage hospitals. The former was defined as a hospital in a large town, staffed entirely by consultants. A district hospital was a hospital in a medium-sized town, staffed partly or wholly by general practitioners. A cottage hospital was a hospital in a small town, village or country district, staffed by local practitioners.[6] The British Medical Association had pressed for years for general practitioner beds to be available everywhere. By implication

[1] ibid., pp. 8–9
[2] ibid., p. 9
[3] ibid., p. 19
[4] ibid., p. 36
[5] ibid., p. 21
[6] ibid., pp. 24–5

the Commission intended there to be no general practitioner beds in large towns.[1]

To undertake the grading of hospitals and to secure a rational use of available accommodation, the Commission suggested the establishment of a strong regional and central organization. The BHA was to form a provincial central council which would in turn initiate the formation of provincial regional councils. Eventually the councils were to be appointed by the hospitals of the region and the regions were in turn to appoint the central council.[2] There were to be effective central and regional offices. The regional office was to receive daily lists of empty beds, was to arrange transfers and generally to take steps to avoid waiting lists at some hospitals and empty beds in others. The office was also to maintain a record of patients, control an ambulance service, maintain a list of blood donors, sponsor joint purchasing schemes, advise on building and enlargements and undertake many other duties.[3] The offices were to be supported by contributions from the hospitals, from regional funds and from government grants.

The Commission recognized that the problem of the distribution of finance was critical to the future of the voluntary hospitals and possibly also to any attempt to secure effective co-ordination. Some hospitals were affluent, others had deficits. If the available finance were distributed according to needs, their financial position would not be unsatisfactory.[4] This could be achieved by establishing a pool into which each hospital would pay a percentage of its income, which could then be redistributed to deserving hospitals, provided they kept uniform accounts and submitted them on time. While this would be the simplest and possibly the most logical solution, the Commission doubted 'whether the minds of the supporters of voluntary hospitals are sufficiently prepared for so fundamental a departure from present methods'.[5] Thus the Commission recommended

[1] When asked why the report had not proposed beds for general practitioners in all hospitals, Sir Henry Brackenbury told the hospitals committee of the BMA that the subject matter had been so vast that some questions had been left out and this was one of them (*BMJ Supplement*, 15 May 1937, p. 293). This may not have been a complete explanation.

[2] ibid., p. 22

[3] ibid., pp. 22–4

[4] ibid., p. 27

[5] ibid.

the creation of regional funds which would receive contributions and endowments on the lines of the King's Fund in London.

As regards the overall financial position, the Commission believed that the hospitals should be prepared to receive grants in aid from the state: 'any traditional disinclination regarding the acceptance of money from the State should disappear.'[1] In particular, the state should contribute towards the treatment of the poor and the education of doctors and nurses. The Commission left the new central council to determine the appropriate method of payment. It recognized that the receipt of funds would lead to a claim for state representation on boards of management. It did not, however, believe that the claim would be 'pressed unduly' and it thought that 'a recognition of it would be advantageous'.[2]

In the case of other sources of finance, the Commission hoped that the regional councils would be able to rationalize arrangements and secure that maximum revenue was obtained. The Commission wanted the main weight of effort to be devoted to securing regular subscriptions: 'sporadic collecting efforts should take a secondary place.'[3] It welcomed the establishment and growth of contributory schemes and laid down principles upon which they should operate. Such schemes were to be regional in character, and there were to be reciprocal arrangements where a patient needed to be admitted to a hospital outside his own region. The income limits recommended by the BMA were accepted without any qualification and it was also suggested that 'rates of contribution to the Scheme should be fixed so as to enable the Scheme Funds to cover the full cost of the provision of hospital and ancillary services of its members'.[4]

The Commission considered the case for the payment of hospital medical staffs. It considered that the wider social group making use of the hospitals had made it necessary for the medical staffs of the hospitals to devote a larger proportion of their time to hospital work and had subtracted from their earnings in private practice. The BMA told the Commission that 'consultants, and particularly the younger consultants, are finding it increasingly difficult to secure and maintain a standard of living

[1] ibid., p. 30
[2] ibid., p. 31
[3] ibid., p. 32
[4] ibid., p. 33

which represents a reasonable reward for their services and enables them to maintain the highest possible standard of professional efficiency'.[1] Faced with this evidence, the Commission conceded the general principle of payment but accepted that there might be some exceptions. In particular, a position at a teaching hospital was 'an asset of considerable value and may in some cases go far to compensate for the time and work voluntarily given to the hospital'.[2] In hospitals with a considerable number of pay beds, particularly where the beds could only be used by the staff of the hospital, there was 'an undoubted material advantage to be gained by the medical staff'.[3] Thus while hospital managements should 'consider' the question of payment 'without delay', there might well be 'exceptions or modifications. Moreover, the circumstances of individual hospitals and the attitude of many members of these staffs vary so widely on this question that no universal application of the principle can be immediately expected.'[4]

As regards the method of payment, the Commission thought that the 'staff pool' system should

> ... be regarded as provisional and temporary, and that ultimately a definite part-time honorarium or salary will be found to be the most satisfactory method. It follows, we think, that, though this may make little, if any, difference in the status of the medical staff, it must involve a statement of the duties undertaken and an obligation to fulfil them more exactly than has sometimes been regarded as essential under existing conditions.[5]

The Commission was not prepared to accept the views of the BMA on the payment of medical staff without qualification. Nor was it prepared to accept the views of the Association on outpatient departments without amendment. The Commission was not willing to see them confined solely to referred cases, emergencies, the follow-up of discharged inpatients, and patients receiving treatment which could only be conveniently given at a hospital.

[1] ibid., p. 42
[2] ibid.
[3] ibid., p. 43
[4] ibid.
[5] ibid.

. . . we think that there is a class of case among persons of small financial means which might be held to make the establishment of such a rule inadvisable at the present time. This consists of the dependants of the lower waged persons insured under the National Health Insurance system, and some others of like status. It is arguable that this class ought to make the necessary provision by some form of contract or voluntary insurance, but they cannot be compelled to do so, and it can scarcely be maintained that, if they care to choose a charitable institution rather than Public Assistance, they should be forbidden such a choice.[1]

The Commission made many further recommendations for improvements in the accounting systems of hospitals, for the training of hospital administrators, for better pay and working conditions for nurses, and for developments in ambulance, convalescent and other related services. In general, the recommendations bore a striking resemblance to those of the only two official committees which had reviewed the problems of the voluntary hospitals (the Lords Committee and the Cave Committee). The BHA regional machinery was, however, to take the place of the exterior bodies which the official committees had favoured. The report suggested as radical a policy as it felt the hospitals could be persuaded to accept. It conceded to the BMA only part of what it wanted. It built upon the precedents of the King's Fund and of the councils which had been established in some areas. It recognized that co-ordination would involve some loss of independence for individual hospital managements.

The hospitals whose independence was most threatened by the Report were the special hospitals. Although the Commission had avoided saying so specifically, it clearly would have welcomed the amalgamation of nearly all of these with general hospitals. Within a few months a meeting was held at Moorfields Hospital of representatives of the 76 special hospitals of London. A committee was set up and, on 5 July 1938, delegates from 63 special hospitals formed a new association.[2]

About the same time, a new edition of the *General Medical Service for the Nation* was published by the BMA. The views of the Sankey Commission were quoted on a number of points, but the Association omitted to stress the difference between its own views

[1] ibid., p. 40
[2] *Lancet*, 16 July 1938, p. 172

and those of the BHA. It argued uncompromisingly that the medical staffs of *all* hospitals should be paid and that the use of the outpatient department should be confined solely to the categories it had recommended. It was not in favour of any services of the general practitioner type being provided to out-patients even at hospitals which had been expressly founded for the benefit of the sick poor.

While conceding the case for hospitals staffed by specialists, it argued that there was

> . . . a growing need for a more extensive provision of a type of hospital or accommodation in which the general practitioner can treat cases falling within his sphere of competence. It commonly happens to-day that for a social reason such as unsatisfactory home surroundings, a patient is admitted to hospital for a condition for which a more fortunately circumstanced patient would be treated at home by the patient's own doctor. It is contrary to the interest of the patient and damaging to the efficiency of general practice if social conditions lead to a discontinuity of medical treatment.[1]

The new edition stated that:

> Hospitals should, as a general rule, be staffed on a part-time basis – that is, by a visiting medical staff of practitioners who are also engaged in private practice. In this way the hospital benefits by the wider experience gained in hospital and private practice by members of its staff, and the general public, whether it seeks its consultant and specialist service at a hospital or privately, can avail itself of the best service in the area.[2]

The Report did not make clear exactly how it was that 'the wider experience' of treating the diseases of paying patients assisted a practitioner in treating the diseases of those less favourably placed.

The BMA did not think that the Sankey Commission's suggestion for regional councils including representatives of local authorities would in fact secure adequate co-operation between voluntary and local authority hospitals. It restated its dissatisfaction with co-operation under the machinery of the Local Government Act.

[1] BMA, *A General Medical Service for the Nation*, p. 66, London, 1938
[2] ibid.

A local authority can discharge its legal obligations . . . by consulting the voluntary hospital committee on the restricted subject of accommodation, and a voluntary hospital can be established or extended regardless of the statutory provisions of the area. In some areas . . . the consultation has been either rigid, limited and official, or completely absent.[1]

The BMA argued that in any consultations all interests should be considered, including those of the general practitioner.[2]

The 1938 edition of the BMA plan included a new section on administration arguing for a unified public authority to be responsible for health matters. It considered the possibility of *ad hoc* authorities with boundaries based on the catchment areas 'of a voluntary hospital or group of such hospitals'. This suggestion was, however, likely to 'detract from interest in the service' and 'so great a departure from past and recent policy in relation to local government [was] outside the realm of practical politics'.[3] It suggested, however, that while insurance committees should be retained and while other health responsibilities should be given only to authorities of 75,000 to 100,000 population, hospitals and related medical services should be treated 'as regional problems'.[4] It was envisaged that local authorities would combine together to provide hospital services on a regional basis.

The new report of the BMA, like its predecessor, was, as *The Hospital* put it, 'a synthesis of suggestions which is likely to commend itself to the medical professions'.[5] In a number of places the report leaned 'heavily – perhaps too heavily – in favour of the general practitioner'.[6] 'Why,' asked the editor, raising a question which was to be vehemently argued over the next decade, 'fix an income limit of £250? Prolonged illness in the home can be a real hardship to the lower middle classes. . . .'[7] *The Lancet* raised the same point and carried the argument one stage further: 'The ultimate solution will lie, we think, in the direction of divorcing the medical service entirely from the

[1] ibid., p. 30
[2] ibid.
[3] ibid., p. 44
[4] ibid.
[5] *Hospital*, Vol. 34, June 1938, p. 191
[6] ibid.
[7] ibid.

insurance system and recognizing it along with all the other public health activities as a service to be supported from the general public funds.'[1] Even if the income limit were retained, the question would undoubtedly arise in some cases whether 'medical remuneration might not be on a salaried basis'.[2]

While Dr Charles Hill, the deputy secretary of the BMA, had been busy preparing the 'redraft' of the *General Medical Service*, with its heavy emphasis on private practice, a stream of letters had been published in the *British Medical Journal* advocating a salaried medical service. The correspondence began with pseudonyms: later contributors used their own names. The first letter from 'Cadaver' at the end of 1937 argued that doctors should be compensated for the loss of the value of their practice and given jobs in health centres.[3] 'Cadaver' was supported by 'Ignotus' who argued that the profession should plan for a salaried service 'while there is yet time'. He feared that the profession would 'wake up one morning to find such a service established and not on our terms and in accord with our own ideas, but forced upon us by an unsympathetic government department'.[4] Ignotus's letter was followed by several signed letters supporting him, including one from a doctor who had 'spent many happy years in the Indian Medical Service'.[5]

The advantages of a state service were pointed out by different correspondents. Inevitably those who troubled to write were those who held extreme views. 'Our homes would be truly private. . . . All expenses of practice . . . would be paid. . . . We should be beyond the whims and caprices of our patients.... We should have right of entry to state hospitals. We should have a fixed hour day and night work on rotation and holidays with pay.'[6] There would be 'a pension at 65'.[7] Doctors would escape 'the indignity of rendering accounts and pin-pricking their patients to pay. . . . Doctors would immediately rise in status'.[8]

A Dr Nathan wrote to say that doctors had been slaves to

[1] *Lancet*, 7 May 1938, p. 1059
[2] ibid.
[3] *BMJ Supplement*, 18 December 1937, p. 373
[4] ibid., 1 January 1938, p. 6
[5] ibid., 29 January 1938, p. 64
[6] ibid., 26 March 1938, p. 159
[7] ibid., 2 April 1938, p. 172
[8] ibid.

... 'free choice'. Whatever may have been the case in the past it is quite apparent to anyone who considers the present position from an unbiased point of view that 'free choice' has become a shibboleth. The public, when given the opportunity, freely chooses the out-patient department or the clinic; it may be unaware of the name of the doctor on duty, but it realizes that he has the backing of many departments for the proper diagnosis of complaints and many facilities for subsequent treatment.

... It should not be impossible for our organization to devise some scheme in which a local consultation centre (or local health centre) would be staffed by all the local doctors; where the patients would get all the medical attention they require in the way which they have shown they are quite happy to obtain it; where medical practitioners on a salaried basis would be working in professional harmony with their colleagues ... instead of being in disastrous competition with them.[1]

At the 1938 annual representative meeting, the redraft of *A General Medical Service for the Nation* was approved unanimously with only very minor amendments.[2] Later at the same meeting Dr Nathan of Kensington moved: 'That in view of the altering outlook of the general public and of the opinions held by many of the younger members of the profession, the Council be asked to give detailed consideration to the case for some form of State medical service, and report thereon.'[3]

He was supported by a Dr Lister from Glasgow. Sir Henry Brackenbury recommended that the motion be rejected.

... A whole-time State medical service would involve such a regimentation of the people of this country as he believed they would never tolerate, such a severe restriction of choice as between doctor and patient as would reduce almost to nothing the mutual confidence which was an essential part of an effective medical service. ...[4]

The motion was lost.

This did not put an end to the debate which rambled on throughout the next year. There were further letters supporting a

[1] ibid., 2 July 1938, p. 7
[2] ibid., 30 July 1938, p. 95
[3] ibid., p. 99
[4] ibid., pp. 100–01

salaried service and further letters opposing it. In April 1939 a Dr E. R. C. Walker wrote suggesting a part-time salaried service to combine the advantages of salaried service with the 'freedom' of the capitation system.[1] There were some, however, who feared that a part-time salaried service would eventually develop into a state medical service.[2]

At the 1939 representative meeting the question was raised again. Doctors from Aberdeen and Edinburgh were particularly keen to modify the insurance basis of the BMA's policy for a general medical service, and also to modify the way in which doctors were to be paid. There was also pressure for a more radical policy for the administration of health services. A resolution was passed:

> That it be remitted to the Council to consider and report on the following modifications of the method advocated in the present scheme for a general medical service for the nation for implementing its four main basic principles:
> 1. Remuneration of medical personnel by graded and adjusted salary with pension;
> 2. Organization of the medical service on a regional basis, centred on base hospitals, as designated in the BMA hospital policy;
> 3. *Ad hoc* administration corresponding to the regional organization.[3]

The resolution was taken by the Council of the BMA in good part. Dr Wand said that 'if the Council was convinced of the correctness of its view he did not see why it should object to putting forward a reasoned statement explaining it. If the Council was going to sit down and entrench itself in one particular policy, well, Heaven help them!'[4]

Thus at the outbreak of war the profession seemed more ready to consider a salaried service if the resolutions at the annual meetings gave a true indication of opinion within the profession. There was certainly a group of doctors who, as Dr Brackenbury pointed out in 1932, were working 'logically and assiduously' to produce a salaried service. Some of them were members of the Socialist Medical Association which had been committed to a salaried

[1] ibid., 28 April 1939, p. 216
[2] ibid., 3 June 1939, p. 311
[3] ibid., 5 August 1939, p. 112
[4] ibid.

service since its inception in 1930. This was a small group but of considerable influence within the Labour Party. The Association had less than a thousand members in 1938.

After its forthright statement of 1922, the Labour Party had retreated from this extreme position, though it continued to have strong leanings towards a salaried service. According to Dr Brackenbury, there had been in 1932 a division of opinion in the Health Advisory Committee of the Labour Party which had prevented it from coming down firmly in favour of a salaried service.[1] From 1934, however, the party adopted a policy broadly on the lines recommended by the Socialist Medical Association.[2] But there remained some leaders of the Party who had far from radical views on hospital policy. Mr Arthur Greenwood made a very moderate speech to hospital officers in 1936, advocating no more than the type of co-ordination envisaged in the Sankey Report. He could not 'conceive of every voluntary hospital being run from Whitehall'.[3] Nor could he 'conceive of any Chancellor of the Exchequer handing out the £15 million needed to support the voluntary hospitals'.[4] The hospitals 'had little to fear from socialist administrators'[5] if Mr Greenwood's views were representative.

---

[1] ibid., 16 April 1932, p. 134
[2] D. Stark Murray et al., *Medical Care and Family Security*, p. 94, London, 1963
[3] *Hospital*, Vol. 32, November 1936, p. 286
[4] ibid.
[5] ibid.

CHAPTER 26

The Second World War

B Y the autumn of 1939, there had been important changes in the opinions of many doctors and some representatives of the voluntary hospitals. There was increasing appreciation that some regional planning of the hospital services was needed. In addition, the British Hospitals Association was willing to accept grants from public funds and the doctors had resolved to consider dispassionately the merits of a salaried service. All these novelties were introduced during the crisis of war.[1]

While plans for the First World War had been based on the need to provide adequate hospital facilities for wounded soldiers and sailors, the plans for the Second World War were dominated by the need to provide hospital care for civilians wounded by air attack. Vast casualties were expected. On highly questionable assumptions, it was estimated that from one to three million hospital beds might be required for air raid casualties alone.[2] At the most there were in England and Wales only half a million beds (or room for beds) in existing hospitals or institutions which could be used as hospitals.[3] Faced with the sheer impossibility of doing more, the Ministry of Health planned to provide 300,000 beds for air raid casualties.[4]

Before 1 June 1938, responsibility for arrangements for air raid casualties was divided between the Ministry of Health and the department responsible for air raid precautions. After this date, the Ministry of Health took on the whole task, but it was never made responsible for hospitals for service patients. Remembering the experience of the First World War, the War Office believed that its patients 'would not be returned to duty from

[1] This chapter draws heavily upon the detailed account of the Emergency Medical Service in Titmuss, *Problems of Social Policy*, London, 1950
[2] ibid., p. 63
[3] ibid., p. 80, including those for mental disease and mental deficiency
[4] ibid., p. 64

civilian hospitals as quickly as if they were in hospitals under military control'.[1] In practice, however, a large proportion of service patients came to be admitted to civilian hospitals under arrangements made through the Ministry of Health.

Faced with the enormous prospective demand for beds, the Ministry decided to carry out the first official survey of the condition of hospitals in Britain. The result was disturbing. There were found to be 'only 80,000 beds in England and Wales which could be used for the prolonged treatment of casualties'.[2] Until that time there had been at the Ministry 'little appreciation of the low standard of hospital accommodation in the country as a whole'.[3] The methods planned to provide this accommodation in the Second World War were similar to those used in the First. Civilian patients were to be overcrowded in every type of hospital; selected hospitals were to be upgraded by the provision of surgical and other equipment; hutted annexes were to be added to existing hospitals and new hutted hospitals were to be constructed.[4] And finally, in view of the urgency with which the accommodation was expected to be required, it was decided to discharge 100,000 patients from existing hospitals on the outbreak of war.[5]

The country was divided into regions under the direction of 'hospital officers'. The hospitals in each region were grouped geographically and graded according to whether they were or were not suitable for the reception of casualties. All the casualty hospitals in the danger area were linked with one another and with suitable institutions outside the area. London was divided into ten sectors radiating from the centre, with each sector based on one or more teaching hospitals. Casualties were to be evacuated outwards along each sector.[6] In view of the location of hospitals, this frequently meant evacuation from voluntary to local authority hospitals.[7]

Next, the Ministry negotiated with the 2,378 hospitals which were to be in the scheme in England and Wales. The government

[1] ibid., p. 57
[2] ibid., p. 63
[3] Memorandum by the Director General of the Emergency Medical Service of August, 1939, quoted in Titmuss, p. 64
[4] ibid., p. 73
[5] ibid., p. 80
[6] ibid., pp. 74–6
[7] *Hospital*, Vol. 35, December 1939, p. 392

stated categorically in July 1939 that there would be 'no interference by the Department in the internal administration of any hospital, voluntary or municipal'.[1] The department was, however, prepared to pay for structural alterations and to issue new equipment where it was needed. Arrangements were made for structural improvements and the issue of equipment. By the outbreak of war, work was planned or in progress at 150 hospitals,[2] and a start was made with a programme of constructing hutted accommodation to provide 40,000 beds.[3] By October 1939, nearly 1,000 new operating theatres had been installed.[4]

The scheme involved using both voluntary and local authority institutions, and it was accepted that the voluntary hospitals would need to be paid for their services. The British Hospitals Association was unwilling to accept a flat-rate payment for both occupied and vacant beds; it drew attention to the wide variation in the cost of different types of hospitals, and explained that many of these variations were due to differences in the quality of service provided. Accordingly it was agreed that the actual running costs of each hospital would be divided between the Ministry and the hospital according to the proportion of beds it was keeping available for the Ministry (whether they were occupied or not).[5]

To provide the medical services for the scheme, a corps of doctors was recruited into an 'Emergency Medical Service'. All grades from house officer to consultant were included, and appropriate military ranks up to and including colonel were distributed.[6] As the doctors had to be prepared to serve anywhere in the country and in any type of hospital (voluntary or municipal), there had to be uniform conditions of service. The

[1] *BMJ Supplement*, 22 July 1939, p. 49. Sir Bernard Docker, as chairman of the British Hospitals Association's War Emergency Committee, had 'impressed upon the Minister of Health the vital importance of linking up the EMS with the voluntary hospitals rather than the taking over of hospitals for the EMS'. (*Hospital*, Vol. 35, November 1939, pp. 388–9)

[2] Titmuss, p. 78

[3] ibid., p. 81

[4] ibid., p. 83

[5] See *Hospital*, Vol. 35, October 1939, p. 333. The full cost (excluding administration) was paid for occupied beds, and the cost less payments for provisions, surgery and dispensary for unoccupied beds.

[6] In April 1942, after representations from the Royal Colleges, two consultants were given the rank of major-general and twenty-two others the rank of brigadier. *BMJ Supplement*, 18 April 1942, p. 62

Ministry decided that in view of these duties, the majority of doctors should, as in the armed forces, be employed on a whole-time basis and thus not be allowed private practice. The Ministry's views may also have been influenced by memories of the 'à la suite' consultants of the First World War. The actual salaries agreed ranged from £450 to £1,500.[1] This represented a large increase in pay for the junior staff, who had always been very badly paid in the voluntary hospitals. The successful consultant, on the other hand, received much less than his peace-time earnings and faced the danger of his practice falling into the hands of a rival who had not joined the service. To deal with this problem, the British Medical Association proposed that no new permanent appointment should be made to a hospital staff throughout the war. It also tried to organize a pool through which the remaining private consultants would hand over one half of any increased earnings to their colleagues on war service.[2] This last scheme was, however, never implemented owing to lack of co-operation from those who would have had to pay into the pool.[3]

The Ministry decided that between 34,000 and 67,000 trained nurses were required for the first-aid posts and emergency hospitals. At this time, there were only about 60,000 trained nurses at work in Britain.[4] It was decided to cut by half the trained staffs of the ordinary civilian hospitals and fill the gaps with untrained staff. A Civil Nursing Reserve was formed to which 7,000 trained nurses and 3,000 assistant nurses were recruited. In addition to this total of 10,000 experienced nurses, untrained volunteers were recruited who were described as 'nursing auxiliaries'. At the outbreak of war, over 20,000 nurses were ready for action, though not all were able and willing to be sent far away from their homes.[5]

Thus when war was declared on 3 September 1939, the government had plans ready to be put into action. In particular, it had been hoped that 100,000 beds could be provided by the simple expedient of discharging their occupants. What actually happened was that about 140,000 patients were ejected in the

[1] For the details, see *Hospital*, 23 September 1939, p. 188.
[2] ibid., 24 June 1939, p. 338
[3] ibid., 9 September 1939, p. 172
[4] Abel-Smith, op. cit., pp. 161–2
[5] ibid.

early days of the war.[1] Instructions were rigorously interpreted. Included in the figure of 140,000 were about 7,000–8,000 tubercular patients 'cleared' from local authority sanatoria, representing nearly 30 per cent of all those receiving residential treatment at the time. In Wales, approximately 60 per cent of tubercular patients were bundled home within twenty-four hours.[2]

The emptied beds were not in fact used for air raid casualties, as there were hardly any in the first nine months of the war. Indeed, throughout the whole war, the number of air raid casualties treated in hospitals was 'roughly 40 per cent less than the number of sick people turned out of hospitals in about two days in September 1939'.[3] Insofar as the beds were used at all in the first nine months, they were primarily used for servicemen who were sick, and secondarily for service casualties admitted mainly in May and June 1940.[4] But the majority of the beds remained empty.

In the first eight months of the war, the Ministry released from the scheme 1,000 hospitals and institutions with about 85,000 beds,[5] partly because they were unsuitable for the purpose for which they were intended to be used, and partly to make more room for sick civilians. It also decided to raise the target of hutted accommodation from 40,000 to 80,000 beds.[6] Thirdly, it was decided in June 1940 to create a large additional reserve of hospital beds in converted houses, schools and other buildings to serve as 'auxiliary hospitals'. The War Office now thought it undesirable for convalescent soldiers to be sent straight from the hospital to their units. Forgetting earlier beliefs about getting soldiers back to the front quickly and forgetting also the ex- periences of the First World War, it was decided that the auxiliary hospitals were to be run on behalf of the Ministry of Health by the War Organization of the British Red Cross Society and Order of St John of Jerusalem. 'By the end of 1940, 140 houses had been turned into annexes with 8,850 beds,

[1] Titmuss, p. 193
[2] ibid., pp. 193–4
[3] ibid., p. 194
[4] ibid., p. 185
[5] ibid.
[6] ibid., p. 187. Construction was suspended when 52,000 beds had been built for the Emergency Medical Service (p. 460).

and 215 auxiliary hospitals with about 5,000 beds had been opened.'[1]

Soon after the great exodus, the Ministry wanted to persuade the voluntary hospitals to admit more civilian sick. The hospitals were, however, receiving about £100,000 a week for keeping their beds empty. Any reduction in casualty beds meant a reduction in subsidy. In October 1939, the Ministry hastened to point out that urgent civilian cases should be admitted to hospital,[2] but hesitated to take any further action because of the 'storm of criticism' it feared from the voluntary hospitals.[3] But in December 1939, the number of beds reserved for casualties was reduced by 20 per cent, and hospitals were allowed to use 'frozen beds' for civilians up to a maximum of 66 per cent total occupancy for all purposes.

There was little response. The proposal would have involved a re-organization of the medical staffing arrangements. Moreover, the voluntary hospitals maintained that the civilian sick were not suffering hardship[4] and that waiting lists had never been so small. Nevertheless, a few more beds were provided for the civilian sick, and under-employed doctors working in casualty stations and hospitals outside London were glad to return to the London patients who needed their services.

This improvement of the London voluntary hospital services for the civilian sick was eased by a change in the terms of service for doctors under the Emergency Medical Service. Within weeks of the outbreak of war, there had been complaints and grousing in medical circles about the ban on private practice by whole-time consultants.[5] It was pointed out that the government would gain in taxation one-third of any earnings,[6] and that some consultants had imagined that they would be allowed private practice when they had signed up.[7] In November 1939 the Minister received a deputation from the profession,[8] and it was decided that doctors of specialist or higher rank should be allowed private practice. They were paid a salary of £500 a year

---

[1] ibid., p. 199
[2] *Hospital*, Vol. 35, October 1939, p. 345
[3] Titmuss, p. 443
[4] ibid.
[5] See, for example, *BMJ Supplement*, 21 October 1939, p. 209
[6] ibid.
[7] ibid., 4 November 1939, p. 215
[8] ibid., 11 November 1939, p. 218

for such duties as might be required of them, on the understanding that if in an acute emergency they were called upon for all their time no extra remuneration would become payable. Although these terms of service were considered by the Select Committee on National Expenditure to be 'neither in the interests of the country nor in accord with the dignity of the profession',[1] they remained throughout the war.

In the late summer of 1940, Britain experienced in terms of hospital casualties the most severe air raids of the war. But on any one day there were never more than 7,380 air raid victims in hospital.[2] Severe air raids continued throughout the winter of 1940–41, but quite apart from reserves, there were never less than 9,000 beds available for immediate occupation in London and a further 25,000 beds were ready and empty in the country surrounding London. In the whole of England and Wales, there were never less than 70,000 to 80,000 available beds.[3]

This does not mean that all hospitals had an easy time. There were local shortages of beds; and while some hospitals and surgical teams were working to the maximum capacity, there were others not far away which were not fully utilized. A certain amount of waste had to be accepted as there was no means of predicting where the enemy would strike next. And throughout there was always reason to fear that the worst was still to come – from gas attacks, secret weapons and the very real possibility of invasion. But the price of this constant readiness for the unknown was paid by the ordinary civilian sick who found it hard to be admitted to any type of hospital – particularly a voluntary hospital.

The voluntary hospitals became even more selective in wartime than they had been in peace-time about the class of cases they would admit. They had always discriminated against chronic sick patients, but now the phrase was given a much wider interpretation. In London, they extended their peace-time policy of transferring 'chronic' cases to the Council hospitals, and such cases ranged from babies with broncho-pneumonia and acute bronchitis to young men and women with influenza and pleurisy.[4] By these policies, the length of stay of the average

[1] Titmuss, p. 199
[2] ibid., p. 443
[3] ibid.
[4] ibid., p. 448

patient in many, if not all, London teaching hospitals was sharply reduced.[1] To a considerable extent the Emergency Medical Service of the London voluntary hospitals consisted of a surgical service to air raid casualties,[2] and a nursing home service to sick officers in the private wing and to sick other ranks in the general wards.

Such policies could not be operated in the London County Council hospitals. They had a statutory duty to admit all sick persons requiring hospital treatment. Thus, their hospitals became dangerously overcrowded and they were forced to use many of their casualty beds for sick civilians. This reacted unfavourably on the casualty service. In heavy air raids, the surgical staff of some of the Council's hospitals were not fully occupied because they lacked beds for further casualties, while overworked operating teams at the voluntary hospitals had more beds than they could use.[3]

The problem of the civilian sick, particularly the chronic sick, demanded urgent attention. In particular, the neglected aged accumulating in air raid shelters were a public disgrace and a dangerous potential source of epidemics. The Ministry determined to put further pressure on the voluntary hospitals to accept more civilian sick and to transfer more civilian patients out of London, and announced that it would pay the cost of maintaining them where necessary. Originally the Emergency Medical Service had been intended for air raid casualties, servicemen and evacuated children. It also became necessary to accept responsibility for hospital patients who were moved into the country to make room for casualties in the city. Now the Ministry decided in September 1940 to make beds available in reception areas 'to aged and infirm persons found in public shelters and rest centres'.[4] By the end of December 1940, 4,000 people had been transferred to emergency hospital beds under this scheme. In addition, 3,500 chronic sick were transferred from Council

[1] ibid., p. 457
[2] Unless there were special medical reasons, civilians could only be given free treatment in the general wards. Air raid casualties asking for treatment in private rooms were required to sign a declaration that they knew that free treatment was available elsewhere (*BMJ Supplement*, 9 August 1941, p. 19).
[3] Titmuss, p. 452
[4] ibid., p. 450

hospitals to the country.[1] After these moves the scheme of transfer from shelters was suspended, as no more beds in reception areas could be spared.

The policy of persuading the voluntary hospitals to take more civilian sick proved to be difficult to implement. In December 1940, the Ministry decided to reduce once again the number of beds reserved for casualties. It was hoped to release some 20–25,000 of the 70–80,000 vacant beds in England and Wales for sick civilians. Although only about 600 beds were involved in London, the hospitals were strongly opposed to any change. They argued that the hardships of sick civilians were exaggerated and that the war situation did not justify any change. The London County Council strongly disagreed and a fierce dispute developed between the Council and the British Hospitals Association.

There is no reason to doubt that the voluntary hospitals were sincere in the views they expressed about the war situation; they had, however, a clear financial incentive to keep beds empty. Indeed, the whole controversy underlined the unsatisfactory nature of the terms upon which the Ministry was paying the hospitals. Running costs were divided between the hospital and the Ministry according to the number of EMS and non-EMS beds. Under this formula, the hospitals gained financially from having EMS beds which were unoccupied. And if the hospital closed beds of its own, a higher proportion of the cost was paid by the Ministry; the average cost was also raised as the overheads of the hospital had to be divided among fewer beds. A hospital could distort the number of its own beds by declaring only those which had been filled, and by other means. And when a hospital was damaged and the number of beds had to be reduced, there was a clear incentive to reduce the beds for the civilian sick, rather than for EMS cases.

Either because of the financial incentives or because of the desire to keep a larger strategic reserve, the voluntary hospitals insisted on keeping a large stock of empty beds. Though there were individual hospitals with financial problems, the failure to fill the beds could not be attributed to shortage of funds. The receipts from voluntary contributions fell slightly during the war and patients' contributions fell considerably as few patients were admitted who might have paid, but the increase in revenue from

[1] ibid., p. 451

public funds was enormous. The receipts per bed more than doubled in London hospitals.[1] Costs also increased considerably, but the finances of hospitals reporting to the *Hospitals Year Book* changed from an overall deficit of about £330,000 in 1938, to a surplus of about £1·8 million in 1940 and £2·2 million in 1941. And while the hospitals were arguing with the Ministry and the London County Council, the overall surplus rose to £3·5 million in 1942.[2]

Eventually the Ministry had to intervene in the dispute between the Council and the British Hospitals Association over the London hospitals. In February it extracted figures from its own records to establish the factual position. They covered forty voluntary and twenty-four London County Council hospitals. It was found that the Council hospitals were nearly 90 per cent occupied, while the voluntary hospitals were less than half occupied. Later information confirmed that this was true of all the voluntary hospitals with over 100 beds in London.[3] Faced with these facts, the voluntary hospitals eventually agreed to accept, with effect from 1 March 1942, the reduction in casualty beds which the Ministry had proposed in December 1940.

This prolonged discussion did not lead to a complete recasting of the financial arrangements operating between the Ministry and the hospitals. One amendment was, however, introduced. A hospital which had its civilian beds reduced because of bombing or other means credited the Ministry with a sum equivalent to the cost of the lost beds. This was to compensate the Ministry for the cost of looking after the extra patients. There was now intended to be no financial advantage gained by a hospital which reduced the number of its civilian beds.

The effect of these changes on the London voluntary hospitals was not dramatic. The occupancy of the hospitals of over 100 beds increased from 49 per cent in 1940 to 52 per cent in 1941 and 59 per cent in 1942.[4] There was only a modest improvement in the provision for the civilian sick.

Meanwhile, the scope of the Emergency Medical Service was

---

[1] ibid., p. 457

[2] ibid., p. 456. The number of hospitals reporting to the *Year Book* was 835 in 1939, 794 in 1940, 713 in 1941 and 806 in 1942.

[3] ibid., p. 457

[4] ibid.

being widened to include more civilians. Munition workers who had been transferred and were living in billets were added at the end of 1940 and all evacuated and homeless people were included in 1941. The fracture service which had been started for the war injured[1] was expanded to include 'certain classes of industrial workers' in 1941, and in 1943 to all manual workers employed in the industries of war-time Britain.[2]

It was hoped that the Red Cross auxiliary hospitals would ease the demand for beds; by 1941 they had available 10,000 beds. Many large country houses had been willingly lent for the war effort, and they were maintained and kept in repair at government expense. Often the owners remained in residence and took charge of the hospital. Most of the equipment was provided by the Ministry, which also paid a fixed rate for occupied and vacant beds to the Red Cross Society.

The Ministry had hoped to use these hospitals as 'a general pool of convalescent accommodation', but their owners preferred the 'blue coated soldier' to the industrial worker, although for most of the war there were very few service patients needing convalescence. The Ministry decided, as it had decided in the case of the voluntary hospitals, to respect the views of the owners of the buildings. And as a result, it found itself paying for hospitals which (up to June 1941) were only about 40 per cent used.[3] After prolonged negotiation, the payment for vacant beds was reduced in the hope that this would lead to a greater incentive for the accommodation to be occupied.

Arrangements for the convalescence of civilian patients continued to be a problem which the development of the auxiliary hospitals did little to ease. Facilities for children were particularly short, with the result that children discharged from hospital were returning with chronic complaints and occupying beds badly needed by other patients. At the end of 1942, the Charity Organization Society, the Invalid Children's Aid Association and the Great Ormond Street Hospital all pressed the Ministry to find more accommodation. The Ministry in turn pressed the Red Cross and after negotiations and investigations lasting over a year, 274 beds were found in several

[1] In July 1940, the British Hospitals Association had pressed the Ministry to start such a scheme. See *Hospital*, Vol. 36, July 1940, p. 155.

[2] Titmuss, p. 470

[3] ibid., p. 461

auxiliary hospitals for convalescent children over the age of five.[1]

The Ministry continued throughout 1942 to worry about the problem of providing adequate hospital accommodation for the civilian sick. Neither air raid casualties nor wounded servicemen were making noticeable demands on the Emergency Medical Service. The auxiliary hospitals were not bringing the relief to the system which had been hoped when the scheme was planned. And the voluntary hospitals were continuing to keep too many reserved beds empty even though they had full authority to use such beds for the civilian sick. Despite all its anxieties, the Ministry was not prepared to use such powers as it possessed or to obtain new powers to direct hospitals.

An inquiry carried out in February 1942 confirmed what the voluntary hospitals had been saying throughout the tedious negotiations which the Ministry had conducted with them. Waiting lists were shorter in most hospitals than they had been before the war; some were much shorter. Valid conclusions could not however be drawn from such information. There had been substantial changes both in the criteria used by general practitioners in asking for a patient to be admitted to hospital and in the willingness of hospitals to admit patients to waiting lists or to maintain lists at all. The former had gained the impression that the hospitals would only accept cases in extreme emergency[2] and the latter tended to restrict their lists to 'surgical cases'. 'Medical cases were not even registered and were usually left to be cared for by overworked general practitioners.'[3]

Doctors and hospitals had developed an unofficial system of priorities. First came the servicemen, second the air raid casualties and then the war-workers and other 'potential effectives'. After their needs were met, some provision was made for women and children. Last of all came the aged and chronic sick. Thus women requiring gynaecological services queued for admission in large numbers, and children waited years for orthopaedic and ophthalmic operations.[4] Many elderly patients were left at home with grossly inadequate care and no prospect of admission at all.

[1] ibid., p. 499
[2] ibid., p. 488
[3] ibid., p. 493
[4] ibid.

In July 1942, the Ministry decided to allow more civilian patients to be 'transferred' to the Emergency Medical Service from hospitals with waiting lists. The hospitals were not told about these arrangements as it could have led to an almost unlimited number of civilian patients being paid for by the Government. The right to use this procedure was given to the responsible officers in each region or sector whenever they thought it was necessary. Originally, transferred patients had been those who had been evacuated from danger areas; now transferred patients had come to mean in practice any patient on a waiting list which the administration chose to designate as such. Under this elastic interpretation of regulations designed for another purpose, the number of transferred patients increased from 59,000 in 1940 to 126,000 in 1943.

Although many hospital beds were put out of action by bomb damage, valiant efforts were made by hospital staffs by improvisation and hasty repairs to keep as many beds in service as was practicable. Detailed statistics of the total number of beds in Britain at different periods of the war are not available. Moreover, war-time hospital capacity cannot be measured by beds alone. The extent of overcrowding which was considered tolerable both for patients and staff varied according to the progress of the war. So also did the quality of service which was thought to be acceptable for casualties. Nevertheless, it is probable that the quantity of usable accommodation increased continuously from the autumn of 1939 to the autumn of 1944. And there is no doubt that the quality of service provided in most acute hospitals was improved in a variety of different ways.

The process of 'upgrading' accommodation was continuous. The hospital officers and sector officers were recruited from doctors who had known the best of Britain's hospitals before the war, and they were grossly dissatisfied with the standards of accommodation in the worst voluntary and Council hospitals and shocked by the standards in the public assistance institutions. There were, however, other pressures for improvements in services. Some middle-class patients were admitted to 'hospitals' which they would never have used before the war and such patients were well able to make their views known.[1] Secondly, the shortage of manpower throughout the war made it essential for the hospitals to restore working capacity as effectively as possible.

[1] ibid., pp. 500-01

Finally, the assumed shortage of hospital accommodation put pressure on all hospitals to discharge patients as soon as they were able to go.

For all these reasons, there were substantial improvements in the quality of hospital services. Orthopaedic and rehabilitation services were rapidly developed.[1] Pathological and blood transfusion services were extended and improved.[2] When hospital diets were examined and found to be seriously delaying the recovery of patients, the Ministry and later the King's Fund conducted a campaign to improve hospital feeding standards.[3] Hospital almoners who had tended to be regarded by hospital managements solely as money raisers, became gradually appreciated as important auxiliaries in the treatment, and particularly the discharge, of the patient.[4] These and many other developments in hospital services were undertaken at a time when Britain's economic resources were greatly depleted by the war. Tacitly, expenditures on medical care came to be regarded less as a form of consumption and more as a positive investment in the war effort.

Thus the hospital services were in much better shape to face the last test of the war. Plans for the invasion of Europe were carefully laid and it was expected that the armed forces would be making great demands on hospital accommodation. Accordingly it was decided that there should be gradual restrictions on the admission of civilian patients. In practice, however, the demands were never excessive. For a few months the auxiliary hospitals were used to an appreciable extent and in August 1944 their beds were 72 per cent occupied.[5] But as the war extended on to the Continent and the fear of air casualties became more remote, the time came when the emergency service could be gradually disbanded.

In some respects, the condition of the hospitals had been improved by the war; there had been substantial up-grading and generous supplies of new equipment. But many major works of maintenance and repair and many plans for rebuilding had been postponed until the war was over. Many hospitals had

[1] ibid., pp. 477–9
[2] ibid., p. 474
[3] ibid., pp. 480–82
[4] ibid., p. 471
[5] ibid., p. 462

suffered severe war damage which had been hastily patched up; heavy expenditure was needed to put the hospitals back in permanent working order.

During the war, the voluntary hospitals had added to their reserves substantially more than £10 million.[1] This did not, however, mean that they were in a stronger overall financial position. At the low prevailing rates of interest, these reserves could not contribute much towards running costs and the price level was much higher after the war than before it. If the higher standards of service achieved in the war were to be maintained in peace-time, much higher expenditure was needed. The hospitals had become heavily dependent on the central government for their maintenance expenditures.

The process had not gone unobserved at the Ministry of Health. As early as October 1940, it had been recognized that the Ministry had gained absolute power over some hospitals which had been heavily damaged by air raids. 'Action by the Ministry may determine their continued existence as independent units, or make such existence impossible.'[2] It was decided that the Ministry would 'preserve those institutions that are of national importance for education and medical progress' and make sure that it had 'at its disposal as many "well managed" beds as possible'.[3] Grants were given to individual hospitals which were in difficulties.

Thus throughout the war, the Ministry did everything possible to retain the independence of the voluntary hospitals. Although it was constantly concerned about the lack of provision for the civilian sick, it was never prepared to direct either the voluntary hospitals or the auxiliary hospitals. Though the Ministry had bought a considerable proportion of the bed days in many hospitals, the hospital managements were paid, when EMS patients were short, for rendering no service at all. Although it was the function of the Government to decide how many beds were needed for war purposes, within limits, it was the governors of the voluntary hospitals who took these decisions. There could be no more forceful demonstration of the status of the voluntary hospitals than that they were allowed throughout the war to retain so many empty beds and accumulate substantial financial

[1] ibid., p. 456
[2] ibid., p. 449
[3] ibid., p. 455

reserves in the process. The hospitals had hesitated to touch public money when they desperately needed it; they showed no hesitation when they did not. The Socialist Medical Association had had some cause to complain to the Minister of Health early in 1940 that the Emergency Medical Service seemed to be designed 'primarily for the benefit of the consultants and the voluntary hospitals'.[1]

Although the Ministry had taken great care not to disturb the system of hospitals over which the Emergency Medical Service had been temporarily superimposed, by 1944 it was clear that some major reorganization was going to take place. Though the hospital system was unchanged by the war, public opinion and medical opinion were not. Opinion was shaped both directly and indirectly by the experiences of the war.

[1] *BMJ Supplement*, 3 February 1940, p. 14

CHAPTER 27

The Doctors' Plan

THE war had led to the first attempt to plan hospitals on a regional basis and the task of organizing and operating the Emergency Medical Service had brought home to all concerned the failings of Britain's hospital system. In view of the vast anticipated demand for beds for war purposes, the unsatisfactory condition of the country's hospitals became a matter of national importance. Previously, Ministry officials had had little cause to visit hospitals – particularly small and ill-equipped hospitals. The war was a major educative experience not only for the Ministry but also for the top doctors and many middle-class patients.

Most of the work of planning the hospital services of each region had been given to senior consultants from the voluntary hospitals. The Ministry had lacked experienced staff members and had appreciated that a consultant was most likely to win the co-operation of all concerned. Thus, for the first time, a group of leading doctors became aware of the state of *all* the hospitals in a given area. Though some consultants from the voluntary hospitals had worked in the best local authority hospitals, they had seldom had cause to visit the accommodation provided for the chronic sick, the mentally ill or those with infectious diseases. Nor had they seen much of the facilities and medical work done in the small rural voluntary hospitals.

Consultants from the best hospitals found themselves allotted beds in rural workhouses and mental hospitals. And they were shocked by what they found. Many of them had also surrendered in the patriotic fervour of the outbreak of war their most precious asset – the goodwill of their practices. They had become wholly dependent on their salary from the state. Indeed, in the early months of war, there was very little private consulting practice – even in London. Nor was it clear that consulting practice would ever play the same role in the nation's health services as before the war. Thus the leaders of the medical profession found themselves with less vested interest in the medical needs of the wealthy and a new familiarity with the unmet needs of the rest of the population.

This new awareness of the medical and social problems of Britain was not confined to doctors and administrators. Men and women of the higher social classes saw the medical care system of the Poor Law as VAD nurses, as voluntary and paid war workers and even as patients and patients' visitors. They saw also the evacuated children and mothers, the occupants of the public air raid shelters and the casualties of the air war. There was more communication between classes and there were more common problems – queueing, rationing, and bereavement. Finally, there was more equality. As the nation united against a common enemy it was more prepared to see individual needs as common needs and to seek national rather than sectional solutions for them. In a sense, Britain's post-war 'Welfare State' was born in the air raid shelters, the community restaurants and the trenches. It is only against this background that the events described in this chapter can be understood.

Between the Munich crisis and the outbreak of war a year later, the *British Medical Journal* had for the first time published a shoal of letters favouring a salaried medical service. And in the last annual meeting before the 'black-out', the BMA had agreed to study this alternative to what had always been the Association's policy. The discussion subsided soon after war was declared and the attention of the profession was concentrated on immediate problems – particularly on terms and conditions of service under the emergency arrangements. The long campaign to get dependents into the national insurance scheme was, however, given a new impetus from the fact that mothers evacuated with children[1] and the wives of servicemen living on meagre allowances were finding it very hard to pay for general practitioner services. The BMA suggested that at least the latter should be brought within the insurance system,[2] but the Ministry insisted that any such needs should be dealt with by the public assistance services. It would not concede that service wives were unable to meet necessary expenses out of their allowances from their husbands in the armed forces.

[1] See *BMJ Supplement*, 15 February 1941, p. 17.
[2] ibid., 18 December 1939, p. 241 and 22 June 1940, p. 100

During the war, the BMA vigilantly watched to see that no dangerous precedents were established. Thus, for example, when the Central London Ophthalmic Hospital set up clinics to provide members of approved societies and contributors to the Hospital Savings Association with private consultations for half a guinea in the northern suburbs, 'inhabited chiefly by a middle-class residential population', the BMA set up a special investigating committee.[1] Strong representations were made to the hospital and the clinics were discontinued. When the hospital contemplated reopening them nine months later on the grounds that bombing made it very difficult for patients to reach the hospital, the Council of the BMA adhered to its previous view. 'Such action by the hospital authority was contrary to the public interest and to medical ethics and presented grave professional risks to the medical staff of such clinics.'[2]

While the BMA headquarters was engaged in these routine operations, there was growing within the ranks of the profession a demand for reform. The under-employed doctors, who were huddled together in hospitals throughout Britain awaiting air raid casualties, were planning a new future for Britain's medical services. In particular there were many doctors who were experiencing regular hours of duty without loss of clinical freedom within a salaried state service, and they were prepared to consider seriously why some such system of providing medical services should not be continued in peace-time. The growing concern about the failings of Britain's hospitals found expression in *The Lancet*. A special commissioner was appointed (Dr Stephen Taylor) and less than two months after the outbreak of war he published 'A Plan for British Hospitals'.[3] He pointed out that there already had been created some sort of a national hospital service run on a regional basis. 'Hitler and the Ministry between them have accomplished in a few months what might have taken the British Hospitals Association twenty years to bring about.'[4] The next step, he argued, should be the creation of a National Hospital Corporation, like the BBC, to take over all hospitals (voluntary and municipal) and run them on a regional basis. 'If the consultant is to be rescued from penury and our hospital

[1] ibid., 2 March 1940, p. 26
[2] ibid., 4 January 1941, p. 4
[3] *Lancet*, 28 October 1939, pp. 946-51
[4] ibid., p. 947

system from chaos or direct governmental control, a scheme such as this is essential.'[1]

The commissioner favoured a whole-time salaried medical staff but laid great stress on the system of internal hospital organization, which he thought would produce the best medical work. In the new services, hospitals should not be run as local authority hospitals had been run in the past, with an all powerful medical superintendent paid £1,500 a year, and far beneath him some five or six junior and senior assistant medical officers paid £350 to £600 a year.[2] Instead, the system of medical administration which had developed in the voluntary hospitals should be extended to all hospitals. There should be well paid consultants serving as equals on a medical committee – each one of them enjoying a wide measure of freedom to act as he thought best. In its editorial, *The Lancet* was cautious on this proposal. It pointed out that there were 'many who doubt whether it is possible to run an efficient institution wholly by a committee, although the voluntary hospital system provides the strongest evidence that it is'.[3]

The plan was discussed in the correspondence column of *The Lancet* for month after month, and the proposal to nationalize the hospitals led to much less opposition than might have been expected. The issue was not seen as one of party politics, as no political party was proposing any action of this kind. Discussion concentrated on details of organization. The proposal for whole-time consultants was the one which led to the most violent criticism.[4]

While correspondents in *The Lancet* were debating the merits of compulsory planning enforced by vesting the ownership of hospitals in one planning authority, a new initiative was taken to encourage *voluntary* co-ordination. Just as the creation of the King's Fund in 1897 made it possible to attempt the type of planning which the Lords Committee had thought necessary for London, so the creation at the end of 1939 of the Nuffield Provincial Hospitals Trust made it possible to try and introduce the type of planning which the Sankey Commission had recommended for the provinces. The trust was endowed with one

1 ibid., p. 951
2 ibid., p. 946
3 ibid., p. 939
4 ibid., 11 November 1939, pp. 1043–4, and 18 November, p. 1095

million Morris Motors shares which could be used for the 'carrying on or extension of such hospital and ancillary medical services as in the opinion of the Governing Trustees are necessary'[1] for co-ordination on a regional basis. The Trust set out 'to establish advisory machinery which it hoped would bring together in a full partnership yet without prejudice to the individuality of each, the various hospitals within a given area'.[2] By 1941, four regional and eleven divisional councils were set up in England and Wales.

Meanwhile, the radical feeling within the profession had percolated through to BMA headquarters. And in August 1940, the British Medical Association set up a medical planning commission 'to study war-time developments and their effects on the country's medical services, both present and future'. There were 73 members of the commission and they were appointed with the full co-operation of the Royal Colleges and the Royal Scottish Corporations. All shades of opinion and experience were represented, and the health departments sent observers.

While the commission was deliberating, a lively debate was conducted in the *British Medical Journal* on the future of the nation's health services. The discussion began with a scheme proposed by Dr S. Terry Pybus, which would give persons with incomes under £500 per year free care from salaried doctors organized on a regional basis.[3] And in the following months correspondents debated once again whether a 'state service' with salaried doctors would be desirable from the profession's point of view. Those who opposed such a service argued that it would 'destroy initiative and ambition',[4] 'produce a semi-paralytic, time-serving, red-tapish type of public servant'[5] under the 'deadening effect of the bonds of the state'.[6] Those who supported such a service stressed the regular working hours and holidays, the freedom from the business side of practice and the access to laboratory services, specialists and possibly hospital beds.[7]

1 Nuffield Provincial Hospitals Trust, *A Report on the Purpose and Activities of the Trust 1939–48*, p. 9, Oxford, 1949
2 ibid., p. 12
3 ibid., 15 March 1941, p. 29
4 ibid., 19 April 1941, p. 47
5 ibid., p. 48
6 ibid., 26 April 1941, p. 49
7 ibid.

By May 1941, discussion in the *British Medical Journal* had focused on the question of whether or not the patients wanted free choice of doctor. Some said that this consideration was 'largely a bogey' and there had always been some restriction of choice.[1] Others stressed the need for competition. And if there were to be competition, one correspondent argued, then hospitals ought to be open to all doctors. 'If we must have competition, let it be open, fair, free and free to all; let every dog have a bite.'[2] Dr Alfred Cox wrote to regret that patients under the existing insurance scheme had made so little use of their right to change doctors. People were not as appreciative of their right to change as he had hoped. If people no longer valued the choice of their own doctor, he would regard it as a 'retrograde tendency' but 'bow to it as a regrettable necessity'.[3] A further correspondent wrote to suggest free choice of doctor was not necessarily incompatible with a 'state service'.[4]

By the summer it was being tacitly assumed by all correspondents that after the war there would be some sort of service which was 'free' to at least the working classes. Local branches of the BMA started meeting to discuss not whether there should be such a service but the principles upon which it should be organized. Thus the Islington and North London branches met and recorded votes in favour of a salaried service[5] while West Somerset favoured a capitation method of paying doctors.[6] And as the demand for reform swept through the profession, the medical planning commission was seen to have increasing importance. A group of younger doctors, feeling that the age group of the commission was too high and that its conclusions would be both unrepresentative and reactionary, formed, through the columns of *The Lancet*, a special association of younger doctors and health service workers called *Medical Planning Research*.[7] Those who joined, eventually some 400 persons, were invited to send in memoranda on the basis of which a report would be prepared. The composition of the profession's planning commission was also criticized at a meeting of representatives of

[1] ibid., 17 May 1941, p. 66
[2] ibid., 24 May 1941, pp. 69–70
[3] *BMJ*, 24 May 1941, pp. 796–7
[4] *BMJ Supplement*, 21 June 1941, p. 83
[5] ibid., 12 July 1941, pp. 4–5 and 13 September 1941, p. 45
[6] ibid., 26 July 1941, pp. 10–11
[7] *Lancet*, 21 June 1941, p. 801

home divisions of the BMA held in September 1941.[1] It was, however, resolved by a large majority that the commission should continue its work, and that divisions should at the same time form study groups to consider the future of medicine.[2] To help divisions with their deliberations the *British Medical Journal* published a series of articles setting out alternative schemes with remarkable objectivity.[3] It was again assumed throughout that medical care ought to be *free* – at least to the bulk of the population.

Up to this point, the debate had been conducted largely in terms of what general practitioners wanted and what patients were assumed to want from general practitioners. But in February 1942, Professor John Ryle from Cambridge widened the discussion by arguing the case for a salaried service as a means of providing a higher quality of care. He stressed the maldistribution of doctors. Where good doctors were most needed, they were least available. In working-class areas, slum surgeries of the poorest type still survived. And even in middle-class practices better equipment and accommodation and better co-operation with the hospital were badly needed. He drew attention to the drastic shortage of consultants and specialists in rural areas where general practitioners did surgery in cottage hospitals and specialist help was 'neither sought nor available'. And he said that consultants were always faced with a constant conflict between their duty to the hospital and their duty to their private patients. Professor Ryle regarded the hospital 'system' as grossly unsatisfactory. The voluntaries were financially embarrassed, the municipals were 'backward but improving' and the Poor Law hospitals were 'antiquated'. The whole system of medical care had to be recast on the basis of Exchequer finance and salaried practice.[4]

Professor Ryle's article was followed by a detailed critique of the organization of hospitals by Dr Himsworth, FRCP.[5] He argued that there were faults in both the voluntary and municipal systems. What was wrong with the voluntary hospitals was that

[1] *BMJ Supplement*, 20 September 1941, p. 49

[2] ibid., 27 September 1941, p. 59

[3] ibid., 3 January 1942, pp. 1-2, 7 February 1942, p. 23, 7 March 1942, p. 41, 4 April 1942, p. 55, and 2 May 1942, p. 69

[4] ibid., 21 February 1942, p. 33

[5] later Sir Harold Himsworth, secretary of the Medical Research Council

his hospital work was not the doctor's 'primary concern'. The hospital was 'a means to an end, the end being an adequately remunerative private practice'.[1] The fault of the municipal system was that the highest earnings were given to the medical administrator, and this deprived the hospitals of the services of the best physicians and surgeons. Moreover the need to refer so many decisions to the lay local authority stifled the initiative of the administrator and produced an essentially authoritarian structure. The medical superintendent had to be both organizer and senior clinical official, and only an exceptional man could discharge both duties effectively. Dr Himsworth thought that it would probably be best if administrators were freed of clinical responsibilities. This was the system of administration which he hoped would develop under a regional plan: and in such circumstances the governing bodies of the voluntary hospitals would tend to become 'superfluous'.

While this fruitful discussion was being conducted in the *British Medical Journal*, the medical planning commission had been hard at work. And in June 1942, it published its draft interim report.[2] It started by drawing attention to the faults of the existing health services – the overlapping health functions of local authorities, the maldistribution of all types of doctor, the isolation of individual general practitioners and the differences between the admissions policies and opportunities for professional practice in different types of hospital. The report then proceeded to criticize the system of control by local government. Not only were many local government units too small to provide a proper service, but local authorities acted 'without adequate consultation with the profession'. Furthermore, 'the rapid advance of medical science and the increasing complexity of medical practice have outstripped the ability of the average local councillor to make informed decisions concerning the provision and management of medical services, and too often policy is determined by local politics and personal factors'.[3]

The commission favoured the organization of the health services by central rather than local government, but stressed the need for considerable delegation of authority and strong representation of the medical profession at every level. Thus a central

---

[1] ibid., 21 March 1942, p. 47
[2] *BMJ*, 20 June 1942, pp. 742–53. No final report was ever published.
[3] ibid., p. 744

authority should be set up which could be either a government department or a corporate body formed under government auspices and responsible through a Minister to Parliament. Its chief officer was to be a doctor and there was to be a strong central medical advisory committee or a medical board with both advisory and executive functions. Local administration was to be on a regional basis. There were either to be regional authorities which delegated authority to non-elected experts, or there were to be regional councils representative of local authorities, voluntary hospitals, the central authority and the doctors. Regions were to cover populations of at least half-a-million and there was to be a teaching hospital in each region.

In the case of general practice, there had to be more co-operation, and the focal point of co-operation was to be the health centre which would be provided or approved by the regional authority. Services at the health centre would be provided to 'all persons with incomes within the current National Health Insurance limits and for their dependants', in effect for about 90 per cent of the population. They would include maternal and child welfare, school health services as well as general practice and specialist consultations. There would normally be between six and ten doctors in each centre who would be paid a basic fixed salary and a capitation fee related to the number of persons or families on their lists. There would be as wide a measure of free choice of doctor as was possible. The majority of the commission were opposed to whole-time salaried practice, and argued that the essential features of the National Health Insurance Scheme should be embodied in any new health plan.

A regional hospital service was 'generally favoured' and at the very least the hospital service had to be unified. 'The voluntary hospitals, however, embodied traditions and standards of service which should not be allowed to disappear. At the same time it was recognized that the potentialities of the council hospitals are great and that they should be developed.' At present they were starved of 'interesting cases'. Moreover the organization of the council hospitals did not encourage a clinical career. In the new service there must be higher clinical posts carrying salaries and status 'no less than those of administrative posts. In other words there should be separate ladders of promotion for clinical and administrative posts.' Doctors should be freed from the domination of medical superintendents. The voluntary system ought to be extended to the council hospitals whereby 'the doctors were given full scope for initiative and responsibility in professional matters'.

As regards the conditions of service for doctors working in the hospitals, the commission thought it satisfactory for appointments, as in the voluntary hospitals, to be full-time up to the level of registrar and chief assistant. Above this level there were to be three types of practice – whole-time salaried posts without rights to private practice, whole-time salaried posts with the right to private practice within the hospital, and part-time salaried posts with the right to private practice inside and outside the hospital. It was particularly hoped that this third type of practice would bring consultants to the smaller hospitals and would ease the situation 'where the hospitals were staffed by general practitioners who may have to undertake work beyond their training or competence'.

These proposals were not to lead to the end of the contributory schemes which were to be extended on a more uniform pattern. There was a 'definite therapeutic as well as a financial value in an arrangement which overcame the necessity for paying a lump sum for medical treatment at the time of illness or immediately afterwards'.[1]

The commission suggested that regional hospital councils should be set up as early as possible with nominees of the central authority, major local authorities, the voluntary hospitals and the doctors. And these councils were to have medical advisory committees. Immediate steps should also be taken to extend services under the National Insurance Scheme to cover consultant, specialist and laboratory services outside hospital. During the interim period, consultants would probably have to be paid on an 'item of service' basis.

The proposals went much further than the second edition of *A General Medical Service for the Nation* (1938) in developing the idea of a comprehensive service based on regions for the poorer 90 per cent of the population. They also incorporated the radical novelty of health centres. Thirdly, the plan accepted the division which had grown up between the general practitioner and the specialist services in urban areas, and planned its extension to rural areas. The commission, upon which the consultants and specialists had been heavily represented, made no mention of

[1] ibid., p. 752

the long campaign to provide hospital beds for general practitioners. The division of function within the medical profession was to be extended into the rural areas.

The commission's report was the principal business discussed at the annual representative meeting of the BMA in September 1942. A motion that the debate should be postponed until after the war was defeated, and the meeting discussed the broad principles of the report. It was resolved right away that there should be a service which would 'render available to every individual all necessary medical services both general and specialist and both domiciliary and institutional'.[1] The council then moved that the provision should be made by the Government 'for a section of the community only', for perhaps 90 per cent. By 94 votes to 92 it was decided that provision should be made 'for the whole of the community',[2] but that patients should have the right to contract out. It was decided that within general practice 'as full a measure as possible of free choice of doctor and patient should be preserved',[3] and that 'group practice should be a feature of any future medical service', but that the groups should be arranged by the doctors themselves. A motion to establish a whole-time salaried government service was defeated by a large majority,[4] but the broad plan for health centres as set out in the report was approved.[5] Apart from referring back to the commission the question of the system of remunerating consultants, the reorganization of the hospitals was not discussed at the meeting.

In January 1943, the bodies which had been represented on the commission expressed views on the report. While the physicians and obstetricians favoured a service for a section of the community, the radiologists and Society of Medical Officers of Health wanted a service for all the community. While the Royal College of Physicians wanted the service to be run by a central board, the Royal College of Surgeons preferred Ministerial control and the latter also put in a special plea for the preservation of the voluntary hospital system. The Society of Medical Officers of Health was alone in recommending control over the service in each area by one single local authority

[1] *BMJ Supplement*, 19 September 1942, p. 31
[2] ibid.
[3] ibid.
[4] 177 to 20
[5] *BMJ Supplement*, 19 September 1942, p. 34

with 'a chief medical officer in executive responsibility'.[1]

A few months after the report of the Medical Planning Commission was published, *The Lancet* printed the draft report of *Medical Planning Research*.[2] Though the report covered much wider ground and was much more radical on some important issues, many of its recommendations were similar to those of the commission. It recommended a 'free' health service available to the *whole* population as part of a comprehensive social security scheme providing generous cash benefits. The proposed health service was to be run by a national corporation operating through eleven regions. Eventually all hospitals might be owned by the corporation. Meanwhile voluntary hospitals and local authority hospitals could continue to own their buildings and appoint governing bodies but hospital staffs would be employed by the corporation and the costs of the hospitals would be met by it. The report condemned in particularly strong terms the hierarchical pattern of medical staffing which existed in local authority hospitals. All hospitals were to adopt the staffing pattern of the voluntary hospitals: consultants and specialists were not to be put under any type of clinical supervisor or medical administrator.

The reports of the Planning Commission and of Planning Research were not the only documents urging the reform of the health services. The Socialist Medical Association had published in 1940 its programme for a unified medical service organized on a regional basis with doctors employed on salaries.[3] The Liberal Party published a programme in 1942 which was similar in some respects to the report of the medical planning commission except that the scheme was based on the local authorities which were to pay grants to the voluntary hospitals without medical schools: the teaching hospitals were to receive their grants from the University Grants Committee. The Liberals favoured health centres but did not wish the doctors to be paid wholly by salary. All medical services, including dental and ophthalmic services, were to be available free to the whole population.[4] The Communist Party published a statement early

[1] ibid., 2 January 1943, p. 2

[2] Supplement to *The Lancet*, 21 November 1942

[3] Socialist Medical Association, *Whither Medicine?*, London, 1940

[4] Liberal Party, *Health for the People; Proposals for a Positive and Active Health Policy for the Nation*, Liberal Publication Dept., London, 1942

in 1943 but the memorandum did little more than stress the need for 'an immediate increase in the efficiency of the health service in order to assist war production and to prepare for and assist the "second front" '.[1]

The Labour Party published its policy for the health services in April 1943.[2] The document had been drawn up in close association with the Socialist Medical Association. The plan was based on the assumption that the system of local government would be completely overhauled: elected regional authorities were to take the place of the existing major authorities. Thus the health services were to be run at the centre by the Ministry of Health and locally by the health committees of the new regional authorities. It was clearly stated that the medical profession would be organized as a 'national, full-time, salaried, pensionable service';[3] 'unless the doctor has a salary and a prospect of pension, which frees him from economic dependence upon paying patients, he cannot devote his full energy to the prevention as well as to the cure of ill health.'[4] The doctors were to work in hospitals, and in district and local health centres.

The voluntary hospitals were to be 'brought within the National Scheme on terms which will satisfy the nation's sense of equity' and 'required' to conform to a plan. A 'simple method' for achieving this would be for hospitals to be paid for cases referred to them by local authorities, and for the authority to gain 'representation and control on the Governing Board'. Thus 'before long the voluntary hospitals will come under the control of the Local Authorities'.[5] Except for hospitals for infectious and mental diseases, special hospitals would be eliminated. Specialized units would instead be included in the general hospitals. 'The General Hospitals should be associated in groups, so that only one hospital out of a group of three or four would admit, say, skin cases, or eye cases; perhaps only one hospital in each Region would undertake rare specialized treatment such as plastic surgery or brain surgery.'[6]

While the political parties had been working out their policies

[1] *BMJ Supplement*, 9 January 1943, p. 7
[2] Labour Party, *National Service for Health: The Labour Party's Post-War Policy*, London, 1943
[3] ibid., p. 18
[4] ibid., p. 12
[5] ibid., p. 16
[6] ibid., p. 15

for a health service, there had been further thinking in Whitehall. In particular, William Beveridge had been presiding over his committee of civil servants which was set up to undertake 'a survey of the existing national schemes of social insurance and allied services, including workmen's compensation and to make recommendations'.[1] Possibly as a result of the work done for this committee or from experience of the Emergency Medical Service, the Minister of Health made an important announcement on post-war hospital policy in October 1941. While immediate reorganization was held to be impracticable, the Government stated that after the war appropriate treatment would be available for all who needed it 'by means of a comprehensive hospital service'.[2] It would be the duty of the major local authorities to secure this though the service would be designed by reference to areas substantially larger than those of individual local authorities:[3] 'the partnership between the local authorities and voluntary hospitals' would be placed 'on a more regular basis'.[4] The local authorities were to be given central government grants and the teaching hospitals would receive increased educational grants. Patients would be 'called on to make a reasonable payment towards the cost whether through contributory schemes or otherwise'.[5]

The Minister had not worked out any detailed plan. A survey of hospitals was, however, set under way – three of them conducted by the Ministry and seven through the Nuffield Provincial Hospitals Trust. It was not going to be easy to design a scheme which preserved the roles of both the local authorities and the voluntary hospitals, and yet constituted a comprehensive service designed by reference to large areas. Several members of parliament asked the Minister to reassure them that there would be full use of, and consultation with, the voluntary hospitals. One member, on the other hand, suggested that the maintenance of voluntary hospitals and their subvention by public funds and flag days was becoming 'increasingly repugnant to the conscience of the public'.[6] It was Aneurin Bevan.

[1] Sir W. Beveridge, *Social Insurance and Allied Services*, Cmd 6404, p. 2, HMSO, 1942

[2] *Hansard* (H of C), Vol. 374, 9 October 1941, col. 1116
[3] ibid.
[4] ibid.
[5] ibid., col. 1117
[6] ibid., col. 1119

The Beveridge Report was published in December 1942. The proposals for an extension and co-ordination of the social insurance schemes were based upon the assumption that there would be a comprehensive national health service to achieve the objectives which the medical planning commission had set out in its reports. Beveridge argued that as the new social insurance scheme would cover all income groups, so the health service should be available to the whole population rather than 90 per cent of the population (the existing insured persons and their dependants).[1] And he proposed that the service should be available without examination of the contributions paid in any individual case. 'Restoration of a sick person to health is a duty of the State and the sick person, prior to any other consideration.'[2]

Beveridge pointed out that this would not, of itself, put an end to private practice.

> Those who have the desire and the means will be able to pay separately for private treatment, if the medical service is organized to provide that, as they may pay now for private schooling, though the public education system is available for all. But no one will be compelled to pay separately. The possible scope of private general practice will be so restricted that it may not appear worthwhile to preserve it. If, therefore, it is desired to preserve a substantial scope for private practice and to restrict the right to service without a charge on treatment to persons below a certain income limit, it will not be possible to include a payment for medical service in an insurance contribution which all are required to pay irrespective of income.[3]

The questions of the organization of such a service and the terms of service of persons employed in it were outside the scope of the report, and Beveridge did not express any views about the place of voluntary and public hospitals in the scheme. He also left open the question of whether a compulsory hospital contribution should be incorporated in the social insurance contribution to replace the existing contributory schemes. Among the considerations which he considered relevant to this question were first, how far people were at present delaying in going to hospital for financial reasons, and secondly, the place of volun-

[1] Beveridge, p. 160
[2] ibid., p. 159
[3] ibid., p. 160

tary hospitals and the terms of service and pay of their staffs. He recognized that this was an awkward dilemma upon which the future of the voluntary hospitals might well depend.

> If a payment for institutional treatment is included in the compulsory insurance contribution . . . an important financial resource of the voluntary hospitals will come to an end. It will then be for the health departments to use the grant they will receive from the Social Insurance Fund in whatever way best fits their hospital policy. [1]

In other words, the health departments would have to use the money for local authority hospitals alone or find some means of making grants to the voluntary hospitals.

The report was debated by the council of the BMA on 3 February 1943. It was agreed that the Association would be willing to co-operate in such a scheme on two conditions.[2] First, 'the character, terms and conditions of the medical service' had to be 'determined by negotiation and agreement with the medical profession'. And secondly,

> . . . those members of the community who decided not to avail themselves in part or in whole of the benefit of the service open to them should not be precluded from obtaining the medical services they desire from hospitals within the scheme, paying for such services privately, with the necessary safeguards to prevent abuse.

The report was debated in Parliament in the same month. The Government announced that it welcomed this conception of a reorganized and comprehensive health service which would cover the people as a whole and include institutional treatment. The ultimate responsibility for the service in any area would be entrusted to 'the well-tried local government machinery, working very often over larger areas perhaps and certainly working in consultation and collaboration with voluntary agencies'. The Government reassured the doctors that it favoured maintaining the principle of free choice of doctor 'to the greatest possible extent' but pointed out that this principle was not necessarily inconsistent with the development of health centres. Also with an eye on the BMA, the Government made

[1] ibid.
[2] *BMJ Supplement*, 13 February 1943, p. 23

it clear that the service was not going to be forced on people who preferred to make private arrangements. The voluntary hospitals were also reassured by being told that their position 'must be safeguarded'. Thus the Government announced that it proposed to 'seek the help of those main organizations – local authority, voluntary or professional – on whose participation the success of any reorganization must depend'. The new service was to be based on 'the co-operation of public authorities, voluntary hospitals and other voluntary agencies and the profession towards one common end'.[1]

The Government was committed to preparing a plan for a National Health Service. It had been led to promote this aspect of post-war planning not only by pressure from the doctors but from the wider public demand for social reform. Moreover, it was a coalition government and there were pressures within the coalition to promote schemes of radical post-war reconstruction. In October 1941, the Government had spoken of a comprehensive *hospital* service available to all who needed it. Now it was committed to preparing plans for a comprehensive *health* service which would cover the people as a whole. Beveridge's plans had been greatly influenced by the report of the medical planning commission. But in one respect his report had led the Government to go further than the commission in recommending a service available to the whole rather than to 90 per cent of the population. Clearly the scope for private practice under such a service would be very limited. It was this fact that contributed to the violent opposition which was soon to be expressed by a powerful section of the medical profession to any government plan for a *national* health service.

Neither the Government nor the medical planning commission had yet faced up to the problem of reconciling the different and somewhat conflicting principles upon which both were agreed. Was it possible to provide a unified hospital service and preserve the independence of the voluntary hospitals? Would voluntary hospitals continue to receive charitable donations if they were given government grants? Would the voluntary hospitals be willing to collaborate fully with 'the well-tried local government machinery'? What was really meant by such words as 'safeguard', 'collaboration', 'co-operation', 'unifica-

[1] Sir John Anderson, *Hansard* (H of C), Vol. 386, 16 February 1943, cols. 1659–64

tion', 'comprehensive', and by the phrase 'ultimate responsi-bility'? The delicate issues could be sidestepped in statements of broad principle but if there were to be a plan, eventually they would have to be faced.

CHAPTER 28

The Government's Plan

IN the middle of the Second World War it seemed even more likely than in the middle of the First World War that there would be a drastic reform of the nation's health services once hostilities were over. The Government and the profession seemed to have agreed on the broad principles of reform. The Beveridge Report was on everyone's lips and Beveridge himself was credited with inventing a national health service. War had once again promoted a widespread but perhaps temporary demand for the institutional changes which would bring about a new era of 'social justice'.

A few weeks after the Government had issued its statement of policy, the Minister of Health (Mr Ernest Brown) called together representatives of the local authorities, the voluntary hospitals and the medical profession. The discussions were meant to be secret and without any commitment, but they did not remain secret for long. Among other papers which the Ministry circulated was a draft scheme for general practice to be conducted on a salaried basis in a comprehensive service.[1] The Minister claimed that the doctors had asked to see such a draft. But two newspapers[2] saw or were told about it and reported that it was the Government's intention to introduce a salaried service. A meeting of the Metropolitan Counties branch of the British Medical Association was hastily called on a Sunday to protest at the intentions of the Ministry. This meeting of 1,000 doctors was addressed by Dr Charles Hill,[3] the deputy secretary of the BMA. In a violent speech he alleged that the Government was proposing 'to recast medical practice and place it *in toto* on a health-

[1] *Hansard* (H of C), Vol. 390, 10 June 1943, col. 974
[2] Neither the Ministry nor the local authorities would have had any incentive to give this information to the newspapers. It is therefore likely that the leak came from one of the doctors.
[3] later Lord Hill of Luton

centre basis'. The Government had decided it needed to control the medical profession so that it could control certification. Dr Hill called for unity and asked the doctors 'to hold their forces until the time comes, as it may come, for a fight'.[1]

The *British Medical Journal* suddenly abandoned the calm and objective tone of the previous year and struck a shrill note of warning.

> If this happens, then doctors will no longer constitute an independent learned and liberal profession, but will instead form a service of technicians controlled by central bureaucrats and by local men and women entirely ignorant of medical matters.[2]

The profession objected to salaries as a mode of remuneration, to the proposed 'subjection' to local government, and, above all, to 'the speed at which the Government was moving'.[3]

This startling change in the attitude of the representatives of the profession cannot be explained as an unfortunate misunderstanding. It was the prelude to a whole new era in the profession's attitude to the Government. It has been suggested that 'as soon as the Government became serious about reforming the medical system, a sort of nameless fear of what might ensue gripped the profession's representatives'.[4] Part of the change could also be attributed to the growing influence of the deputy secretary, Dr Charles Hill, who was to succeed to the secretaryship within a year. In devising its own plans, the profession had been acting purely as an expert body. But once the Government started negotiations, the BMA had instinctively begun to act as a trade union, and thus to obstruct, in the hope of obtaining thereby the most favourable terms of service. Finally, it should be remembered that the Government was insisting on a service for the *whole* population and thus greatly limiting the scope for private practice.

For whatever reason, the first shot had been fired in what was to be a long and often unintelligible dispute between Ministers and the profession. Negotiations were, however, soon resumed. The negotiating committee made it clear that the discussion of a

---

[1] *Hansard* (H of C), Vol. 390, 10 June 1943, col. 964
[2] *BMJ Supplement*, 29 May 1943, p. 670
[3] H. Eckstein, *The English Health Service*, p. 142, Harvard, 1959
[4] ibid., p. 143

salaried service would be 'unfruitful' and the Minister agreed 'to relegate the proposals to the discard'. And the talks progressed within the limits set by the Minister: discussion was confined to a comprehensive service administered by local authorities, available not to 90 per cent but 100 per cent of the community.[1] It was known to all concerned that on the basis of these talks the Minister would prepare a White Paper which was intended to appear in mid-1943.

The White Paper was not completed until February 1944, by which time a new Minister had been appointed – Mr Willink. The rationale of a national health service was stated by analogy.

> Just as people are accustomed to look to public organization for essential facilities like a clean and safe water supply or good highways, accepting these as things which the community combines to provide for the benefit of the individual without distinction of section or group, so they should now be able to look for proper facilities for the care of their personal health to a publicly organized service available to all who want to use it – a service for which all would be paying as taxpayers and ratepayers and contributors to some national scheme of social insurance.[2]

At present the availability of health services depended on where people happened to live or work, on what age or vocational group they happened to belong to, on the nature of their illness and to some extent on their ability to pay. The Government wanted to rationalize the distribution of medical services. It also wanted to encourage early treatment not just to mend ill-health but to increase 'good health and the sense of well-being'.[3]

In applying these objectives, the Government made it clear that it did not intend to disregard the past and 'invent *ad hoc* a completely new organization for all health requirements'. Rather it wished 'to use and absorb the experience of the past and the present, building it into a wider service'.[4] In practice this meant rejecting any proposal for an organization divorced from local government, in which the profession would have

---

[1] *BMJ Supplement*, 15 January 1944, p. 9. See also *Hansard* (H of C), Vol. 398, 16 March 1944, col. 440.

[2] Ministry of Health and Department of Health for Scotland, *A National Health Service*, Cmd 6502, p. 6, HMSO, 1944

[3] ibid., p. 8

[4] ibid.

substantial power. The machinery of local government was to be adapted to provide the hospital and other services for which they had been traditionally responsible. The administration of the existing health insurance services was also to be adapted, partly by greater centralization to secure a more even distribution of general practitioners over the country, and partly by creating greater co-ordination between these services and those of the local authorities. But at both central and local levels there were to be advisory committees (Health Services Councils) drawn largely from the medical profession.

The central control of the service was to rest with the Minister. An independent executive body could not be given control over major questions of finance because of the need for parliamentary control: nor could local government authorities be placed in the position of being overruled by a body which was not answerable to Parliament.[1] Similarly, a regional *ad hoc* authority would conflict with democratic principles and the Government did not intend 'needlessly to interfere with the well-tested machinery of local government'.[2] Nor was the Government prepared to allow professional representatives to have seats on the local authority and its committees. 'The risk of impairing the principle of public responsibility – that effective decisions on policy must lie entirely with elected representatives answerable to the people for the decisions that they take – outweighs any advantage likely to accrue.'[3]

General practice was to be based on 'a combination of grouped practice and of separate practice side by side'.[4] And grouped practice was to include both practices in ordinary doctors' premises and in specially designed premises. Thus there would be experimental health centres. While the health centres would be owned by local authorities, the doctors would be under contract with the central authority. The White Paper stated that there was a strong case for paying doctors in health centres on a salaried basis.[5]

The White Paper pointed out that the existing counties and county boroughs (with the exception of London) were too small

[1] ibid., p. 13
[2] ibid., p. 15
[3] ibid., p. 20
[4] ibid., p. 28
[5] ibid., p. 32

to provide a full hospital service. Moreover, the distinction between separate urban and rural authorities was unsuited for hospital organization as the towns largely served the rural areas. If the existing authorities were asked to provide a full range of services, there would be overlapping and duplication. If arrangements were made for each local authority to pay for services rendered to their population by other authorities, there would be 'a mass of financial adjustments'. Finally, the creation of *ad hoc* health authorities covering wide areas would be opposed to the trend in government towards all-purpose authorities. Thus the Government proposed the combination of counties and county boroughs into joint boards to provide the hospital services.

This raised the problem of the voluntary hospitals. The Government had no wish to 'destroy or to diminish a system which is so well rooted in the goodwill of its supporters'.[1] Thus a way had to be found

> . . . of combining the general responsibility of the new joint authority for the service with the continued participation in that service of the voluntary movement . . . of securing a whole service under one ultimate public responsibility without destroying the independence and traditions to which the voluntary hospitals attach value.[2]

It was hoped that this could be achieved by voluntary hospitals freely entering into contractual arrangements with local authorities.

Thus it would be the duty of the joint authority to survey the hospital needs of its area and make a plan about how these needs could best be met and to do this in consultation with the voluntary hospitals. The plan would then be approved by the Minister who would hear objections from the local health services council (the local advisory body) and the voluntary hospitals. A voluntary hospital which agreed to provide certain services on a contractual basis under the plan would have to observe certain general conditions – the implementation of nationally-agreed salary scales, the adoption of a nationally-agreed system of appointing medical staff, the acceptance of public inspection and the standardization of accounts.[3]

---

[1] ibid., p. 21
[2] ibid.
[3] ibid., p. 23

The local authorities were to pay the voluntary hospitals for services rendered on a scale which would be centrally determined. Hospitals, both municipal and voluntary, would also receive a share of any sum collected for the hospitals as part of the social insurance scheme. This would compensate hospitals for the loss of money which patients would otherwise have provided. 'In the case of voluntary hospitals it would be feasible, if so desired, to regard the aggregate of their share of the payments as a central pool from which payments to individual hospitals could be varied according to the needs and resources of each.'[1] The White Paper emphasized, however, that it was essential that

> the hospitals should still look substantially to their own financial resources, to personal benefactors and the continuing support of those who believe in the voluntary hospital movement. So long, and so long only, can they retain their individuality. If once the situation were to arise in which the whole cost of the voluntary hospitals' part in the public service (a service designed for the whole population) was repaid from public money, or indeed it was recognized that public funds were to be used to guarantee those hospitals' financial security, the end of the voluntary movement would be near at hand.[2]

The Government envisaged a system of inspection for all hospitals in the scheme similar to that developed over many decades for the education service. The inspectors would be employed on both a 'part-time and a whole-time basis' and would include doctors from both voluntary and municipal hospitals as well as 'administrators, nurses, catering experts and others'.[3] It would be the duty of inspectors to bring to the notice of the Minister and the joint authority defects of organization or management and to enable individual hospitals to be kept in touch with the latest practice and ideas.

It was envisaged that consultants would receive 'proper and regular remuneration' on a centrally regulated scale. Some would be employed on a whole-time basis and others on a part-time basis. And there were to be 'more regular attendances and duties than is often the case now'.[4] Each consultant would

---

[1] ibid.
[2] ibid.
[3] ibid., p. 24
[4] ibid.

normally be associated 'with more than one major hospital, so as to enable the sharing of a common consultant staff to become an effective link between hospitals'. There would be a special machinery for the appointment of consultants to avoid the danger of 'in-breeding'. And as there were not yet enough men and women 'of real consultant status',[1] there would have to be 'more consultants and a better distribution of them'.[2]

Two weeks after the White Paper was published and two days after he had been appointed Secretary of the British Medical Association, Dr Charles Hill addressed a mass meeting of 1,200 doctors at BMA House. He regretted that there was not to be a corporate body at the top of the service and that the Government 'had been unwilling to dilute the democratic principle by including, in the public interest, some non-elected professional expert members in the joint authorities'.[3] The Government would 'need to be converted' on the issue of salaried practice in health centres. He regretted that the voluntary hospitals would have to be subsidized by the Government or 'thrown back on the old methods of public appeal unrelated to services rendered'.[4] Although he emphasized the need to watch any tendency for a salaried service to be imposed, he welcomed the other basic principles of the White Paper. The final passage of the speech struck a curious note. 'You may think as I do that it is a pity that we should be called on to devote our time and thought to this subject when we are approaching the critical stage in the bloodiest war in history.'[5] Had he forgotten that the initiative for reform had come as much from the profession as from the Government?

The Council of the BMA gave the White Paper formal consideration in March 1944. Criticisms were mainly concentrated on the proposals for general practice which, it was said, would lead to a fall in the capital values of practices and might also 'lead to a whole-time salaried service'. The Council did not at this stage make an issue of the whole question of local authority control of hospitals. It contented itself by regretting the position of the voluntary hospitals. The White Paper would destroy the

[1] ibid., p. 25
[2] ibid.
[3] *BMJ Supplement*, 11 March 1944, p. 42
[4] ibid.
[5] ibid.

motive for contributory schemes and throw the hospitals back on the old methods of charitable collection. Moreover, they were given no special representation on the local health authorities.[1]

The White Paper was debated in the House of Commons shortly afterwards and the Minister of Health (Mr Willink) took the opportunity to explain further the financial position of the voluntary hospitals under the scheme. He pointed out that 'to launch a major social insurance scheme which did not cover the contributors against perhaps the greatest normal contingency of life, prolonged illness involving residence in hospital, would be impossible'.[2] This meant that the contributory schemes would have to go and the Minister was sure that the voluntary hospitals would be 'the last to suggest that contributory schemes should be maintained simply in order to continue the existing basis of their finances'.[3] The receipts from this source would be more than compensated by the new Exchequer payment to the hospitals and the Government would certainly 'review the question of financial assistance in respect of teaching work at the teaching hospitals'.[4]

The Minister also stated categorically that the Government did not intend 'to establish a fully salaried State medical service'.[5] But the charge that it did was repeated immediately by the spokesman for the profession in the House of Commons[6] and in the correspondence columns of the British Medical Journal over the following months.[7] Sympathy with the position of the voluntary hospitals was also expressed. Many letters also came in which criticized the administration of local authority hospitals. As the report of Medical Planning Research had shown, this was the issue about which the younger doctors felt most strongly. One correspondent wrote to quote a local councillor as saying, 'We have bought the services of the medical officer, and he belongs to us, body and soul.'[8] And Squadron-Leader O. M. Kelly, FRCS, contributed an article which consisted of a fierce

[1] ibid., 18 March 1944, p. 52
[2] Hansard (H of C), Vol. 398, 16 March 1944, cols. 436–7
[3] ibid.
[4] ibid.
[5] ibid., col. 432
[6] ibid., col. 443 (Sir E. Graham-Little)
[7] BMJ Supplement, 1 April 1944, pp. 66–7, and 22 April 1944, pp. 81–4
[8] ibid., 8 April 1944, pp. 71–2

attack on the local authority system of medical administration. The medical superintendent was 'in a position of supreme power over his medical staff, and a position of no power whatsoever with his immediate superiors'.[1] The medical staff had no say in the running of their hospitals: they could appeal to the local authority, which would do as much good as

> ... to bang their heads against the nearest stone wall. ... The shadow of 'County Hall' hovers like a bird of ill-omen over all. The medical and nursing staffs have no more standing than the porters, perhaps less, as the latter have their own trade union. And the policy of safety-first, combined with the 'Fuehrer' complex which the system inevitably produces in the medical superintendent to a greater or lesser degree, is felt throughout the whole institution.[2]

Squadron-Leader Kelly attracted a number of letters opposing his views, but he also had many letters of support.[3] And by June 1944, the Council of the BMA had decided that the question of administration was fundamental.

> There should be no negotiations on detail and terms of service until the profession was satisfied as to the method of administration. ... The profession must have effective and adequate representation at all stages. ... The profession would not agree to be employed by local authorities. ... The Joint Board plan was unacceptable.

Voluntary hospitals must be given a place in the scheme and the plan should be based upon regions. Finally there was no need for a 100 per cent service.[4]

While the BMA was gradually moving into a position of firm opposition to the White Paper, the organizational pattern of the service received strong support in a pamphlet published by Political and Economic Planning, an independent research institute. The pamphlet emphasized the need for consumer sovereignty, which ruled out 'the variety of syndicalist or technocratic alternatives',[5] which had been suggested. 'The doctor's wish to "keep medicine out of politics" is no different

[1] ibid., 3 June 1944, p. 130
[2] ibid.
[3] ibid., 24 June 1944, p. 158
[4] ibid., 17 June 1944
[5] PEP, *Medical Care for Citizens*, Planning No. 222, p. 7, London, 1944

from the professional soldier's desire to escape control by "the civilians in Whitehall". It derives partly from an evasion of the responsibilities of democratic citizenship, but also from past experience of bad administration.'[1] PEP concluded, however, that 'inflexible and pettifogging lay control of doctors, out of date methods of appointing and promoting hospital medical staffs, narrow-mindedness and lack of imagination, are still far too prevalent among local health authorities'.[2]

PEP also supported the principle of making the free service available to all who wanted it as distinct from all who were thought to need it. The Council of the BMA was still arguing that it was 'unnecessary for the State to make provision for those who are both willing or able, indeed prefer, to make it for themselves'.[3] But PEP pointed out that this category could not be defined by an income limit as 'medical needs may be unlimited, while incomes never are'.[4] It was held to be 'wrong in principle to establish by statute a compulsory fee-paying class'.[5] On the question of private practice, it argued that if the public service was to be the best

> there is every reason why doctors entering into general practice should be spared this dilemma of how to take a fee without giving anything in return; they should be offered the straight choice between devoting themselves to full-time public service or exclusively to private work outside it.[6]

PEP's contribution to the discussion was not well received by the *British Medical Journal*.[7]

By the summer the British Hospitals Association had formed its views on the White Paper.

> If it were the intention of the government to destroy the voluntary hospitals, no surer method could have been devised than the administrative structure as set out in the White Paper which places them in a position of complete subservience to the local authorities

---

[1] ibid.
[2] ibid., p. 6
[3] *BMJ*, 13 May 1944, p. 644
[4] PEP, *Medical Care*, p. 3
[5] ibid.
[6] ibid., p. 7
[7] *BMJ Supplement*, 8 July 1944, p. 8

and gives them no voice in the planning of the hospital services, national or local.[1]

The elimination of voluntary schemes would 'deprive the voluntary hospitals not only of a large part of the incomes raised voluntarily on their behalf but of a real personal contact between the hospitals and the people whom they serve'.[2] The Association wanted the whole of the Exchequer payment for services to be paid to them direct and not through the local authorities. This would remove from the local authorities the opportunity of 'using the power of the purse to gain control of voluntary hospitals'.[3] The White Paper as it stood would lead to the disappearance of the voluntary hospitals.

The British Hospitals Association accordingly proposed that there should be a central hospitals board, representative of both voluntary and local authority hospitals. The Minister would consult this Board on all matters of hospital planning. For the lower level of the administration, it argued that the proposed areas were too small for efficient planning. Thus the Association proposed larger regional councils, which would be statutory bodies consisting of an equal number of representatives of local authority and voluntary hospitals and would be wholly responsible for planning in their areas. Each region should as far as possible have a teaching hospital.[4]

The King's Fund advocated a similar plan based on twelve regions, and asked for direct Exchequer payments to the voluntary hospitals on a triennial or quinquennial basis on the lines of the grants paid by the University Grants Committee.[5] The arguments it used to support this approach were similar to those used by the British Hospitals Association. 'There could be no partnership if one party is put into the position of paymaster to the other.'[6] Exchequer grants had to be strictly on a per bed basis. The governors of St Thomas' Hospital also produced a statement. They were strongly opposed to hospitals being dependent on rates and taxes. In particular they feared that the

[1] quoted in *BMJ Supplement*, 26 August 1944, p. 45
[2] ibid.
[3] ibid.
[4] ibid.
[5] ibid., 16 September 1944, p. 59
[6] ibid.

power to be vested in the London County Council would make the 'development of the present happy and equal partnership a matter of much greater and possibly insurmountable difficulty'.[1] 'The personal and spiritual aspect of all hospital and health activities are of an importance at best equal to the administrative and financial.'[2]

Meanwhile the BMA had conducted a poll of the whole profession, which gained a high response rate and was analysed by the British Institute of Public Opinion.[3] The majority against the actual proposals of the White Paper was not large (53 per cent as against 39 per cent). But to the embarrassment of the leadership of the profession, 60 per cent of the doctors favoured a free service for 100 per cent of the population.[4] But perhaps the most significant result of all concerned the control of hospitals by joint authorities: 78 per cent of doctors were opposed to this and only 13 per cent were in favour. Feeling was strongest among consultants who, as Lord Moran pointed out, feared interference by local authorities in clinical work.[5] The leadership had a clear mandate to fight the joint authority proposal but not much else.

Thus the British Medical Association decided that it would only agree to negotiate with the Minister if the administrative structure were discussed first. Agreement on this issue was made a prerequisite to discussion of other subjects. This was the position adopted by the council in November 1944[6] and ratified by the annual representative meeting in December of the same year.[7] Between mid-January and mid-March the negotiating committee held eight meetings with the Ministry of Health: the Minister himself was present at six of these meetings.[8] By July 1945 some concessions appear to have been obtained. Health centres were now to be 'experimental' and private practice was to be allowed in them.[9] Moreover, there were

[1] ibid., 9 September 1944, p. 54
[2] ibid.
[3] The detailed results of the poll are analysed in Eckstein, pp. 147–50.
[4] Later Dr Dane, the Chairman of the council, tried to use ingenious arguments to escape this. See *BMJ Supplement*, 16 September 1944, p. 63.
[5] ibid., 21 April 1945, p. 60
[6] ibid., 18 November 1944, p. 112
[7] ibid., 16 December 1944, p. 161
[8] ibid., 24 March 1945, p.43
[9] *Hansard* (H of C), Vol. 409, 12 April 1945, cols. 1958–9

indications that the Government was prepared to modify the
whole system of administration to meet the wishes of the
BMA.[1] New proposals were discussed at a special and secret
representative meeting in July 1945 which were very different
from those in the White Paper. One correspondent to the
British Medical Journal described these proposals as 'a betrayal
of both the nation and the medical profession'.[2]

The Minister was in a difficult position. His White Paper had
followed earlier statements of Government policy by giving wide
responsibility to the local authorities but, in doing so, he had
antagonized both the doctors and the voluntary hospitals. If
it had been amended to meet the doctors' wishes by introducing
some measure of professional control, it would have been opposed
by the local authorities. The London County Council made it
quite clear that 'no right of nomination or appointment by
professional or other bodies to membership of any committees
of the Council charged with the administration of the scheme
could be acceptable'.[3] Moreover, the governors of voluntary
hospitals wanted to share the responsibility for planning the
hospital services with the local authorities, and preferred to see
doctors kept in an advisory position.

The medical profession's antagonism towards the local
authorities was proving to be a major stumbling block. And
much of this was directed against the medical superintendent
system. Those who held these posts were not respected by the
leaders of the medical profession. The ablest doctors had always
been unwilling to apply for jobs which were primarily administrative and offered no opportunities for private practice, from
which the highest incomes could be earned. The governors of
the voluntary hospitals felt much the same about the local
authorities. And the London teaching hospitals claimed the
wide measure of freedom from parliamentary control which
had been achieved by the universities.

Thus the Minister of Health, responsible as he also was for
local government as a whole, was under great pressure to dilute
the principle of local democracy by introducing some measure
of medical syndicalism. By the early summer of 1945, a revised
plan was taking shape. No longer were local authorities to join

[1] ibid., Vol. 413, 17 August 1945, col. 258, and 21 August 1945, cols. 568-9
[2] *BMJ Supplement*, 13 January 1945, p. 5
[3] ibid., 13 January 1945, p. 5

with others to provide hospital services. Each authority would continue to run its own hospitals. But for planning the hospital services, thirty to thirty-five area bodies would be set up, consisting of representatives of local authorities and of voluntary hospitals. Other health services would be similarly planned by bodies consisting solely of the local authority representatives of each area, and the two plans would be considered and possibly amended by about ten regional bodies. Once the Minister had accepted a plan built up in this way, it would be binding on all concerned.[1]

This was the somewhat clumsy structure which was evolved to give the voluntary hospitals a right to participate in health planning without interfering with the ultimate authority of the democratically elected bodies, both local and central. While this concession was made to meet the wishes of the voluntary hospitals, there is no evidence of any concession having been made to meet the wishes of the doctors by allowing them to participate in the organization of hospital services.

Such was the stage reached in planning at the time of the General Election. In August 1945, the Government was overwhelmingly defeated. The first Labour Government to hold an absolute majority in the House of Commons had come to power. There was a new Minister of Health – Mr Aneurin Bevan.

[1] A. J. Willcocks, 'A Process of Erosion', *The Sociological Review, Monograph No. 5*, p. 16, Keele, 1962

CHAPTER 29

Bevan Decides

B Y the time the new Minister took office, every shade of opinion had been expressed about the future of Britain's health services. It was clearly impossible to please everyone. The voluntary hospitals wanted to keep their independence but lacked the financial resources to do so. The local authorities were eager to add to their services, and were not prepared to share any of their existing powers with doctors or governors of voluntary hospitals. The doctors were demanding what neither the voluntary hospitals nor the local authorities were prepared to grant them – a major say in the direction of the hospital system.

At first sight, the local authorities would seem the most formidable group for a Minister to antagonize, as local councillors are usually also leading figures in the constituency parties. Those who controlled the voluntary hospitals also seemed to wield considerable influence, both in the Conservative Party and in the House of Lords. Though some northern and Welsh voluntary hospitals were controlled and financed by persons active in the Labour movement, a Labour Minister did not have to pay undue attention to the views of national hospital representatives. The doctors were the third pressure group. They were not, perhaps, credited with much effective power by the two political parties but there was always a danger that they might succeed in swaying opinion against the Government.

Superficially the Government appeared to be facing three united power blocks. This was, however, an over-simplification. Two of the groups were far from united, as the new Minister was not slow to appreciate. The teaching hospitals, and particularly the London teaching hospitals, had always been inclined to act apart from the British Hospitals Association, and by doing so had probably stopped the latter from ever becoming an effective organization. In London, the teaching hospitals tended instead to give their allegiance to the influential King's Fund. Quite apart from connections of family and lineage which brought these interests together, there was the subtle relationship with 'the City'. The latter had, however, close connections both with the 'Royal hospitals' and with the Royal charity whose offices were near the Mansion House. The Royal Colleges were closely allied with this nexus of power. In 1945, as in 1745, the physicians were the practitioners of the ruling class – the only doctors to be accepted or nearly accepted in the highest social circles. The Royal Colleges tended to stand apart from the British Medical Association, just as the teaching hospitals stood apart from the British Hospitals Association. Indeed the physicians and surgeons tended to identify more with their lay governors and the King's Fund than with their fellow doctors.

Any scheme had to win the co-operation of the medical profession if it was to run smoothly. But if a particular proposal commanded strong public support, the profession could not – and in time would appreciate that it could not – defy public opinion. While it was important to have widespread medical participation to create any sort of service, it was essential to gain the participation of those doctors who had the highest standing in Britain – the leading figures in the Royal Colleges – or else the service would not command status and prestige among all classes of patients. Though these doctors were not averse to being paid for their hospital work, they did not want a full-time contract. They wanted to continue their role of 'visiting' consultant, much as it had evolved over the years, and to have time over for private practice with all its status, money and social connections. If driven to choose between hospital work and private practice, it was conceivable that they might choose the latter.

The British Medical Association had for years been debating within itself and with successive ministers the question of whether general practitioner services should be available to 90 per cent or 100 per cent of the population. In the hospital service the question of whether the service would be *used* by 90 per cent or 98 per cent of the population might depend on the participation of the top doctors. The principle of having a national rather than a sectional service was one which had a special appeal for the Labour Party. A 'universal' service was certainly regarded as more *socialist* in the sense in which the term was used in Britain. But this 'socialist' aim came in conflict with other socialist aims. The members of the Labour Party most actively interested in the health service belonged to the Socialist Medical Association – a body which had for many years been committed to the principle of a salaried medical service run by local authorities. This principle was strenuously opposed by the representatives of physicians and surgeons. Thus attempts to impose a salaried service were sure to lead to a very bitter fight, not only with the British Medical Association, but also with the Royal Colleges. And even if this battle were won, it was clear that a salaried service would be less 'universal' than some alternative to which the organized profession might agree.

Such was the dilemma facing Aneurin Bevan when he took over as Minister in August 1945. His appointment inevitably created concern in medical circles as he was reported to be a 'left-wing' member of the Party and thus more likely to adopt extremist policies. Moreover, the election of a Labour Government had put back into the melting pot all the provisional agreements which had been reached between Willink, the former Minister, and the profession. Mr Bevan made it perfectly clear that he did not consider himself bound by any decisions reached by the previous government: many leading figures in the Labour Party objected publicly to the 'unnecessary concessions' which Willink had made.[1]

Officially the Party Conference, under pressure from Socialist Medical Association speakers, had committed the Labour Party to the principle of a salaried service run by local authorities.[2] The Prime Minister and his Government were, however, well able to duck or ignore conference resolutions if they decided to do so. A second influence on the new government was the fact that several of its senior members had been in the war-time coalition government and were thus associated with the 1944 White Paper. Herbert Morrison, the Lord President of the Council in the new government and former leader of the London County Council, was known to favour the control of hospitals by local

[1] *BMJ Supplement*, 8 September 1945, p. 60

[2] Almont Lindsey, *Socialized Medicine in England and Wales*, p. 50, London, 1962. See also *BMJ Supplement*, 2 June 1945, p. 99, for resolutions and debate at the 1945 Labour Party Conference. See also *Hansard* (H of C) Vol. 422, 30 April 1946, col. 142. The policy statement for the election, 'Let us Face the Future', was much more general though it emphasized the importance of health centres. See *BMJ Supplement*, 30 June 1945, p. 130.

government. Indeed, he had even been opposed to the joint board solution, and had pressed Willink to leave hospitals in the hands of existing authorities.[1] In view of the many different opinions held within the Cabinet, it was clear that much depended on the views of the Minister principally concerned, and on his influence with his colleagues.

The department which Bevan directed had for more than a century operated through locally elected bodies. If the major authorities were to channel finance to virtually all the nation's hospitals, enormous grant aid from the central government would be essential. Indeed, the level of grant needed was so high and the proportion of expenditure which could be locally financed was so low that the Ministry would be under constant pressure from the Treasury to interfere in local affairs. Was it possible for local government to run a service of this size when so much money came from the central government?

Despite its name, the Ministry of Health was in reality the department responsible for local government, and it had a long tradition of keeping its medical officers at some distance from the principal arteries where policy was formed. In 1945, the post of Chief Medical Officer was held by a man of exceptional sagacity – Sir Wilson Jameson. He was closely in touch with the more progressive thinkers in the profession – particularly those associated with *The Lancet*. And it was not long before he won the confidence of his new Minister. Though Bevan never accepted an idea without testing it and often adapting it, his thinking was influenced as much by Sir Wilson as by any of his colleagues in the Labour Party.

At his first public meeting with the doctors, Bevan was at his most winsome. In an after-dinner speech, he stressed the importance of free choice of doctor, of professional freedom and of the privacy of the doctor-patient relationship. Combining tact with a love of paradox, he said that as a Socialist he believed in industrial democracy. 'I want for the miners, the railwaymen, the engineers, a far greater share in the management of their work and the policies that govern it, and I say no less for the doctors.'[2] He promised a plan within a year which would make

---

[1] This was later alleged by Willink in the House of Commons and not denied. Herbert Morrison did not speak in the debate on the National Health Service. See *Hansard* (H of C) Vol. 422, 1 May 1946, col. 226.

[2] *BMJ Supplement*, 15 September 1945, p. 63

Great Britain 'the envy of the world'.[1] The British Medical
Association found the new Minister 'clever and charming', and
liked his disarming confession of ignorance of medical matters.[2]

While Bevan was happy to attend a variety of official recep-
tions and to delight his hosts, he was not anxious to enter into a
further series of formal negotiations. The profession had appointed and briefed its negotiating committee but no summons
came from Whitehall. Bevan was opposed to the principle of
negotiation in such circumstances, which he regarded as con-
stitutionally improper.[3] The doctors' negotiating committee
politely wrote suggesting a meeting and Bevan indicated that
he would be happy to meet the committee 'before the Government finally decide what proposals they will submit to Parliament. . . . Neither of us, I think, contemplates beginning afresh a
long series of protracted negotiations. Indeed, to do so would
mean covering all over again ground which has been repeatedly
tilled and so wasting time which we cannot now afford.'[4]

In early November 1945, only two months after the new
government had taken office, the press carried reports that Mr
Bevan had firm proposals for a National Health Service and had
obtained the Cabinet's agreement in principle.[5] It was reported
that he wanted to nationalize all hospitals, both voluntary and
municipal, and place them under twelve regional boards. The
rumours turned out to be broadly correct. Cabinet approval to
this scheme was not, however, easily obtained. Behind the scenes
Bevan was having difficulty with those of his colleagues, led by
Herbert Morrison, who wanted the local authorities to keep
their hospitals and who preferred, as Hugh Dalton put it, 'to
proceed by stages, spread over years, and not by one bold
stroke'.[6]

[1] ibid.
[2] ibid., 1 December 1945, p. 119
[3] In negotiating with outside bodies two things happen. They are
made aware of the nature of the proposals before the House of Commons
itself; and, furthermore, the Minister puts himself into an impossible position,
because if he has agreed things with somebody outside, he is bound to resist
amendments from Members in the House. Otherwise he does not play fair
with them. (Mr Aneurin Bevan) Hansard (H of C) Vol. 422, 30 April 1946,
col. 60
[4] BMJ Supplement, 24 November 1945, p. 113
[5] ibid., 10 November 1945, p. 101
[6] Hugh Dalton, High Tide and After, p. 106, London, 1962

Though the rumours about Bevan's plan were greeted with relief in medical circles, there was concern about the lack of 'consultation'. The press reported that when the British Medical Association was invited to meet the Minister it would not be to discuss the form of the health service, but to settle terms of service within it. The Minister was also expected to offer terms on the lines of the recommendations of the Spens Committee.[1] The *British Medical Journal* complained that the Minister had failed to consult the local authorities, the voluntary hospitals and 'the profession's own representative body'.[2]

Early in January the negotiating committee had its long postponed meeting with the Minister and were informed of the Minister's intentions. Similar meetings were also held with the TUC, with the local authorities, with hospital representatives and many other bodies. In total the Minister held twenty conferences.[3] After its meeting with the Minister, the BMA Committee sent a set of questions to clarify a number of points and wanted 'to ascertain to what extent the Minister would modify his proposals before he introduced his Bill'.[4] Meanwhile an 'emergency guarantee fund' was set up which could be used 'to further the professional cause in any major dispute which might occur between the Government and the profession'.[5]

Further rumours appeared in the press. It was by now generally expected that the country would be divided into regions, but now it seemed that the teaching hospitals were to be handled separately. And specialists were to be allowed to work part-time in the health service. The *New Statesman and Nation* hastened to criticize the idea of allowing the medical staff of teaching hospitals to function 'as professors and lecturers and physicians and at the same time earning as fat fees as they can in the tradition of Harley Street'.[6] It was predicted that not only conservative but socialist councils would resent the loss of their hospitals.[7] And it was widely known that Herbert Morrison was strongly opposed to this solution. His views had been expressed

[1] *BMJ Supplement*, 10 November 1945, p. 101
[2] ibid.
[3] *Hansard* (H of C), Vol. 422, 30 April 1946, col. 60
[4] *BMJ Supplement*, 9 February 1946, p. 25
[5] ibid., 9 March 1946, p. 363
[6] quoted, ibid., 23 February 1946, p. 39, from *New Statesman and Nation*, 2 February
[7] *BMJ Supplement*, 23 February 1946, p. 39

publicly in a debate in the House of Commons a year earlier.[1]

The Minister's proposals were published as a White Paper in March 1946.[2] Both the local authority and the voluntary hospitals were to be appropriated by the Minister. The bulk of them were to be administered by regional boards consisting of 'people chosen and appointed by the Minister for their individual suitability for the task'.[3] But before making appointments the Minister was 'to consult any university with a medical school in the region, bodies representative of the medical profession, the local authorities of the area and others concerned, including, initially, those with experience of the voluntary hospital system'.[4] For day-to-day management, the boards were to appoint management committees for each large hospital or a group of related hospitals. The members of this body were to be appointed after consultation with the local authorities of the area, the medical and dental staffs of the hospitals concerned and others.

The endowments of the hospitals for which the regional boards were to be responsible were to be removed from the individual hospitals and handed over to a central Hospital Endowment Fund to be controlled by the Minister. After paying off debts on the appointed day, the remaining fund would be apportioned among the regional boards who could spend the income on specified types of expenditure, and could spend the capital on any purpose which the Minister approved. As endowments were extremely unevenly distributed, hospitals who had had large funds were sure to see little of them after the appointed day.

The White Paper made no attempt to conceal the Minister's wide powers. Though he had a duty to consult various bodies before making appointments, he needed to accept none of their recommendations. In practice the plan could involve, as in fact it did, the representation of all existing interests – doctors, local councillors and voluntary hospital committee men and women. In a sense Bevan was taking over two hospital 'systems' and handing them back to committees of persons drawn from both, to which he was adding representatives of the medical profession. But Bevan made it quite clear that members of hospital

[1] *Hansard* (H of C), Vol. 408, 15 February 1945, cols. 506 and 512
[2] Ministry of Health, *National Health Service Bill* (Cmd 6761)
[3] ibid., p. 6
[4] ibid.

authorities were in no sense to owe any allegiance to the bodies
from which they had been drawn. They were there to do the
job and not to represent any sectional interest. Bevan was
anxious to have hospitals controlled by reasonably homo-
geneous Boards rather than by 'conferences of persons representing different interests and organizations. . . . Any system
which made the boards conferences, any proposal which made
the representatives delegates, would at once throw the hospital
administration into chaos.'[1] He thought it 'a wise thing to give
the doctors full participation in the administration of their own
profession',[2] but he was only prepared to concede part of what
the British Medical Association was demanding. And though
the local authorities were to be given a large role in the administration of other parts of the health service, they were to be
deprived of any formal participation in the provision or administration of hospital services.

Such was the plan for the vast majority of the hospitals and
for the vast majority of hospital beds. The teaching hospitals
were, however, given separate and different treatment outside
the regional structure, despite the fact that the location and
number of teaching hospitals were the determining factors in
fixing regional boundaries. The Bill laid it down that the
Minister was to *constitute* a separate board of governors for each
teaching hospital or group of such hospitals. These bodies were,
as in the case of regional boards, to include 'members appointed
after consultation with the major local authorities and other
organizations concerned, including the previous governing
bodies' but they were also to include members *nominated* 'by the
University, the Regional Board for the area, and the senior staff
of the hospital itself'. In other words, an element of self-government was to be introduced by allowing teaching hospital doctors
to sit on their own governing bodies. And while non-teaching
hospitals were to have their endowments put into a central pool,
each board of governors was to receive the endowments of the
teaching hospital which it inherited. And the new governors
would be 'free to use them as they think best but are required, so
far as practicable, to see that the purposes for which they were
previously usable are still observed'.[3]

[1] *Hansard* (H of C), Vol. 422, 30 April 1946, col. 51
[2] ibid., col. 52
[3] *National Health Service Bill*, p. 5

Throughout the whole hospital service, medical staffs were to be employed either whole-time or part-time. In the latter case, they were not debarred 'from also continuing any private practice outside the service which individual patients may wish them to undertake'.[1] Medical staffs were also to be allowed to have private patients in Health Service hospitals. Bevan thought himself forced to make this concession as 'unless we permit some fee-paying patients in the public hospitals, there will be a rash of nursing homes all over the country. . . . I believe that nursing homes ought to be discouraged. They cannot provide general hospital facilities.'[2] The whole Bill was indeed remarkably generous to the hospital medical staffs. Not only were they to be paid for what they had previously done for nothing, they were also to have private patients and be allowed to treat them on the spot. As Bevan remarked to a friend: 'I stuffed their mouths with gold.'

Such were the plans for hospitals. The administration of the general practitioner service, the pharmaceutical service, the dental service and the ophthalmic service was to be undertaken by new bodies called executive councils, which would be similar to the insurance committees set up under the Insurance Act of 1911. There was to be a council in the area of each county and county borough, and each council was to consist of half professional members and half laymen. Health centres provided by local authorities were to be a main feature of the general practitioner services. Doctors were to be paid partly by capitation fees and partly by fixed salaries – the latter taking account of different circumstances and experience and the conditions of practice in different areas. After the appointed day, doctors would not be able to start practice in every area without restriction, and the sale of the goodwill of practices would in future be prohibited. A sum of £66 million would be allocated to compensate practitioners for the loss of this right in Great Britain.

The remaining local and domiciliary services were to be the responsibility of counties and county boroughs. The range of such services was, however, to be greatly extended by the Bill and many of them were to be made mandatory. The services covered maternity, child care, health visiting, home nursing, domestic help, ambulances and others – on the whole those

[1] ibid., p. 8
[2] *Hansard* (H of C), Vol. 422, 30 April 1946, col. 57

services in which doctors played no part, or only a minor part. On the same day as the proposals were published, the British Medical Association despatched a copy of them and a copy of the Council's detailed criticisms of them to all its members. The County Councils Association hastened to protest at the loss of their hospitals, but the Labour-controlled London County Council loyally supported the Government, though not without an expression of pained regret.[1] Lord Moran, the President of the Royal College of Physicians, also publicly endorsed the Minister's proposals, though he failed to carry his colleagues with him. He was reported as saying that 'by preserving the teaching hospitals, this new scheme preserved the essence of the voluntary system'.[2] The British Hospitals Association, as might have been expected, emitted a shrill cry of anguish and indignation.

A few weeks later, when Bevan presented his Bill to Parliament, he started by emphasizing the importance of hospital planning – the issue upon which his case was strongest. He stressed the maldistribution of existing hospital facilities, their variable quality and the fact that there were so many small hospitals – 70 per cent with less than 100 beds and 30 per cent with less than 30 beds. 'I would rather be kept alive in the efficient if cold altruism of a large hospital than expire in a gush of warm sympathy in a small one.'[3] Small hospitals were liable to attempt treatments which were beyond their capacity and thus 'the welfare of patients is sacrificed to the vaulting ambitions of those in charge of the hospital'.[4]

Control by local authorities could not solve the problem of the hospital services. They were too poor and also too small. Moreover they varied so much in size and wealth that there would be serious anomalies – the worst hospitals in places where good hospitals were most needed. It was these considerations which made him reject any solution based on local authorities while their boundaries remained unreformed. Thus he had been driven to accept the principle of administration by large regions centred on teaching hospitals.

[1] *Hansard* (H of C), Vol. 422, 1 May 1946, col. 271
[2] quoted, ibid., 1 May 1946, col. 293. See also ibid., 2 May 1946, col. 374.
[3] ibid., 30 April 1946, col. 44
[4] ibid., col. 48

The Conservative Party expressed its opposition in the form of a reasoned amendment. The faults of the Bill were that it

> retards the development of the hospital services by destroying local ownership, and gravely menaces all charitable foundations by diverting to purposes other than those intended by the donors the trust funds of the voluntary hospitals; and . . . weakens the responsibility of local authorities without planning the health services as a whole.[1]

It was held that the 'vast non-elective bodies' were unnecessary as local authorities could do the job if they were given the money. It was said that the division between the hospital services and the local authority services would be bad for continuity of care – particularly in the case of maternity patients. And the Minister was accused of wanting to create eventually a full-time salaried service[2] – a charge which he not only failed to deny, but at one stage almost admitted.[3]

The Bill was changed little in committee. It was made clear that doctors in the service would not be subject to the restrictions on civil liberties imposed on civil servants. They would be free to publish what they wanted and even to be members of parliament. The hospital management committees also emerged with a somewhat larger role than had earlier been intended for them.[4] Apart from the issue of a salaried service, the debate focused on the questions of prohibiting the sale of goodwill and redistributing the endowments of hospitals. Bevan defended the distinction he was making between the treatment of endowments of non-teaching and teaching hospitals by pointing out that a considerable part of the latter were given for specific research purposes.[5]

[1] ibid., 1 May 1946, col. 222

[2] ibid., cols. 225 and 242

[3] Bevan had said in his opening speech that he was not in favour of a full salaried service and added, 'I do not believe that the medical profession is ripe for it.' (ibid., 30 April, col. 55). When questioned about the significance of this, Bevan interjected, 'There is all the difference in the world between plucking fruit when it is ripe and plucking it when it is green.' (ibid., 1 May 1946, col. 392.) Much significance was attached to this remark at the time, but Bevan was probably exhibiting his impish debating skill rather than any premeditated intention.

[4] ibid., Vol. 425, 22 July 1946, col. 1696, and Vol. 426, 26 July 1946, col. 429

[5] ibid., Vol. 425, 22 July 1946, col. 1795

To the charge that he was discouraging voluntary effort,[1] Bevan could argue that he was widening the scope for voluntary services.[2] The only voluntary part of the hospital service he was destroying was 'the necessity to sell flags and to collect money'.[3] The most penetrating criticism the Minister encountered from his own side of the House came from Dr Stephen Taylor (later Lord Taylor). He feared that, by the attempt to combine 'industrial democracy' with 'general democracy', there was 'a danger that we may impose on ourselves a medical dictatorship, and a very bad thing that would be'.[4]

While Parliament was debating the fate of voluntary hospitals and the rights of donors, the various groups of doctors were examining further how their position would be affected by the Service. The greatest concern, as might be expected, was expressed by general practitioners, and it was their dissatisfaction and their fears of the Minister's ultimate intentions which gave the leaders of the profession enough support to hold out against the Service until almost the last moment.[5] The consultants and specialists greeted the proposals with perceptible relief. The local authorities who had built up the hierarchical pattern of hospital administration were to have nothing to do with hospitals. The consultants liked the proposed arrangements for the regional planning and organization of hospitals. They were all in favour of the planning of hospitals on a regional basis, even though the teaching hospitals – the linchpin of the whole new organization – were to be independent. At a special meeting of the British Medical Association to consider the Bill, it was suggested that the governors of teaching hospitals 'should be responsible to the regional body to ensure that its services were carried out with due regard to the hospital needs of patients'. This motion was decisively rejected as this would 'tie the teaching hospitals down . . . and one of the possible freedoms still left would be removed'.

[1] ibid., Vol. 426, 25 July 1946, col. 400
[2] ibid., 26 July 1946, col. 471
[3] ibid., col. 470
[4] ibid., col. 423
[5] On 7 April 1948, Bevan undertook to sponsor a statutory provision prohibiting a full-time salaried service. A further poll of the profession was conducted by the BMA and on 28 May 1948 – a week before the new service was to start – the Council of the BMA announced that it favoured acceptance of the National Health Service. See Almont Lindsey, pp. 60–62.

The consultants and specialists, at their own meeting called to consider the Bill, contented themselves by pointing out that there was no 'proved necessity' for changing the ownership of hospitals or hospital endowments. But if the new system were to be introduced, they were anxious to be able to appoint the medical representatives who were to sit on all hospital authorities. And on no account should any of these bodies be composed of a majority of local authority representatives. A further important source of concern was the right to private practice. They wanted the right of private practice in a health service hospital to be given to all consultants and specialists whether they joined the service or not. They insisted also that all designated pay beds in existing hospitals should continue to be used for this purpose.[1] The consultants and specialists expressed no concern about the loss of their 'honorary' status. Indeed it was decided late in 1946

> to recommend to voluntary hospitals that, without prejudice to future arrangements under the National Health Service, the visiting specialist staff of such hospitals be paid salaries during the interim period, assessed on the basis of five guineas a session and to urge the Minister to provide the financial assistance necessary to enable the hospitals to adopt this course.[2]

While the consultants were anxious to strengthen their position in the hospitals by contractual arrangements long before the appointed day, the general practitioners were afraid that the limited part which they already played in the hospital system would be taken away when the health service started. The lobby within the British Medical Association for general practitioner hospitals and for rights for general practitioners in other hospitals, which had been somewhat quiescent since before the war, suddenly took on a new life. An amendment to the Bill was sought 'whereby family doctors would be assured of the right to assume personal responsibility in hospital for such patients as came within their scope'.[3] It was argued that every doctor should have the same privileges, rights and facilities for treating his patients, and more specifically that general practitioners

[1] *BMJ Supplement*, 18 May 1946, p. 151
[2] ibid., 23 November 1946, p. 134
[3] ibid., 11 May 1946, pp. 120–22

should have the same privileges as specialists and consultants with regard to pay beds in hospitals.[1]

The general practitioners did win a limited concession as regards the chronic sick. In the committee stage of the Bill, Bevan quoted the case of chronic sick patients going into hospital because they could not get treatment at home. 'It may be that they suffer from something which does not require specialist treatment but treatment by a general practitioner. I want to make it clear that the general practitioner should give that kind of treatment in a general practitioner hospital.'[2] But the general practitioners also wanted facilities to treat their own maternity cases, privately or otherwise. According to one such practitioner, the attitude of the obstetricians in this matter was 'trade unionism run mad'.[3]

The general practitioners were right in assuming that the scope for their work in hospitals would be reduced by the health service. Where it had been impossible for a whole-time consultant or specialist to make a living, hospitals had had to be staffed by general practitioners with a special interest in particular types of diseases or with some specialist training. Now such hospitals would be able to combine to support their own specialist staffs. Moreover, subtler changes in the relationship between general practitioners and consultants were foreseen with the large decline in private consulting practice which was anticipated. No longer would the consultant curry favour with all general practitioners in the hope of receiving private referred cases. The practitioner without private patients to bestow would not be treated with the same courtesy. And instead of general practitioners complaining about 'abuse' if hospital doctors took their cases from them, in future it would be hospital doctors who would be complaining of 'abuse' if general practitioners sent them work they did not want. General practitioners would find 'a change of front from the usual "kind regards" and "Christmas cards" '.[4] Instead of the nineteenth-century battle to get patients, the second half of the twentieth century might see doctors scrambling to foist patients on to their colleagues.

Over the years, the hospital had gained an aura of prestige

[1] ibid., pp. 133 and 135
[2] quoted, ibid., 3 August 1946, p. 51
[3] ibid.
[4] ibid., 10 May 1947, pp. 98–9

and this was one reason why general practitioners sought access to it. As the new service defined the line between hospital and other practice with greater precision, it was feared that general practice would lose prestige. It would become less general and more trivial. These fears added to general practitioners' more direct anxieties about the new health service. The more weight Bevan placed upon the role of health centres and the role of salary within practitioners' remuneration, the greater the support he gained from his own turbulent left wing and the greater opposition he generated in professional circles. It was not only lay control that the general practitioner feared, but the wider, almost catastrophic, experience of being bundled out of his home and into a health centre to work under the critical gaze of colleagues he had not chosen.

Bevan could continue to hold out against the general practitioners and the British Medical Association because he knew that his proposals had won support, or at least acceptance, in the most influential part of the hospital world. In deciding whom to woo and whom to fight, Bevan had been realistic. It was no concern of his which individual general practitioners joined the service and which did not, and he knew that many who opposed the service would be carried into it by pressure from their own patients. But the participation of the top hospital doctors was essential to the prestige and therefore 'universality' of the service. He wanted a service of high quality and high prestige, and he wanted to get it without greatly antagonizing the left wing of his own party. Bevan was remarkably successful as a conciliator of such diverse interests. Even the Socialist Medical Association was prepared to accept the final compromise though it 'retained a certain amount of privilege in the Health Service'.[1]

Bevan's plan differed from earlier plans principally in the concessions it made to the views of the Royal Colleges. While the negotiating committee under the aegis of the British Medical Association was awaiting a summons to Whitehall, Bevan was dining with Lord Moran (President of the Royal College of Physicians) at Prunier's restaurant in St James's Street. Thus the top doctors obtained *à la suite* terms in the Health Service: part-time payment for loosely defined sessions, the secret disposal

---

[1] Dr Starke Murray speaking at the Labour Party Conference of 1946. Quoted in *BMJ Supplement*, 29 June 1946, p. 202

of Treasury funds to those of their number whom Lord Moran and his two colleagues thought more meritorious, the lion's share of the endowments of the teaching hospitals to pay the costs of their researches, and the right to private practice – much as before. The consultants had gained regular remuneration without any loss of freedom and were being trusted to use this freedom responsibly.

Deliberately Bevan had played on the ancient split in the medical profession. Deliberately, too, he had exploited the breach among the voluntary hospitals. The teaching hospitals had retained their independence, whatever nonsense it made of the regional design: the special relationship which these hospitals achieved was similar to that which their medical schools had gained as parts of universities. The compliance of the teaching hospitals gained at this price was enough to kill at birth any attempt to organize a voluntary hospital protest movement. The most aristocratic and reactionary bodies had found it easiest to come to terms with 'socialism'.

CHAPTER 30

The Impact of National Ownership

ON 5 July 1948, most of Britain's hospitals were taken into national ownership. Only three years earlier there had been hardly any advocate of such an extreme solution to the problems of hospital planning and hospital administration. The pressures which led to this development came not from any doctrines of the Labour Party, which by 1945 was confining its proposals for nationalization to the industrial sector, but from the aspirations of parts of the medical profession. Nationalization seemed the only way by which the consultants and specialists could achieve their principal objectives – adequate financial support for the hospitals in which they worked, the retention of private practice and an effective 'say' in the running of all hospital services.

Thus on the appointed day, the local authorities lost their hospitals. The need to transfer hospital services to the major authorities had been widely accepted for many years. The decision to take them away was sudden and unexpected. The counties and county boroughs had been major hospital authorities for only eight years before the dislocation of the war: they had had little time to show failure or success. But most of them were too small and too poor to provide an adequate hospital service with all the specialized units which modern treatment required. The standards achieved by some authorities – particularly the largely rural authorities – left much to be desired. Transport facilities revolved around the towns and cities, making them the 'natural' places for siting hospitals. But the boundaries of local authorities did not facilitate such planning arrangements, as urban areas and the surrounding country were often controlled by different authorities. These difficulties had led to plans for joint authorities, but such plans had proved unacceptable to the doctors.

The medical profession feared authoritarianism from medical

superintendents and narrow-mindedness from the distant committees and functionaries of County Hall. It was not inevitable that local authorities would retain the medical superintendent system, for it had already been modified in some areas.[1] And even if it had been retained, persons commanding more respect in the profession might have gradually been appointed. Similarly the various personnel in the local authority administration might have learnt to understand the susceptibilities of the medical profession with its tradition of individualism. But however false all the associations may have been, local government was judged not by what it could do but by what it had done and failed to do. Many hospitals had remained under the Poor Law. And though transferred hospitals did not seem to be disliked by their patients, even these hospitals were disliked by their doctors.

Under the National Health Service, planning was undertaken by fourteen (later fifteen) regional boards which had responsibility for all hospitals other than teaching hospitals. Outside London each region had one teaching hospital and this was made the rationale for the number of regions. Provided close working relations developed between the regional board and the board of governors (and such relationships were encouraged by a considerable element of common membership), the task of planning could be undertaken despite the somewhat anomalous independence of the teaching hospital itself. The problem of London was, however, complicated by the existence of twelve undergraduate teaching hospitals and fourteen post-graduate institutions, all concentrated near the centre of the conurbation. The solution adopted was to carve London into four sectors which met at the centre and set up four separate regional boards, whose authority stretched right to the coast to the East and South and far into the country to the West and North. This arrangement owed much to the administrative structure of the war-time services: the swift movement of patients from the centre to the surrounding country had made it possible to keep some beds in the central area empty for air raid casualties. It was, moreover, believed that by embodying this 'sector' plan in the peace-time hospital services, the influence of the teaching hospitals would be

[1] Before 1948, Middlesex had redefined the clinical position of its medical superintendents as only *primus inter pares vis-à-vis* their consultant colleagues. Acton Society Trust, *The Impact of the Change*, p. 12, London, 1956

extended into areas which lacked such concentrations of specialized facilities and medical skill. It was a solution intended to benefit the periphery more than the centre and it had the consequence of making yet more complex the task of planning London's hospital services.

The number of members of boards varied from twenty-two in one of the London-based boards to thirty-two in Wales.

Of the first 364 appointments made in 1947, more than 120 were doctors (40 university professors and teachers of medicine and allied subjects, 60 specialists and 20 general practitioners). Members of other professions in the medical field numbered 20, including 10 matrons and 2 dentists. The remainder included holders of non-medical university appointments (including several vice-chancellors), local government members and members of the governing bodies of former voluntary hospitals. According to an analysis made in 1951, 41 per cent of the members were aged 60 or over, and 85 per cent had had previous experience of hospital work.[1]

These were the members selected by the Minister to plan the hospitals services. Regional boards were also intended to act as an administrative link in seeing that the plan was executed, and to exercise general supervision over the hospital services of their areas.[2] Their agents in this were the hospital management committees. Thus the first task of the boards when they were set up in 1947 was to allot hospitals to groups, and appoint members to their management committees so that the new services could come into operation on the appointed day. Thus in the course of 1947 and 1948, 377 management committees were set up. The number of such committees per regional board varied from fourteen in East Anglia to fifty-two in one of the London-based boards (South-West Metropolitan).

With few exceptions, mental and mental deficiency hospitals were formed into separate groups apart from the general hospitals. A few of the general hospital groups were responsible for as many as twenty hospitals, but the typical group had between six and ten hospitals and between 500 and 1,500 beds. A general group was thought of as providing the equivalent of a single large

[1] Acton Society Trust, *Groups, Regions and Committees: Part II Regional Hospital Boards*, pp. 4–5, London, 1957
[2] ibid., p. 31

general hospital for the district[1] 'with the former separate hospitals constituting sub-units in the nature of departments of a single hospital housed in separate premises'.[2]

Hospitals which had previously been voluntary or local authority were brought together into the same groups. In total, 1,145 voluntary hospitals with some 90,000 beds were taken over, and 1,545 municipal hospitals with about 390,000 beds. Of this latter number some 190,000 beds were occupied by patients in mental and mental deficiency hospitals, and there were about 80,000 beds which were administered under the Poor Law at the time of transfer.[3] Much of this accommodation was in institutions which were still partly used for the chronic sick and partly for aged and other persons needing residential care. In such cases it was frequently decided to divide the institution so that part became administered by the hospital service and part by the local authority.

The group was the main local administrative agency. And the Ministry laid it down that the management committee was to have 'one officer to whom it can look for securing that its policy is carried out in all hospitals in the group and for co-ordinating and reviewing all group activities'. In non-mental groups this chief officer was nearly always a layman. The Group Secretary had the duty of acting as the representative of the governing body where policy had been clearly defined, or where the matter in question was not of such importance as to require the governing body's authority.

Hospital management committees worked through a series of sub-committees whose recommendations were ratified or amended at the monthly meeting of the main committee. The system was an amalgamation of the practices of local authorities and those of voluntary hospitals. The Ministry discouraged delegation to powerful 'house' committees responsible for individual hospitals. It was therefore at group level that the diverse traditions of different individual hospitals had to be reconciled.

Though there had been some tendency to give added responsibility to matrons and lay-clerks, the typical pattern of admini-

[1] Acton Society Trust, *Groups, Regions and Committees: Hospital Management Committees*, p. 7, London, 1957

[2] *The Impact of the Change*, p. 4

[3] P. Townsend, *The Last Refuge*, p. 33, London, 1962

stration in local authority hospitals remained much as it had been laid down by the Poor Law Board for infirmaries some eighty years earlier. The hospitals had been administered by medical superintendents who were responsible through the Medical Officer of Health to the Public Health Committee of the Council 'for the whole administration of the hospitals (excluding such matters as finance, building and stores, in which the clerk, steward or engineer of the hospital might be responsible to the local authority's treasurer, clerk, stores purchasing department or engineer)'.[1] The superintendent was held responsible for both the lay and nursing administration, and both the matron and the clerk or steward were subordinate to him. In some cases there were hospital committees, but the chairman of such a committee never had the authority and status of the chairman of a voluntary hospital.

In the voluntary hospitals the pattern of administration had varied according to both tradition and size, but for larger hospitals a system of tripartite administration had been the usual practice. The lay administrator (house governor, secretary or clerk), the matron and the chairman of the medical staff committee all reported direct to the governors or a committee appointed by them. The matron had complete authority over 'the nursing care of the patients as well as the control of the training school',[2] and also usually over domestic staff and all catering arrangements. 'The medical care of the patients was entrusted to the visiting physicians and surgeons, etc.'[3] The chairman of the medical staff co-ordinated the medical policy of the hospital though the actual authority which he could exercise over the unpaid colleagues who elected him was necessarily limited. The day-to-day medical administration was 'in the hands of a relatively junior resident medical officer without authority over the consultants and limited to dealing with such matters as emergency admissions'.[4] The remaining staff of the hospital were directed by the senior lay officer, who also kept the minutes and conducted correspondence on behalf of the governors. In view of the extensive delegation of responsibilities for the medical

[1] ibid., p. 64
[2] Evidence of the King's Fund. Ministry of Health, *Report of the Committee on the Internal Administration of Hospitals*, p. 5, HMSO, 1954
[3] ibid.
[4] *The Impact of the Change*, p. 11

care and nursing of the patients, 'the governing body of the hospital was primarily concerned with the enlightened pursuit of economy, so far as is consistent with the requirements of the sick'.[1]

Such were the traditions – one almost strictly hierarchical, the other multilateral, with the actual power relationships varying according to the hospital and the personalities of those holding particular posts. The voluntary hospitals had managed with a minimum of administrative staff and had taken full advantage of the flexibility which arose from their independence. Not all of them observed the salary scales negotiated during and after the war. Accountancy and records were generally kept to the minimum: most hospitals employed 'glorified book-keepers under the control of the secretary, whose duties were considered complete once the transactions were recorded in the books. There was little attempt to interpret these records or to give advice to the finance committee.'[2] By contrast the local authority hospitals had to conform to the dictates of a district County or Town Hall and all the specialist departments which grew up within the large authority. There was limited scope for action without application well in advance to the appropriate committee for financial authority.

Henceforth, the formulation of group, regional or national policy on a certain issue involved choosing between two or more established practices. Some decisions which had major implications for individual hospitals were taken nationally. Thus the national negotiating machinery was extended and, to prevent auctions by competing hospitals for scarce grades of staff, it was decided that terms and conditions of service, once nationally agreed, should be uniformly applied. Secondly, national systems of accounting and stores control were introduced for all hospitals. Thus in such matters ex-voluntary hospitals found themselves working within a structure similar to that of a local authority hospital.

But in most other respects the voluntary hospital system was imposed on the former local authority hospitals. The Ministry recommended that all beds should be allotted to the charge of individual consultants. This meant that the principal role of the medical superintendent as the doctor in charge of all beds was

[1] *Report on the Internal Administration of Hospitals*, p. 5
[2] ibid., p. 53

taken from him.[1] And on the appointed day, medical superintendents 'were given the opportunity to qualify as consultants with all the ensuing privileges appertaining to consultant rank. The majority in fact did this, and only very few remained as administrative superintendents at the lower salary.'[2] In those hospitals which had had medical superintendents the title was allowed to continue under the National Health Service, but it carried much less status or authority. Under the terms of service, less was paid for administrative than clinical work. It was the Ministry's policy 'to reduce to a minimum the time given by medical staff to administrative duties, to enable them to devote their energies to clinical work in their appropriate grade'.[3] Thus the terms of service 'removed that part of the social and professional status of medical superintendents which was bound up with their holding the most highly paid post in the hospital'.[4]

The creation of hospital groups acted in a further way to undermine the authority of those medical superintendents who remained in post. Group medical advisory committees were formed to guide management committees generally on medical policy. Each member of the senior medical staff of the group was represented on this committee which took on the same relationship to the management committee as that which had evolved between voluntary hospital governors and their medical staffs. Thus where there were medical superintendents, management committees were faced with more than one source of advice about policy. The views of the medical superintendent could be challenged by a committee composed of doctors, most of whom might not even work in the hospital concerned. Most of the senior medical staff of the hospital service were drawn from the former voluntary hospitals, and thus were likely to favour the patterns of behaviour which had grown up in the voluntary hospitals. In addition, as had been the practice in many governing bodies of voluntary hospitals, there was strong medical representation on the hospital management committee itself. Most of those who occupied these strategic positions were also drawn from the former voluntary hospitals.

[1] See *Report on the Internal Administration of Hospitals*, p. 11.
[2] *The Impact of the Change*, p. 12
[3] ibid.
[4] ibid.

The existence of group secretaries further reduced the authority of medical superintendents. The lay hospital secretary was able to turn to the group secretary for guidance, rather than to the medical superintendent. Although the responsibilities of the medical superintendent and the secretary were rarely defined, the latter acted more and more independently.[1] Sometimes the powers of medical superintendents remained impervious to all these possible sources of erosion. Their lay secretaries still looked to them rather than to the group secretary for guidance on a wide range of policy questions. And the latter, particularly if his experience of hospital administration was limited, did not attempt to interfere. But all this depended on the support of the hospital management committee and the compliance of the group medical advisory committee.

What was true of the secretary of a former local authority hospital was also true of the matron. She might, from habit established over the years, look to the medical superintendent for policy guidance in nursing affairs. She was, however, appointed by the group and could appeal to the management committee direct or through the group secretary, and thus bypass the medical superintendent. In this way a former local authority matron could enhance her status towards that customarily accorded to the matron of a former voluntary hospital.

While medical staffs hastened to accept the group as the main administrative unit and adjust their advisory committees accordingly, matrons were slow to adjust their arrangements to suit the new pattern of administration. Those who had previously worked in voluntary hospitals retained their previous relationship with the house committees of their hospitals only to find that the main decisions were being taken at management committee level. Many groups did establish nursing committees, but they were composed predominantly of lay members of the management committee. It was imagined that housewives had obtained as a birthright an instinctive knowledge of the housekeeping arrangements of large institutions and of the principles of nursing administration. These nursing committees were rarely regarded as of the same standing as the medical advisory committees. And where lay domination had not been imposed, it was not easy for matrons to agree upon a common policy, particularly when the professional status of the various matrons

[1] *Report on the Internal Administration of Hospitals*, p. 13

within a group could vary enormously. Miss Nightingale had insisted at the start of the nursing revolution that the matron should be the undisputed head of nursing services within each hospital. Thus matrons had not been accustomed to working in partnership with other matrons. There were, moreover, many management committees which did not accept the right of matrons or a representative from the matrons to attend their meetings. Finally, while doctors typically made up a quarter or more of the management committee, there was not always even one, and hardly ever more than one, nurse on the committee. For all these reasons, the matron, who had previously worked on terms of equality with a lay house governor and in co-operation with the chairman of the visiting medical staff, now found herself under the control of a lay group secretary without any effective access to the management committee in which power was vested.

Matrons also saw their role being reduced by changes in hospital administration which had been developing before the Health Service but which were hastened by it. Specialist officers were being used to assume functions which had previously been the responsibility of matrons. Officers were appointed to look after the catering arrangements[1] and superintendents to supervise the domestic staff. Matrons tended to blame the National Health Service for these changes, although they originated long before 1948.

In time, matrons, supported by the Ministry of Health, were to obtain the right to representation or attendance at management committee meetings, but there is reason to doubt whether their position, except in a few hospitals, was as powerful after 1948 as it had been before in some voluntary hospitals. Nevertheless the tripartite system became the accepted form of administration for all non-mental hospitals. In this respect, the nationalization of Britain's hospitals involved a triumph for the former voluntary hospitals over the local authorities, and for the doctors over democratic representatives. Committees of unpaid persons, not very different from the governors of the voluntary hospitals they were replacing, exercised a wide

---

[1] 'In 1943, the King Edward's Hospital Fund . . . had recommended the appointment of specialist catering officers; and in 1945 the Ministry of Health issued a circular to the then existing hospital authorities also advocating the appointment of a "full-time and suitably trained officer".' *The Impact of the Change*, p. 16

measure of authority over groups of hospitals. Though this happened very rarely, their decisions could, in theory, be over-ruled by higher authority, but, in practice, the position of hospital management committees was similar to that of voluntary hospital governors – 'primarily concerned with the enlightened pursuit of economy so far as is consistent with the requirements of the sick'.

Those who had previously served as governors of voluntary hospitals drew attention to the limitations of their powers under the new service. They could no longer settle the remuneration of their staff, but restrictions of this kind had already begun to be imposed on them as the strength of trades unions and pro-fessional associations increased. They were required to try and keep their expenditure within a figure determined in advance, and could do almost nothing to increase their income. Never-theless the sums of money they received were on the whole greater than virtually any hospital had enjoyed before: in this respect their freedom was increased. From time to time, com-mittees were hamstrung by establishment controls and severe limitations over capital construction, but these limitations became less acute later on. Those who had previously exercised responsibilities over hospitals from the public health committees of local authorities were accustomed to restrictions imposed by higher authority on expenditure, on establishments and on wages and salaries. The main new limitation which they experienced was the powerful position which medical staffs had gained throughout the hospital service.

What was expected of part-time medical staffs under the National Health Service was not very different from what had been expected in the voluntary hospitals. Though payment made it possible for more time to be given to hospital work, no mechanism was created for supervising the quality of the work which was performed. Terms of service did not quote any specific hours or times for attendance, or specify any closely defined duties. Each consultant remained responsible to his own code of professional ethics for the care he gave to his patients. Though there were formal mechanisms by which the complaints of patients could be channelled, there was no system of medical inspection and no chain of authority. In the 1944 White Paper a national hospital inspectorate, on the lines of that long operated for schools, was envisaged. This proposal was dropped. While in

the United States some hospitals have 'Chiefs of Service' to whom
specialists in the various departments are responsible, no system
developed in Britain to replace what had previously been done,
however ineptly, by the medical superintendent of the local
authority hospital. Moreover, the wider professional disciplines
imposed as a condition of accreditation in the United States
had no parallel in the conditions of service under the National
Health Service. To a very large extent the rights which doctors
had obtained when or because they were working in a voluntary
hospital on an unpaid basis were extended to all consultants and
specialists when doctors came to be paid for their work. In
practice, the National Health Service became a means by which
doctors working in local authority hospitals widened their
professional freedom.

Such was the impact of the change of ownership on hospital
staffs and hospital managements. The impact on hospital patients
is much harder to assess. The most noticeable change must have
been in the easing of financial restrictions. Suddenly there were
more medical staff giving more time to their hospital work.
Similarly standards of feeding and general amenity must have
increased considerably in those hospitals where they had been
low. Members of management committees who had previously
known only hospitals in good financial circumstances were
shocked by the standards of care provided in some of the
hospitals which they had taken over. More uniform standards
of amenity were provided within groups of hospitals by the
deliberate policy of up-grading the worst hospitals. Differentials
which were tolerated under different managements were seen
to be anomalous once a common management was established.

For some patients and some hospitals the availability of free
care without any account being taken of national insurance
records or membership of contributory schemes represented an
important change. No longer had almoners a duty to extract
from patients such 'voluntary' contributions as they could
afford. The exact number of patients affected by this change is
not known, nor is it possible to give any clear picture of the
amounts involved. But the principles of providing free care where
it was needed, and of admitting patients before any consideration
was given to their financial circumstances were long established
practices in both the voluntary and the local authority hospitals.

The distinction between 'free' patients and paying patients, which had grown up in most hospitals because of the professional difficulties of implementing any other arrangement, was applied in the National Health Service with little difficulty[1] though a new intermediate category of amenity beds was introduced.[2] It was laid down that paying patients should be those who paid the whole cost or virtually the whole cost of the services they received from the hospital. Such patients could pay separately for medical services.

The introduction of a free hospital service for anyone who wished to use it was by no means as revolutionary in Britain as it would have been in some other countries. Nor did it generate great opposition. With the possible exception of the HSA, the pre-payment agencies operating in Britain were unbusinesslike, ineffectively co-ordinated and run by persons without power or influence. They were swept into the background without antagonizing any important section of opinion. If the large profit-making insurance interests had ever entered the hospital field, the replacement of 'voluntary' pre-payment with a scheme based on taxation and compulsory 'contributions' would have been less easily accomplished.

The virtual elimination all on one day of the historic voluntary hospital movement would have been regarded as politically impossible by virtually all sections of opinion before the war. Outside the great teaching hospitals, however, medical staffs had been growing more and more dissatisfied with the inability and unwillingness of voluntary hospital managements to give payment for all medical work. It is true that the doctors had asked for the best of both worlds – the full pay of the local authority hospital and the honorary status of the voluntary hospital. But, paradoxically, the nationalization of all hospitals proved to be a means of granting it. Nationalization was accepted as nearly all

---

[1] In hospitals where there had been part-pay beds, the rigid distinction between free beds and pay-beds created considerable ill-feeling. A former member of the governing body of a voluntary hospital complained that he had raised £100,000 for people unable to pay the full cost of hospital care. 'Now the fees for pay-beds are being based on the estimated economic costs of treating a patient in the hospital, about £14 a week, and people are being made to pay the very prices which the donors of the money wanted to avoid for them.' *The Impact of the Change*, p. 23

[2] Where such beds were available, a patient was able to obtain a private or semi-private room for a modest weekly charge. Such a patient was entitled to the services of the medical staff without any further cost.

hospital doctors had something to gain from it. The staffs of the voluntary hospitals gained pay without supervision and the staffs of local authority hospitals were paid more for working without supervision.

Voluntary hospital managements could not stand out for independence because of the formidable financial difficulties which faced them after the war. They had become dependent on the central government for much of their maintenance expenditure. And though their capital position was better after than before the war, this could not go far towards meeting the costs of maintaining hospitals at the higher post-war standards – particularly when they were faced with a steadily rising price level. It is conceivable that by a strenuous policy of charging patients and by a drastic overhaul and expansion of the contributory schemes, the hospitals could have been kept open. But the large increase in flat-rate insurance contributions, which was the essence of the Beveridge plan for social security, restricted the ability of working people to pay a further contribution for hospital services on the scale required. The voluntary hospitals might have had to concentrate on paying patients. Instead, they accepted nationalization and continued to count among their patients the poor for whose benefit they had been founded.

Their fight to remain independent was half-hearted. So also was the political opposition to the plan to appropriate them. The case against nationalization was not argued by leading opposition speakers in either House as an issue of free enterprise versus socialism. The issue was not regarded as one of political philosophy but as one of political method. The broad principles which underlay the Health Service were by 1946 ostensibly common ground between the political parties and accepted by the vast majority of the British public. For a century or more medical care in hospital had been regarded, as the education of children was always regarded in the United States, as a responsibility for which the community should in some form provide. It was this heritage of shared opinion which was responsible for the widespread acceptance in Britain of what others chose to call 'socialized medicine'.

In many respects the National Health Service extended and developed practices which had been built up over many generations. Despite the collectivist implications of its title, the service is still, though in a special sense, a blend of public and private effort. Thousands of unpaid but appointed 'volunteers' drawn from a variety of different fields play an executive role within a service controlled by a Minister. There is also no small element of professional self-rule. While the nationalization of hospitals represented a large increase in government ownership, it also involved a substantial transfer of power to the medical profession. Local government authorities had for a century accepted doctors as advisers but they had always refused to give them the right to vote as medical representatives at health committees. Only doctors who had been elected as councillors had the right to vote on policy. General practitioners had, however, been represented on their governing bodies ever since the National Insurance Act of 1911. This practice was extended to the hospital services when the National Health Service Act of 1946 came into force. Regional boards, boards of governors and hospital management committees were all given a generous proportion of medical representatives.

Though the National Health Service operates under one Act, this does not make it a cohesive whole. It is in fact three health services – a hospital service, a family doctor service and a home nursing service – each controlled by different authorities. The National Insurance Act set up a family doctor service which gradually took over the care, outside hospital, of those patients who had previously been the responsibility of local authorities. The National Health Service Act took the hospital services away from the local authorities, leaving them with a rag-bag of health functions which there seemed no good reason to transfer elsewhere.

While the health service increased co-ordination within the hospital services, it made it harder to co-ordinate hospitals with services outside. In many areas hospital doctors and home doctors found themselves more separated than before. But separation had been growing for over a century. The changes of 1948 in this field, as elsewhere, extended trends which were long established.

The nationalization of the hospitals and other developments which are collectively described as the creation of the National Health were not, as some would imply, an aberration produced by a band of socialist revolutionaries. Socialists had, however, been among the early advocates of health planning and this major reform of the nation's health services owed much to the resolute actions of a left-wing socialist Minister. What he achieved was not in any sense a final or perfect solution to the need for co-ordination. The start of the health service was no more than a stage in the evolution of the nation's social services: it expressed values and embodied traditions both of long duration. It cannot be fully understood without a knowledge of what preceded it. And this knowledge may assist those who plan further steps in the development of Britain's health services.

Bibliography

This bibliography includes the principal manuscript and printed sources consulted in the course of this study. Newspaper and periodical references are indicated in footnotes throughout the text.

ABEL-SMITH, B.: *A History of the Nursing Profession*, London, 1960

ACTON SOCIETY TRUST: *Groups, Regions and Committees*, Part I: *Hospital Management Committees*, London, 1957

ACTON SOCIETY TRUST: *Groups, Regions and Committees, Part II: Regional Hospital Boards*, London, 1957

ACTON SOCIETY TRUST: *Hospitals and the State: Background and Blueprint*, London, 1955

ACTON SOCIETY TRUST: *The Impact of the Change*, London, 1956

AIKMAN, J.: *Surgical Operations in Private Practice*, London, 1904

BETTANY, G. T.: *Eminent Doctors*, 2 vols., London, 1885

BEVERIDGE, SIR W.: *Social Insurance and Allied Services*, HMSO, 1942

BRISTOWE AND HOLMES: *The Hospitals of the United Kingdom*, HMSO, 1864

BRITISH MEDICAL ASSOCIATION: *A General Medical Service for the Nation*, London, 1938

BRITISH MEDICAL ASSOCIATION: *Proposals for a General Medical Service for the Nation*, London, 1929

BROCKBANK, E.M.: *The Foundation of Provincial Medical Education in England*, Manchester, 1936

BRUCE, M.: *The Coming of the Welfare State*, London, 1961

BUCKLE, F.: *Vital and Economical Statistics of the Hospitals for the Year 1863*, London, 1865

BURDETT, H. C.: *Cottage Hospitals, General, Fever, and Convalescent*, London, 1896

BURDETT, H. C.: *Hospitals and Asylums of the World*, 4 vols., London, 1891–3

BURDETT, H. C.: *Hospitals and the State*, London, 1881

BURDETT, H. C.: *Pay Hospitals and Paying Wards throughout the World*, London, 1880

CAMERON, H. C.: *Mr Guy's Hospital 1726–1948*, London, 1954

CHALMERS, R. W.: *Hospitals and the State*, London, 1928

The Life of Sir Robert Christison, Bart (edited by his sons), Edinburgh, 1885–6

CLARKE, J. F.: *Autobiographical Recollections of the Medical Profession*, London, 1874

COLE, MARGARET: *Beatrice Webb's Diaries 1912–24*, London, 1952

COLLINS, E. T.: *The History and Traditions of the Moorfields Eye Hospital*, London, 1929

COPE, Z.: *The Versatile Victorian, Being the Life of Sir Henry Thompson, Bt, 1820–1904*, London, 1951

DALE, W.: *The State of the Medical Profession in Great Britain and Ireland*, Dublin, 1875

DALTON, HUGH: *High Tide and After*, London, 1962

DAVIS, M.: *Dispensaries: their Management and Development*, New York, 1918

ECKSTEIN, H.: *The English Health Service*, Harvard, 1959

FEILING, K.: *The Life of Neville Chamberlain*, London, 1946

GIBSON, A. G.: *The Radcliffe Infirmary*, Oxford, 1926

GRAHAM, H.: *Eternal Eve*, London, 1950

GRAHAM, H.: *Surgeons All*, London, 1939

GRAVES, C.: *The Story of St Thomas's, 1106–1947*, London, 1947

GWYNN, S., and GERTRUDE TUCKWELL: *The Life of the Rt. Hon. Sir Charles W. Dilke*, 2 vols., London, 1917

HAMMOND, J. L. and BARBARA: *James Stansfeld – A Victorian Champion of Sex Equality*, London, 1932

HART, E.: *The Sick Poor in Workhouses*, London, 1894

HIGGINS, T.: *Great Ormond Street 1852–1952*, London, 1952

HIGHMORE, A.: *Pietas Londinensis: The History, Design and Present State of the various Public Charities In and Near London*, 2 vols., London, 1810

HOLMES, G.: *The National Hospital, Queen Square*, London, 1954

HOWARD, J.: *An Account of the Principal Lazarettos in Europe*, Warrington, 1789

JACOB, F. H.: *A History of the General Hospital near Nottingham*, Bristol and London, 1951

JEWESBURY, E. C. O.: *The Royal Northern Hospital 1856–1956*, London, 1956

KERR, J. M. M. *et al*: *Historical Review of British Obstetrics and Gynaecology*, 1800–1950, Edinburgh and London, 1954

KING EDWARD'S HOSPITAL FUND: *Patients' Waking Hours in London Voluntary Hospitals*, London, 1931

LABOUR PARTY: *The Organization of the Preventive and Curative Medical Services and Hospital and Laboratory Systems under a Ministry of Health*, London, 1918

LAMBERT, R.: *Sir John Simon (1816–1904), and English Social Administration*, London, 1963

LANGDON-DAVIES, J.: *Westminster Hospital – Two Centuries of Voluntary Service, 1719–1948*, London, 1952

LEADER, J. D.: *Sheffield General Infirmary, now the Sheffield Royal Infirmary, 1797–1897*, Sheffield, 1897

LIBERAL PARTY, *Health for People: Proposals for a Positive and Active Health Policy for the Nation*, London, 1942

LINDSEY, ALMONT: *Socialized Medicine in England and Wales*, London, 1962

LONG, F. D.: *King Edward's Hospital Fund for London: The Story of its Foundations and Achievements 1897–1942*, London, 1942

LONG, VISCOUNT: *Memories*, London, 1923

LOW, S.: *The Charities of London in 1861*, London, 1862

MCCURRICH, H. J.: *The Treatment of the Sick Poor of this Country*, London, 1929

MCINNES, E. M.: *St Thomas' Hospital*, London, 1963

MACPHERSON, SIR W. G.: *History of the Great War, Medical Services, General History*, HMSO, 1921

MAPOTHER, E.: *The Medical Profession*, Dublin, 1868

MINNEY, R. F.: *Viscount Addison: Leader of the Lords*, London, 1958

MOBERLEY BELL, E.: *The Story of Hospital Almoners – The Birth of a Profession*, London, 1961

MOORE, N.: *The History of St Bartholomew's Hospital*, London, 1918

MORRIS, E. W.: *A History of the London Hospital*, London, 1926

MORSON, C.: *St Peter's Hospital for Stone 1860–1960*, London, 1960

MURRAY, D. STARK *et al*: *Medical Care and Family Security*, London, 1963

NEWMAN, C.: *The Evolution of Medical Education in the Nineteenth Century*, Oxford, 1957

NEWSHOLME, SIR ARTHUR: *International Studies on the Relation between the Private and Official Practice of Medicine*, London, 1931

NIGHTINGALE, FLORENCE: *Notes on Hospitals*, London, 1863

NUFFIELD PROVINCIAL HOSPITALS TRUST: *Studies in the Functions and Design of Hospitals*, London, 1955

NUFFIELD PROVINCIAL HOSPITALS TRUST: *The Hospital Surveys*, Oxford, 1946

OPPERT, F.: *Hospitals, Infirmaries and Dispensaries*, London, 1883

PARSONS, F. G.: *The History of St Thomas's Hospital*, 3 vols., London, 1932–6

POLITICAL AND ECONOMIC PLANNING: *Medical Care for Citizens*, London, 1944

POLITICAL AND ECONOMIC PLANNING: *Report on British Health Services*, London, 1937

POWELL, SIR A.: *The Metropolitan Asylums' Board and Its Work 1867–1930*, London, 1930

POWER, SIR D'ARCY and WARING, H. J.: *A Short History of St Bartholomew's Hospital 1123–1923*, London, 1923

ROGERS, J.: *Reminiscences of a Workhouse Medical Officer*, London, 1889

ROSS, ELIZABETH M.: 'Women and Poor Law Administration 1857–1910', London M.A. thesis, 1956

PRESTON-THOMAS, H.: *The Work and Play of a Government Inspector*, London, 1909

SAUNDERS, H. ST GEORGE: *The Middlesex Hospital, 1745–1948*, London, 1949

SHEEN, A.: *The Workhouse and Its Medical Officer*, Cardiff, 1875

SIMON, J.: *On the Aims and Philosophic Method of Pathological Research*, London, 1848

SIMON, SIR J.: *English Sanitary Institutions*, London, 1890

SOCIALIST MEDICAL ASSOCIATION: *Whither Medicine?* London, 1940

SPENCER, H. R.: *The History of British Midwifery from 1650 to 1800*, London, 1927

SPRIGGE, S.: *The Life and Times of Sir Thomas Wakley*, London, 1899

STILL, G. F.: *The History of Paediatrics*, London, 1931

TITMUSS, R. M.: *Problems of Social Policy*, London, 1950

TOWNSEND, P.: *The Last Refuge*, London, 1962

THE TRADES UNION CONGRESS AND THE LABOUR PARTY: *The Labour Movement and the Hospital Crisis*, London, 1922

TWINING, LOUISA: *Recollections of Workhouse Visiting and Management during Twenty-Five Years*, London, 1880

WARING, E. J.: *Cottage Hospitals*, London, 1867

WEBB, BEATRICE: *The Coming of a Unified Medical Service and how it will affect the Voluntary Hospitals*, Glasgow, 1910

WEBB, SIDNEY and BEATRICE: *English Local Government: English Poor Law History* (Private Subscription Edition) 1929

WEBB, SIDNEY and BEATRICE: *Our Partnership*, London, 1948

WEBB, SIDNEY and BEATRICE: *The State and the Doctor*, London, 1000

WILSON, E.: *The History of the Middlesex Hospital*, London, 1845

WILSON, N.: *Public Health Services*, Glasgow, 1938

WOLFF, L.: *In Flanders Fields*, London, 1963

WOODHAM-SMITH, CECIL: *Florence Nightingale*, London, 1951

WOODWARD, C.: 'The Rise of the Charity Organization Society', Cambridge University Ph.D thesis, 1961

Index

239–40; on national medical services, 459; on pay hospitals and pay beds, 138, 139–51, 195–6; on special hospitals, 28–9, 30, 157, 158

British Provident Association, 328, 339, 398

British Red Cross Society, in world wars, 253*ff*., 428

Brodie, Sir Benjamin (surgeon), 18

Brown, Ernest (Minister of Health) and national medical services, 458–71

Brown, Dr George, 166

Buchman, J. Courtenay (Metropolitan Hospital), 243

Burdett (Sir) Henry C., 25*n*., 41*n*., 136, 218, 289, 295; and National Insurance Act, 243–4; on wartime medical services, 263, 271, 280; portrait *facing 242*; support for pay hospitals, 138

Burns, John (Pres., Local Govt. Board), and Poor Law reforms, 233–4

CARLISLE, Sir Anthony (surgeon), 20–1

Cave Committee, 307–10, 323, 326, 384, 409

Chadwick, Edwin (Poor Law Commissioner), 47, 76

Chamberlain, Neville, and Poor Law reform, 358–63

chaplains, 155: *see also* hospitallers

Charing Cross Hospital, 17, 42; house committee, 34; outpatients, 117; admission of women students, 278

Charity Organization Society, 86, 92, 101, 106–10, 163, 166, 174*ff*., 200, 276

children and hospital care, 13–14, 24–5, 38

chronic cases, 26, 39, 45, 49, 190–1, 208–10, 373–4

Churchill, Winston, and hospitals and Poor Law reforms, 233, 359

civilian sick in wartime, 259–64, 278, 280–1, 425, 427*ff*.

Clark, Sir Andrew, 163, 169

Communist Party and national health services, 451–2

consultants, medical, and National Health Service, 480, 483, 497–8; BMA on, 110–16, 176–7

convalescent homes, 133, 254, 265, 395

Cooper, Sir Astley, 26

cottage hospitals, 102–4, 106, 138, 197, 264, 408

Coulson, Walter John (surgeon), 30

Cox, Dr Alfred, 313, 445

Cranbrook, Viscount, 165

cross-infection, 1: *see also* hygiene; infectious diseases

DALTON, Hugh, 476

Davy, J. S. (Chief Poor Law Inspector), 89, 201, 219; and 'public health idea', 231; and Royal Commission on the Poor Laws, 220–1

Dawson, Sir Bernard, 288, 289; Committee on medical care, 290–4, 298, 301; press reactions to, 292–3

Devon, Earl of, 83

Dickens, Charles, and workhouse reform, 73

diet in hospitals and workhouses, 10, 42–3, 55, 336

Dill, Dr Gordon, 311

dispensaries, 13, 29, 84, 85, 90

Docker, Sir Bernard, 401

EDUCATION, medical, 16*ff*.; cost of, 18, 19*n*.; and National Insurance Act, 245, 246: *see also* teaching hospitals

Emergency Medical Service, 426–39

endowments, 5, 478

eye diseases, dispensaries and hospitals for, 24, 26, 30, 41, 442

'FAGGOT' votes for hospital appointments, 20

Farnall, H. B. (Poor Law Inspector), 48, 50, 51, 73; influence of Florence Nightingale on, 75–6